LINEAR APPROXIMATION

MATHEMATICAL SURVEYS · *Number 9*

LINEAR APPROXIMATION

BY

ARTHUR SARD

1963

AMERICAN MATHEMATICAL SOCIETY

190 Hope Street, Providence, Rhode Island

The writing of this book was supported in part by the Aeronautical Research Laboratories and the Office of Scientific Research, both of the United States Air Force.

Library of Congress Catalog Number: 63-11988

Preface

The form in which I have written "Linear approximation" seems to me to be suited to the subject, and to the use of mathematicians, scientists, and engineers.

Readers interested in the applications may wish to start with the illustrative examples and the statements of theorems. All readers are urged to skip boldly and to sample where they will.

I am grateful to my wife and to many men and women for help and teaching. In the words of David, Psalm 16, 6,

חבלים נפלו לי בנעימים אף נחלת שפרה עלי.

The lines are fallen unto me in pleasant places;
yea, I have a goodly heritage.

ARTHUR SARD

July 21, 1962

QUEENS COLLEGE
THE CITY UNIVERSITY OF NEW YORK
FLUSHING, NEW YORK

Table of Contents

Introduction

Many approximations of integrals, derivatives, functions, or sums are linear, and continuous relative to a suitable norm. The linearity and continuity provide a means to establish known properties of the approximations and to discover other properties.

Design, analysis, and appraisal all are illuminated and advanced by the theory in this book.

§ 1. **Functionals.** If a quantity e is a linear function on a three-dimensional linear space X, that fact alone permits us to gain a complete knowledge of e. We may introduce coordinates

$$x = (x^1, x^2, x^3), \qquad x \in X,$$

in X. Then the value of e at x is

(2) $$e(x) = \alpha^1 x^1 + \alpha^2 x^2 + \alpha^3 x^3, \qquad x \in X,$$

where α^1, α^2, α^3 are appropriate numbers which characterize e and which can be calculated by putting x equal to

(3) $$(1, 0, 0), \quad (0, 1, 0), \quad (0, 0, 1)$$

successively in (2).

For an infinite dimensional space the generalization of the above remark is interesting.

Suppose that X is a normed† linear space. By a functional F on X we mean a map of X into the numbers N, where N will be either the reals R or the complex numbers C. The set X^* of linear continuous functionals on X is known as the adjoint space. If

$$F \in X^*,$$

that is, if F is a linear continuous functional on X, then this fact alone tells us much about F.

If X is finite dimensional, the dimension of X characterizes X^*. This case is like the three-dimensional one alluded to earlier. If X is infinite dimensional, the dimension of X does not of itself characterize X^*.

For the most part we deal with spaces X of dimension $\aleph_0$ (aleph$_0$). For some such spaces, the adjoint X^* is well known and our knowledge includes an explicit direct procedure for obtaining a standard formula for an arbitrary element of X^*. This is important in the theory of approximation because

† Precise definitions of technical terms are in later chapters; exact references thereto are in the index.

remainders are often elements of X^* for suitable X. If the standard formula leads to sharp appraisals, it is particularly useful.

Consider $C_0(I)$, for example, the space of continuous functions on $I = \{\alpha \leqq s \leqq \tilde{\alpha}\}$ to R, with norm

$$\|x\|_{C_0(I)} = \sup_{s \in I} |x(s)|, \qquad x \in C_0(I). \tag{4}$$

An arbitrary element F of $C_0(I)^*$, that is, an arbitrary linear continuous functional F on $C_0(I)$, may be written

$$Fx = \int_I x(s)\, df(s), \qquad x \in X, \tag{5}$$

where f is a suitable function of bounded variation on I. Furthermore f may be calculated from the formula

$$f(t) = \begin{cases} \lim_{\nu \to \infty} F\theta^\nu(t, s) & \text{if } t > \alpha, \\ 0 & \text{if } t \leqq \alpha, \end{cases} \tag{6}$$

where $\{\theta^\nu\}$, $\nu = 1, 2, \cdots$, is a standard sequence of continuous functions which approach the Heaviside step function θ monotonely (Theorem 3 : 34).†

To apply this theorem of F. Riesz's to a particular functional F we need only recognize F as an element of $C_0(I)^*$, which is easily done by § 3 : 8 or otherwise, calculate f by (6) or its equivalent, and conclude that (5) is valid. Note that (5) is the analogue of (2) and the use of (6) is the analogue of the substitution of (3) in (2).

One may deduce from Riesz's theorem the corresponding result for the space $C_n(I)$ of functions on I n-fold continuously differentiable, with norm

$$|||x|||_{C_n(I)} = \max_{i=0,1,\cdots,n} \sup_{s \in I} |x_i(s)|, \qquad x \in C_n(I),$$

where x_i denotes the ith derivative of x (Theorem 3 : 39). The standard form of an element F of $C_n(I)^*$ is

$$Fx = \sum_{i<n} c^i x_i(a) + \int_I x_n(s)\, df(s), \qquad x \in C_n(I), \tag{7}$$

† In our cross-references a number before a colon is a chapter number and a number after a colon is the number of the object referred to within the designated chapter. If no colon is present, the reference is to the numbered object in the current chapter.

Thus in Chapter 2, for example, (3: 4) would refer to item (4) of Chapter 3; (3: 4, 5) would refer to items (4) and (5) of Chapter 3; and (6) would refer to item (6) of Chapter 2 itself. Theorem 7: 8 would refer to Theorem 8 of Chapter 7. Theorem 7: 8 is not necessarily the 8th theorem in that chapter, but the 8th numbered object, which happens to be a theorem. Similarly § 1: 2 is the section labeled 2 in Chapter 1. Chapter numbers will appear in the captions of left-hand pages.

References to the bibliography are in square brackets, near the author's name or including his name. Thus [Newton 3] or . . . Newton . . . [3] would refer to the 3rd work listed under Newton.

where the constants c^i and the function f of bounded variation are given in (3 : 40, 41) and a is an arbitrary fixed element of I. The relation (7) leads to sharp appraisals of Fx, $x \in C_n(I)$, because the elements

$$x_0(a), x_1(a), \cdots, x_{n-1}(a); \qquad x_n \in C_0(I),$$

that describe x are independent of one another: For any set $b^0, b^1, \cdots, b^{n-1}$ of numbers and any function $y \in C_0(I)$, there is a function $x \in C_n(I)$ such that

$$x_i(a) = b^i, \qquad i < n;$$

$$x_n(s) = y(s), \qquad s \in I.$$

The function f in (7) is determined by the functional F. If f is absolutely continuous, then

$$df(s) = f_1(s)\, ds;$$

and the integral in (7) becomes an ordinary integral. Ordinary integrals have the advantage of being appraisable by all the Hölder inequalities (§ 1 : 21).

In actual practice the functional F is often given as a linear combination of integrals. Then relations like (7) may be established by a transformation of formulas. For functions of one variable, the powerful and elementary Theorem 1 : 8 states this fact. The theorem is due to Peano and dominates the subject. The theorem provides a standard form (7) in which f is absolutely continuous and a direct procedure for calculating the density f_1, for certain functionals F.

Every formula for a remainder in Steffensen's useful book [1], for example, can be deduced from Theorem 1 : 8. The theorem provides alternative formulas also, which are useful and have been neglected.

There are illustrations in Chapter 1 and extensive applications in Chapter 2.

In the approximation of a given functional G, we often consider a family $\mathscr{A}$ of functionals and put to ourselves the problem of choosing one functional $A \in \mathscr{A}$ to serve as the approximation of G. For each $A \in \mathscr{A}$, there is a remainder

$$Rx = Gx - Ax, \qquad x \in X.$$

A procedure often followed is to choose $A \in \mathscr{A}$ so that R vanish for polynomials of as high degree, say $n - 1$, as possible. Such a criterion of choice seems to me to be indirect. What it achieves is that Rx is expressible in terms of the nth derivative x_n. What we want is that Rx be as small as possible in some sense for the set of functions x on which we will operate, or that the appraisal of Rx that we use be as small as possible.

Various criteria of choice of $A \in \mathscr{A}$ are discussed in § 2 : 1 and in Chapters 9, 10.

§ 8. **Several variables.** For spaces X of functions of a single real variable, our knowledge of the adjoint space X^* is usually adequate. This is not the case for spaces of functions of several variables.

Consider a normed space X of functions on a closed bounded region D of the s, t-plane to the reals R. For some such spaces a standard form of elements in X^* and a direct procedure for finding sharp appraisals are not known.

An example is the space $C_1^2(D)$ of functions which have continuous first partial derivatives on D, with norm

$$\|x\|_{C_1^2(D)} = \max\,[\sup |x(s, t)|, \sup |x_{1,0}(s, t)|, \sup |x_{0,1}(s, t)|], \qquad x \in C_1^2(D),$$

where the suprema are taken for $(s, t) \in D$. There is no known procedure for calculating a standard form of an element F of $C_1^2(D)^*$, even when D is an interval. We know that Fx may be written as a sum of Stieltjes integrals on x, $x_{1,0}$, $x_{0,1}$; but we do not know a direct way of obtaining such a formula for an arbitrary $F \in C_1^2(D)^*$. Nor, if we have such a formula, do we know how to obtain effectively a sharp appraisal of Fx, $x \in C_1^2(D)$. The difficulties here are related to the fact that the derivatives $x_{1,0}$ and $x_{0,1}$ are not independent on D.

Thus it is important to discover particular spaces X for which we can find direct procedures of obtaining standard forms and sharp appraisals of arbitrary elements of X^*. Our spaces B, K, Z of Chapters 4, 5, 6, 7 are of this sort.

The spaces B, K and the related spaces $\mathscr{B}^*$, $\mathscr{K}^*$ have the following properties:

(i) Elements of B^*, K^*, $\mathscr{B}^*$, or $\mathscr{K}^*$ are readily recognizable (§§ 4 : 80; 6 : 13, 21, 47).

(ii) Remainders in approximation are often elements of suitable B^*, K^*, $\mathscr{B}^*$, or $\mathscr{K}^*$.

(iii) Each element of B^*, K^*, $\mathscr{B}^*$, or $\mathscr{K}^*$ may be written in a standard form. There is an explicit direct procedure for obtaining that form and sharp appraisals thereof.

Chapter 4 provides the elementary part of the theory. It is the counterpart for functions of two variables of Chapter 1.

Chapter 5 discusses applications to integration, substitution (interpolation or smoothing), and differentiation.

Chapter 6 provides the complete theory of the spaces B, K and their adjoints. The functionals which are elements of B^*, K^* are considered intrinsically; it is not required that such elements be given as sums of Stieltjes integrals. The culmination of the chapter is Theorem 6 : 58 which gives a standard form for Fx in terms of ordinary integrals, when $F \in K^*$ and $x \in B$. It is Theorem 6 : 58 which motivates the definition of the space K and which shows that K is the proper companion of B.

The spaces B, K are defined in terms of a compact interval

$$I = I_s \times I_t, \qquad I_s = \{\alpha \leqq s \leqq \tilde{\alpha}\}, \qquad I_t = \{\beta \leqq t \leqq \tilde{\beta}\},$$

of the s, t-plane; and an arbitrary fixed point (a, b) of I. The spaces B, K consist of functions x on I for which certain specified partial derivatives $x_{i,j}$ are continuous on I, and other specified partial derivatives $x_{i,j}$, with $s = a$, are continuous on I_t, and other specified partial derivatives $x_{i,j}$, with $t = b$, are continuous on I_s. There is a great variety of spaces B and K (§ 4 : 49; § 6 : 38).

The spaces B and K have a rectangular character which may appear to give our theory a limited scope but which on the contrary is a source of strength. Each condition that restricts a space X at the same time broadens the adjoint space X^*. Now our principal hypothesis in the first chapters is that

$$F \in K^* \quad \text{and} \quad x \in B.$$

The condition $x \in B$ is easily carried by functions that we encounter, as a rule. Indeed x usually has more than enough continuous differentiability. And the condition $F \in K^*$, because of the narrowness of K, is relatively broad. The functional F need not have a rectangular character but may depend entirely on an arbitrary subset of the interval I that enters in the definition of B and K. Cf. the illustrations in §§ 5 : 2, 18, 26. Thus the weight of our hypothesis falls on x rather than on F.

Furthermore, and this point is compelling, the hypotheses of our theorems are necessary as well as sufficient for the conclusions.

In Chapter 7, the theory is extended to spaces of functions of m variables.

Chapters 1–7 consider functions on compact intervals. Compactness makes the formulas for masses and kernels simpler than they otherwise would be (cf. Theorem 6 : 9). This gain in simplicity is important in the theory of approximation where the task to be done includes the calculation of masses and kernels as means to obtain explicit formulas and sharp appraisals.

§ 9. **General linear formulas**. In the first part of the book functionals are evaluated in terms of derivatives. It is natural to ask what objects, if any, other than derivatives may be used. We give a complete answer to this question for linear continuous operators, in† Chapter 8.

By an operator F we mean a map of a function space X into a space Y. In many cases Y is itself a function space. If Y is the space N of numbers, then the operator F is a functional.

The spaces that we consider are normed. Different norms and different sorts of norms are useful in the theory of approximation. There are norms based on suprema such as those in the spaces C_n, B, K; and norms based on averages (§ 9 : 1). There are norms based on the function itself, such as the norm in C_0; and norms based on certain derivatives of the function, such as the norm in C_2. The norms in X and Y determine the open sets and the meaning of continuity of operators.

† Chapter 8 does not depend on its predecessors.

In approximation we often start with a preproblem and then construct a precise problem which is an acceptable instance of the preproblem. If we are interested in an operator (F) vaguely defined on a vague space (X) to a vague space (Y), we replace these vague objects by precise ones F, X, Y. Whenever possible we arrange our choice of F, X, Y so that F be continuous. The wide choice of norms and of normed function spaces is very helpful here. It is natural to require continuity of F because otherwise a small change in input might induce a large change in output. But the meaning of smallness is to an extent at our disposal.

What we seek is a problem which fits the preproblem and which allows strong conclusions from relatively weak hypotheses.

Continuity is desirable and often attainable. Linearity is less universal. We say that an operator F on X is linear if

$$F(ax + by) = aFx + bFy$$

whenever

$$x, y \in X; \qquad a, b \in \mathsf{N}.$$

In this book we consider only linear operators. The hypothesis of linearity is very rewarding, as will be seen. Furthermore the preproblem often permits hypotheses of linearity, because derivatives, integrals, sums, and values of a function all are linear.

Minimax approximation is an example of a nonlinear process. Nonlinear theories tend to involve greater computational difficulties than do linear theories.

In the study of linear continuous operators we often seek to describe one operator in terms of another. Suppose that R is a linear continuous operator on X to Y and that U is a linear continuous operator on X to all of $\tilde{X}$, where X, $\tilde{X}$, Y are normed linear complete spaces. In order that there exist a linear continuous operator Q on $\tilde{X}$ to Y such that

$$Rx = QUx, \qquad x \in X; \tag{10}$$

it is necessary and sufficient that

$$Rx = 0 \quad \text{whenever} \quad Ux = 0, \qquad x \in X. \tag{11}$$

This is the quotient theorem of Chapter 8.

That the operator Q is continuous is important here. The relation (10) implies the sharp appraisal

$$\|Rx\|_Y \leqq \|Q\| \, \|Ux\|_{\tilde{X}}, \qquad x \in X, \tag{12}$$

where $\|Q\|$ is a finite number determined by Q.

It is striking that the simple condition (11) and the preliminary hypotheses permit one to deduce the representation (10) and the appraisal (12).

The representations of elements of C_n^*, B^*, K^*, and Z^* of the earlier chapters all are instances of (10). In Theorem 3: 39, for example, U is the operator which assigns to $x \in C_n$ the ordered set

$$x(a), x_1(a), \cdots, x_{n-1}(a), \quad \text{and} \quad x_n \in C_0(I).$$

In this case Ux is a set of n numbers and one function.

When studying an approximation in which the remainder is Rx, $x \in X$, a mathematician may review the variety of ways to construct operators U and spaces $\tilde{X}$ for which the hypotheses of the quotient theorem would be valid. Thus Ux, instead of being a derivative or set of derivatives as in earlier chapters, may be a specified linear combination of derivatives or sets thereof or a difference or a specified linear combination of differences or other things.

§ 13. **The effect of error in input.** We often wish to approximate

$$Gx, \qquad x \in X,$$

by

$$A(x + \delta x), \qquad x + \delta x \in X,$$

where

- X is a space of functions (or equivalence sets of functions) on a space S;
- Y is a space;
- G is a given operator on X to Y;
- A is an operator on X to Y.

We may say that x is the ideal input, $x + \delta x$ the actual input, δx the error in the input, Gx the desired output, and $A(x + \delta x)$ the actual output. The error in the approximation is

$$e = A(x + \delta x) - Gx \tag{14}$$

and is an element of Y.

The theory of approximation is concerned with the calculation of $A(x + \delta x)$, the appraisal of e, and the choice of $A \in \mathscr{A}$ when a family $\mathscr{A}$ of admissible approximations is given.

It is sometimes advantageous to write

$$e = e_A + e_{\delta x}, \tag{15}$$

where

$$e_A = Ax - Gx,$$
$$e_{\delta x} = A(x + \delta x) - Ax.$$

We may call e_A the truncation error or error due to A and $e_{\delta x}$ the error due to δx. We may put

$$R = G - A,$$
$$Rx = -e_A,$$

and study the operator R by the quotient theorem.

If A is linear, then

$$e_{\delta x} = A\delta x$$

and $e_{\delta x}$ is independent of x.

The above decomposition of e into e_A and $e_{\delta x}$ may be useful when our knowledge or hypotheses about x and δx are of different sorts. For example, we may know that δx is small in one sense and that Ux is small in another sense, for suitable U.

§ 16. **The use of probability.** In the problem of the preceding section more than one x and one δx enter. Either the operator A is to be used repeatedly on different inputs or, if A is to be used only once, we nonetheless do not know precisely what x and δx will be and we must provide for a number of possibilities.

There are two ways of describing the multiplicity of inputs. For brevity let us consider the input x. Our comments will apply similarly to the input δx.

We may say that x is an arbitrary element of a specified set $M \subset X$ and we may treat all elements of M as equally important. Alternatively we may introduce a probability to indicate the anticipated importance of different $x \in X$.

Each element of X is a function on S. We may introduce a probability as follows. Let Ω be a space and let p be a probability defined on Ω. Assume that there is given a function x on $S \times \Omega$ and that, for each fixed $\omega \in \Omega$ with null exceptions,

$$x_\omega \in X$$

and x_ω is a possible ideal input of § 13 above, where x_ω is the function on S obtained by fixing ω in $x(s, \omega)$, $s \in S$, $\omega \in \Omega$. Assume further that

$$p(\Omega_1)$$

is the probability that the ideal input of § 13 will be x_ω with $\omega \in \Omega_1$, where Ω_1 is an arbitrary measurable subset of Ω (§§ 9 : 174, 175). Thus $p(\Omega_1)$ is a measure of the anticipated frequency of occurrence of inputs x_ω with $\omega \in \Omega_1$. Alternatively $p(\Omega_1)$ is a measure of the anticipated importance of such inputs. Since x is a function on $S \times \Omega$, x is now a stochastic process.

Similarly δx may be a stochastic process and the same number $p(\Omega_1)$ may be the probability that the input error of § 13 will be δx_ω with $\omega \in \Omega_1$.

The space Ω and the probability p may be simple or not. In many pre-problems it is natural to suppose that an appropriate Ω and p exist. If p is not known we may attempt to estimate p by some statistical technique. Known and future statistical theories of stochastic processes may afford effective methods of estimating p and x or δx (§§ 9 : 175, 304). Even without a technique of statistical estimation we may assume that p and x or δx are of a specified reasonable type, draw conclusions from the assumptions, and, in the manner of inductive science, acquire evidence that the assumptions (and conclusions) are valid in those cases in which observations seem to fit theoretical conclusions. A simple analogy is the following: We may profitably study the anticipated action of a new medicine in terms of the probability p_0 that it will be effective, even though we do not know the exact value of p_0.

§ 17. **Hilbert spaces.** In Chapters 9 and 10 we deal with separable Hilbert spaces and with direct products of pairs of such spaces.† Our technical hypotheses fit the preproblem, and allow the use of projections and the extension of operators. One of the hypotheses, for example, is that

$$\delta x \in X\Psi, \tag{18}$$

where X is a separable Hilbert space (which may or may not be an L^2-space), Ψ is a separable L^2-space of functions absolute square integrable p on Ω, and $X\Psi$ is the direct product of X into Ψ (§ 9 : 70).

What we want is that δx be a manageable function on $S \times \Omega$. Now (18) satisfies this desideratum and at the same time gives us an immense choice of possible spaces X, Ψ (§ 9 : 27). The fact that any two Hilbert spaces of the same dimension are isomorphic does not imply that the spaces are equivalent in the theory of approximation, because the isomorphism between the spaces may fail to preserve the qualities which interest us.

The use of Hilbert spaces leads to a unity of method with a large variety of interpretation and application. The technical hypothesis (18) will often be satisfied, for suitable Ψ and X.

It is my opinion that stochastic processes which are elements of direct products of Hilbert spaces will be important in many theories.

§ 19. **Efficient approximation.** Chapter 9 considers the problem of choosing one approximation from a given family $\mathscr{A}$ of approximations. The choice depends on the anticipated character of the inputs. The data of the problem include a space T and a measure m on T, a space Ω and a probability p on Ω. We denote expected value by

$$E \cdots = \int_{\Omega} \cdots \, dp.$$

For each approximation $A \in \mathscr{A}$, there is a stochastic process e which is a function on $T \times \Omega$ absolute square integrable mp. For each fixed $\omega \in \Omega$, with null exceptions, e_ω is a function on T absolute square integrable m and is the error in the approximation if the inputs arise from ω. We say that $A \in \mathscr{A}$ is strongly efficient if

$$E|e_\omega(t)|^2$$

† Chapters 9 and 10 do not depend on their predecessors.

is minimal for each $t \in T$ with null exceptions, and that A is efficient if

$$\int_T E|e_\omega(t)|^2 \, dm(t)$$

is minimal (§ 9: 176). We define nearly strongly efficient and nearly efficient operators in the natural way. Such operators are characterized completely in Theorem 9: 189 and Lemma 9: 220.

Efficiency is said to be strong if, for all $\rho > 0$, any operator within ρ of efficiency is surely within ρ of strong efficiency. In this case a weak minimization is in fact strong. Theorem 9: 232 gives a necessary and sufficient condition that efficiency be strong. Theorem 9: 253 asserts that efficiency is strong if $\mathscr{A}$ contains all operators of finite rank.

Illustrations and applications are in §§ 9: 267 ff.

We consider stationary data and Wiener-Kolmogorov Theory in §§ 9: 311 ff.

§ 20. **Minimal response to error. Variance.** In the problem of efficient approximation of Chapter 9, both inputs x and δx are stochastic processes. In Chapter 10, the input δx is again taken to be a stochastic process, now assumed to be unbiased

$$E\delta x = 0;$$

but x is an arbitrary element of a given linear set $M \subset X$. We say that an operator A is minimal if A minimizes the expected response to δx, for each $x \in M$, among all linear continuous operators on X which are unbiased on M (§ 10: 2). Theorem 10: 27 characterizes minimal and nearly minimal operators. The theorem involves the knowledge of δx as a stochastic process (element of $X\Psi'$).

The variance V of δx is a nonnegative operator of finite trace, determined by δx (§ 10: 70). Theorem 10: 104 characterizes minimal operators in terms of the variance V rather than in terms of the stochastic process δx itself. Theorem 10: 137 gives a usable sufficient condition involving V and not δx that a sequence of operators be minimizing.

In the example of §§ 10: 150 ff., the search for minimal operators is carried out in two ways, by the use of variance and by the use of projection.

§ 21. **Other topics.** Chapters 11 and 12 are of general mathematical interest.

Chapter 11 constructs a table of integrals of step functions. The results are used in the theory of the spaces B^*, Z^*, and K^*. I believe that the formulas of Chapter 11 will have applications elsewhere, since step functions and their integrals occur in nature.

Chapter 12 discusses single and multiple Stieltjes integrals. The chapter includes the formula of W. H. Young for multiple integration by parts, a formula extremely useful in the study of integrals which are not themselves products of simpler integrals.

CHAPTER 1

Functionals in Terms of Derivatives

§ 1. **Introduction.** In the approximation of the integral

$$\int_{-1}^{1} x(s)\, ds$$

by the trapezoidal rule, the remainder is

$$Rx = \int_{-1}^{1} x(s)\, ds - [x(-1) + x(1)].$$

This expression assigns to the function x the number Rx and thereby defines a functional R. The form itself of R is such that Theorem 8 of the present chapter, with $n = 1, 2, \cdots$, applies to R. The functional R is a simple instance of what we study in this chapter.

Theorems 8 and 43 provide standard forms for certain functionals and a direct procedure for obtaining the forms. The standard forms lead to sharp appraisals.

Illustrations of the use of the theorems are given in §§ 49, 56, 57, 59 and in Chapter 2.

§ 2. **The spaces C_n, $\boldsymbol{C}_n$, V of functions.** Let I be the interval

$$\alpha \leqq s \leqq \tilde{\alpha},$$

where

$$-\infty < \alpha < \tilde{\alpha} < \infty;$$

and let n be a nonnegative integer. We denote by C_n or $C_n(I)$ the space† of functions on I to the reals R which are continuous on I together with their derivatives of order $\leqq n$. The space C_n depends on I, but usually I is fixed in each discussion.

Consider a function x on I. We write

$$x_i = \frac{d^i x}{ds^i}$$

for the ith derivative of x with respect to s, and $x_i(s)$ for the value thereof at s. The use of subscript instead of superscript conforms to the notation

---

† By a space we mean a set. Later we may mean a set together with addition and scalar multiplication and perhaps a norm.

for partial derivatives in later chapters. Here and elsewhere indices stand for nonnegative integers unless other specifications are given. We use

iff

as an abbreviation for

if and only if.

Thus

$$x \in C_n$$

iff x_n exists and

$$x_n \in C_0.$$

The definition of C_n implies that

$$C_0 \supset C_1 \supset C_2 \supset \cdots.$$

We may call C_n the *space of functions with continuous nth derivative.*

In addition to C_n, we consider the space $\mathbf{C}_n$ (bold C_n) of functions with *absolutely continuous* $(n-1)$*th derivative,* defined as follows:

$x \in \mathbf{C}_0$ iff x is an integrable function on I; that is, x is defined almost everywhere on I and is integrable in the sense of Lebesgue.

For $n \geqq 1$, $x \in \mathbf{C}_n$ iff the derivative x_{n-1} is absolutely continuous† on I; that is, $x_n(s)$ exists almost everywhere on I and is an element of $\mathbf{C}_0$; and x_{n-1} is an indefinite integral of x_n.

Thus

$$\mathbf{C}_0 \supset C_0 \supset \mathbf{C}_1 \supset C_1 \supset \mathbf{C}_2 \supset C_2 \supset \cdots.$$

We say that a function y is *piecewise continuous* on I if it is possible to subdivide I into a finite number of intervals on the interior of each of which y is uniformly continuous. The values of y at the endpoints of the subintervals are immaterial. Indeed y need not be defined at those endpoints. If x_n is piecewise continuous and x_{n-1}, $n \geqq 1$, is continuous, then x is an element of $\mathbf{C}_n$. A reader wishing to simplify our discussion may in many instances interpret $\mathbf{C}_n$ as the space of functions with continuous $(n-1)$th and piecewise continuous nth derivative.

It will be convenient to write

$$(s-a)^{(i)} = \begin{cases} \dfrac{(s-a)^i}{i!}, & i = 1, 2, \cdots; \\ 1, & i = 0; \\ 0, & i = -1, -2, \cdots. \end{cases}$$

† Cf. § 12 : 44.

We may refer to $(s - a)^{(i)}$ as a *normalized power*. The jth derivative of $(s - a)^{(i)}$ with respect to s is $(s - a)^{(i-j)}$, whether $i - j$ is positive, zero, or negative.

The space $\boldsymbol{C}_n$, $n \geqq 1$, is precisely the space of functions x which are such that Taylor formulas with integral remainders in terms of x_n hold for x and all its derivatives of order $< n$. That is, $x \in \boldsymbol{C}_n$ iff $x_n \in \boldsymbol{C}_0$ and

$$x_i(s) = \sum_{i \leqq j < n} (s - a)^{(j-i)} x_j(a) + \int_a^s (s - t)^{(n-i-1)} x_n(t)\, dt, \qquad s \in I, \quad i < n.$$

We denote by V the space of functions of *bounded variation* on I (cf. § 12: 14).

§ 3. The space $\mathscr{C}_n^*$ of functionals. By a *functional* F we mean a map of a space X of functions into the real or complex numbers N; that is, a correspondence which assigns to each $x \in X$ a number Fx.

The *space* $\mathscr{C}_n^*$ (script C_n star) *of functionals* is defined as follows. A functional F is an element of $\mathscr{C}_n^*$ iff Fx is of the form

$$Fx = \sum_{i \leqq n} \int_I x_i(s)\, d\mu^i(s), \tag{4}$$

where $\mu^i \in V$ and the superscript i merely distinguishes different functions μ^i, all in V. Then Fx is surely defined whenever $x \in \boldsymbol{C}_n$. In fact Fx is defined if $x \in \boldsymbol{C}_n$ and x_n is integrable relative to $d\mu^n$. The formula (4) fails to be precise if $x_n(s)$ does not exist at a point s at which $\mu^n(s)$ has a jump. All the lower derivatives $x_i(s)$, $i < n$, are continuous everywhere in I and so the terms in (4) with $i < n$ cause no complication, if $x \in \boldsymbol{C}_n$.

Integrals are to be understood in the sense of Lebesgue, although for many purposes the reader may interpret integrals in the sense of Riemann. Aspects of the theory of integration are discussed in Chapter 12.

If $\mu(s)$ is absolutely continuous, the integral

$$\int_I y(s)\, d\mu(s)$$

equals the ordinary integral

$$\int_I y(s)\kappa(s)\, ds,$$

where

$$\kappa(s) = \frac{d\mu(s)}{ds}.$$

Each integral in (4) may be an ordinary integral, or the sum of an ordinary integral and a linear combination of values of the integrand at a finite number of points in I, or something more complicated.

In practice the mass $\mu(s)$ that occurs will often be such that

$$\int_I y(s)\,d\mu(s) = \int_I y(s)\kappa(s)\,ds + \sum_{\nu \leqq N} c^\nu y(s_\nu), \tag{5}$$

where $\kappa(s)$ is piecewise continuous on I and

$$s_\nu \in I, \quad c^\nu \in \mathsf{R}; \qquad \nu = 0, 1, \cdots, N.$$

We may say here that

$$d\mu(s) = \kappa(s)\,ds \text{ plus jumps of } c^\nu \text{ at the points } s = s_\nu.$$

The space $\mathscr{C}_n^*$ is important because, as we shall see, many expressions of interest to mathematicians and scientists are in fact elements of $\mathscr{C}_n^*$ and because each element of $\mathscr{C}_n^*$ can be written in useful standard forms which are readily calculable and appraisable.

The definition of $\mathscr{C}_n^*$ implies that

$$\mathscr{C}_0^* \subset \mathscr{C}_1^* \subset \mathscr{C}_2^* \subset \cdots.$$

If F, $G \in \mathscr{C}_n^*$ and $a, b \in \mathsf{R}$, then

$$aF + bG \in \mathscr{C}_n^*.$$

If $F \in \mathscr{C}_n^*$ and if x, y are such that Fx, Fy are defined, then $F(ax + by)$ is defined and

$$F(ax + by) = aFx + bFy \tag{6}$$

whenever $a, b \in \mathsf{R}$.

Suppose that $F \in \mathscr{C}_n^*$. It will be convenient to define the *jump set* $\mathscr{J}_{F,n}$ of F as the set of points s in I at which the function $\mu^n(s)$ in (4) is discontinuous. Since $\mu^n \in V$, the set $\mathscr{J}_{F,n}$ is countable (that is, finite or countably infinite). If the last integral in (4) is of the form (5), then $\mathscr{J}_{F,n}$ will be finite. If $F \in \mathscr{C}_n^*$, then $F \in \mathscr{C}_{n+1}^*$ also and the set $\mathscr{J}_{F,n+1}$ is empty.

§ 7. **A standard form for elements of $\mathscr{C}_{n-1}^*$.** We now state and establish the principal result of the present chapter.

8. Kernel theorem. *Suppose that*

$$F \in \mathscr{C}_{n-1}^*, \qquad n \geqq 1,$$

and that a is an arbitrary element of I. Then a function $\kappa \in V$ and constants c^i, $i < n$, exist such that

$$Fx = \sum_{i<n} c^i x_i(a) + \int_I x_n(s)\kappa(s)\,ds \tag{9}$$

whenever $x \in \boldsymbol{C}_n$. Furthermore

$$c^i = F[(s - a)^{(i)}], \qquad i < n; \tag{10}$$

and κ *may be taken so that*

$$\kappa(t) = F[(s - t)^{(n-1)}\psi(a, t, s)] \tag{11}$$

for all t *not in the jump set* $\mathscr{J}_{F,n-1}$, *where*

$$\psi(a, t, s) = \begin{cases} 1 & \textit{if } a \leqq t < s, \\ -1 & \textit{if } s \leqq t < a, \\ 0 & \textit{otherwise.} \end{cases} \tag{12}$$

A few observations before the proof may be of interest.

We call Theorem 8 a kernel theorem because it involves $\kappa(s)\,ds$. Later theorems involving $d\lambda(s)$, where $\lambda \in V$, may be called mass theorems.

The formula (9) does not give Fx for all x for which Fx is defined, but only for $x \in \boldsymbol{C}_n$. If $x \in C_{n-1}$, for example, Fx is well defined by (4) with n replaced by $n - 1$, but the derivative x_n need not exist. An advantage of (9) is that Fx is expressed in terms of an ordinary rather than a Stieltjes integral.

The terms of (9) are independent of one another. This may be seen as follows. Put

$$x(s) = (s - a)^{(j_0)}, \qquad j_0 < n,$$

in (9). Then (9) reduces to $Fx = c^{j_0}x_{j_0}(a)$. On the other hand if

$$x(s) = \int_a^s y(t)(s - t)^{(n-1)}\,dt,$$

where y is an arbitrary continuous function on I, then

$$x_i(a) = 0, \quad i < n; \qquad x_n(s) = y(s), \quad s \in I.$$

(Cf. Lemmas 3:70 and 74.) It follows that Fx reduces to the last term in (9). Thus it is possible for any term of (9) to be different from zero while all other terms vanish.

In (11) t is a parameter, as may be seen from its being on both sides of the equation. The functional F operates on its argument

$$(s - t)^{(n-1)}\psi(a, t, s) \tag{13}$$

as a function of s, and the s disappears after the operation, as if s were the variable of integration in a definite integral. Note that (13) as a function of s is an element of $\boldsymbol{C}_{n-1}$, but not of C_{n-1}, since its $(n - 1)$th derivative with respect to s is $\psi(a, t, s)$, which has a jump at $s = t$. This point will be discussed in the proof.

The fact that (11) may fail on $\mathscr{J}_{F,n-1}$ causes no complication, because the ambiguity of $\kappa(t)$ on a countable set is immaterial to the use of (9).

If the hypothesis of Theorem 8 holds for $n = n_0$, it holds a fortiori for $n > n_0$. The constants c^i, $i < n_0$, will be the same whether $n = n_0$ or $n > n_0$.

Theorem 8 not only asserts the existence of the formula (9) but it also

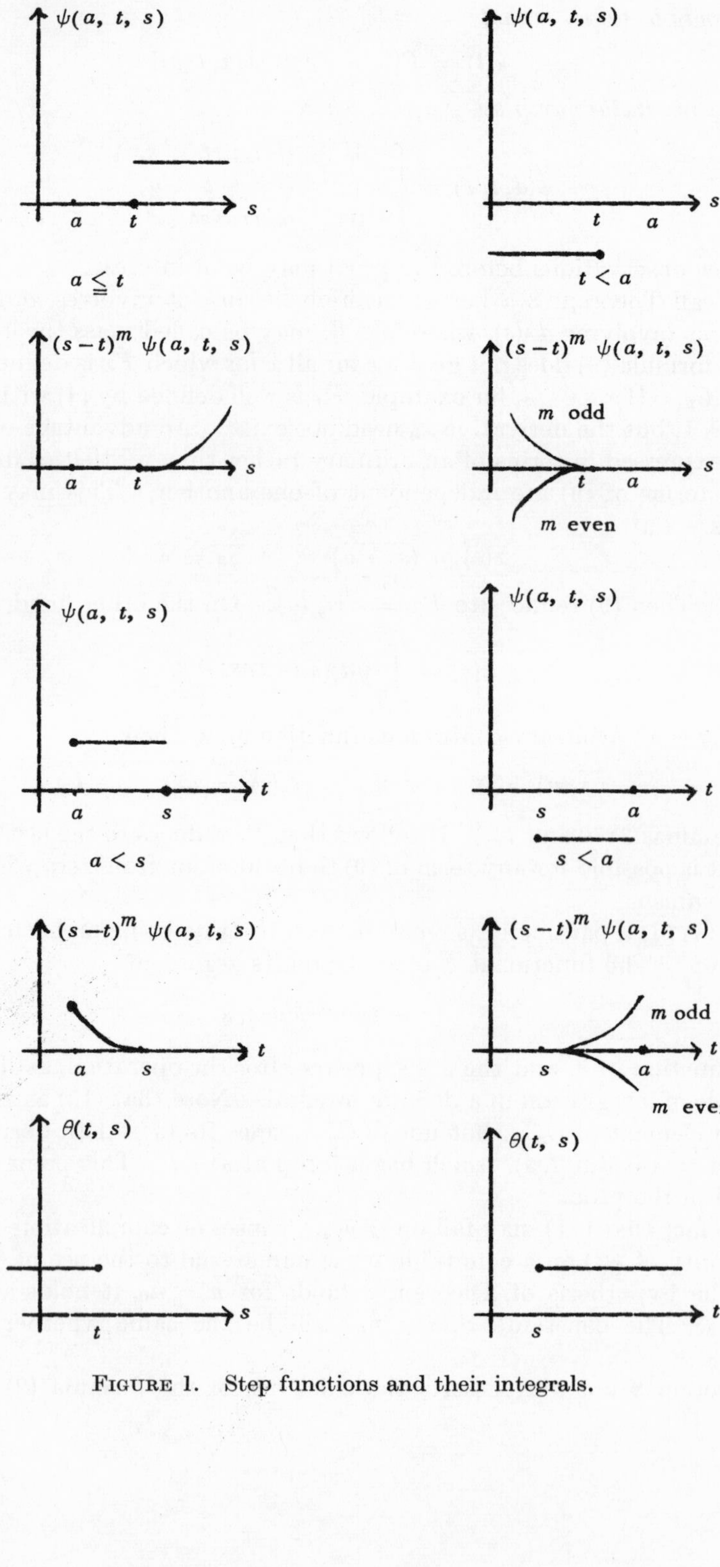

FIGURE 1. Step functions and their integrals.

provides through (10) and (11) means actually to calculate c^i, $i < n$, and κ; that is, to obtain (9) explicitly.

The proof of Theorem 8 depends on Taylor's formula with integral remainder, Fubini's Theorem, and the following relation [Sard 5, p. 326]:

$$\int_a^s y(t)\,dt = \int_\alpha^{\tilde{\alpha}} y(t)\psi(a, t, s)\,dt, \qquad \alpha \leqq a, s \leqq \tilde{\alpha}, \tag{14}$$

where $y(t)$ is an arbitrary integrable function on $[\alpha, \tilde{\alpha}]$. To establish (14), suppose first that $a > s$. Then $\psi(a, t, s)$ vanishes unless $s \leqq t < a$ in which case $\psi(a, t, s) = -1$, by (12). Hence (14) holds. Likewise if $a < s$. Finally, if $a = s$, then $\psi(a, t, s)$ is identically zero and (14) is correct. Note that (14) converts a directed integral with variable limits into an integral with fixed limits.

Proof of Theorem 8. Suppose that $x \in C_n$. By Taylor's formula applied to x_i, $i < n$, and (14), since $a \in I = [\alpha, \tilde{\alpha}]$,

$$\begin{aligned} x_i(s) &= \sum_{i \leqq j < n} (s - a)^{(j-i)} x_j(a) + \int_a^s (s - t)^{(n-i-1)} x_n(t)\,dt \\ &= \sum_{i \leqq j < n} (s - a)^{(j-i)} x_j(a) + \int_I (s - t)^{(n-i-1)} x_n(t)\psi(a, t, s)\,dt, \end{aligned} \tag{15}$$

$$s \in I, \quad i < n.$$

Also

$$Fx = \sum_{i<n} \int_I x_i(s)\,d\mu^i(s), \qquad \mu^i \in V; \tag{16}$$

since

$$F \in \mathscr{C}^*_{n-1}.$$

Hence

$$Fx = \sum_{i<n} \int_I d\mu^i(s) \left[\sum_{i \leqq j < n} (s - a)^{(j-i)} x_j(a) + \int_I dt (s - t)^{(n-i-1)} x_n(t)\psi(a, t, s) \right].$$

By Fubini's Theorem

$$\int_I d\mu^i(s) \int_I dt\,(s - t)^{(n-i-1)} x_n(t)\psi(a, t, s) = \int_I dt \int_I d\mu^i(s) \cdots,$$

providing that the integrand is integrable relative to $t\mu^i(s)$. Now $(s - t)^{(n-i-1)} x_n(t)$ is integrable; and $\psi(a, t, s)$ is certainly bounded and measurable. It follows that the product is indeed integrable. Hence

$$Fx = \sum_{j<n} c^j x_j(a) + \int_I x_n(t)\kappa(t)\,dt,$$

where

$$c^j = \sum_{i \leqq j} \int_I (s-a)^{(j-i)}\,d\mu^i(s), \qquad j < n,$$

$$\kappa(t) = \sum_{i<n} \int_I (s-t)^{(n-i-1)}\psi(a,t,s)\,d\mu^i(s), \qquad t \in \mathsf{R}. \tag{17}$$

The function $\kappa(t)$ defined by (17) is of bounded variation on I, since the variation with respect to t of each integrand is bounded, for each fixed $s \in I$, uniformly over I (cf. Figure 1).

Thus (9) is established, with $\kappa \in V$.

The relation (9) itself implies (10). For we may put

$$x(s) = (s-a)^{(j_0)}, \qquad j_0 < n,$$

in (9). Then

$$x_n(s) = 0 \quad \text{for all } s;$$
$$x_i(a) = 0 \quad \text{if } i \neq j_0; \quad x_{j_0}(a) = 1;$$

and (9) reduces to (10).

We now show that $\kappa(t)$ as defined by (17) satisfies (11) for all t not in $\mathscr{J}_{F,n-1}$; that is, for all t except those which are discontinuities of the function $\mu^{n-1}(t)$ of (16).

Consider the argument

$$y(s) \underset{\text{def}}{=} (s-t)^{(n-1)}\psi(a,t,s)$$

of F in (11). Since $\psi(a,t,s)$, as a function of s, is locally constant except at $s = t$, all derivatives $\partial^i y/\partial s^i$ exist except at $s = t$ and

$$y_i(s) = \frac{\partial^i y}{\partial s^i} = (s-t)^{(n-i-1)}\psi(a,t,s), \qquad s \neq t, \quad i \leqq n-1. \tag{18}$$

Furthermore, since $s - t = 0$ when $s = t$, the equality (18) holds even at $s = t$ providing that $i < n - 1$. The $(n-1)$th derivative y_{n-1} does not exist at $s = t$ if $n > 1$; $y_{n-1}(s)$ is given by (18) for $s \neq t$ and has a jump of 1 at $s = t$. Thus $y \in C_{n-1}$ but $y \notin C_{n-1}$ (cf. Figure 1).

By (16) the missing value $s = t$ is immaterial and Fy is well defined, except when $s = t$ is a discontinuity of $\mu^{n-1}(s)$ and $n > 1$. Suppose that $s = t$ is a point of continuity of $\mu^{n-1}(s)$. Then (16) implies that

$$Fy = \sum_{i<n} \int_I (s-t)^{(n-i-1)}\psi(a,t,s)\,d\mu^i(s).$$

Hence

$$Fy = \kappa(t), \qquad t \notin \mathscr{J}_{F,n-1},$$

as was to be shown. This completes the proof of the theorem.

19. Remark. The function $\kappa(t)$ defined by (17) is continuous from above for all real t:

$$\kappa(t + 0) = \kappa(t), \qquad t \in \mathsf{R}.$$

To establish this assertion, consider $\kappa(t')$ and $\kappa(t)$, $t' > t$. Let t' approach t monotonely. Then, if $a \leqq t$,

$$(20) \qquad (s - t')^{(n-i-1)}\psi(a, t', s) \to (s - t)^{(n-i-1)}\psi(a, t, s)$$

monotonely for each fixed s (cf. Figure 1). If $a > t$, the convergence (20) may not be monotone to start with but it becomes and remains monotone after t' becomes $< a$. By the classical theorem on the integration of monotone sequences, it follows that

$$\kappa(t') \to \kappa(t)$$

without exception.

An alternative form of (17), which however we do not need, is

$$\kappa(t) = \begin{cases} \sum_{i<n} \int_{[\alpha, t]} -(s - t)^{(n-i-1)}\, d\mu^i(s) & \text{if} \quad \alpha \leqq t < a, \\ \sum_{i<n} \int_{(t, \tilde{\alpha}]} (s - t)^{(n-i-1)}\, d\mu^i(s) & \text{if} \quad a \leqq t \leqq \tilde{\alpha} \quad \text{and} \quad a < \tilde{\alpha}, \\ 0 & \text{if} \quad t < \alpha \quad \text{or if} \quad t \geqq \tilde{\alpha}, \end{cases}$$

by (12). In notations like $(t, \tilde{\alpha}]$, the square bracket indicates inclusion of the endpoint, the round parenthesis exclusion.

The function κ in (9) is unique in the following sense. If (9) holds with $\kappa = \kappa^0 \in V$ and also with $\kappa = \kappa^1 \in V$, then

$$\kappa^0(t) = \kappa^1(t), \qquad t \in I,$$

with countable exceptions. This is because the equality must hold at each point of continuity of κ^0 and κ^1.

In practice, as we shall see in the illustrative examples below and in Chapter 2, functionals are often given explicitly as elements of $\mathscr{C}^*_{n-1}$, for suitable n. If a functional is defined in some other fashion than by an explicit formula of the form (16), the question of whether it is an element of $\mathscr{C}^*_{n-1}$ is interesting. This question will be studied in Chapter 3.

§ 21. **Inequalities.** Theorem 8 leads to appraisals of Fx, if

$$F \in \mathscr{C}^*_{n-1}, \qquad x \in \boldsymbol{C}_n,$$

as follows. Take $a \in I$, and write

$$F = G + H,$$

$$Gx = \sum_{i<n} c^i x_i(a),$$

$$Hx = \int_I x_n(s)\kappa(s)\,ds,$$

where c^i and $\kappa \in V$ are given in Theorem 8.

By customary inequalities,

$$(22) \qquad |Gx| \leqq M \max_{i<n} |x_i(a)|, \qquad M = \sum_{j<n} |c^j|,$$

$$(23) \qquad |Hx| \leqq N \sup_{s \in I} |x_n(s)|, \qquad N = \int_I |\kappa(t)|\,dt,$$

where sup stands for supremum, that is, least upper bound.

Alternatively, the rôles of x and (c^i, κ) may be interchanged:

$$(24) \qquad |Gx| \leqq M \sum_{i<n} |x_i(a)|, \qquad M = \max_{j<n} |c^j|,$$

$$(25) \qquad |Hx| \leqq N \int_I |x_n(s)|\,ds, \qquad N = \sup_{t \in I} |\kappa(t)|.$$

The Hölder inequalities may be used [Hardy-Littlewood-Pólya 1, pp. 24–26, 139–142; Riesz-Nagy 1, pp. 41–43, 73–74]. Suppose that e and e' are two positive numbers such that

$$\frac{1}{e} + \frac{1}{e'} = 1.$$

Then

$$(26) \qquad |Gx| \leqq M\left[\sum_{i<n} |x_i(a)|^e\right]^{1/e}, \qquad M = \left[\sum_{j<n} |c^j|^{e'}\right]^{1/e'},$$

$$(27) \qquad |Hx| \leqq N\left[\int_I |x_n(s)|^e\,ds\right]^{1/e}, \qquad N = \left[\int_I |\kappa(t)|^{e'}\,dt\right]^{1/e'}.$$

The simplest case occurs when

$$e = e' = 2.$$

Then

$$(28) \qquad (Gx)^2 \leqq M^2 \sum_{i<n} [x_i(a)]^2, \qquad M^2 = \sum_{j<n} [c^j]^2,$$

$$(29) \qquad (Hx)^2 \leqq N^2 \int_I [x_n(s)]^2\,ds, \qquad N^2 = \int_I [\kappa(t)]^2\,dt.$$

All the above inequalities are the best possible or, as we say, *sharp*, in the following strong sense. Let $\rho > 0$. Any one of the inequalities with M replaced by $M - \rho$ or N replaced by $N - \rho$ would be false for a suitably chosen x, even if x were restricted to be an element of C_n (rather than $\mathbf{C}_n$). Indeed the inequality would be false for a suitably chosen polynomial x, by Weierstrass's Theorem [Graves 1, pp. 122-125]. As regards (25) we assume here without essential loss of generality that the function κ of bounded variation is such that $\kappa(t)$ lies between $\kappa(t - 0)$ and $\kappa(t + 0)$ for all t.

The suprema in (23) and (25) may be replaced by essential suprema (also called effective suprema or true maxima; cf. § 2: 100). For our purposes there is little advantage in such replacement. The inequalities (26) and (27) may be interpreted as reducing to (22) and (23) when

$$e = \infty, \qquad e' = 1,$$

and to (24) and (25) when

$$e = 1, \qquad e' = \infty,$$

respectively, it being supposed that the suprema are replaced by essential suprema.

It is interesting to note which functions x create the extreme cases in the above appraisals. One might say that such functions are in *resonance* with κ and $c^0, \cdots, c^{n-1}$ in (9).

If x is such that†

$$(30) \qquad x_i(a) = p \text{ signum } c^i, \qquad i < n,$$

$$(31) \qquad x_n(s) = p \text{ signum } \kappa(s),$$

where p is a positive constant, then the equality (9) implies that equality holds in the appraisals (22), (23), since

$$\sum_{i<n} c^i x_i(a) = p \sum c^i \text{ signum } c^i = p \sum |c^i| = \max_{i<n} |x_i(a)| \sum_{j<n} |c_j|,$$

$$\int_I x_n(s)\kappa(s)\, ds = p \int_I |\kappa(s)|\, ds = \sup_{s \in I} |x_n(s)| \int_I |\kappa(t)|\, dt.$$

Now the relation (31) cannot necessarily be satisfied with x in C_n since κ and signum κ are not necessarily continuous on I. For any $\rho > 0$, however, there is a function x in C_n such that (30) holds, (31) holds approximately, and

---

† signum c is defined as 0 if $c = 0$ and $|c|/c$ otherwise, where c is a complex number. Thus

$$c \text{ signum } c = |c|$$

without exception. If $0 \neq c \in \mathbf{R}$ then signum c is $+1$ or -1 according as c is positive or negative.

$$|Gx| = M \max_{i<n} |x_i(a)|,$$

$$|Hx| > (N - \rho) \sup_{s \in I} |x_n(s)|,$$

where M, N are given in (22), (23). This assertion may be established by the use of Taylor's formula and the technique of establishing the inequality (23). The function x may be taken to be a polynomial, by Weierstrass's Theorem.

If x is such that

$$x_i(a) = \begin{cases} p & \text{if } i = i_0, \\ 0 & \text{if } i \neq i_0, \quad i < n, \end{cases} \tag{32}$$

$$x_n(s) = \begin{cases} p & \text{if } s \text{ is near a suitably chosen point at which } |\kappa| \text{ is near its supremum}, \\ 0 & \text{elsewhere}, \end{cases} \tag{33}$$

where p is a positive constant and i_0 is an integer such that

$$|c^{i_0}| = \max_{i<n} |c^i|;$$

then the equality (9) implies that equality holds in (24) and nearly holds in (25). There exist functions x of this sort which are polynomials.

Suppose that

$$\frac{1}{e} + \frac{1}{e'} = 1, \qquad e, e' > 0.$$

If x is such that

$$x_i(a) = p|c^i|^{e'/e} \operatorname{signum} c^i, \qquad i < n, \tag{34}$$

$$x_n(s) = p|\kappa(s)|^{e'/e} \operatorname{signum} \kappa(s), \tag{35}$$

where p is a positive constant, then the equality (9) implies that equality holds in the appraisals (26), (27). The relation (35) cannot necessarily be satisfied by an x in C_n. For any $\rho > 0$, however, there is a polynomial x such that (34) holds, (35) holds approximately, and

$$|Gx| = M\left[\sum_{i<n} |x_i(a)|^e\right]^{1/e},$$

$$|Hx| > (N - \rho)\left[\int_I |x_n(s)|^e \, ds\right]^{1/e},$$

where M, N are given by (26), (27).

The appraisals (22)–(27) do not exhaust the possible sharp appraisals of (9). We may introduce weights as follows. Let

$$w^0, w^1, \cdots, w^{n-1}$$

be arbitrary positive constants and let $w(s)$ be an arbitrary positive measurable function on I bounded away from 0 and from ∞. We may write (9) as

$$Fx = \sum_{i<n} \frac{c^i}{w^i} w^i x_i(a) + \int_I x_n(s) w(s) \frac{\kappa(s)}{w(s)} \, ds,$$

and apply the same analysis. Thus we obtain (22)–(29) with

$$\begin{array}{llll} c^i & \text{replaced by} & \dfrac{c^i}{w^i}, & \\ x_i(a) & \quad " \quad " & x_i(a) w^i, & i < n, \\ \kappa(s) & \quad " \quad " & \dfrac{\kappa(s)}{w(s)}, & \\ x_n(s) & \quad " \quad " & x_n(s) w(s). & \end{array}$$

All these appraisals are sharp.

In the literature there has been what seems to me an undue emphasis on kernels κ which do not change sign. This is perhaps because of the fact that

$$\int_I x_n(s)\kappa(s)\, ds = x_n(\sigma) \int_I \kappa(s)\, ds,$$

for a suitable $\sigma \in I$, if κ does not change sign and if $x_n \in C_0$. In practice this relation is usually used for getting the sharp appraisal (23) of the integral on the left, an appraisal which we have obtained directly and which is just one of many possible appraisals.

I do not share the view that it is desirable that κ be of one sign. Quite the opposite. If κ changes sign, then the different contributions of x_n to the integral will tend to offset one another when x_n is of constant sign. If κ does not change sign, one can obtain a lower bound for the absolute value of the integral; but it is usually upper bounds that one seeks.

§ 36. **Symmetry and skew symmetry.** The following corollaries to Theorem 8 are useful.

37. Corollary (The symmetric case). *Suppose in Theorem* 8 *that* $a = 0$, *that* a *is the midpoint of* I, *and that*

$$F[x(-s)] = F[x(s)] \tag{38}$$

for all x *in* C_n. *Then*

$$c^i = 0 \quad \textit{if } i \textit{ is odd};$$

and

$$\kappa(-t) = (-1)^n \kappa(t) \tag{39}$$

at all points of continuity of $\kappa(t)$ *and* $\kappa(-t)$.

PROOF. If

$$y(x) = x(-s), \qquad x \in C_n,$$

then

$$\frac{d^i y}{ds^i} = y_i(s) = (-1)^i x_i(-s), \qquad i \leqq n.$$

Now

$$Fy = Fx,$$

by (38). Hence, by (9),

$$\sum_{i<n} c^i(-1)^i x_i(0) + \int_{-\tilde{\alpha}}^{\tilde{\alpha}} (-1)^n x_n(-s)\kappa(s)\,ds = \sum_{i<n} c^i x_i(0) + \int_{-\tilde{\alpha}}^{\tilde{\alpha}} x_n(s)\kappa(s)\,ds, \qquad x \in C_n. \tag{40}$$

Put

$$x(s) = (s - 0)^{(j)}, \qquad j < n,$$

in (40). The relation reduces to

$$(-1)^j c^j = c^j.$$

Hence $c^j = 0$ if j is odd.

Now put

$$x(s) = \int_0^s (s - t)^{(n-1)} z(t)\,dt$$

in (40), where z is an arbitrary function in C_0. Then

$$x_i(0) = 0, \qquad i < n,$$

and

$$x_n(s) = z(s).$$

Hence (40) reduces to

$$\int_{-\tilde{\alpha}}^{\tilde{\alpha}} (-1)^n z(-s)\kappa(s)\,ds = \int_{-\tilde{\alpha}}^{\tilde{\alpha}} z(s)\kappa(s)\,ds, \qquad z \in C_0.$$

Thus

$$\int_{-\tilde{\alpha}}^{\tilde{\alpha}} (-1)^n z(t)\kappa(-t)\,dt = \int_{-\tilde{\alpha}}^{\tilde{\alpha}} z(s)\kappa(s)\,ds;$$

and

$$\int_{-\tilde{\alpha}}^{\tilde{\alpha}} z(s)[\kappa(s) - (-1)^n\kappa(-s)]\,ds = 0$$

for all z in C_0. Hence

$$\kappa(s) = (-1)^n \kappa(-s)$$

at each point of continuity of $\kappa(s)$ and $\kappa(-s)$. This completes the proof.

41. COROLLARY (THE SKEW-SYMMETRIC CASE). *Suppose in Theorem 8 that $a = 0$, that a is the midpoint of I, and that*

$$F[x(-s)] = -F[x(s)]$$

for all x in C_n. Then

$$c^i = 0 \quad \text{if } i \text{ is even};$$

and

$$\kappa(-t) = (-1)^{n-1}\kappa(t)$$

at all points of continuity of $\kappa(t)$ and $\kappa(-t)$.

The proof is similar to that of Corollary 37.

§ 42. **Functionals that vanish for degree $n - 1$.** We say that x is a polynomial of degree n if

$$x(s) = a_0 + a_1 s + a_2 s^2 + \cdots + a_n s^n, \qquad a_0, \cdots, a_n \in \mathsf{N},$$

whether or not $a_n \neq 0$. This usage is a matter of convenience, not necessity. We say that a functional F *vanishes for degree n* if $Fx = 0$ whenever x is a polynomial of degree n.

The following theorem is due to Peano who, however, did not give a complete statement [1]. The theorem is a corollary of Theorem 8.

43. KERNEL THEOREM. *Suppose that*

$$F \in \mathscr{C}^*_{n-1}, \qquad n \geqq 1,$$

and that F vanishes for degree $n - 1$. Then a function $\kappa \in V$ exists such that

$$Fx = \int_I x_n(s)\kappa(s)\, ds \tag{44}$$

whenever $x \in \boldsymbol{C}_n$. Furthermore κ may be taken so that

$$\kappa(t) = -F[(s - t)^{(n-1)}\theta(t, s)] = F[(s - t)^{(n-1)}\phi(t, s)] \tag{45}$$

for all t not in the jump set $\mathscr{J}_{F,n-1}$, where

$$\theta(t, s) = \begin{cases} 0 & \text{if } t < s, \\ 1 & \text{if } t \geqq s, \end{cases} \tag{46}$$

$$\phi(t, s) = 1 - \theta(t, s) = \begin{cases} 1 & \text{if } t < s, \\ 0 & \text{if } t \geqq s; \end{cases} \tag{47}$$

or, what is the same, κ may be taken so that

$$\kappa(t) = F[(s - t)^{(n-1)}\psi(a, t, s)], \qquad t \notin \mathscr{J}_{F,n-1}, \tag{48}$$

with a in I but otherwise arbitrary.

In (45) and (48) F operates on its arguments as functions of s; t is a parameter. The function ψ is defined in (12).

Some books state Theorem 43 in a weak form, assuming that $F \in \mathscr{C}^*_{n-2}$, $n \geqq 2$, which implies that $F \in \mathscr{C}^*_{n-1}$.

PROOF. Let a be any number in I. Then, by Theorem 8, (9) holds with

$$c^i = F[(s - a)^{(i)}] = 0, \qquad i < n,$$

since F vanishes for degree $n - 1$. This establishes (44), with κ satisfying (11) = (48).

It is easily verified that

$$\psi(a, t, s) = \theta(t, a) - \theta(t, s),$$

by considering the cases $a < s$, $a > s$, $a = s$ (cf. Chapter 11). By (6), then,

$$\begin{aligned}
\kappa(t) &= F[(s - t)^{(n-1)}\{\theta(t, a) - \theta(t, s)\}] \\
&= \theta(t, a)F[(s - t)^{(n-1)}] - F[(s - t)^{(n-1)}\theta(t, s)] \\
&= -F[(s - t)^{(n-1)}\theta(t, s)] \\
&= F[(s - t)^{(n-1)}] - F[(s - t)^{(n-1)}\theta(t, s)] \\
&= F[(s - t)^{(n-1)}\{1 - \theta(t, s)\}] \\
&= F[(s - t)^{(n-1)}\phi(t, s)], \qquad t \notin \mathscr{J}_{F, n-1},
\end{aligned}$$

since F is zero for degree $n - 1$. This establishes (45) and completes the proof.

If $F \in \mathscr{C}^*_m$ for some m, then F will be zero for degree n iff $Fx = 0$ when

$$x(s) = 1, s, \cdots, s^n.$$

This follows immediately from (6).

§ 49. **Illustration. One approximation of $\int_{-1}^{1} x(s)\, ds$.** Suppose that we approximate

$$\int_{-1}^{1} x(s)\, ds$$

by

$$2x(0).$$

The remainder is the functional R, where

$$Rx = \int_{-1}^{1} x(s)\, ds - 2x(0). \tag{50}$$

We shall study this functional. Take

$$I = \{-1 \leqq s \leqq 1\}.$$

Since Rx is a Stieltjes integral on $x(s)$ (of the form (5)), $R \in \mathscr{C}_0^*$. Hence

$$R \in \mathscr{C}_{n-1}^*, \qquad n = 1, 2, 3, \cdots;$$

and we may apply Theorem 8 to R with $n = 1, 2, 3, \cdots$. Since R is symmetric, we may also apply Corollary 37.

By direct substitution

$$Rx = 0 \quad \text{when} \quad x(s) = 1 \quad \text{or} \quad x(s) = s,$$

and

$$Rx \neq 0 \quad \text{when} \quad x(s) = s^2.$$

Hence we may apply Theorem 43 with $n = 1$ or 2.

We now obtain different formulas for Rx.

CASE i. *Theorem* 43 *with* $n = 1$. Here

$$(51) \qquad Rx = \int_{-1}^{1} x_1(s)\kappa^1(s)\,ds, \qquad x \in \boldsymbol{C}_1,$$

where

$$(52) \qquad \kappa^1(t) = -R[\theta(t, s)] = R[\phi(t, s)], \qquad t \neq 0.$$

The superscript in κ^1 is intended merely to distinguish the present kernel from later ones. The jump set $\mathscr{J}_{R,0}$ consists of the single point $s = 0$, because the mass in (50) relative to $x_0 = x$ is discontinuous only at $s = 0$. Hence the only value excluded in (52) is $t = 0$.

To evaluate $\kappa^1(t)$, suppose first that $0 < t \leqq 1$. Then

$$\kappa^1(t) = R[\phi(t, s)] = \int_{-1}^{1} \phi(t, s)\,ds - 2\phi(t, 0)$$

$$= \int_{t}^{1} ds - 0 = 1 - t,$$

by (47). The reader may check this result by working out $-R[\theta(t, s)]$.

One may similarly calculate $\kappa^1(t)$ for $-1 \leqq t < 0$, by (52). However, such calculation is not needed here since, by Corollary 37,

$$\kappa^1(-t) = -\kappa^1(t).$$

Thus if $-1 \leqq t < 0$,

$$\kappa^1(t) = -\kappa^1(-t) = -[1 - (-t)] = -1 - t.$$

Thus (51) is established, with

$$\kappa^1(t) = \begin{cases} -1 - t & \text{if} \quad -1 \leqq t < 0, \\ 1 - t & \text{if} \quad 0 < t \leqq 1. \end{cases}$$

The value of $\kappa^1(t)$ at $t = 0$ is immaterial to (51).

Of the possible inequalities, we now note (23) and (29):

$$|Rx| \leqq \sup_{-1<s<1} |x_1(s)|,$$

$$|Rx| \leqq \left[\frac{2}{3}\int_{-1}^{1} x_1(s)^2\, ds\right]^{1/2}, \qquad x \in \boldsymbol{C}_1.$$

These are valid because

$$\int_{-1}^{1} |\kappa^1(t)|\, dt = 2\int_{0}^{1} |\kappa^1(t)|\, dt = 2\int_{0}^{1} (1 - t)\, dt = 1,$$

$$\int_{-1}^{1} \kappa^1(t)^2\, dt = 2\int_{0}^{1} \kappa^1(t)^2\, dt = 2\int_{0}^{1} (1 - t)^2\, dt = \frac{2}{3}.$$

The importance of Theorems 8 and 43 is that they assert the validity of the formulas for Fx and afford a direct way to calculate the formulas. Once a formula like (51) is obtained, it may be checked directly. Thus

$$\int_{-1}^{1} x_1(s)\kappa^1(s)\, ds = \int_{-1}^{0} x_1(s)(-1 - s)\, ds + \int_{0}^{1} x_1(s)(1 - s)\, ds;$$

and integration by parts shows that the second member is indeed

$$\int_{-1}^{1} x(s)\, ds - 2x(0).$$

When functions of two variables are involved, however, a check of this sort is much more complicated and, in fact, often completely impracticable (cf. § 5: 26).

Another approach to the study of Rx is to start with the Stieltjes integrals. Thus (50) may be written

$$Rx = \int_{-1}^{1} x(s)\, d\mu(s) \tag{53}$$

where μ may be taken as

$$\mu(s) = \begin{cases} 1 + s & \text{if } -1 \leqq s < 0, \\ -1 + s & \text{if } \quad 0 \leqq s \leqq 1, \end{cases}$$

the essential properties of μ being that

$$d\mu = ds \qquad \text{for } s \neq 0,$$

$$d\mu = -2 \quad \text{for } s = 0,$$

and

$$\mu(s) = 0 \qquad \text{at } s = -1.$$

Now evaluate (53) by parts (Theorem 12: 8):

$$Rx = 0 - \int_{-1}^{1} \mu(s)\, dx(s),$$

$$Rx = -\int_{-1}^{1} \mu(s) x_1(s)\, ds, \qquad x \in \boldsymbol{C}_1.$$

This is precisely (51) with

$$\kappa^1(s) = -\mu(s).$$

When functions of two variables are involved, however, a calculation of the sort in this paragraph is often impracticable (cf. § 5: 26).

Note that (51) does not necessarily hold if $x \in C_0$. For Rx is surely defined then, but $x_1(s)$ need not exist. One strength of (51) is that advantage is taken of the existence of $x_1(s)$ when it is known that $x \in \boldsymbol{C}_1$.

Case ii. *Theorem* 43 *with* $n = 2$. A similar calculation based on the formulas

$$\kappa(t) = \kappa^2(t) = -R[(s - t)\theta(t, s)] = R[(s - t)\phi(t, s)]$$

applies. Since the mass in (50) corresponding to $x_{n-1} = x_1$ has no discontinuities (being identically zero), the jump set $\mathscr{J}_{R,1}$ is empty, and the above formula holds without exception.

Suppose that $0 < t \leqq 1$. Then

$$\kappa^2(t) = R[(s - t)\phi(t, s)] = \int_{-1}^{1} (s - t)\phi(t, s)\, ds + 2t\phi(t, 0)$$

$$= \int_{t}^{1} (s - t)\, ds = \frac{(1 - t)^2}{2}.$$

By Corollary 37 (or by a similar calculation for $-1 \leqq t < 0$),

$$\kappa^2(-t) = \kappa^2(t).$$

Hence

(54) $$Rx = \int_{-1}^{1} x_2(s)\kappa^2(s)\, ds, \qquad x \in \boldsymbol{C}_2,$$

where

$$\kappa^2(t) = \frac{(1 - |t|)^2}{2}.$$

Also

$$|Rx| \leqq \frac{1}{3} \sup_{-1<s<1} |x_2(s)|,$$

$$|Rx| \leqq \left[\frac{1}{10}\int_{-1}^{1} x_2(s)^2\, ds\right]^{1/2}, \qquad x \in \boldsymbol{C}_2,$$

since

$$\int_{-1}^{1} |\kappa^2(t)|\, dt = 2\int_0^1 \frac{(1-t)^2}{2}\, dt = \frac{1}{3},$$

$$\int_{-1}^{1} \kappa^2(t)^2\, dt = 2\int_0^1 \frac{(1-t)^4}{4}\, dt = \frac{1}{10}.$$

The formulas (54) and (51) are related. Indeed

$$d\kappa^2(s) = -\kappa^1(s)\, ds,$$

and one formula can be derived from the other by an integration by parts. For functions of two variables, analogous shifting from one valid formula to another is often impracticable (Chapters 4, 5).

Case iii. *Theorem* 8 *with* $n = 3$, $a = 0$. The final result is that

$$(55) \qquad Rx = \frac{1}{3}\, x_2(0) + \int_{-1}^{1} x_3(s)\kappa^3(s)\, ds, \qquad x \in C_3,$$

where

$$\kappa^3(t) = \begin{cases} \dfrac{-(1+t)^3}{6} & \text{if } \; -1 \leqq t < 0, \\ \dfrac{(1-t)^3}{6} & \text{if } \; 0 \leqq t \leqq 1. \end{cases}$$

The direct application of Theorem 8 to obtain (55) is as follows. By (10),

$$c^2 = R[s^{(2)}] = \int_{-1}^{1} \frac{s^2}{2}\, ds - (2)(0) = \frac{1}{3},$$

$$c^1 = c^0 = 0.$$

By (11)

$$\kappa^3(t) = R\left[\frac{(s-t)^2}{2}\, \psi(0, t, s)\right]$$

without exception, since the mass in (50) corresponding to x_{n-1} has no discontinuities.

Suppose that $0 < t \leqq 1$. Then

$$\psi(0, t, s) = \theta(t, 0) - \theta(t, s) = 1 - \theta(t, s) = \phi(t, s),$$

$$\kappa^3(t) = \int_{-1}^{1} \frac{(s-t)^2}{2}\, \phi(t, s)\, ds - 2\,\frac{t^2}{2}\, \phi(t, 0)$$

$$= \int_t^1 \frac{(s-t)^2}{2}\, ds = \frac{(1-t)^3}{6}.$$

If $-1 \leqq t < 0$, then

$$\kappa^3(t) = -\kappa^3(-t) = \frac{-(1+t)^3}{6},$$

by Corollary 37 or by a similar calculation.

Theorem 8 may also be applied with other values of a and n.

§ 56. **Illustration. One approximation of $\int_0^1 x(s)\, ds/\sqrt{s}$.** Suppose that we choose to approximate the integral

$$\int_0^1 \frac{x(s)\, ds}{\sqrt{s}}$$

by

$$[4x(0) + 2x(1)]/3,$$

an approximation which is exact for degree 1. The remainder is

$$Rx = 2\int_0^1 x(s)\, d(s^{1/2}) - \frac{4x(0) + 2x(1)}{3}.$$

The infinity in the integrand has been absorbed in the differential.

The functional Rx is a Stieltjes integral on $x(s)$; and $R \in \mathscr{C}_0^*$. Hence Theorem 8 applies with $n = 1, 2, \cdots$. Since R vanishes for degree 1, Theorem 43 applies with $n = 1$ or 2. For $n = 2$, the result is

$$Rx = \int_0^1 x_2(s)\kappa(s)\, ds, \qquad x \in C_2,$$

where

$$3\kappa(s) = -4s + 4s^{3/2}.$$

§ 57. **Illustration. One approximation of the derivative $x_1(s)$ at $s = 1/4$.** Suppose that we choose to approximate the value of dx/ds at $s = 1/4$ by

$$\frac{-x(-1) - 2x(0) + 3x(1)}{4},$$

an approximation which is exact for degree 2. The error in the approximation is

$$Rx = \frac{-x(-1) - 2x(0) + 3x(1)}{4} - x_1\left(\frac{1}{4}\right). \tag{58}$$

Here Rx is the sum of two Stieltjes integrals, one on x and one on x_1. Hence $R \in \mathscr{C}_1^*$, and Theorem 8 applies to R with $n = 2, 3, \cdots$. Theorem 8 does not apply with $n = 1$. This is reasonable, since an integral

$$\int_{-1}^1 x_1(s)\kappa(s)\, ds$$

could not possibly produce the term $x_1(1/4)$.

Since

$$Rx = 0 \quad \text{when} \quad x(s) = 1, s, s^2,$$

R vanishes for degree 2. Since $R[s^3] \neq 0$, R does not vanish for degree 3. Hence Theorem 43 applies to R with $n = 2$ and $n = 3$.

The result for $n = 3$ is

$$Rx = \int_{-1}^{1} x_3(s)\kappa(s)\,ds, \qquad x \in C_3,$$

where

$$\kappa(s) = \begin{cases} \dfrac{(1+s)^2}{8} & \text{if } -1 < s < 0, \\ \dfrac{1+2s+3s^2}{8} & \text{if } \ 0 < s < \dfrac{1}{4}, \\ \dfrac{3(1-s)^2}{8} & \text{if } \ \dfrac{1}{4} < s < 1; \end{cases}$$

the omitted values of κ are immaterial. The calculation starts with the equations

$$\kappa(t) = -R[(s-t)^{(2)}\theta(t,s)] = R[(s-t)^{(2)}\phi(t,s)].$$

These equations hold without exception, since the jump set $\mathscr{J}_{R,2}$ is empty because the Stieltjes mass in (58) corresponding to x_2 has no discontinuities.

If $1/4 < t < 1$,

$$\begin{aligned} \kappa(t) &= R\left[\frac{(s-t)^2}{2}\phi(t,s)\right] \\ &= \frac{-(1+t)^2\phi(t,-1) - 2t^2\phi(t,0) + 3(1-t)^2\phi(t,1)}{8} - [(s-t)\phi(t,s)]_{s=1/4} \\ &= \frac{3(1-t)^2}{8} - 0. \end{aligned}$$

If $0 < t < 1/4$,

$$\kappa(t) = R\left[\frac{(s-t)^2}{2}\phi(t,s)\right] = \frac{3(1-t)^2}{8} - \left(\frac{1}{4} - t\right) = \frac{1+2t+3t^2}{8}.$$

If $-1 < t < 0$,

$$\kappa(t) = -R\left[\frac{(s-t)^2}{2}\theta(t,s)\right] = \frac{+(1+t)^2}{8} - 0.$$

§ 59. **Illustration. Linear interpolation.** If we approximate $x(u)$ by a linear interpolation based on $x(0)$ and $x(1)$, the error is

$$Rx = (1-u)x(0) + ux(1) - x(u).$$

Here u is a fixed real number, Rx is a Stieltjes integral on x, and

$$R \in \mathscr{C}_0^*$$

if we take I as the smallest interval containing $s = 0, 1$, and u. Theorem 8 applies with $n = 1, 2, 3, \cdots$; Theorem 43 with $n = 1, 2$.

If $0 \leqq u \leqq 1$, the result for $n = 2$ is

$$Rx = \int_0^1 x_2(s)\kappa(s)\,ds, \qquad x \in \boldsymbol{C}_2 = \boldsymbol{C}_2[0, 1],$$

where

$$\kappa(s) = \kappa(s, u) = \begin{cases} s(1 - u) & \text{if } 0 < s < u, \\ u(1 - s) & \text{if } u < s < 1. \end{cases}$$

Since $\kappa(s, u) \geqq 0$,

$$\int_0^1 |\kappa(s, u)|\,ds = \int_0^1 \kappa(s, u)\,ds = \int_0^u s(1 - u)\,ds + \int_u^1 u(1 - s)\,ds$$

$$= (1 - u)\frac{u^2}{2} + u\frac{(1 - u)^2}{2} = \frac{u(1 - u)}{2}.$$

Hence, by (23),

$$|Rx| \leqq \frac{u(1 - u)}{2} \sup_{0<s<1} |x_2(s)|, \qquad x \in \boldsymbol{C}_2[0, 1], \qquad 0 \leqq u \leqq 1,$$

an inequality often given in the literature.

Alternatively,

$$\int_0^1 \kappa(s, u)^2\,ds = \int_0^u s^2(1 - u)^2\,ds + \int_u^1 u^2(1 - s)^2\,ds = \frac{u^2(1 - u)^2}{3}.$$

Hence, by (29)

$$|Rx| \leqq \frac{u(1 - u)}{\sqrt{3}}\left[\int_0^1 x_2(s)^2\,ds\right]^{1/2}, \qquad x \in \boldsymbol{C}_2[0, 1], \quad 0 \leqq u \leqq 1;$$

an inequality in terms of the root-mean-square of the second derivative of the function operated on.

§ 60. **A theorem on convex families of functions.** The following theorem will be an aid in certain calculations where it will reduce by half the number of unknowns to be determined.

Let us say that K is a *convex family* if K is a set whose elements are measurable functions on

$$I = \{\alpha \leqq s \leqq \tilde{\alpha}\}$$

and if

$$(1 - t)\kappa^0 + t\kappa^1 \in \mathsf{K} \quad \text{whenever } \kappa^0, \kappa^1 \in \mathsf{K} \text{ and } 0 \leqq t \leqq 1.$$

61. THEOREM. *Suppose that* K *is a convex family and that*

$$e > 1.$$

If there is an element κ *in* K *for which*

$$J = \int_I |\kappa(s)|^e \, ds$$

is minimal and finite, then κ *is unique to within a set of measure zero.*

The conclusion may be expressed as follows: If $\kappa^0 \in \mathsf{K}$ and $\kappa^1 \in \mathsf{K}$ minimize J, then

$$\kappa^0 = \kappa^1 \quad \text{almost everywhere on } I. \tag{62}$$

PROOF. By way of introduction, consider the case $e = 2$. Suppose that J is minimal both for $\kappa^0 \in \mathsf{K}$ and $\kappa^1 \in \mathsf{K}$. Define the function f as follows:

$$f(t) = \int_I [(1 - t)\kappa^0(s) + t\kappa^1(s)]^2 \, ds = \int_I \{[\kappa^1(s) - \kappa^0(s)]t + \kappa^0(s)\}^2 \, ds,$$
$$0 \leqq t \leqq 1.$$

By hypothesis, $f(t)$ is a value taken on by J with $\kappa \in \mathsf{K}$, for each t such that $0 \leqq t \leqq 1$. By construction $f(t)$ is minimal for $t = 0$ and for $t = 1$. Now $f(t)$ is a quadratic function of t, with nonnegative leading coefficient. Such a function cannot take on its minimum at both ends of an interval unless it is quadratic in appearance only, indeed, unless both its coefficient of t^2 and of t vanish. Hence

$$\int_I [\kappa^1(s) - \kappa^0(s)]^2 \, ds = 0.$$

This implies (62).

Now consider the general case $e > 1$. Suppose that $J < \infty$ is minimal for both $\kappa^0 \in \mathsf{K}$ and $\kappa^1 \in \mathsf{K}$. Define the function g as follows:

$$g(t) = \left[\int_I |(1 - t)\kappa^0(s) + t\kappa^1(s)|^e \, ds\right]^{1/e}, \qquad 0 \leqq t \leqq 1.$$

Then $g(t)$ is minimal both at $t = 0$ and at $t = 1$; and

$$g(0) = g(1).$$

The idea of the present proof is that unless (62) held g would be a strictly convex function, a contradiction of its being minimal at two points.

By Minkowski's inequality [Hardy-Littlewood-Pólya 1, p. 146],

$$\begin{aligned} g(t) &< \left[\int_I |(1 - t)\kappa^0(s)|^e \, ds\right]^{1/e} + \left[\int_I |t\kappa^1(s)|^e \, ds\right]^{1/e} \\ &= (1 - t)\left[\int_I |\kappa^0(s)|^e \, ds\right]^{1/e} + t\left[\int_I |\kappa^1(s)|^e \, ds\right]^{1/e} \\ &= (1 - t)g(0) + tg(1) = g(0), \qquad 0 < t < 1, \end{aligned}$$

unless $|(1-t)\kappa^0(s)|$ and $|t\kappa^1(s)|$ are effectively proportional, that is, unless constants a and b exist, not both zero, such that

$$a|\kappa^0(s)| = b|\kappa^1(s)| \qquad \text{almost everywhere.}$$

This last relation must therefore hold; otherwise $g(0)$ could not be minimal. Now suppose, for example, that $b \neq 0$. Then

$$|\kappa^1(s)| = c|\kappa^0(s)|, \qquad c \in \mathsf{R},$$

and

$$g(1) = cg(0).$$

Hence

$$g(0) = g(1) = 0 \quad \text{or} \quad c = 1.$$

In the first case,

$$\kappa^0(s) = \kappa^1(s) = 0 \quad \text{almost everywhere,}$$

and the theorem is proved.

If $c = 1$, then

$$|\kappa^1(s)| = |\kappa^0(s)| \quad \text{almost everywhere,}$$

(63) $$\kappa^1(s) = \pm\kappa^0(s) \quad \text{almost everywhere.}$$

We now show that the upper sign holds except on a set of measure zero. Let A be the set of points in I at which

(64) $$\kappa^1(s) = -\kappa^0(s) \neq 0.$$

Put

$$B = I - A;$$

then, by (63),

$$\kappa^1(s) = \kappa^0(s) \quad \text{for almost all } s \text{ in } B.$$

Hence

$$\begin{aligned} g(t) &= \left[\int_A |(1-t)\kappa^0(s) - t\kappa^0(s)|^e\, ds + \int_B |(1-t)\kappa^0(s) + t\kappa^0(s)|^e\, ds\right]^{1/e} \\ &= \left[|1-2t|^e \int_A |\kappa^0(s)|^e\, ds + \int_B |\kappa^0(s)|^e\, ds\right]^{1/e}. \end{aligned}$$

Hence

$$g\left(\frac{1}{2}\right) = \left[\int_B |\kappa^0(s)|^e\, ds\right]^{1/e} < g(0),$$

unless

$$\int_A |\kappa^0(s)|^e\, ds = 0,$$

that is, unless A is a set of measure zero, by (64). Since A is of measure zero, (63) implies (62); and the proof is complete.

Chapter 2

Applications

This chapter consists of four parts which consider the approximation of integrals, values, derivatives, and sums related to a function of one real variable.

Part 1. Integrals

§ 1. **Introduction. Best formulas.** Suppose that we wish to approximate the integral

$$\int_{-1}^{1} x(s)\, ds,$$

say, by Ax. We must decide what approximation Ax to use and we should, if possible, study the remainder R, where

$$Rx = \int_{-1}^{1} x(s)\, ds - Ax.$$

If we could choose Ax so that Rx were small for all integrands x that would be considered, such a choice of A would be compelling. There is usually no satisfactory way to make Rx small for all pertinent x. The choice of A is influenced by questions of practicality and convenience also.

Let us specify, in this illustration, that A be of the form

$$(2) \qquad Ax = ux(-1) + vx(0) + wx(1), \qquad u, v, w \in \mathsf{R}.$$

Thus A will be determined by the choice of the three real numbers u, v, w. The remainder in the approximation is the Stieltjes integral

$$(3) \qquad Rx = \int_{-1}^{1} x(s)\, ds - ux(-1) - vx(0) - wx(1)$$

on the function x. Hence

$$R \in \mathscr{C}_0^* \subset \mathscr{C}_1^* \subset \mathscr{C}_2^* \subset \cdots;$$

and Theorem 1 : 8 applies with $n = 1, 2, \cdots$; $F = R$; a arbitrary; and the interval I the smallest closed interval that contains $s = -1$, 1, and a. We shall assume that

$$-1 \leqq a \leqq 1,$$

so that

$$I = [-1, 1].$$

Then

$$Rx = c^0x_0(a) + \cdots + c^{n-1}x_{n-1}(a) + \int_{-1}^{1} x_n(s)\kappa^n(s)\,ds, \tag{4}$$

whenever $x \in \boldsymbol{C}_n$. The superscript n in κ^n here merely distinguishes different kernels κ^n that occur for different values of n.

We may study R and determine our choice of A by means of (3) or (4) or in other ways.

We shall consider a series of cases. In the first cases, we arrange that

$$c^i = 0, \qquad i < n, \tag{5}$$

and we study R by (4). Then we consider cases in which c^i, $i < n$, do not all vanish. Finally we consider (3) directly.

The condition (5) is equivalent to the condition that R vanish for degree $n - 1$, by (1 : 10), in which case Theorem 1 : 43 applies.

CASE i. $n = 1$ *and* $c^0 = 0$. We specify that A shall be chosen so that

$$n = 1, \qquad c^0 = 0.$$

Then

$$Rx = \int_{-1}^{1} x_1(s)\kappa^1(s)\,ds, \qquad x \in \boldsymbol{C}_1. \tag{6}$$

Thus the remainder is completely determined by x_1. We propose to analyze Rx in terms of x_1, the first derivative of the function operated on.

The condition $c^0 = 0$ will be satisfied iff

$$Rx = 0 \quad \text{when} \quad x(s) = 1, s \in \boldsymbol{I};$$

that is, iff

$$R[1] = \int_{-1}^{1} 1\,ds - u - v - w = 0,$$

$$u + v + w = 2, \tag{7}$$

by (3). Then

$$\kappa^1(t) = -R[\theta(t, s)] = R[\phi(t, s)], \qquad t \neq -1, 0, 1,$$

by (1 : 45), since $\mathscr{J}_{R,0}$ is $s = -1, 0, 1$. Take $-1 < t < 1$. Then, by (1 : 46),

$$\kappa^1(t) = -\int_{-1}^{1} \theta(t, s)\,ds + u\theta(t, -1) + v\theta(t, 0) + w\theta(t, 1)$$

$$= -\int_{-1}^{t} 1\,ds + u + v\theta(t, 0) + 0 = -t - 1 + u + v\theta(t, 0).$$

Hence

$$\kappa^1(t) = \begin{cases} -t - 1 + u & \text{if } -1 < t < 0, \\ -t - 1 + u + v = -t + 1 - w & \text{if } \quad 0 < t < 1. \end{cases} \tag{8}$$

There are two degrees of freedom in our choice of u, v, w, because of the constraint (7). Let us take u and w as independent variables, v as dependent.

The next step depends on our information about the functions x on which we will operate. Suppose that we know or have a bound for one of the quantities

$$\sup_{-1 \leqq s \leqq 1} |x_1(s)|, \qquad \int_{-1}^{1} [x_1(s)]^2 \, ds, \qquad \int_{-1}^{1} |x_1(s)| \, ds.$$

(We could also consider

$$\int_{-1}^{1} |x_1(s)|^e \, ds, \qquad 2 \neq e > 1,$$

but this is perhaps not of practical interest.) By (1 : 23, 25, 29),

$$|Rx| \leqq M \sup_{s \in I} |x_1(s)|, \qquad M = \int_{-1}^{1} |\kappa^1(t)| \, dt, \tag{9}$$

$$[Rx]^2 \leqq J \int_{-1}^{1} [x_1(s)]^2 \, ds, \qquad J = \int_{-1}^{1} [\kappa^1(t)]^2 \, dt, \tag{10}$$

$$|Rx| \leqq N \int_{-1}^{1} |x_1(s)| \, ds, \qquad N = \sup_{t \in I} |\kappa^1(t)|, \tag{11}$$

it being assumed in the last supremum that κ^1 is defined suitably† at $t = -1, 0, 1$. The constants M, J, and N in these inequalities are the best possible, even if x is restricted to be a polynomial rather than an element of C_1.

We now define best formulas as follows. A formula (2) is *best relative to*

$$\sup_{s \in I} |x_1(s)|$$

if it minimizes M; it is *best relative to*

$$\int_I [x_1(s)]^2 \, ds$$

if it minimizes J; it is *best relative to*

$$\int_I |x_1(s)| \, ds$$

if it minimizes N. Best formulas give the appraisals (9, 10, 11) with the least possible right side, respectively. We shall calculate these three best formulas.

† $\kappa^1(t)$ is to lie between $\kappa^1(t + 0)$ and $\kappa^1(t - 0)$ for all t.

CASE i_1. *The best formula relative to* $\int_I [x_1(s)]^2\, ds$. Here we shall choose u, w so as to minimize

$$J = \int_{-1}^{1} \kappa^1(t)^2\, dt = \int_{-1}^{0} (u - t - 1)^2\, dt + \int_{0}^{1} (1 - t - w)^2\, dt.$$

Since u, w are independent variables, the two terms are independent. To minimize J it is therefore necessary and sufficient to minimize each term. Consider the last term, for example.

$$\int_0^1 (1 - t - w)^2\, dt = \int_0^1 (s - w)^2\, ds = \frac{1 - 3w + 3w^2}{3}.$$

This quadratic function is minimal iff $w = 1/2$; its minimal value is†

$$\frac{(1 - 3w/2)}{3} = \frac{1}{12}.$$

The first term may be treated similarly or by observing that it is the term just studied with (t, w) replaced by $(-t, u)$.

Thus J takes on its minimal value $1/6$ when

$$u = w = \frac{1}{2}, \qquad v = 1.$$

The best formula relative to

$$\int_I [x_1(s)]^2\, ds$$

is therefore the iterated trapezoidal rule; and

$$Rx = \int_{-1}^{1} x(s)\, ds - [.5x(-1) + x(0) + .5x(1)], \tag{12}$$

$$Rx = \int_{-1}^{1} x_1(s)\kappa^1(s)\, ds \quad \text{if } x \in \boldsymbol{C}_1,$$

$$\kappa^1(s) = \begin{cases} -.5 - s & \text{if } s < 0, \\ .5 - s & \text{if } s > 0, \end{cases}$$

$$|Rx| \leqq \left[\frac{1}{6}\int_{-1}^{1} x_1(s)^2\, ds\right]^{1/2}, \qquad x \in \boldsymbol{C}_1. \tag{13}$$

CASE i_2. *The best formula relative to* $\sup_{s \in I} |x_1(s)|$. Continuing to use (8), we now determine u, w so as to minimize

$$M = \int_{-1}^{1} |\kappa^1(t)|\, dt = \int_{-1}^{0} |1 + t - u|\, dt + \int_{0}^{1} |1 - t - w|\, dt.$$

† Cf. Lemma 46 below.

Since u and w are independent, it is necessary and sufficient to minimize each term on the right separately. Consider

$$M' \underset{\text{def}}{=} \int_0^1 |1 - t - w|\, dt.$$

It is clear from the graph of $1 - t - w$ vs. t that M' will not be minimal when $w < 0$ or $w > 1$. Suppose that $0 \leqq w \leqq 1$. Then

$$\begin{aligned} M' &= \int_0^{1-w} (1 - t - w)\, dt + \int_{1-w}^1 (t + w - 1)\, dt \\ &= \int_w^1 (s - w)\, ds + \int_0^w (w - s)\, ds = .5 - w + w^2. \end{aligned}$$

Hence M' is minimal when $w = .5$ and then equals

$$.5 - .5w = .25.$$

The other term equals M' with (t, w) replaced by $(-t, u)$. Hence the minimal value of M is .5 and occurs when

$$u = w = .5, \qquad v = 1.$$

The best formula relative to

$$\sup_{s \in I} |x_1(s)|$$

is again the trapezoidal rule (12), and

$$|Rx| \leqq .5 \sup_{s \in I} |x_1(s)|, \qquad x \in C_1. \tag{14}$$

CASE i_3. *The best formula relative to* $\int_I |x_1(s)|\, ds$. Continuing to use (8) we now determine u, w so as to minimize

$$N = \sup_{t \in I} |\kappa^1(t)| = \max \left[\sup_{-1<t<0} |1 + t - u|, \sup_{0<t<1} |1 - t - w| \right].$$

The two suprema in the bracket are independent. Consider

$$N' \underset{\text{def}}{=} \sup_{0<t<1} |1 - t - w| = \begin{cases} 1 - w & \text{if } w < 0, \\ \max(1 - w, w) & \text{if } 0 \leqq w \leqq 1, \\ w & \text{if } 1 < w, \end{cases}$$

as may be seen from the graph of $1 - t - w$ vs. t. The other supremum equals N' with w replaced by u.

The minimal N' is .5 and occurs when $w = .5$. Hence the minimal N is .5 and occurs when

$$u = w = .5, \qquad v = 1.$$

Thus the best formula relative to

$$\int_I |x_1(s)|\, ds$$

is again the trapezoidal rule (12), and

$$|Rx| \leqq .5 \int_{-1}^{1} |x_1(s)|\, ds, \qquad x \in C_1. \tag{15}$$

According to all three criteria, the iterated trapezoidal rule is best in Case i.

CASE ii. $n = 2$ *and* $c^0 = c^1 = 0$. We specify that A shall be chosen so that

$$n = 2; \qquad c^0 = c^1 = 0.$$

Then

$$Rx = \int_{-1}^{1} x_2(s)\kappa^2(s)\, ds, \qquad x \in C_2;$$

the remainder is completely determined by x_2. We propose to analyze Rx in terms of x_2, the second derivative of the function operated on. In Case i we considered the analysis of Rx in terms of x_1.

The conditions $c^0 = c^1 = 0$ will be satisfied iff

$$Rx = 0 \quad \text{when} \quad x(s) = s \quad \text{and when } x(s) = 1;$$

that is, iff

$$\int_{-1}^{1} s\, ds - (-u + 0 + w) = 0 \quad \text{or} \quad u = w,$$

and

$$u + v + w = 2,$$

by (3). Then, by (1:45),

$$\kappa^2(t) = -R[(s - t)\theta(t, s)] = R[(s - t)\phi(t, s)],$$

without exception since $\mathscr{J}_{R,1}$ is empty. If $-1 < t < 0$,

$$\begin{aligned}\kappa^2(t) &= -\int_I (s - t)\theta(t, s)\, ds + (-1 - t)\theta(t, -1)u + (-t)\theta(t, 0)v \\ &\quad + (1 - t)\theta(t, 1)w \\ &= -\int_{-1}^{t} (s - t)\, ds + (-1 - t)u = .5(1 + t)^2 - u(1 + t),\end{aligned}$$

by the expression containing $\theta(t, s)$. If $0 < t < 1$, by the dual expression,

$$\kappa^2(t) = \int_t^1 (s - t)\, ds - (1 - t)w = .5(1 - t)^2 - w(1 - t);$$

this result may also be obtained by a change of variable of integration in Rx.

There is one degree of freedom, since the parameters u, v, w are subject to two constraints. Take v as the independent variable. Then

$$u = w = 1 - .5v$$

and

$$\kappa^2(t) = \begin{cases} .5(1 + t)(v - 1 + t) & \text{if } -1 \leqq t \leqq 0, \\ .5(1 - t)(v - 1 - t) & \text{if } 0 \leqq t \leqq 1. \end{cases} \tag{16}$$

The condition $u = w$ has made R symmetrical, so $\kappa^2(t)$ is an even function, in conformity to Corollary 1 : 37.

The value of v is at our disposal. We suppose that we will use one of the inequalities

$$|Rx| \leqq M \sup_{s \in I} |x_2(s)|, \qquad M = \int_I |\kappa^2(t)|\, dt;$$

$$(Rx)^2 \leqq J \int_I [x_2(s)]^2\, ds, \qquad J = \int_I [\kappa^2(t)]^2\, dt;$$

$$|Rx| \leqq N \int_I |x_2(s)|\, ds, \qquad N = \sup_{t \in I} |\kappa^2(t)|.$$

CASE ii$_1$. *The best formula relative to* $\int_I [x_2(s)]^2\, ds$. This is defined as the formula which minimizes

$$J = \int_{-1}^{1} \kappa^2(t)^2\, dt = 2\int_0^1 \kappa^2(t)^2\, dt = .5\int_0^1 (1 - t)^2(v - 1 - t)^2\, dt$$

$$= .5\int_0^1 s^2(v - 2 + s)^2\, ds = \frac{10v^2 - 25v + 16}{60}.$$

Now J is minimal iff $v = 5/4$, in which case

$$J = \frac{(16 - 125/8)}{60} = \frac{1}{160}.$$

Then

$$u = w = \frac{3}{8}.$$

Thus the best formula relative to

$$\int_I x_2(s)^2\, ds$$

is the 3, 10, 3 rule; and for this rule

$$Rx = \int_{-1}^{1} x(s)\, ds - \frac{3x(-1) + 10x(0) + 3x(1)}{8},$$

$$Rx = \int_{-1}^{1} x_2(s)\kappa^2(s)\,ds \qquad \text{if } x \in C_2,$$

$$\kappa^2(s) = \frac{(1 - |s|)(1 - 4|s|)}{8},$$

$$|Rx| \leqq \left[\frac{1}{160}\int_{-1}^{1} x_2(s)^2\,ds\right]^{1/2}, \qquad x \in C_2.$$

CASE ii$_2$. *The best formula relative to* $\sup_{s\in I}|x_2(s)|$. This is defined as the formula which minimizes

$$M = \int_{-1}^{1} |\kappa^2(t)|\,dt = 2\int_0^1 .5|(1 - t)(v - 1 - t)|\,dt = \int_0^1 (1 - t)|t - v'|\,dt,$$

where

$$v' = v - 1.$$

It is clear from the graph of $t - v'$ vs. t that M will not be minimal when $v' < 0$ or $v' > 1$. Suppose that $0 \leqq v' \leqq 1$. Then

$$M = \int_0^{v'} (1 - t)(v' - t)\,dt + \int_{v'}^1 (1 - t)(t - v')\,dt = \frac{1 - 3v' + 6v'^2 - 2v'^3}{6}.$$

Hence

$$\frac{dM}{dv'} = 0 \quad \text{iff} \quad v' = 1 \pm \frac{1}{\sqrt{2}}.$$

The minimum of M occurs at

$$v' = 1 - \frac{1}{\sqrt{2}}$$

and is

$$M = \frac{2 - \sqrt{2}}{6} = .09763.$$

Then

$$v = 2 - 1/\sqrt{2} = 1.2929, \qquad u = w = 1/2\sqrt{2} = .3536.$$

Thus for the best formula relative to

$$\sup_{s\in I}|x_2(s)|,$$

the following relations hold:

$$Rx = \int_{-1}^{1} x(s)\,ds - \left\{\frac{1}{2\sqrt{2}}[x(-1) + x(1)] + \left(2 - \frac{1}{\sqrt{2}}\right)x(0)\right\},$$

$$Rx = \int_{-1}^{1} x_2(s)\kappa^2(s)\,ds, \qquad x \in C_2,$$

$$|Rx| \leqq \frac{2 - \sqrt{2}}{6} \sup_{s \in I} |x_2(s)|;$$

and κ^2 is given by (16) with $v = 2 - 1/\sqrt{2}$.

CASE ii3. *The best formula relative to* $\int_I |x_2(s)|\,ds$. This is defined as the formula which minimizes

$$N = \sup_{-1<t<1} |\kappa^2(t)| = \sup_{0<t<1} |.5(1 - t)(v - 1 - t)|$$

$$= \sup_{0<t<1} .5(1 - t)|v' - t|,$$

where

$$v' = v - 1.$$

As before the minimum of N cannot occur for $v' < 0$ or $v' > 1$. Suppose that $0 \leqq v' \leqq 1$. Then

$$N = \max\left[\sup_{0<t<v'} .5(1 - t)(v' - t),\ \sup_{v'<t<1} .5(1 - t)(t - v')\right]$$

$$= \max\,[v'/2,\ (1 - v')^2/8].$$

The minimum N then occurs when

$$N = v'/2 = (1 - v')^2/8,$$

$$v'^2 - 6v' + 1 = 0,$$

$$v' = 3 - \sqrt{8}.$$

Then

$$v = 4 - \sqrt{8} = 1.1716, \qquad u = w = \sqrt{2} - 1 = .4142,$$

$$N = 1.5 - \sqrt{2} = .08579.$$

Thus for the best formula relative to

$$\int_I |x_2(s)|\,ds,$$

the following relations hold:

$$Rx = \int_{-1}^{1} x(s)\,ds - [(\sqrt{2} - 1)\{x(-1) + x(1)\} + (4 - \sqrt{8})x(0)],$$

$$Rx = \int_{-1}^{1} x_2(s)\kappa^2(s)\,ds, \qquad x \in C_2,$$

$$|Rx| \leqq (1.5 - \sqrt{2}) \int_{-1}^{1} |x_2(s)|\, ds;$$

and κ^2 is given by (16) with $v = 4 - \sqrt{8}$.

It is interesting to compare the three best formulas in Case ii. Consider the middle coefficient v, for example. The best formulas relative to

$$\sup_{s \in I} |x_2(s)|, \qquad \int_I x_2(s)^2\, ds, \qquad \int_I |x_2(s)|\, ds$$

have

$$v = 1.29,\ 1.25,\ 1.17,$$

respectively. We are dealing here with three cases of the generalized Hölder inequality in which $e = \infty, 2, 1$. It is natural that the value of v for $e = 2$ lie between the values for $e = \infty$ and $e = 1$.

Of the three formulas, then, it would seem reasonable to favor the one based on $\int_I x_2^2$, unless specific information about $\sup |x_2|$ or $\int_I |x_2|$ is in fact available. The best formula is simpler in the case $e = 2$ than in the other cases. Its derivation also is simpler, because absolute values are achieved by squaring.

For situations more complicated than that of the present section, in which after all we are merely approximating

$$\int_{-1}^{1} x(s)\, ds$$

by

$$ux(-1) + vx(0) + wx(1),$$

the differences just noted will be more marked. In the search for best formulas in later sections, we will therefore concentrate on the case $e = 2$: *Best formulas will be best relative to*

$$\int_I x_n^2,$$

for some n, unless we state otherwise.

Case iii. $n = 3$ *and* $c^0 = c^1 = c^2 = 0$. We specify that A shall be chosen so that

$$n = 3; \qquad c^0 = c^1 = c^2 = 0.$$

For this it is necessary and sufficient that, in addition to the constraints of Case ii,

$$Rx = 0 \quad \text{when} \quad x(s) = s^2;$$

that is,

$$\int_{-1}^{1} s^2\,ds - (u + w) = 0,$$

$$u + w = \frac{2}{3}.$$

Hence

$$u = w = \frac{1}{3}, \qquad v = \frac{4}{3}.$$

There is only one formula satisfying the constraints; it is Simpson's rule. Since the set of formulas under consideration consists of a single element, there is no question of choosing a formula which is best.

For Simpson's rule,

$$\begin{aligned}\kappa^3(t) &= R[(s-t)^2\phi(t,s)/2] = -R[(s-t)^2\theta(t,s)/2] \\ &= \int_{-1}^{1} (s-t)^2\phi(t,s)\,ds/2 \\ &\quad - \frac{(-1-t)^2\phi(t,-1) + 4(-t)^2\phi(t,0) + (1-t)^2\phi(t,1)}{6}.\end{aligned}$$

If $0 < t < 1$,

$$\kappa^3(t) = \int_{t}^{1} (s-t)^2\,ds/2 - \frac{(1-t)^2}{6} = \frac{-t(1-t)^2}{6}.$$

By Corollary 1: 37, or in other ways,

$$-\kappa^3(t) = \kappa^3(-t).$$

Hence

$$Rx = \int_{-1}^{1} x(s)\,ds - \frac{x(-1) + 4x(0) + x(1)}{3},$$

$$Rx = \int_{-1}^{1} x_3(s)\kappa^3(s)\,ds, \qquad x \in \boldsymbol{C}_3,$$

$$\kappa^3(s) = -s(1-|s|)^2/6;$$

and

$$|Rx| \leqq \frac{1}{36}\sup_{s\in I}|x_3(s)|,$$

$$|Rx| \leqq \left[\frac{1}{1890}\int_{-1}^{1} x_3(s)^2\,ds\right]^{1/2},$$

$$|Rx| \leqq \frac{4}{27}\int_{-1}^{1} |x_3(s)|\,ds;$$

since

$$\int_{-1}^{1} |\kappa^3(t)|\, dt = 2\int_0^1 t(1-t)^2\, dt/6 = \frac{1}{36},$$

$$\int_{-1}^{1} \kappa^3(t)^2\, dt = \frac{1}{1890},$$

$$\sup_{t\in I} |\kappa^3(t)| = \frac{4}{27}.$$

CASE iv. *$n = 4$ and $c^0 = c^1 = c^2 = c^3 = 0$.* Here there is an extra condition, over and above those of Case iii, on u, v, w. The condition

$$R(x) = 0 \quad \text{when} \quad x(s) = s^3$$

is in fact satisfied by the values of u, v, w of the previous case. Here too there is one and only one formula, Simpson's rule. For it,

$$Rx = \int_{-1}^{1} x(s)\, ds - \frac{x(-1) + 4x(0) + x(1)}{3},$$

$$Rx = \int_{-1}^{1} x_4(s)\kappa^4(s)\, ds, \qquad x \in \boldsymbol{C}_4,$$

$$\kappa^4(t) = R[(s-t)^3\phi(t,s)/6] = -(1+3|t|)(1-|t|)^3/72;$$

and

$$|Rx| \leqq \frac{1}{90}\sup_{s\in I} |x_4(s)|,$$

$$|Rx| \leqq \frac{1}{36\sqrt{7}}\left[\int_{-1}^{1} x_4(s)^2\, ds\right]^{1/2},$$

$$|Rx| \leqq \frac{1}{72}\int_{-1}^{1} |x_4(s)|\, ds,$$

since

$$\int_{-1}^{1} |\kappa^4(t)|\, dt = \frac{1}{90},$$

$$\int_{-1}^{1} \kappa^4(t)^2\, dt = \frac{1}{(36)^2\, 7},$$

$$\sup_{t\in I} |\kappa^4(t)| = \frac{1}{72}.$$

CASE v. *$n \geqq 5$ and $c^i = 0$, $i < n$.* Since Simpson's rule is not exact for $x(s) = s^5$, these conditions cannot be satisfied. There are no formulas in Case v.

The above five cases exhaust the applications of Theorem 1:43. There are also applications of Theorem 1:8. To get an insight into these, consider, for preciseness, the case

$$n = 1, \qquad -1 \leqq a \leqq 1,$$

where a is specified and fixed. Then, by (1:9),

$$\begin{aligned} Rx &= \int_{-1}^{1} x(s)\,ds - [ux(-1) + vx(0) + wx(1)] \\ &= c^0 x(a) + \int_{-1}^{1} x_1(s)\kappa(s)\,ds, \quad x \in \boldsymbol{C}_1. \end{aligned} \tag{17}$$

Here Rx is expressed in terms of both $x_1(s)$, $s \in \boldsymbol{I}$, and $x(a)$. In Case i above we arranged to make $c^0 = 0$. We might, however, be in a situation in which we know and want to use $x(a)$. Suppose, for example, that we know that $x(a) = 0$. The value of c^0 is then immaterial.

CASE vi. $n = 1$, *a fixed*, $0 < a < 1$. Here (17) holds, with

$$\kappa(t) = R[\psi(a, t, s)], \qquad t \neq -1, 0, 1;$$

$$c^0 = R[1] = 2 - (u + v + w).$$

We shall apply (17) to a set of functions x for each of which

$$x(a) = 0, \qquad x \in \boldsymbol{C}_1.$$

From the relation

$$\kappa(t) = \int_{-1}^{1} \psi(a, t, s)\,ds - [u\psi(a, t, -1) + v\psi(a, t, 0) + w\psi(a, t, 1)]$$

and (1:12), it follows that

$$\kappa(t) = \begin{cases} \displaystyle\int_t^1 ds - w = 1 - t - w & \text{if } a < t < 1, \\ \displaystyle -\int_{-1}^{t} ds + u + v = -1 - t + u + v & \text{if } 0 < t < a, \\ \displaystyle -\int_{-1}^{t} ds + u = -1 - t + u & \text{if } -1 < t < 0. \end{cases}$$

We shall determine the three independent variables u, v, w so that

$$J = \int_{-1}^{1} \kappa(t)^2\,dt$$

is minimal. Now

$$J = \int_{-1}^{0} (1 + t - u)^2\,dt + \int_0^a (1 + t - u - v)^2\,dt + \int_a^1 (1 - t - w)^2\,dt.$$

Consider J as a function of the independent variables

$$u' = u,$$
$$v' = u + v,$$
$$w' = w.$$

Each term then depends on one and only one variable, and J will be minimal iff

$$u' = u = \frac{0 + 1}{2} = \frac{1}{2},$$

$$v' = u + v = \frac{1 + (1 + a)}{2} = 1 + \frac{a}{2}, \qquad v = \frac{1 + a}{2},$$

$$w' = w = \frac{1 - a + 0}{2} = \frac{1 - a}{2};$$

in which case

$$c^0 = 2 - (u + v + w) = \frac{1}{2}.$$

Thus

$$Rx = \int_{-1}^{1} x(s)\, ds - \frac{x(-1) + (1 + a)x(0) + (1 - a)x(1)}{2},$$

$$Rx = \frac{x(a)}{2} + \int_{-1}^{1} x_1(s)\kappa(s)\, ds, \qquad x \in \boldsymbol{C}_1,$$

$$\kappa(s) = \begin{cases} -s - \dfrac{1}{2} & \text{if } -1 < s < 0, \\[2ex] -s + \dfrac{a}{2} & \text{if } \quad 0 < s < a, \\[2ex] -s + \dfrac{a + 1}{2} & \text{if } \quad a < s < 1. \end{cases}$$

Also, omitting details,

$$J = \int_{-1}^{1} \kappa(s)^2\, ds = \frac{2 - 3a + 3a^2}{12};$$

and therefore

$$|Rx| \leqq \left[J \int_{-1}^{1} x_1(s)^2\, ds\right]^{1/2} \quad \text{if } x(a) = 0, \qquad x \in \boldsymbol{C}_1.$$

We have obtained the best formula relative to

$$\int_I x_1(s)^2\,ds,$$

under the condition (assumed known) $x(a) = 0$.

Considerations of the present sort may be worthwhile if repeated use is to be made of the formula of approximation. For example, repetition of an experiment or engineering trial might yield outputs $x(s)$ for all of which it is known that $x(a) = 0$.

CASE vii. *Direct study of the Stieltjes integral.* Consider the initial Stieltjes integral

$$Rx = \int_{-1}^{1} x(s)\,ds - ux(-1) - vx(0) - wx(1)$$

itself. This relation defines Rx if $x \in C_0$ and if $x(s)$ is defined at $s = -1, 0, 1$. We assume that x satisfies these conditions throughout the present case. Then

$$|Rx| \leqq [2 + |u| + |v| + |w|] \sup_{s \in I} |x(s)|, \tag{18}$$

by the usual inequality (12: 16) which may be written

$$\left|\int_{-1}^{1} x(s)\,d\mu(s)\right| \leqq \sup_{s \in I} |x(s)| \int_{-1}^{1} d|\mu|(t), \qquad \mu \in V.$$

Furthermore (18) cannot be strengthened: If the factor $2 + |u| + |v| + |w|$ were reduced by a positive quantity, the resulting inequality would be false, even if x were restricted to be a polynomial.

Suppose that we intend to use (18). Then it would be natural to choose u, v, w so as to minimize

$$2 + |u| + |v| + |w|.$$

This quantity is a minimum when $u = v = w = 0$. Then the approximation Ax of

$$\int_I x(s)\,ds$$

is merely zero. Not only is this approximation best relative to

$$\sup_{s \in I} |x(s)|,$$

it is also the simplest of all possible approximations and is often uninteresting.

We may summarize our study of

$$Rx = \int_{-1}^{1} x(s)\,ds - ux(-1) - vx(0) - wx(1)$$

as follows. The analysis based on knowing that $x(a) = 0$ (Case vi) seems special. Similar attacks will not be pursued further here, although they are of real usefulness. The direct study of the formula itself (Case vii) is easily accomplished. The remaining cases involve Theorem 1: 43 with $n = 1, 2, 3, 4$. If $n = 3$ or 4 there is a unique formula, Simpson's rule (Cases iii and iv). If $n = 1$ or 2 there is a real choice of coefficients. If $n = 2$ there are three different best formulas, relative to

$$\sup |x_2|, \qquad \int x_2^2, \qquad \int |x_2|,$$

respectively.

In this chapter we will study formulas of approximation which are best relative to criteria that involve $\int x_n^2$ for some n. Such criteria are often as pertinent as those based on $\int |x_n|^e$, $e \geqq 1$. Our case $e = 2$ leads to formulas which are easier to derive and to use.

The theory of this chapter was given in [Sard 3], a paper which suggests the minimization of the factor $\int |\kappa|^2$ in (1: 29) and of $\int |\kappa|$ in (1: 23). The paper [3] suggests also the minimization of the modulus (§ 86 below), where applicable. The paper [3] considers a broad class of approximations, one which includes all subsequent formulas of the present chapter.

S. M. Nikolskii's work on approximate integration is of interest. Nikolskii has, among other things, determined a number of formulas which minimize the factor $\int |\kappa|$ in (1: 29) in the cases $n = 1$ and 2 [1, § 2; 3, § 10].

Golomb and Weinberger [1] consider questions of best approximation from another point of view.

When a formula of approximation will be repeatedly used—as, for example, by a computing machine—it may be important to study the set of all possible pertinent formulas with a view to choosing one which is best in a reasonable sense relative to the information available or expected about the input functions x.

§ 19. **The approximation of $\int_0^m x(s)\,ds$ by $c_0x(0) + c_1x(1) + \cdots + c_mx(m)$.** Approximations A of the form

$$(20) \qquad Ax = c_0x(0) + c_1x(1) + \cdots + c_mx(m)$$

are convenient and often used. In this section and the next, we find the best formulas Ax for

$$\int_0^m x(s)\,ds$$

relative to

$$\int_0^m x_n(s)^2\,ds,$$

for different m and n; $m, n \geqq 1$. The 3, 10, 3 formula of Case ii$_1$ in the preceding section will appear here as the case $m = n = 2$.

Let $\mathscr{A}^*_{m,n}$ denote the family of those formulas (20) which are equal to

$$\int_0^m x(s)\,ds$$

whenever x is a polynomial in s of degree $n - 1$. The remainder

$$Rx \underset{\text{def}}{=} \int_0^m x(s)\, ds - c_0 x(0) - \cdots - c_m x(m) \tag{21}$$

vanishes for degree $n - 1$, when $A \in \mathscr{A}^*_{m,n}$. By Theorem 1 : 43, then,

$$Rx = \int_0^m x_n(s)\kappa(s)\, ds, \qquad x \in \boldsymbol{C}_n, \tag{22}$$

$$(Rx)^2 \leqq J \int_0^m x_n(s)^2\, ds, \tag{23}$$

where

$$\kappa(t) = -R[(s - t)^{(n-1)}\theta(t, s)] = R[(s - t)^{(n-1)}\phi(t, s)], \tag{24}$$

$$J = \int_0^m \kappa(t)^2\, dt; \tag{25}$$

the formula (24) holds without exception if $n > 1$ and for $t \neq 0, 1, \cdots, m$ if $n = 1$.

In considering $\mathscr{A}^*_{m,n}$, we in effect specify that Rx is determined by x_n, because of the validity of (22). We choose to use the inequality (23) and we therefore will minimize J.

The family $\mathscr{A}^*_{m,n}$ may be empty, but this will surely not occur if $m \geqq n - 1$. Indeed $\mathscr{A}^*_{m,n}$ is empty iff m is less than the largest even number contained in $n - 1$.

We say that a formula A in $\mathscr{A}^*_{m,n}$ is *best* if it minimizes J. If $\mathscr{A}^*_{m,n}$ is not empty, it contains a unique best formula, as we will prove in the next section. The best formula is symmetric:

$$c_i = c_{m-i}, \qquad i \leqq m.$$

The best formulas for the cases

$$\begin{aligned} n &= 1, & &\text{all } m; \\ n &= 2, & m &\leqq 20; \\ n &= 3, & m &\leqq 12; \\ n &= 4, & m &\leqq 9; \end{aligned}$$

will be given. The use of these best formulas is direct and free of complexity. The derivation of the formulas will be discussed in the next section.

If $n = 1$, the best formula is the iterated trapezoidal rule, for all m. That is, the best formula in $\mathscr{A}^*_{m,1}$ is given by the coefficients

$$c_0 = c_m = \frac{1}{2},$$

$$c_i = 1, \qquad 0 < i < m;$$

and for this formula

$$J = \frac{m}{12}.$$

TABLE 1

BEST APPROXIMATE INTEGRATION FORMULAS

$n = 2$

m	1	2	3	4	5	6	7	8	9	10	11	12
δ	2	8	10	28	38	104	142	388	530	1448	1978	5404
$c_0\delta$	1	3	4	11	15	41	56	153	209	571	780	2131
$c_1\delta$		10	11	32	43	118	161	440	601	1642	2243	6128
$c_2\delta$				26	37	100	137	374	511	1396	1907	5210
$c_3\delta$						106	143	392	535	1462	1997	5456
$c_4\delta$								386	529	1444	1973	5390
$c_5\delta$										1450	1979	5408
$c_6\delta$												5402
J	$\frac{1}{120}$	$\frac{1}{160}$	$\frac{1}{120}$	$\frac{1}{105}$	$\frac{5}{456}$	$\frac{77}{6240}$	$\frac{39}{2840}$	$\frac{22}{1455}$	$\frac{7}{424}$	$\frac{311}{17376}$	$\frac{763}{39560}$	$\frac{419}{20265}$

m	13	14	15	16	17	18	19	20
δ	7382	20168	27550	75268	102818	280904	383722	1048348
$c_0\delta$	2911	7953	10864	29681	40545	110771	151316	413403
$c_1\delta$	8371	22870	31241	85352	116593	318538	435131	1188800
$c_2\delta$	7117	19444	26561	72566	99127	270820	369947	1010714
$c_3\delta$	7453	20362	27815	75992	103807	283606	387413	1058432
$c_4\delta$	7363	20116	27479	75074	102553	280180	382733	1045646
$c_5\delta$	7387	20182	27569	75320	102889	281098	383987	1049072
$c_6\delta$	7381	20164	27545	75254	102799	280852	383651	1048154
$c_7\delta$		20170	27551	75272	102823	280918	383741	1048400
$c_8\delta$				75266	102817	280900	383717	1048334
$c_9\delta$						280906	383723	1048352
$c_{10}\delta$								1048346
J	$\frac{9773}{442920}$	$\frac{28381}{1210080}$	$\frac{8213}{330600}$	$\frac{2468}{94085}$	$\frac{170393}{6169080}$	$\frac{162977}{5618080}$	$\frac{699869}{23023320}$	$\frac{8331}{262087}$

$n = 3$

m	2	3	4	5	6	7	8	9	10	11	12
δ	3	8	60	312	155	86736	80388	522320	3457287	253598280	11937836
$c_0\delta$	1	3	21	112	55	30927	28603	186016	1230777	90294905	4250217
$c_1\delta$	4	9	76	379	192	106573	99124	643081	4259404	312347051	14705148
$c_2\delta$			46	289	132	76573	69874	457051	3016564	221544971	10423398
$c_3\delta$					172	89503	85684	549131	3656464	267523241	12607228
$c_4\delta$							76534	515161	3358804	247986521	11640978
$c_5\delta$									3528844	255093851	12084348
$c_6\delta$											11831398
J	$\frac{1}{1890}$	$\frac{11}{8960}$	$\frac{11}{12600}$	$\frac{73}{69888}$	$\frac{11}{10850}$	$\frac{134081}{124899840}$	$\frac{3961}{3617460}$	$\frac{662807}{584998400}$	$\frac{507029}{435618162}$	$\frac{3062211497}{2556270662400}$	$\frac{1028343}{835648520}$

$n = 4$

m	2	3	4	5	6	7	8	9
δ	3	8	7248	86568	3290014	23997936	1537281648	32364150256
$c_0\delta$	1	3	2349	29392	1082811	8013897	509110987	10764281184
$c_1\delta$	4	9	9932	110209	4409946	31412443	2040010996	42647140119
$c_2\delta$			4430	76819	2225043	18665443	1105566730	24253340709
$c_3\delta$					4304484	25900993	1867200148	37040022813
$c_4\delta$							1254475462	30933891327
J	$\frac{1}{9072}$	$\frac{13}{17920}$	$\frac{6557}{36529920}$	$\frac{61633}{193912320}$	$\frac{210047}{921203920}$	$\frac{56097271}{207342167040}$	$\frac{2876254589}{11621849258880}$	$\frac{18892720083}{72495696573440}$

TABLE 2

NEARLY BEST FORMULAS

$n = 2$

m	4	5	6
δ	100	100	100
$c_0\delta$	39	40	40
$c_1\delta$	115	112	112
$c_2\delta$	92	98	98
$c_3\delta$			100
$\tilde{J}$	$\frac{143}{15000}$	$\frac{11}{1000}$	$\frac{31}{2500}$
$\tilde{J}/J$	1.0010	1.0032	1.0049

$n = 3$

m	5	6
δ	120	1000
$c_0\delta$	43	355
$c_1\delta$	146	1238
$c_2\delta$	111	853
$c_3\delta$		1108
$\tilde{J}$	$\frac{79}{75600}$	$\frac{7097}{7000000}$
$\tilde{J}/J$	1.0004	1.00003

$n = 4$

m	4	5	5	6	6
δ	300	240	1200	100	1000
$c_0\delta$	97	81	407	33	329
$c_1\delta$	412	307	1529	134	1341
$c_2\delta$	182	212	1064	67	675
$c_3\delta$				132	1310
$\tilde{J}$	$\frac{10193}{56700000}$	$\frac{46987}{145152000}$	$\frac{1154043}{3628800000}$	$\frac{1487}{6300000}$	$\frac{31923}{140000000}$
$\tilde{J}/J$	1.0015	1.0185−	1.0006	1.0352	1.00003

Table 2 gives formulas which are exact for degree $n - 1$ and nearly best in the sense of making

$$\tilde{J} = \int_0^m \kappa(t)^2\, dt$$

close to its minimal value J. The extent to which the appraisal of Rx by (23) is increased (weakened) by the use of a nearly best formula instead of the best formula of Table 1 is measured by one-half the percentage increase of $\tilde{J}$ over J.

As an illustration of the use of Table 1, the best formula in $\mathscr{A}^*_{3,2}$ is

$$Ax = 0.4[x(0) + x(3)] + 1.1[x(1) + x(2)].$$

This formula gives the best approximation of

$$\int_0^3 x(s)\, ds,$$

relative to

$$\int_0^3 x_2(s)^2\, ds.$$

For this formula,

$$Rx = \int_0^3 x(s)\, ds - Ax = \int_0^3 x_2(s)\kappa(s)\, ds, \qquad x \in C_2,$$

and

$$|Rx| \leqq \left[\frac{1}{120}\int_0^3 x_2(s)^2\, ds\right]^{1/2}.$$

In the case $n = 2$, explicit formulas have been obtained for the coefficients c_i for all m. There are striking recursions in the numerators $c_i\delta$ and in the denominators δ. For example, minus any entry for $n = 2$ plus four times the entry two places on its right equals the entry four places on its right [Meyers-Sard 1, pp. 121–122]. Cf. §§ 27, 49, 63 below.

The essential property of the formulas in $\mathscr{A}^*_{m,n}$ is that they involve $m + 1$ equally spaced values of the integrand $x(s)$, including the end values. A linear transformation of the s-axis is easily managed: Translation of the origin does not change the coefficients c_i or J. A change of scale, from the variable s to t, where

$$\Delta t = h\,\Delta s, \qquad h > 0,$$

replaces c_i by hc_i, Rx by hRx, and J by $h^{2n+1}J$. Thus, suppose that

$$t = hs + k, \qquad h > 0, \quad k \in \mathsf{R},$$

$$y(t) = x(s),$$

$$R'y \underset{\text{def}}{=} \int_k^{k+mh} y(t)\, dt - [c_0'y(k) + c_1'y(k + h) + \cdots + c_m'y(k + mh)],$$

$$Rx = \int_0^m x(s)\, ds - [c_0x(0) + c_1x(1) + \cdots + c_mx(m)]$$

$$= \int_0^m x_n(s)\kappa(s)\, ds, \qquad x \in C_n[0, m].$$

Then, if $c_i' = hc_i$,

$$R'y = hRx = \int_k^{k+mh} y_n(t)\kappa'(t)\, dt, \qquad y \in C_n[k, k + mh],$$

where

$$\kappa'(t) = h^n\kappa(s);$$

and

$$J' \underset{\text{def}}{=} \int_k^{k+mh} \kappa'(t)^2\, dt = h^{2n+1}\int_0^m \kappa(s)^2\, ds = h^{2n+1}J.$$

If one needs a formula in $\mathscr{A}^*_{m,n}$, where m is beyond the range given in our table, one may construct a good (but not best) formula by combining best formulas that are given. For example, the best formula for

$$\int_0^{m'} x$$

plus the best formula for

$$\int_{m'}^{m'+m''} x$$

is a good formula for

$$\int_0^{m'+m''} x.$$

The minimal property of the best formulas implies that

$$J_{m',n} + J_{m'',n} \geqq J_{m'+m'',n}, \tag{26}$$

where

$$J_{m,n} = \int_0^m \kappa(t)^2\, dt$$

is the value of J for the best formula in $\mathscr{A}^*_{m,n}$.

In many computations, the mathematician has to decide what value of n to use. The best formula in $\mathscr{A}^*_{m,n}$ is pertinent if an appraisal in terms of

$$\int x_n^2$$

is involved. Often there will be no compelling reason for using such an appraisal. Indeed, there will often be no compelling information at hand as to the size of

$$\int x_n^2.$$

The man of action might then estimate

$$\int x_n^2,$$

perhaps by calculating nth differences of x and taking x_n as approximately equal to $\Delta^n x/\Delta s^n$. Alternatively he might consider the approximations given by the best formulas in $\mathscr{A}^*_{m,1}$, $\mathscr{A}^*_{m,2}$, $\cdots$ and retain the one with lowest n that seems consistent with the others.

Strictly speaking an argument which leads to the conclusion that one formula is good in a specific situation can be based only on knowledge of some sort about the input functions x. If such knowledge is not at hand, the choice of a procedure of approximation must be guesswork.

A common practice in the past has been to recommend that for a given m, the integer n be taken as large as possible. The family $\mathscr{A}^*_{m,n}$ then consists of a single element (the Newton-Cotes formula). Because of (22) the error of approximation then is entirely determined by the nth derivative x_n, if $x \in C_n$; the error will be proportional to x_n, and maximal when x_n is in resonance with κ. We may have to operate on a function x which does not have an nth derivative or one about whose nth derivative we have no information. Engineers have been aware of the possible unsuitability of the Newton-Cotes formulas when n is large and have therefore at times preferred the iterated trapezoidal or Simpson rules.

As a precise example, suppose that

$$m = 6, \qquad n = 2;$$

$$Rx = \int_0^6 x(s)\,ds - c_0x(0) - c_1x(1) - \cdots - c_6x(6).$$

We will appraise Rx in terms of

$$\int_0^6 x_2(s)^2\,ds.$$

Then

$$|Rx| \leqq \left[J \int_0^6 x_2(s)^2\,ds\right]^{1/2}, \qquad x \in C_2.$$

For the best formula in $\mathscr{A}^*_{6,2}$,

$$J = \frac{77}{6240} = .0123, \qquad c_0 = c_6 = \frac{41}{104}, \qquad c_1 = c_5 = \frac{118}{104},$$

$$c_2 = c_4 = \frac{100}{104}, \qquad c_3 = \frac{106}{104};$$

by Table 1 with $m = 6$, $n = 2$.

For the iterated trapezoidal rule,

$$J = 6\,\frac{1}{120} = .05, \qquad c_0 = c_6 = \frac{1}{2}, \qquad c_1 = c_2 = c_3 = c_4 = c_5 = 1;$$

by iteration of Table 1 with $m = 1$, $n = 2$.

For the Newton-Cotes formula, which many conventional treatments recommend,

$$J = \frac{27}{350} = .077, \qquad c_0 = c_6 = \frac{41}{140}, \qquad c_1 = c_5 = \frac{216}{140},$$

$$c_2 = c_4 = \frac{27}{140}, \qquad c_3 = \frac{272}{140}.$$

The above value of $J = 2H$ may be computed from (33) below.

TABLE 3

BEST APPROXIMATE INTEGRATION FORMULAS IN DECIMAL FORM

$n = 2$

m	p	e_0	$e_{1/2}$	e_1	$e_{3/2}$	e_2	$e_{5/2}$	e_3	$e_{7/2}$	e_4	$e_{9/2}$	e_5	$e_{11/2}$	e_6	$e_{13/2}$	e_7	$e_{15/2}$	e_8	$e_{17/2}$	e_9	$e_{19/2}$	e_{10}	J
1	1/2		.500000																				.008333
2	1	1.250000		.375000																			6250
3	3/2		1.100000		.400000																		8333
4	2	.928571		1.142857		.392857																	9524
5	5/2		.973684		1.131579		.394737																.010965 –
6	3	1.019231		.961538		1.134615		.394231															.012340
7	7/2		1.007042		.964789		1.133803		.394366														.013732
8	4	.994845		1.010309		.963918		1.134021		.394330													.015120
9	9/2		.998113		1.009433		.964151		1.133962		.394340												.016509
10	5	1.001381		.997238		1.009669		.964088		1.133978		.394337											.017898
11	11/2		1.000506		.997472		1.009606		.964105		1.133974		.394338										.019287
12	6	.999630		1.000740		.997409		1.009622		.964101		1.133974		.394338 –									.020676
13	13/2		.999865 –		1.000677		.997426		1.009618		.964102		1.133975 –		.394338								.022065 –
14	7	1.000099		.999802		1.000694		.997422		1.009619		.964102		1.133975 –		.394338							.023454
15	15/2		1.000036		.999819		1.000690		.997423		1.009619		.964102		1.133975 –		.394338						.024843
16	8	.999973		1.000053		.999814		1.000691		.997423		1.009619		.964102		1.133975 –		.394338					.026232
17	17/2		.999990		1.000049		.999815 +		1.000691		.997423		1.009619		.964102		1.133975 –		.394338				.027620
18	9	1.000007		.999986		1.000050 –		.999815 –		1.000691		.997423		1.009619		.964102		1.133975 –		.394338			.029009
19	19/2		1.000003		.999987		1.000050 –		.999815 –		1.000691		.997423		1.009619		.964102		1.133975		.394338		.030398
20	10	.999998		1.000004		.999987		1.000050 –		.999815 –		1.000691		.997423		1.009619		.964102		1.133975 –		.394338	.031787

$n = 3$

m	p	e_0	$e_{1/2}$	e_1	$e_{3/2}$	e_2	$e_{5/2}$	e_3	$e_{7/2}$	e_4	$e_{9/2}$	e_5	$e_{11/2}$	e_6	J
2	1	1.333333		.333333											.000529
3	3/2		1.125		.375										.001228
4	2	.766667		1.266667		.35									.000873
5	5/2		.926282		1.214744		.358974								.001045 –
6	3	1.109677		.851613		1.238710		.354839							.001014
7	7/2		1.031901		.882828		1.228705		.356565 –						.001074
8	4	.952058		1.065880		.869209		1.233070		.355812					.001095 –
9	9/2		.986294		1.051331		.875040		1.231201		.356134				.001133
10	5	1.020697		.971514		1.057611		.872523		1.232008		.355995			.001164
11	11/2		1.005897		.977871		1.054910		.873606		1.231661		.356055 –		.001198
12	6	.991084		1.012273		.975133		1.056073		.873140		1.231810		.356029	.001231

$n = 4$

m	p	e_0	$e_{1/2}$	e_1	$e_{3/2}$	e_2	$e_{5/2}$	e_3	$e_{7/2}$	e_4	$e_{9/2}$	e_5	J
2	1	1.333333		.333333									.000110
3	3/2		1.125		.375								.000725
4	2	.611203		1.370309		.324089							.000179
5	5/2		.887383		1.273092		.339525 –						.000318
6	3	1.308348		.676302		1.340403		.329120					.000228
7	7/2		1.079301		.777794		1.308964		.333941				.000271
8	4	.816035 –		1.214612		.719170		1.327025 –		.331176			.000247
9	9/2		.955807		1.144477		.749389		1.317728		.332599		.000261

The best formula is more than twice as good as the iterated trapezoidal rule under the present conditions, because

$$\frac{6}{120} \div \frac{77}{6240} > 4.$$

The comparison of the best formula with the Newton-Cotes formula is even more favorable.

Table 3 gives the best approximate integration formulas in decimal form. To illustrate certain numerical trends, we have changed notation and put

$$p = \frac{m}{2}$$

and

$$e_j = c_{p+j} = c_{p-j}, \qquad j = p, p - 1, p - 2, \cdots, \zeta;$$

where

$$\zeta = \begin{cases} 0 & \text{if } m \text{ is even,} \\ \frac{1}{2} & \text{if } m \text{ is odd.} \end{cases}$$

Thus the index j ranges over integers if m is even and over odd multiples of $1/2$ if m is odd.

In Table 3 it appears that the entries converge to unity as one moves down each column and converge to specific limits as one moves down parallel to the sloping edge. Both convergences appear to be alternating. Formal statements are as follows.

The index n is fixed throughout. To indicate the dependence on m we write

$$e_j = e_{m,j} = e_{2p,j}, \qquad m = 2p.$$

Then it appears that

$$\text{(i)} \quad e_{2p,j} \to 1 \text{ as } p = j, j + 1, j + 2, \cdots$$

for each fixed integer or half-integer $j \geqq 0$.

$$\text{(ii)} \quad e_{2p,p-j} \text{ converges as } p = j,\ j + \frac{1}{2},\ j + 1, \cdots$$

for each fixed integer $j \geqq 0$.

$$\text{(iii)} \quad J_m - J_{m-1} \text{ converges as } m = 2, 3, 4, \cdots.$$

For $n = 1$, all these assertions are trivially true, since

$$e_{m,p} = \frac{1}{2}; \qquad e_{m,j} = 1, \quad 0 \leqq j < p; \qquad J_m = \frac{m}{12}.$$

For $n = 2$, assertions (i) and (ii) have been established by means of the known recursions. Indeed the limits in (ii) are known [Meyers-Sard 1]: for each fixed positive integer j,

$$e_{2p,p-j} \to 1 - \frac{(-1)^j(2-\sqrt{3})^j}{2} \quad \text{as} \quad p = j, j + \frac{1}{2}, j+1, \cdots;$$

and

$$e_{2p,p} \to \frac{3+\sqrt{3}}{12} \quad \text{as} \quad p = \frac{1}{2}, 1, \frac{3}{2}, \cdots.$$

Assertion (iii) is a consequence of relation (7) in the paper just referred to. The truth or falsity of (7) for all values of its index could be established by a straightforward but long algebraic calculation.

For $n \geqq 3$, it is not known whether assertions (i), (ii), (iii) are true.

Assertion (i) implies that the interior coefficients a fixed number of positions from the center approach unity as $m \to \infty$. Assertion (ii) implies that the coefficients a fixed number of positions from the end of the range approach specific values as $m \to \infty$.

§ 27. **Derivation of the preceding formulas.** Consider $\mathscr{A}^*_{m,n}$, $m, n \geqq 1$. It is advantageous to translate the s-axis and to write each remainder as

$$(28) \qquad Rx = \int_{-p}^{p} x(s)\,ds - \sum_j e_j x(j) = \int_{-p}^{p} x_n(s)\kappa(s)\,ds, \qquad x \in \boldsymbol{C}_n,$$

where

$$p = \frac{m}{2}$$

and the index j ranges over the $m + 1$ values

$$(29) \qquad -p, \quad -p+1, \quad -p+2, \cdots, \quad p-1, \quad p.$$

The coefficient e_j of (28) is the coefficient c_{j+p} of (21).

Throughout §§ 27–64 the indices j and k range over the values (29) or indicated subsets of (29). For example if we write $j > 0$, j is to range over those elements of (29) which are positive.

If m is even, (29) consists of integers and includes zero. If m is odd, (29) consists of odd halves.

The functional R will vanish for degree $n - 1$ iff

$$Rx = 0 \quad \text{for} \quad x(s) = 1, s, s^2, \cdots, s^{n-1};$$

that is, iff

$$(30) \qquad \sum_j e_j j^r = \begin{cases} \dfrac{2p^{r+1}}{r+1} & \text{if } r \text{ is even,} \\ 0 & \text{if } r \text{ is odd,} \end{cases} \qquad r = 0, 1, \cdots, n-1,$$

where $e_0 0^0$ is understood as e_0.

Our problem is to determine e_j so that the constraints (30) are satisfied and so that

$$J = \int_{-p}^{p} \kappa(t)^2\,dt$$

is minimal, where $\kappa(t)$ is given by (24). As we shall see, J is a function of $m + 1$ variables subject to n constraints. In the process of solution we will show that

$$e_{-j} = e_j.$$

To obtain a formula for J, we calculate κ in the interval $0 < t < p$ and in the interval $-p < t < 0$, using first one part of (24) and then the other part. Now

$$\int_{-p}^{p} (s - t)^{(n-1)}\phi(t, s)\,ds = \int_{t}^{p} (s - t)^{(n-1)}\,ds = (p - t)^{(n)}.$$

By (24) then,

$$\kappa(t) = R[(s - t)^{(n-1)}\phi(t, s)] = (p - t)^{(n)} - e_p(p - t)^{(n-1)} \quad \text{if } p - 1 < t < p,$$

$$\kappa(t) = (p - t)^{(n)} - e_p(p - t)^{(n-1)} - e_{p-1}(p - 1 - t)^{(n-1)} \quad \text{if } p - 2 < t < p - 1,$$

$$\vdots$$

$$\kappa(t) = (p - t)^{(n)} - e_p(p - t)^{(n-1)} - e_{p-1}(p - 1 - t)^{(n-1)} - \cdots - e_\zeta(\zeta - t)^{(n-1)} \quad \text{if } 0 < t < \zeta;$$

where

$$\zeta = \begin{cases} 1 & \text{if } m = 2p \text{ is even,} \\ \frac{1}{2} & \text{if } m = 2p \text{ is odd.} \end{cases} \tag{31}$$

Put

$$H = \int_{0}^{p} \kappa(t)^2\,dt. \tag{32}$$

Then

$$H = \alpha - 2 \sum_{j>0} \beta_j e_j + \sum_{j,k>0} \gamma_{j,k} e_j e_k, \tag{33}$$

where

$$\alpha = \int_{0}^{p} [(p - t)^{(n)}]^2\,dt = \frac{p^{2n+1}}{(2n + 1)n!^2}, \tag{34}$$

$$\beta_j = \int_{0}^{j} (p - t)^{(n)}(j - t)^{(n-1)}\,dt = \int_{0}^{j} (p - j + t)^{(n)} t^{(n-1)}\,dt, \tag{35}$$

$$
(36)\qquad \begin{aligned}
\gamma_{k,j} = \gamma_{j,k} &= \int_0^j (j - t)^{(n-1)}(k - t)^{(n-1)}\, dt \\
&= \int_0^j (k - j + t)^{(n-1)} t^{(n-1)}\, dt, \qquad j \leqq k.
\end{aligned}
$$

Thus H is a function of the variables e_j, $j > 0$, alone. On occasion we will write

$$H = H(e_p, e_{p-1}, \cdots, e_\zeta).$$

In a similar fashion we put

$$H^* = \int_{-p}^{0} \kappa(t)^2\, dt$$

and evaluate $\kappa(t)$, $-p < t < 0$, by means of the dual part of (24). Thus

$$-\int_{-p}^{p} (s - t)^{(n-1)}\theta(t, s)\, ds = -\int_{-p}^{t} (s - t)^{(n-1)}\, ds = (-p - t)^{(n)};$$

and

$$\kappa(t) = -R[(s - t)^{(n-1)}\theta(t, s)] = (-p - t)^{(n)} + e_{-p}(-p - t)^{(n-1)} \qquad \text{if } -p < t < -p + 1,$$

$$\kappa(t) = (-p - t)^{(n)} + e_{-p}(-p - t)^{(n-1)} + e_{-p+1}(-p + 1 - t)^{(n-1)} \qquad \text{if } -p + 1 < t < -p + 2,$$

$$\vdots$$

$$\kappa(t) = (-p - t)^{(n)} + e_{-p}(-p - t)^{(n-1)} + e_{-p+1}(-p + 1 - t)^{(n-1)} + \cdots + e_{-\zeta}(-\zeta - t)^{(n-1)} \qquad \text{if } -\zeta < t < 0.$$

Hence

$$H^* = \alpha - 2 \sum_{j>0} \beta_j e_{-j} + \sum_{j,k>0} \gamma_{j,k} e_{-j} e_{-k};$$

the coefficients α, β_j, $\gamma_{j,k}$ are exactly the same as before, as follows from a change of variable in the integrals defining the coefficients. Thus H^* is merely H with e_j replaced by e_{-j}, $j > 0$.

The following lemmas give useful formulas for the coefficients β_j and $\gamma_{j,k}$ in H.

37. LEMMA. *The coefficient β_j equals $(-1)^n/(2n)!$ times the sum of the first $n + 1$ terms of the binomial expansion of $(j - p)^{2n}$. Thus*

$$(-1)^n (2n)! \beta_j = \sum_{h=0}^{n} C_{2n,h} j^{2n-h} (-p)^h,$$

where

$$C_{q,r} = \frac{q!}{(q - r)!\, r!}.$$

PROOF. For all positive integers q, n

$$\sum_{i=0}^{q} \frac{(-1)^i C_{q,i}}{n+i} = \frac{(n-1)!q!}{(n+q)!}, \tag{38}$$

as may be shown by induction on q or by the use of the beta function $B(n, q+1)$.

Since

$$(p - j + t)^n = \sum_{h=0}^{n} \sum_{i=0}^{n-h} \frac{n! p^h (-j)^{n-h-i} t^i}{h! i! (n-h-i)!},$$

(35) implies that

$$\begin{aligned}
\beta_j &= \frac{1}{n!(n-1)!} \int_0^j (p - j + t)^n t^{n-1}\, dt \\
&= \frac{1}{(n-1)!} \sum_h \sum_i \frac{p^h (-j)^{n-h-i}}{h! i! (n-h-i)!} \int_0^j t^{n+i-1}\, dt \\
&= \frac{1}{(n-1)!} \sum_h \frac{(-1)^{n-h} p^h j^{2n-h}}{h!} \sum_i \frac{(-1)^i}{i!(n-h-i)!(n+i)} \\
&= \frac{1}{(n-1)!} \sum_h \frac{(-1)^{n-h} p^h j^{2n-h}}{h!(n-h)!} \sum_i \frac{(-1)^i C_{n-h,i}}{n+i} \\
&= \frac{1}{(n-1)!} \sum_h \frac{(-1)^{n-h} p^h j^{2n-h}}{h!(n-h)!} \frac{(n-1)!(n-h)!}{(2n-h)!}
\end{aligned}$$

by (38). Hence

$$\beta_j = \sum_h \frac{(-1)^{n-h} p^h j^{2n-h}}{h!(2n-h)!} = \frac{(-1)^n}{(2n)!} \sum_{h=0}^{n} C_{2n,h} j^{2n-h} (-p)^h,$$

as was to be shown.

39. LEMMA. *The coefficient* $\gamma_{j,k}$ *equals* $(-1)^{n-1}/(2n-1)!$ *times the sum of the first* n *terms of the binomial expansion of* $(j-k)^{2n-1}$, $0 < j \leqq k$. *Thus*

$$(-1)^{n-1}(2n-1)!\gamma_{j,k} = \sum_{h=0}^{n-1} C_{2n-1,h} j^{2n-h-1} (-k)^h.$$

PROOF. Since

$$(k - j + t)^{n-1} = \sum_{h=0}^{n-1} \sum_{i=0}^{n-h-1} \frac{(n-1)! k^h (-j)^{n-h-i-1} t^i}{h! i! (n-h-i-1)!},$$

(36) implies that

$$\begin{aligned}\gamma_{j,k} &= \frac{1}{(n-1)!^2}\int_0^j (k-j+t)^{n-1}t^{n-1}\,dt \\ &= \frac{1}{(n-1)!}\sum_h\sum_i \frac{k^h(-j)^{n-h-i-1}}{h!i!(n-h-i-1)!}\int_0^j t^{n+i-1}\,dt \\ &= \frac{1}{(n-1)!}\sum_h \frac{(-1)^{n-h-1}k^hj^{2n-h-1}}{h!}\sum_i \frac{(-1)^i}{i!(n-h-i-1)!(n+i)} \\ &= \frac{1}{(n-1)!}\sum_h \frac{(-1)^{n-h-1}k^hj^{2n-h-1}}{h!(n-h-1)!}\sum_i \frac{(-1)^iC_{n-h-1,i}}{n+i} \\ &= \frac{1}{(n-1)!}\sum_h \frac{(-1)^{n-h-1}k^hj^{2n-h-1}}{h!(n-h-1)!}\,\frac{(n-1)!(n-h-1)!}{(2n-h-1)!}\end{aligned}$$

by (38). Hence

$$\gamma_{j,k} = \frac{(-1)^{n-1}}{(2n-1)!}\sum_{h=0}^{n-1} C_{2n-1,h}j^{2n-h-1}(-k)^h,$$

as was to be shown.

The coefficients $\gamma_{j,k}$ occur not only in the present study of approximate integration, but in other approximations also where quantities of the form

$$Ax = c_0x(0) + c_1x(1) + \cdots + c_mx(m)$$

are involved.

The matrix $\{\gamma_{j,k}\}$, $0 < j, k \leqq p$, is positive definite [Meyers-Sard 2, p. 204]. Since $\gamma_{j,k}$ is a function of j, k, and n only, the coefficients $\gamma_{j,k}$ that occur in the case $n = n_0$, $p = p_0$ occur also in the cases $n = n_0$, $p > p_0$.

We now turn our attention to the problem of minimizing

$$J = \int_{-p}^{p} \kappa(t)^2\,dt = H^* + H,$$

subject to the constraints (30). Here H is a function of the variables e_j, $j > 0$, and H^* is the same function of the variables e_{-j}, $j > 0$. Thus J is a function of the variables e_j, $j \neq 0$.

For simplicity of exposition we discuss separately the cases in which m is even or odd.

§ 40. ***m* even.** Suppose that m is even. Then $p = m/2$ is an integer, the variables are e_0, e_j, e_{-j}, $j = 1, 2, \cdots, p$. The variable e_0 does not enter in J; nor in any constraint (30) except

$$e_0 + \sum_{j\neq 0} e_j = 2p, \tag{41}$$

the constraint (30) corresponding to $r = 0$. Thus (41) determines e_0. Our problem is to minimize the function J of the variables e_j, $j \neq 0$, subject to the constraints

$$\sum_{j\neq 0} e_j j^r = \begin{cases} \dfrac{2p^{r+1}}{r+1} & \text{if } r \text{ is even,} \\ 0 & \text{if } r \text{ is odd,} \end{cases} \qquad r = 1, \cdots, n-1. \tag{42}$$

Since e_j and e_{-j}, $j > 0$, may be interchanged in J and in (42), it will be sufficient to minimize

$$H = \alpha - 2 \sum_{j>0} \beta_j e_j + \sum_{j,k>0} \gamma_{j,k} e_j e_k,$$

subject to the constraints

$$\sum_{j>0} e_j j^r = \frac{p^{r+1}}{r+1}, \qquad r \text{ even}, \quad 2 \leqq r \leqq n-1. \tag{43}$$

(If $n \leqq 2$, there are no constraints.) To prove this assertion, suppose that $e_j = e_j^0$, $j > 0$, minimize H, subject to (43). Then $e_{-j} = e_j^0$ minimize

$$H^* = \alpha - 2 \sum_{j>0} \beta_j e_{-j} + \sum_{j,k>0} \gamma_{j,k} e_{-j} e_{-k},$$

subject to

$$\sum_{j>0} e_{-j}(-j)^r = \frac{p^{r+1}}{r+1}, \qquad r \text{ even}, \quad 2 \leqq r \leqq n-1, \tag{44}$$

since only a change of name of variables is involved. Put

$$(e_j, e_{-j}) = (e_j^0, e_j^0).$$

Then (43) and (44) imply (42), since $j^r + (-j)^r = 0$ when r is odd. Thus $(e_j, e_{-j}) = (e_j^0, e_j^0)$ minimize H and H^* separately subject to (42) and therefore a fortiori minimize $J = H + H^*$ subject to (42). The minimal J is $2H(e_j^0)$.

Furthermore, whenever the linear equations (43) are consistent, it is certainly possible to minimize H subject to (43), since $H = \int_0^p \kappa(t)^2\, dt$ is nonnegative and a quadratic function of its independent variables.

Finally, the set of values e_j, $j > 0$, which minimizes H subject to (43) is unique. This may be proved in various ways, one of which is the following. Suppose that A^0, A^1 are elements of $\mathscr{A}^*_{m,n}$. Then kernels κ^0, κ^1 exist, such that

$$\int_{-p}^{p} x(s)\, ds - A^0 x = \int_{-p}^{p} x_n \kappa^0\, ds,$$

$$\int_{-p}^{p} x(s)\, ds - A^1 x = \int_{-p}^{p} x_n \kappa^1\, ds, \qquad x \in C_n.$$

For any real number t, then,

$$\int_{-p}^{p} x(s)\, ds - [(1-t)A^0(x) + tA^1(x)] = \int_{-p}^{p} [(1-t)\kappa^0 + t\kappa^1] x_n\, ds.$$

Hence $(1 - t)A^0 + tA^1$ is an element of $\mathscr{A}^*_{m,n}$ with kernel $(1 - t)\kappa^0 + t\kappa^1$; and the family K of kernels corresponding to $\mathscr{A}^*_{m,n}$ satisfies the hypothesis of Theorem 1:61. Hence there is a unique κ in K which minimizes $J = \int_{-p}^{p} \kappa(t)^2\, dt$, two kernels being considered equivalent if equal almost everywhere. But kernels which are equal almost everywhere must correspond to the same element A in $\mathscr{A}^*_{m,n}$, since

$$\int_{-p}^{p} x(s)\, ds - Ax$$

would be the same for all x in $\boldsymbol{C}_n$. Hence the minimizing A in $\mathscr{A}^*_{m,n}$ is unique.

By (41),

$$e_0 = 2p - 2 \sum_{j>0} e_j. \tag{45}$$

For any positive integers p, n, one now proceeds to minimize the quadratic function H of the p variables $e_1, \cdots, e_p$ subject to (43). One may use Lagrange's multipliers or directly eliminate variables chosen to be dependent. In our calculation below we shall make use of the following elementary lemma.

46. Lemma. *Consider the quadratic function*

$$f(z) = a + 2\sum_r a_r z_r + \sum_{r,s} a_{r,s} z_r z_s$$

of the independent real variables z_r, where the indices r, s vary over a finite set and a, a_r, $a_{r,s}$ are real constants. If z minimizes f, then the minimal value of f is

$$f(z) = a + \sum_r a_r z_r.$$

More generally the last relation holds whenever z is a point at which the differential df vanishes.

§ 47. **The cases** $n = 1$, $p = 1, 2, \cdots$. Here there are no constraints. By Lemmas 37 and 39,

$$\alpha = \frac{p^3}{3}; \qquad \beta_j = \frac{2jp - j^2}{2}; \qquad \gamma_{j,k} = \gamma_{k,j} = j, \quad j \leqq k. \tag{48}$$

We seek the solution of the equations

$$\frac{\partial H}{\partial e_j} = 0, \qquad 1 \leqq j \leqq p;$$

that is,

$$\sum_{k>0} \gamma_{j,k} e_k = \beta_j.$$

The solution e_j, as given in § 19, is

$$e_p = \frac{1}{2}; \qquad e_k = 1, \quad 1 \leqq k < p.$$

It is sufficient to verify that these values are indeed a solution:

$$\sum_{k \leqq j} k + (p - j - 1)j + \frac{j}{2} = jp - \frac{j^2}{2}.$$

By Lemma 46,

$$H = \alpha - \sum_{j>0} \beta_j e_j = \frac{p^3}{3} - \sum_{j=1}^{p} \left(jp - \frac{j^2}{2}\right) + \frac{1}{2}\frac{p^2}{2} = \frac{p}{12}.$$

Hence

$$J = 2H = \frac{2p}{12} = \frac{m}{12}.$$

Finally, by (45),

$$e_0 = 2p - 2\left(p - \frac{1}{2}\right) = 1.$$

Thus the results for $n = 1$ (and m even) of § 19 are established.

§ 49. **The cases** $n = 2, p = 1, 2, \cdots$. Here again there are no constraints. By Lemmas 37 and 39,

$$(50) \quad \alpha = \frac{p^5}{20}; \quad \beta_j = \frac{6j^2p^2 - 4j^3p + j^4}{24}; \quad \gamma_{j,k} = \gamma_{k,j} = \frac{3j^2k - j^3}{6}, \quad j \leqq k.$$

Although the solutions e_j for all p are known by means of the recursion described in § 19, the general treatment is too long to be included here. We will give the details for $p = 1$ and $p = 2$. The results up to $p = 10$ are in Table 1.

THE CASE $n = 2, p = 1$ ($m = 2$). Here

$$\alpha = \frac{1}{20}, \qquad \beta_1 = \frac{1}{8}, \qquad \gamma_{1,1} = \frac{1}{3}; \qquad H = \frac{1}{20} - \frac{e_1}{4} + \frac{e_1^2}{3}.$$

The minimum of H occurs when

$$\frac{2e_1}{3} = \frac{1}{4}, \qquad e_1 = \frac{3}{8},$$

and is

$$H = \frac{1}{20} - \frac{e_1}{8} = \frac{1}{20} - \frac{3}{64} = \frac{1}{320}.$$

Then by (45),

$$e_0 = 2 - 2\cdot\frac{3}{8} = \frac{10}{8}.$$

Thus we confirm the entries of Table 1 for $\mathscr{A}^*_{2,2}$:

$$e_1 = c_2 = c_0 = \frac{3}{8}, \qquad e_0 = c_1 = \frac{10}{8}, \qquad J = 2H = \frac{1}{160}.$$

THE CASE $n = 2, p = 2$ $(m = 4)$. Here

$$\alpha = \frac{8}{5}, \qquad \beta_1 = \frac{17}{24}, \qquad \gamma_{1,1} = \frac{1}{3}, \qquad \gamma_{1,2} = \frac{5}{6},$$

$$\beta_2 = 2, \qquad \gamma_{2,1} = \frac{5}{6}, \qquad \gamma_{2,2} = \frac{8}{3}.$$

H is a function of the variables e_1, e_2. H is minimal when

$$\frac{1}{3}e_1 + \frac{5}{6}e_2 = \frac{17}{24}, \qquad \frac{5}{6}e_1 + \frac{8}{3}e_2 = 2.$$

The solution according to Table 1 is

$$e_2 = c_4 = c_0 = \frac{11}{28}, \qquad e_1 = c_3 = c_1 = \frac{32}{28},$$

as is indeed the fact. The minimal H is

$$\frac{8}{5} - \frac{17}{24}\cdot\frac{32}{28} - 2\cdot\frac{11}{28} = \frac{1}{210}.$$

Hence $J = 1/105$. Finally, by (45),

$$e_0 = c_2 = 2\left(2 - \frac{32}{28} - \frac{11}{28}\right) = \frac{26}{28}.$$

We omit the calculations for the cases $n = 2, p \geqq 3, m$ even.

§ 51. **The cases** $n = 3, p = 1, 2, \cdots$. Here the constraints (43) reduce to

(52) $$\sum_{j>0} e_j j^2 = \frac{p^3}{3}.$$

Also

(53) $$\alpha = \frac{p^7}{252}, \qquad \beta_j = \frac{j^3(20p^3 - 15p^2j + 6pj^2 - j^3)}{720},$$

$$\gamma_{j,k} = \gamma_{k,j} = \frac{j^3(10k^2 - 5jk + j^2)}{120}, \qquad 1 \leqq j \leqq k \leqq p.$$

The solutions for $p = 1, \cdots, 6$ are given in Table 1. We shall give the details for $p = 1$ and $p = 2$ only.

THE CASE $n = 3$, $p = 1$ $(m = 2)$. Here the constraint

$$e_1 = \frac{1}{3}$$

completely determines e_1. There is only one formula in $\mathscr{A}^*_{2,3}$, which is therefore the best formula in $\mathscr{A}^*_{2,3}$. For it,

$$H = \frac{1}{252} - 2\frac{1}{72}\cdot\frac{1}{3} + \frac{1}{20}\cdot\frac{1}{9} = \frac{1}{27\cdot 4\cdot 5\cdot 7},$$

$$J = \frac{1}{1890},$$

$$e_0 = 2\left(1 - \frac{1}{3}\right) = \frac{4}{3}.$$

THE CASE $n = 3$, $p = 2$ $(m = 4)$. Here the constraint is

$$e_1 + 4e_2 = \frac{8}{3}.$$

$$\alpha = \frac{32}{63}, \qquad \beta_1 = \frac{111}{720}, \qquad \gamma_{1,1} = \frac{1}{20}, \qquad \gamma_{1,2} = \frac{31}{120},$$

$$\beta_2 = \frac{8}{9}, \qquad \gamma_{2,1} = \frac{31}{120}, \qquad \gamma_{2,2} = \frac{8}{5}.$$

We use the constraint to express H as a function of the independent variable e_2, taking e_1 as dependent. Thus,

$$H = \frac{32}{63} - \frac{111}{360}e_1 - \frac{16}{9}e_2 + \frac{1}{20}e_1^2 + \frac{31}{60}e_1e_2 + \frac{8}{5}e_2^2,$$

$$H = \frac{13}{315} - \frac{7e_2}{30} + \frac{e_2^2}{3}.$$

Hence H is minimal when

$$\frac{2e_2}{3} = \frac{7}{30}, \qquad e_2 = \frac{7}{20},$$

and the minimal value of H is

$$\frac{13}{315} - \frac{7}{60}\frac{7}{20} = \frac{11}{2^4 3^2 5^2 7},$$

and

$$J = \frac{11}{12600}, \qquad e_2 = c_4 = c_0 = \frac{7}{20},$$

$$e_1 = c_3 = c_1 = \frac{8}{3} - 4e_2 = \frac{19}{15},$$

$$e_0 = c_2 = 2\left(2 - \frac{19}{15} - \frac{7}{20}\right) = \frac{23}{30}.$$

§ 54. **The cases** $n = 4$, $p = 1, 2, \cdots$. There is one constraint (52). The solutions for $p = 1, 2, 3, 4$ are given in Table 1. We omit the details.

§ 55. m **odd.** Suppose that m is odd. Then $p = m/2$ is an odd number of halves. The variables are e_j, e_{-j}, with

$$j = \frac{1}{2}, \frac{3}{2}, \cdots, p.$$

Our problem is to minimize

$$J = H^* + H,$$

subject to the constraints (30). For this it will be sufficient to minimize

$$H = \alpha - 2 \sum_{j>0} \beta_j e_j + \sum_{j,k} \gamma_{j,k} e_j e_k$$

subject to the constraints

(56) $$\sum_{j>0} e_j j^r = \frac{p^{r+1}}{r+1}, \qquad r \text{ even}, \quad 0 \leqq r \leqq n - 1.$$

Furthermore whenever the constraints (56) are consistent, there is a unique minimizing set e_j, $j > 0$. The minimal J is twice the minimal H and occurs with $e_{-j} = e_j$. These facts are proved exactly as before. In the present case there is no variable e_0; and constraints on e_j, $j > 0$, are always present.

§ 57. **The cases** $n = 1$, $p = 1/2, 3/2, \cdots$. Here the constraint is

(58) $$\sum_{j>0} e_j = p.$$

The formulas for α, β_j, $\gamma_{j,k}$ are precisely (48) (although the indices j, k take on different values). If $p = 1/2$, (58) reduces to

$$e_{1/2} = \frac{1}{2}.$$

There is only one formula in $\mathscr{A}^*_{1,1}$. For it

$$H = \frac{1}{24} - \frac{e_{1/2}}{4} + \frac{e_{1/2}^2}{2} = \frac{1}{24}, \qquad J = \frac{1}{12}, \qquad c_0 = c_1 = e_{1/2} = \frac{1}{2}.$$

The cases

$$p = \frac{3}{2}, \frac{5}{2}, \frac{7}{2}, \cdots$$

may be treated in a similar fashion. It is perhaps preferable to avoid the complication of using the constraint (58), in the following way. We have proved that the best formula in $\mathscr{A}^*_{m,1}$ is the (iterated) trapezoidal rule and that for it

$$J = \frac{m}{12}, \tag{59}$$

in the cases $m = 2, 4, 6, \cdots$ and $m = 1$. We shall now deduce that the same is true in the cases

$$m = 3, 5, 7, \cdots.$$

Let J_m be the minimal value of $\int_0^m \kappa(t)^2\,dt$, corresponding to formulas in $\mathscr{A}^*_{m,1}$. Suppose that m is odd and > 1. Apply the trapezoidal rule on m ordinates to $\int_0^{m-1}$ and the trapezoidal rule on two ordinates to $\int_{m-1}^m$. The result is the trapezoidal rule on $m+1$ ordinates, an element of $\mathscr{A}^*_{m,1}$. For the combination of the two trapezoidal rules, by (59) for established values,

$$\int_0^m \kappa(t)^2\,dt = \int_0^{m-1} + \int_{m-1}^m = \frac{m-1}{12} + \frac{1}{12} = \frac{m}{12} \geqq J_m, \tag{60}$$

since J_m is the minimal value (cf. (26)). On the other hand, the combination of iterated trapezoidal rules on $m+1$ ordinates for $\int_0^m$ and $\int_m^{2m}$ gives the trapezoidal rule on $2m+1$ ordinates for $\int_0^{2m}$, an element of $\mathscr{A}^*_{2m,1}$. Hence

$$J_m + J_m = 2J_m \geqq J_{2m},$$

since J_{2m} is minimal. By (59)

$$J_{2m} = \frac{2m}{12},$$

since $2m$ is even. Hence

$$2J_m \geqq \frac{2m}{12}, \qquad J_m \geqq \frac{m}{12}.$$

As we have already established the reverse inequality, it follows that

$$J_m = \frac{m}{12}.$$

Thus (59) holds for all m. Finally the trapezoidal rule on $m+1$ ordinates for $\int_0^m$ yields a kernel κ for which

$$\int_0^m \kappa^2\,dt = \frac{m}{12}$$

by (60). Since the best formula in $\mathscr{A}^*_{m,1}$ is unique, it must be this trapezoidal rule.

§ 61. **The cases** $n = 2$, $p = 1/2, 3/2, \cdots$. Here the constraint is (58). The formulas for α, β_j, $\gamma_{j,k}$ are (50). The solutions for

$$p = \frac{1}{2}, \frac{3}{2}, \frac{5}{2}, \ldots, \frac{19}{2}$$

are given in Table 1. We will give the details for $p = 1/2$ and $p = 3/2$ only. The solution for all p is known by means of the recursion described in § 19.

THE CASE $n = 2$, $p = 1/2$ ($m = 1$). As in the case $n = 1$, $p = 1/2$, there is only one formula in $\mathscr{A}^*_{1,2}$. It is the trapezoidal rule. For it, by (50),

$$H = \frac{1}{640} - \frac{e_{1/2}}{64} + \frac{e_{1/2}^2}{24} = \frac{1}{640} - \frac{1}{64 \cdot 2} + \frac{1}{24 \cdot 4} = \frac{1}{240},$$

$$J = \frac{1}{120}, \qquad e_{1/2} = c_0 = c_1 = \frac{1}{2}.$$

THE CASE $n = 2$, $p = 3/2$ ($m = 3$). Here the constraint (58) is

$$e_{1/2} + e_{3/2} = \frac{3}{2}.$$

Also, by (50),

$$\alpha = \frac{243}{640}, \qquad \beta_{1/2} = \frac{43}{384}, \qquad \gamma_{1/2,1/2} = \frac{1}{24}, \qquad \gamma_{1/2,3/2} = \frac{1}{6},$$

$$\beta_{3/2} = \frac{81}{128}, \qquad \gamma_{3/2,1/2} = \frac{1}{6}, \qquad \gamma_{3/2,3/2} = \frac{9}{8}.$$

Take $e_{3/2}$ as the independent variable.

$$H = \frac{243}{640} - \frac{43e_{1/2}}{192} - \frac{81e_{3/2}}{64} + \frac{e_{1/2}^2}{24} + \frac{e_{1/2}e_{3/2}}{3} + \frac{9e_{3/2}^2}{8}$$

$$= \frac{11}{80} - \frac{2e_{3/2}}{3} + \frac{5e_{3/2}^2}{6}.$$

Hence the minimal H occurs at

$$e_{3/2} = \frac{2}{5}$$

and is

$$\frac{11}{80} - \frac{1}{3} \cdot \frac{2}{5} = \frac{1}{240}.$$

Hence

$$J = \frac{1}{120}, \qquad e_{1/2} = \frac{11}{10} = c_2 = c_1, \qquad e_{3/2} = \frac{2}{5} = c_3 = c_0.$$

§ 62. **The cases $n = 3$, $p = 1/2, 3/2, \cdots$.** Here the constraints (56) are

$$\sum_{j>0} e_j = p, \tag{63}$$

$$\sum_{j>0} e_j j^2 = \frac{p^3}{3}.$$

The coefficients α, β_j, $\gamma_{j,k}$ are given by (53). The constraints (63) are inconsistent for $p = 1/2$. The results for

$$p = \frac{3}{2}, \frac{5}{2}, \cdots, \frac{11}{2}$$

are given in Table 1. We omit the details.

§ 64. **The cases $n = 4$, $p = 1/2, 3/2, \cdots$.** Here again the constraints are (63). The results for

$$p = \frac{3}{2}, \frac{5}{2}, \frac{7}{2}, \frac{9}{2}$$

are given in Table 1.

§ 65. **The approximation of $\int_{-1}^{1} x(s)\,ds$ by a formula of Gaussian type involving two ordinates.** In an approximation of this sort the remainder will be

$$Rx \underset{\text{def}}{=} \int_{-1}^{1} x(s)\,ds - ux(a) - vx(b).$$

Our object is to choose u, v, a, b as effectively as possible. Let us specify that

$$-1 \leqq a \leqq b \leqq 1.$$

Actually we could allow a or b to be outside the interval $[-1, 1]$. Several additional cases to those that we will analyze would have to be considered; and it would undoubtedly turn out to be advantageous to take a, b in $[-1, 1]$.

For reasons of symmetry one would expect that $u = v$ and $a = -b$. This will indeed be the case. But there does not appear to be an easy way to prove in advance that this is so. We therefore treat u, v, a, b as parameters, and show in several cases that the minimizing values are such that $u = v$, $a = -b$. Our calculations would be considerably simpler if we could put $u = v$ and $a = -b$ at the beginning.

CASE i. *Best formula relative to* $\int_I x_1(s)^2\,ds$. Here we will specify that R vanish for degree 0. Then

$$Rx = \int_{-1}^{1} x_1(s)\kappa^1(s)\,ds, \qquad x \in C_1;$$

and we shall determine u, v, a, b so that

$$\int_{-1}^{1} \kappa^1(s)^2\,ds$$

is minimal.

There is one constraint,

$$R[1] = 0 \quad \text{or} \quad u + v = 2.$$

Also,

$$\kappa^1(t) = -R[\theta(t, s)] = R[\phi(t, s)].$$

If $b < t < 1$,

$$\kappa^1(t) = \int_{-1}^{1} \phi(t, s)\,ds - u\phi(t, a) - v\phi(t, b) = \int_t^1 ds = 1 - t.$$

If $a < t < b$,

$$\kappa^1(t) = 1 - t - v.$$

If $-1 < t < a$,

$$\kappa^1(t) = -R[\theta(t, s)] = -\int_{-1}^{t} ds = -1 - t.$$

Let us take v, a, b as the independent parameters and determine u by the constraint.

$$J = \int_{-1}^{1} \kappa^1(t)^2\,dt = \int_{-1}^{a} (1 + t)^2\,dt + \int_a^b (1 - t - v)^2\,dt + \int_b^1 (1 - t)^2\,dt.$$

$$J = \int_{-1}^{a} (1 + t)^2\,dt + \int_a^1 (1 - t)^2\,dt - 2v\int_a^b (1 - t)\,dt + v^2\int_a^b dt.$$

$$J = \frac{(1 + a)^3}{3} + \frac{(1 - a)^3}{3} - v[(1 - a)^2 - (1 - b)^2] + v^2(b - a).$$

$$J = \frac{2(1 + 3a^2)}{3} - v[2(b - a) - (b^2 - a^2)] + v^2(b - a).$$

If $b - a = 0$, J is independent of v and is minimal when $a = 0$, in which case $J = 2/3$. We shall see that $J = 2/3$ is not the absolute minimum of J.

Suppose that $b - a \neq 0$. Let us first minimize J, for each a, b, by taking

$$v = \frac{2(b - a) - (b^2 - a^2)}{2(b - a)} = \frac{2 - a - b}{2} = 1 - \frac{a + b}{2}.$$

Then

$$J = \frac{2 + 6a^2}{3} - \frac{2 - a - b}{4}[2(b - a) - (b^2 - a^2)],$$

$$J = \frac{2}{3} + 2a^2 - \frac{(b - a)(2 - b - a)^2}{4}.$$

It is convenient to replace the independent variables (a, b) by (r, s), where

$$r = b + a,$$
$$s = b - a.$$

Then

$$J = \frac{2}{3} + \frac{(r - s)^2}{2} - \frac{s(2 - r)^2}{4} = \frac{2}{3} + \frac{2r^2 + 2s^2 - sr^2 - 4s}{4};$$

$$\frac{\partial J}{\partial r} = \frac{2r - sr}{2}; \qquad \frac{\partial J}{\partial s} = \frac{4s - r^2 - 4}{4}.$$

Hence

$$dJ = 0 \quad \text{iff} \quad r = 0, \quad s = 1 \quad \text{or} \quad r = \pm 2, \quad s = 2;$$

that is, iff

$$b = \frac{1}{2} = -a \quad \text{or} \quad b = 2, \quad a = 0 \quad \text{or} \quad b = 0, \quad a = -2.$$

The last two sets of values are extraneous. Hence if J has an interior minimum, it must be at

$$b = \frac{1}{2} = -a, \qquad v = 1, \qquad u = 1.$$

Then

$$J = \frac{1}{6},$$

which is indeed an absolute minimum.

Thus the best formula of Gaussian type relative to

$$\int_{-1}^{1} x_1(s)^2 \, ds$$

is such that

$$Rx = \int_{-1}^{1} x(s)\,ds - x\left(-\frac{1}{2}\right) - x\left(\frac{1}{2}\right) = \int_{-1}^{1} x_1(s)\kappa^1(s)\,ds, \qquad x \in \boldsymbol{C}_1,$$

$$\kappa^1(t) = \begin{cases} -1 - t & \text{if } -1 < t < -\frac{1}{2}, \\ -t & \text{if } -\frac{1}{2} < t < \frac{1}{2}, \\ 1 - t & \text{if } \frac{1}{2} < t < 1, \end{cases}$$

$$|Rx| \leqq \frac{1}{\sqrt{6}}\left[\int_{-1}^{1} x_1(s)^2\,ds\right]^{1/2}.$$

CASE ii. *Best formula relative to* $\int_{-1}^{1} x_2(s)^2\,ds$. Here we specify that R vanish for degree 1. The constraints are

$$u + v = 2,$$
$$au + bv = 0,$$

the last equation being equivalent to the statement that

$$Rx = 0 \quad \text{when} \quad x(s) = s.$$

Then

$$Rx = \int_{-1}^{1} x_2(s)\kappa^2(s)\,ds, \qquad x \in \boldsymbol{C}_2,$$

where

$$\kappa^2(t) = -R[(s - t)\theta(t, s)] = R[(s - t)\phi(t, s)].$$

If $b < t < 1$,

$$\kappa^2(t) = \int_{t}^{1} (s - t)\,ds = \frac{(1 - t)^2}{2}.$$

If $a < t < b$,

$$\kappa^2(t) = \frac{(1 - t)^2}{2} - v(b - t).$$

If $-1 < t < a$,

$$\kappa^2(t) = -\int_{-1}^{t} (s - t)\,ds = \frac{(1 + t)^2}{2}.$$

Hence

$$J = \int_{-1}^{1} \kappa^2(t)^2\,dt = \int_{-1}^{a} \frac{(1 + t)^4}{4}\,dt + \int_{a}^{b}\left[\frac{(1 - t)^2}{2} - v(b - t)\right]^2 dt$$
$$+ \int_{b}^{1} \frac{(1 - t)^4}{4}\,dt,$$

$$J = \int_{-1}^{a} \frac{(1+t)^4}{4}\,dt + \int_{a}^{1} \frac{(1-t)^4}{4}\,dt - v\int_{a}^{b} (1-t)^2(b-t)\,dt + v^2\int_{a}^{b} (b-t)^2\,dt.$$

Now

$$\int_{a}^{b} (1-t)^2(b-t)\,dt = \int_{0}^{b-a} (1-b+s)^2 s\,ds = \frac{(1-b)^2(b-a)^2}{2} + \frac{2(1-b)(b-a)^3}{3} + \frac{(b-a)^4}{4}.$$

Hence

$$J = \frac{(1+a)^5}{20} + \frac{(1-a)^5}{20} - v\left[\frac{(1-b)^2(b-a)^2}{2} + \frac{2(1-b)(b-a)^3}{3} + \frac{(b-a)^4}{4}\right] + \frac{v^2(b-a)^3}{3}.$$

There are two degrees of freedom. Let us take a and b as the independent variables. The constraints imply that

$$-v(b-a) = 2a.$$

Hence

$$J = \frac{1+10a^2+5a^4}{10} + 2a\left[\frac{(1-b)^2(b-a)}{2} + \frac{2(1-b)(b-a)^2}{3} + \frac{(b-a)^3}{4}\right] + \frac{4a^2(b-a)}{3}.$$

$$J = \frac{1}{10} + ab - \frac{2}{3}ab^2 + \frac{2}{3}a^2b + \frac{ab^3+a^2b^2+a^3b}{6}.$$

$$\frac{\partial J}{\partial a} = b - \frac{2}{3}b^2 + \frac{4}{3}ab + \frac{b^3+2ab^2+3a^2b}{6}.$$

$$\frac{\partial J}{\partial b} = a - \frac{4}{3}ab + \frac{2}{3}a^2 + \frac{3ab^2+2a^2b+a^3}{6}.$$

Hence $dJ = 0$ iff

$$b(6+8a-4b+3a^2+2ab+b^2) = 0,$$
$$a(6+4a-8b+a^2+2ab+3b^2) = 0.$$

If $a = 0$, then $b = 0$ (since $6 - 4b + b^2 = 0$ has only imaginary roots) and $J = 1/10$. Suppose that $a \neq 0$. Then $b \neq 0$ and (a, b) must satisfy the equations

$$6+8a-4b+3a^2+2ab+b^2 = 0,$$
$$6+4a-8b+a^2+2ab+3b^2 = 0.$$

Therefore

$$4a + 4b + 2a^2 - 2b^2 = 0,$$

$$(a + b)(2 + a - b) = 0.$$

Now

$$a = b - 2$$

leads to values of a or b outside $[-1, 1]$. Hence

$$a = -b,$$

and, since $b \leqq 1$,

$$b = 3 - \sqrt{6} = .55051,$$

$$J = \frac{1}{10} + \frac{ab}{6}[6 - 4b + 4a + b^2 + ab + a^2]$$

$$= 19.6 - 8\sqrt{6} = .00408.$$

Thus

$$b = 3 - \sqrt{6}$$

makes J an absolute minimum. Then

$$v = 1 = u.$$

The best formula of Gaussian type relative to

$$\int_{-1}^{1} x_2(s)^2\, ds$$

is therefore such that

$$Rx = \int_{-1}^{1} x(s)\, ds - [x(-3 + \sqrt{6}) + x(3 - \sqrt{6})]$$

$$= \int_{-1}^{1} x_2(s)\kappa^2(s)\, ds, \qquad x \in C_2;$$

and

$$|Rx| \leqq (19.6 - 8\sqrt{6})^{1/2}\left[\int_{-1}^{1} x_2(s)^2\, ds\right]^{1/2} = .064\left[\int_{-1}^{1} x_2(s)^2\, ds\right]^{1/2}.$$

CASE iii. *Best formula relative to* $\int_{-1}^{1} x_3(s)^2\, ds$. Here we specify that R vanish for degree 2. The constraints are

$$u + v = 2,$$

$$ua + vb = 0,$$

$$ua^2 + vb^2 = \frac{2}{3}.$$

Thus there is one degree of freedom. If we assume that the best formula will be symmetric

$$u = v,$$
$$a = -b,$$

the degree of freedom disappears and we immediately obtain the formula with

$$\begin{aligned} u &= v = 1, \\ b &= 1/\sqrt{3} = -a = .5774. \end{aligned} \tag{66}$$

CASE iv. *Best formula relative to* $\int_{-1}^{1} x_4(s)^2\, ds$. Here we specify that R vanishes for degree 3. The constraints are those of the preceding case and

$$ua^3 + vb^3 = 0.$$

These constraints determine the formula uniquely. It is given by (66).

§ 67. **Approximation of $\int_I x(s)\, ds$ by formulas of Gaussian type.** Here we specify that the integral is to be approximated by a linear combination of $m + 1$ ordinates optimally chosen. The case $m = 1$ has been considered in the preceding section. Let n, m be specified. We study

$$Rx \underset{\text{def}}{=} \int_I x(s)\, ds - u_0 x(a_0) - u_1 x(a_1) - \cdots - u_m x(a_m), \tag{68}$$

$$Rx = \int_I x_n(s)\kappa(s)\, ds, \qquad x \in C_n, \tag{69}$$

where $u_0, \cdots, u_m, a_0, \cdots, a_m \in \mathsf{R}$ are to be chosen so that

$$J = \int_I \kappa(s)^2\, ds$$

is minimal. Translate the origin so that the interval I becomes $[-c, c]$. Then the constraints necessary to insure (69) are

$$\sum_{i=0}^{m} u_i a_i^j = \frac{c^{j+1} - (-c)^{j+1}}{j+1}, \qquad j = 0, \cdots, n-1.$$

We may and shall assume that

$$a_0 \leqq a_1 \leqq \cdots \leqq a_m.$$

The calculation has not been carried out, except for $m = 1$; it would seem an important enterprise. It is to be anticipated that the best formulas are symmetric:

$$u_i = u_{m-i}, \qquad a_i = -a_{m-i}; \qquad i \leqq m.$$

The proof of symmetry in the simpler case of § 27 does not carry over to the present case.

For an alternative class of formulas we may specify that the coefficients u_i, $i \leqq m$, be all equal in (68) and then choose $a_0, \cdots, a_m$ optimally.

§ 70. **Approximations of $\int_I x$ that involve derivatives of x.** Thus far we have approximated the integral by linear combinations of values of the integrand $x(s)$. One may also approximate by a linear combination of values of the integrand $x(s)$ and of the derivative $x_1(s)$ and of higher derivatives.

As an illustration, let $\mathscr{R}^*$ be the family of functionals R such that

$$(71) \qquad Rx \underset{\text{def}}{=} \int_{-1}^{1} x(s)\,ds - [\tilde{u}x(-1) + ux(1) + \tilde{v}x_1(-1) + vx_1(1)]$$

and such that R vanishes for degree 1. Then, by Theorem 1 : 43, $\kappa \in V$ exists such that

$$(72) \qquad Rx = \int_{-1}^{1} x_2(s)\kappa(s)\,ds, \qquad x \in \boldsymbol{C}_2.$$

Note that Theorem 1 : 43 with $n = 1$ does not apply, since $R \notin \mathscr{C}_0^*$ except in the case $v = \tilde{v} = 0$. The best formula in $\mathscr{R}^*$ is the one which minimizes

$$J = \int_{-1}^{1} \kappa(s)^2\,ds.$$

The best formula is unique by Theorem 1 : 61, since

$$(1 - t)R^0 + tR^1 \in \mathscr{R}^*$$

whenever R^0, $R^1 \in \mathscr{R}^*$ and t is real.

The uniqueness of the best formula implies that

$$\tilde{u} = u, \qquad \tilde{v} = -v.$$

To establish this fact, put $t = -s$ and $y(s) = x(t)$. Then

$$\int_{-1}^{1} y(s)\,ds = \int_{-1}^{1} x(t)\,dt,$$

and

$$y_1(s) = -x_1(t).$$

Let R' be the functional

$$R'x = \int_{-1}^{1} x(s)\,ds - [ux(-1) + \tilde{u}x(1) - vx_1(-1) - \tilde{v}x_1(1)],$$

and let R be the functional (71). Then

$$R'x = Ry.$$

Consequently, if $R \in \mathscr{R}^*$, then $R' \in \mathscr{R}^*$ and, by (72), the values of J for R and R' must be the same. Hence if R minimizes J, so must R'. Since the minimizing R in $\mathscr{R}^*$ is unique, it follows that $R = R'$, that is, that

$$\tilde{u} = u, \qquad \tilde{v} = -v.$$

Then R will vanish for degree 1 iff $u = 1$.

In the search for the best formulas we need therefore consider only the functionals

$$Rx = \int_{-1}^{1} x(s)\,ds - \{x(1) + x(-1) + v[x_1(1) - x_1(-1)]\}, \qquad v \in \mathsf{R}.$$

Then, if $-1 < t < 1$,

$$\kappa(t) = R[(s-t)\phi(t, s)] = \int_t^1 (s-t)\,ds - (1-t) - v = -\frac{1-t^2}{2} - v.$$

Hence

$$J = 2\int_0^1 \kappa(t)^2\,dt = 2\int_0^1 \left(\frac{1-t^2}{2} + v\right)^2 dt = 2v^2 + \frac{4v}{3} + \frac{4}{15}.$$

The minimal J occurs when

$$v = -\frac{1}{3}$$

and is

$$J = \frac{2}{45}.$$

The calculation of further best formulas involving derivatives of the integrand would seem an important enterprise.

§ 73. **Stepwise solution of differential equations.** In the stepwise approximate solution of a differential equation

$$x_1(s) = \frac{dx}{ds} = g(x, s),$$

where the function g is known, there is occasion to approximate

$$x(m)$$

in terms of the previously calculated values

$$x(m-1), \quad x(m-2), \cdots, x(1), \quad x(0)$$

and the derivatives

$$x_1(m-1), \quad x_1(m-2), \cdots, x_1(1), \quad x_1(0)$$

and perhaps

$$x_1(m).$$

We may call such an approximation *closed* if $x_1(m)$ is used and *open* if $x_1(m)$ is not used, expanding a terminology of Steffensen's. The open formulas afford an explicit calculation for each forward step of the approximate solution.

One may define and determine best open and closed formulas relative to criteria of the sort that we have been using rather than the conventional criterion of making the approximation exact for as high a degree as possible.

Omitting details, we state the following results as an indication of a theory that could be explored.

Of all approximations of

$$x(2)$$

by linear combinations of

$$x(1), \quad x(0); \qquad x_1(2), \quad x_1(1), \quad x_1(0)$$

which are exact whenever x is a polynomial of degree 3, the best is

$$\frac{8}{43}\,x(1) + \frac{35}{43}\,x(0) + \frac{15}{43}\,x_1(2) + \frac{52}{43}\,x_1(1) + \frac{11}{43}\,x_1(0).$$

The error in this approximation is at most

$$\left(\frac{13}{13545}\right)^{1/2}\left(\frac{1}{2}\int_0^2 x_4(s)^2\,ds\right)^{1/2}, \qquad x \in \boldsymbol{C}_4.$$

The approximation is best in the sense that this appraisal is minimal among appraisals that use the root-mean-square of the fourth derivative x_4 (cf. § 86 below).

Stability of an appropriate sort is desirable in any procedure that is to be iterated. Now the above closed formula is stable and convergent in the sense of Dahlquist [1]; cf. [Henrici 1, pp. 209–246]. This follows from the facts that the approximation is exact for degree 1 and that the roots of the equation

$$z^2 - \frac{8}{43}\,z - \frac{35}{43} = 0$$

lie in or on the unit circle, all roots on the circle being simple.

We now consider an open formula.

Of all approximations of

$$x(2)$$

by linear combinations of

$$x(1), \quad x(0), \quad x_1(1), \quad x_1(0)$$

which are exact whenever x is a polynomial of degree 2, the best is

$$-\frac{3}{2}\,x(1) + \frac{5}{2}\,x(0) + \frac{11}{4}\,x_1(1) + \frac{3}{4}\,x_1(0).$$

The error in this approximation is at most

$$\left(\frac{13}{80}\right)^{1/2}\left(\frac{1}{2}\int_0^2 x_3(s)^2\,ds\right)^{1/2}, \qquad x \in \boldsymbol{C}_3.$$

The approximation is best in the sense that this appraisal is minimal among appraisals that use the root-mean-square of the third derivative x_3.

The above open formula is not stable in the sense of Dahlquist. It may nonetheless be useful where it is not to be iterated. For example the unstable open formula may be used to provide starting values in a calculation by closed formulas.

One may seek the best open approximation of $x(2)$ among those which are stable and exact for degree 2. The result is

$$x(0) + 2x_1(1).$$

Alternatively one may consider approximations of

$$x(m)$$

by $x(m - 1)$ plus a linear combination of

$$x_1(m - 1),\ x_1(m - 2), \cdots, x_1(0)$$

and perhaps $x_1(m)$. If the approximation is exact for degree $n - 1 \geqq 1$, then it will be stable and convergent and free of extraneous transients, since Dahlquist's polynomial is $z - 1$. In the Adams method the approximation is taken so as to be exact for as high a degree as possible. Instead one may choose the approximation to be best relative to

$$\frac{1}{m}\int_0^m x_n^2,$$

for suitable n.

Part 2. Values of functions

§ 74. **Conventional interpolation with distinct arguments.** Suppose that we wish to approximate the value $x(u)$ of a function x in terms of the values of $x(s)$ and perhaps its derivatives at $s = a_1, a_2, \cdots, a_m$. The conventional practice is to approximate $x(u)$ by

$$\begin{aligned} p(u) &= x(a_1) + (u - a_1)x(a_1, a_2) + (u - a_1)(u - a_2)x(a_1, a_2, a_3) + \cdots \\ &\quad + (u - a_1)\cdots(u - a_{m-1})x(a_1, \cdots, a_m), \end{aligned} \tag{75}$$

where $x(a_1, \cdots, a_{r+1})$ denotes the rth divided difference of x based on the arguments $a_1, \cdots, a_{r+1}$. The error in the approximation is then

$$-\ Rx = p(u) - x(u).$$

For each fixed u, R is a functional. The interpolating function $p(u)$ is a polynomial in u of degree $m - 1$.

Suppose first that $a_1, \cdots, a_m$ are distinct. Then, by Lagrange's formula,

$$p(u) = \sum_{i=1,\cdots,m}' x(a_i) \frac{(u - a_1)\cdots(u - a_m)}{(a_i - a_1)\cdots(a_i - a_m)}, \tag{76}$$

where the $'$ indicates that the factors $(u - a_i)$ and $(a_i - a_i)$ are omitted from the multiplier of $x(a_i)$. Let us consider $u, a_1, \cdots, a_m$ to be fixed. Then

$$Rx = x(u) - p(u)$$

is merely a linear combination of values $x(s)$ at $s = u, a_1, \cdots, a_m$, with coefficients of combination depending on $u, a_1, \cdots, a_m$. Thus Rx is an elementary Stieltjes integral on x and

$$R \in \mathscr{C}_0^*.$$

Furthermore $Rx = 0$ if x is a polynomial of degree $m - 1$. This may be seen as follows. If x is a polynomial of degree $m - 1$, then $Rx = x(u) - p(u)$ is a polynomial in u of degree $m - 1$ which vanishes at the distinct values $x = a_1, \cdots, a_m$ and therefore vanishes identically in u.

Hence R vanishes for degree $m - 1, m - 2, \cdots, 3, 2, 1, 0$ and Theorem 1:43 applies to R with $n = 1, 2, \cdots, m$. Hence

$$Rx = x(u) - p(u) = \int_I x_n(t)\kappa^n(t)\, dt, \qquad x \in \boldsymbol{C}_n, \tag{77}$$

where I is the smallest interval containing $a_1, \cdots, a_m$ and u,

$$\kappa^n(t) = \kappa^n(t, u) = -R[(s - t)^{(n-1)}\theta(t, s)] = R[(s - t)^{(n-1)}\phi(t, s)], \tag{78}$$

and

$$n = 1, \cdots, m. \tag{79}$$

In (78), R acts on its argument as a function of s. To emphasize the dependence on u, we sometimes write $\kappa^n(t, u)$ for $\kappa^n(t)$.

If we choose not to use (78), we may calculate $\kappa^n(t)$ from Hermite's formula and the transformation of iterated integrals. Thus, by Newton's divided difference formula and Hermite's formula,

$$Rx = (u - a_1)\cdots(u - a_m)x(u, a_1, \cdots, a_m),$$

$$Rx = (u - a_1)\cdots(u - a_m) \int_0^1 dt_1 \int_0^{t_1} dt_2 \cdots \int_0^{t_{m-1}} dt_m x_m(\tau), \qquad x \in \boldsymbol{C}_m, \tag{80}$$

where

$$\tau = a_1 + t_1(u - a_1) + t_2(a_2 - u) + t_3(a_3 - a_2) + \cdots + t_m(a_m - a_{m-1}).$$

Since a divided difference is a symmetric function of its arguments, $u, a_1, \cdots, a_m$ may be permuted in any fashion in the formula for τ. The permutation used above is such that $\tau = a_1$ when $t_1 = \cdots = t_m = 0$ and $\tau = a_m$ when $t_1 = \cdots = t_m = 1$.

The iterated integral in (80) may be transformed into a single integral on $x_m(\tau)\,d\tau$. The relation (80) thereby becomes (77) with $n = m$. Thereafter (77) with $n = m - 1$ can be deduced by an integration by parts combined with an extension of the resultant formula from $\boldsymbol{C}_m$ to the larger space $\boldsymbol{C}_{m-1}$. Integrating by parts again, one may obtain (77) with $n = m - 2, \cdots, 1$. The successive integrations by parts are successful in producing all the cases of (77) because the actual kernel $\kappa^m(t)$ is sufficiently differentiable and vanishes with its derivatives at the endpoints of I. The calculation is more complicated than the use of (78).

§ 81. **Illustration. The case $m = 2$; ordinary linear interpolation.** Assume that

$$a_1 = a, \qquad a_2 = b, \qquad a < u < b.$$

Then

$$p(u) = x(a) + (u - a)x(a, b) = x(a) + (u - a)\,\frac{x(b) - x(a)}{b - a}.$$

$$\begin{aligned} Rx &= (u - a)(u - b)x(u, a, b) \\ &= (u - a)(u - b)\int_0^1 dt_1 \int_0^{t_1} dt_2 x_2(\tau), \qquad x \in \boldsymbol{C}_2, \\ \tau &= u + t_1(a - u) + t_2(b - a). \end{aligned}$$

Now

$$\int_{t_2=0}^{t_1} dt_2 x_2(\tau) = \frac{1}{b - a}\int_{u+t_1(a-u)}^{u+t_1(b-u)} d\tau x_2(\tau),$$

since $d\tau = (b - a)\,dt_2$ when $dt_1 = 0$. Hence

$$\begin{aligned} Rx &= \frac{(u - a)(u - b)}{b - a}\int_0^1 dt_1 \int_{u+t_1(a-u)}^{u+t_1(b-u)} d\tau x_2(\tau) \\ &= \frac{(u - a)(u - b)}{b - a}\left\{\int_a^u d\tau x_2(\tau)\int_{(\tau-u)/(a-u)}^1 dt_1 \right. \\ &\qquad\qquad \left. + \int_u^b d\tau x_2(\tau)\int_{(\tau-u)/(b-u)}^1 dt_1\right\} \\ &= -\int_a^u x_2(\tau)\,\frac{(\tau - a)(b - u)}{b - a}\,d\tau - \int_u^b x_2(\tau)\,\frac{(u - a)(b - \tau)}{b - a}\,d\tau, \end{aligned}$$

$$Rx = \int_a^b x_2(\tau)\kappa^2(\tau)\,d\tau, \qquad x \in \boldsymbol{C}_2, \tag{82}$$

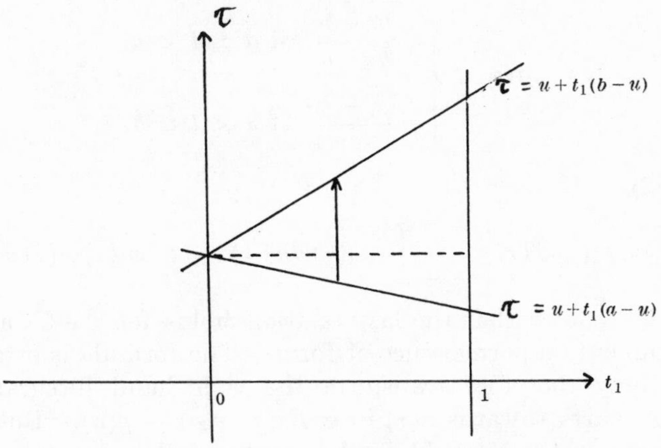

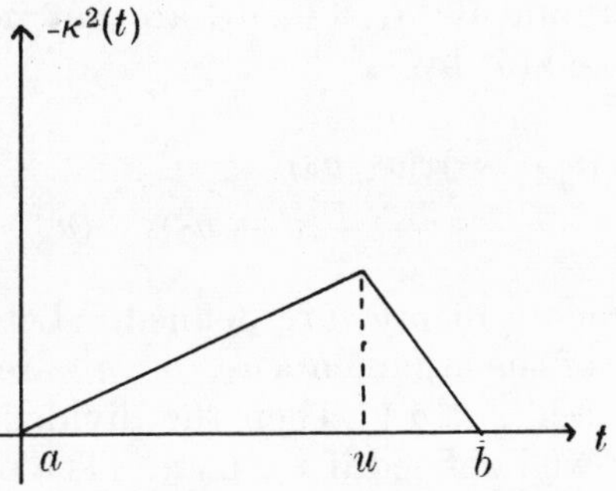

where

$$\kappa^2(t) = \kappa^2(t, u) = \begin{cases} -\dfrac{(b - u)(t - a)}{b - a} & \text{if } a \leqq t < u, \\ -\dfrac{(u - a)(b - t)}{b - a} & \text{if } u \leqq t \leqq b. \end{cases}$$

Thus (77) is established at least for $x \in C_2$. The result agrees with § 1 : 59, where $a = 0$, $b = 1$, and the functional is the negative of the present R.

Now $\kappa^2(t)$, despite its corner at $t = u$, is absolutely continuous, with

$$d\kappa^2(t) = \left(\frac{d\kappa^2(t)}{dt}\right) dt = -\kappa^1(t)\, dt, \qquad t \neq u,$$

where

$$\kappa^1(t) = \begin{cases} \dfrac{b-u}{b-a} & \text{if } a \leqq t < u, \\[2ex] -\dfrac{u-a}{b-a} & \text{if } u < t \leqq b. \end{cases}$$

Hence, by (82),

$$Rx = x_1(\tau)\kappa^2(\tau)\Big|_{\tau=a}^{b} - \int_a^b x_1(\tau)\, d\kappa^2(\tau) = \int_a^b x_1(\tau)\kappa^1(\tau)\, d\tau$$

for $x \in \boldsymbol{C}_2$. It follows that the last relation holds for $x \in \boldsymbol{C}_1$ also, by the following argument on permanence of form. The formula is established for $x \in \boldsymbol{C}_2$. We may therefore transform the right-hand integral by direct integration by parts towards $x(\tau)$ into $Rx = x(u) - p(u)$. But that same series of transformations would apply equally well to $x \in \boldsymbol{C}_1$. Hence the formula is valid for $x \in \boldsymbol{C}_1$.

§ 83. **Conventional interpolation with at most q coincident arguments.** Suppose that the arguments $a_1, \cdots, a_m$ are not necessarily distinct. We may still approximate $x(u)$ by

$$p(u) = x(a_1) + (u - a_1)x(a_1, a_2) \\ + \cdots + (u - a_1)\cdots(u - a_{m-1})x(a_1, \cdots, a_m),$$

if the divided differences in $p(u)$ are defined. Let q be a positive integer such that any $q + 1$ of the arguments $a_1, \cdots, a_m$ are not all identical. (The number of coincidences is $\leqq q$.) Then the divided differences in $p(u)$ and $p(u)$ itself are surely well defined if $x \in C_{q-1}$. The divided differences are in fact linear combinations of values of $x(s)$ and the derivatives $x_1(s), \cdots, x_{q-1}(s)$ at $s = a_1, \cdots, a_m$.

The polynomial $p(u)$ interpolates to $x(u)$ in the strong sense that

$$p(a_{i_1}, \cdots, a_{i_j}) = x(a_{i_1}, \cdots a_{i_j}),$$

where $a_{i_1}, \cdots, a_{i_j}$ is any subset of $a_1, \cdots, a_m$. (If $a_1 = a_2$, for example, then $p(a_1) = x(a_1)$ and $p_1(a_1) = x_1(a_1)$.)

Put

$$Rx = x(u) - p(u).$$

For each u, Rx is a linear combination of x and its derivatives of order $\leqq q - 1$. Hence

$$R \in \mathscr{C}^*_{q-1}.$$

Furthermore R vanishes for degree $m - 1$. For, if $x(s)$ is a polynomial in s of degree $m - 1$,

$$x(u) = p(u) + (u - a_1)\cdots(u - a_m)x(u, a_1, \cdots, a_m) = p(u)$$

by the divided difference formula for $x(u)$ and the fact that the mth differences of a polynomial of degree $m - 1$ vanish identically.

It follows that Theorem 1: 43 applies to R with

$$n = q, q + 1, q + 2, \cdots, m;$$

that is, (77) and (78) hold for these values of n. Thus we have kernel forms (77) of the remainder in conventional interpolation, whether the arguments $a_1, \cdots, a_m$ are coincident or not.

§ 84. **Illustration. The case $m = 2$ with coincident arguments.** Let

$$a_1 = a_2 = a.$$

Then $q = 2$. Theorem 1: 43 applies with

$$n = q = m = 2,$$

and for no other values of n. As an alternative to the use of (78) we shall carry out the analogue of the calculation in the illustration of § 81.

$$p(u) = x(a) + (u - a)x(a, a) = x(a) + (u - a)x_1(a).$$

$$Rx = x(u) - p(u) = (u - a)^2x(u, a, a)$$

$$= (u - a)^2 \int_0^1 dt_1 \int_0^{t_1} dt_2 x_2(\tau), \qquad x \in \boldsymbol{C}_2,$$

where

$$\tau = u + t_1(a - u) + t_2(a - a) = u + t_1(a - u).$$

Since τ is independent of t_2,

$$Rx = (u - a)^2 \int_0^1 dt_1 x_2(\tau) t_1 = \frac{(u - a)^2}{a - u} \int_u^a \frac{\tau - u}{a - u} x_2(\tau)\, d\tau.$$

$$Rx = \int_a^u (u - \tau) x_2(\tau)\, d\tau, \qquad x \in \boldsymbol{C}_2.$$

Thus, if $a < u$,

(85) $$Rx = \int_a^u x_2(\tau)\kappa^2(\tau)\, d\tau, \qquad x \in \boldsymbol{C}_2,$$

with

$$\kappa^2(\tau) = \kappa^2(\tau, u) = \begin{cases} u - \tau & \text{if } a < \tau < u, \\ 0 & \text{otherwise.} \end{cases}$$

A similar relation holds if $u < a$.

Integration of (85) by parts, in either direction, fails to give a formula for Rx as a single integral relative to $d\tau$.

§ 86. **Interpolation.** Suppose that tabular values

(87) $$x(a_0), x(a_1), \cdots, x(a_m), \qquad a_0 < a_1 < \cdots < a_m,$$

of a function $x(s)$ are given; and suppose that we wish to approximate the value $x(u)$ by

(88) $$Ax = \alpha_0 x(a_0) + \alpha_1 x(a_1) + \cdots + \alpha_m x(a_m),$$

where the coefficients $\alpha_0, \cdots, \alpha_m$ depend on u. We describe the approximation of $x(u)$ by Ax as an interpolation. We distinguish between *narrow interpolation* and *broad interpolation.* In narrow interpolation, the investigator is interested in a single value of u; in broad interpolation, he is interested in many values of u.

Conventional interpolation based on distinct arguments is an instance of approximation of $x(u)$ by Ax. Thus, in conventional interpolation a positive integer n is given and fixed, $n \leqq m + 1$; and $x(u)$ is approximated by the Lagrange polynomial $p(u)$ based on the n arguments $a_0, a_1, \cdots, a_m$ which are closest to u. By Lagrange's formula (76), $p(u)$ is precisely of the form (88) with $m - n + 1$ coefficients equal to zero and n coefficients equal to polynomials in u of degree $n - 1$. As u takes on different values the base of the interpolation may change. Hence conventional interpolation is an approximation of the form (88) in which the coefficients $\alpha_0, \cdots, \alpha_m$ are piecewise polynomials in u of degree $n - 1$. At transition points the coefficients may be discontinuous in u. For example, consider quadratic interpolation ($n = 3$) based on arguments $s = 0, 1, 2, 3, \cdots$. For $u < 1.5$, the interpolation is based on $x(0), x(1), x(2)$. For $1.5 < u < 2.5$, the interpolation is based on $x(1), x(2), x(3)$. There is a transition at $u = 1.5$ at which α_0 and α_3 are discontinuous, since

$$\alpha_0 = -.125, \quad \alpha_3 = 0 \quad \text{at} \quad u = 1.5-0,$$

$$\alpha_0 = 0, \quad \alpha_3 = -.125 \quad \text{at} \quad u = 1.5 + 0.$$

To design and justify a practice of interpolation, suppose that a positive integer n is given and fixed and that we choose to consider only approximations Ax of the form (88) which are such that

(89) $$Rx = x(u) - Ax = \int_I x_n(s)\kappa(s)\,ds, \qquad x \in C_n(I),$$

where I is the smallest interval containing $u, a_0, \cdots, a_m$ and κ is a suitable function of s and u.

Let $\mathscr{A}^*$ be the set of approximations A of the form (88) which are exact whenever x is a polynomial of degree $n - 1$. We know from Theorem 1 : 43 that $\mathscr{A}^*$ consists precisely of all those approximations A of the form (88) for which (89) holds, since for each fixed u, $-\infty < u < \infty$,

$$R \in \mathscr{C}_0^* \subset \mathscr{C}_{n-1}^*.$$

We seek criteria on the basis of which to choose preferred elements of $\mathscr{A}^*$.

Consider A in $\mathscr{A}^*$. For each fixed u, the corresponding function $\kappa(s)$ may vanish on appreciable parts of I. We define the *support* S of κ for each u as the closure of the set of points s in I at which $\kappa(s) \neq 0$. The support S may be identical with I. Equation (1 : 45) implies that S is always a finite number of intervals.

Since κ vanishes on $I - S$, (89) implies that

$$(90) \qquad Rx = \int_S x_n(s)\kappa(s)\,ds, \qquad x \in C_n(I).$$

Let $|S|$ be the sum of the lengths of the constituent intervals of S. If $|S| = 0$, (90) reduces to

$$Rx = 0.$$

In this case the approximation is perfect and there is no need for further study of R. If $|S| \neq 0$, Schwarz's inequality (1: 29) applied to (90) implies that

$$(91) \qquad |Rx| \leqq M\left[\frac{\int_S x_n(s)^2\,ds}{|S|}\right]^{1/2}, \qquad x \in C_n(I),$$

where

$$(92) \qquad M = \left[|S| \int_S \kappa(s)^2\,ds\right]^{1/2}.$$

We call M the *modulus* of the formula A [Sard 3, § 5]. The modulus M is a function of u. We define the *best narrow* formula in $\mathscr{A}^*$ as the one which minimizes M for each u, $-\infty < u < \infty$.

The advantage of the appraisal (91) is that it involves an average of x_n, viz., the root-mean-square of x_n on S. Suppose that we have no basis for preferring an average of x_n on one set to an average on another set. The best narrow formula will then give the appraisal (91) with the least second member.

In addition to the best narrow formula, we define also the *special* formula B in $\mathscr{A}^*$ as follows. The special formula B is that element A of $\mathscr{A}^*$ which minimizes

$$(93) \qquad J = \int_I \kappa(s)^2\,ds$$

for each u, $-\infty < u < \infty$. The special formula is unique, by Theorem 1: 61.

By Schwarz's inequality applied to (89),

$$(94) \qquad |Rx| \leqq J^{1/2}\left[\int_I x_n(s)^2\,ds\right]^{1/2}, \qquad x \in C_n(I).$$

The special formula gives the strongest instance of (94) in $\mathscr{A}^*$.

One may prove that the coefficients $\alpha_0, \cdots, \alpha_m$ in the special formula are smooth functions of u, with derivatives of order $\leqq 2n - 2$ continuous on $-\infty < u < \infty$, at least in the case in which $a_0, \cdots, a_n$ are regularly spaced.

The coefficients $\alpha_0, \cdots, \alpha_m$ in the best narrow formula, considered for all u, are discontinuous in u at certain transition values. Since only one value of u is involved in narrow interpolation, the discontinuity of the coefficients of the best narrow formula may be immaterial.

At times we may prefer the special formula, even in narrow interpolation. For example, we may choose to confine our attention to those elements of $\mathscr{A}^*$ for which $S = I$. Thus, if the tabular entries

$$x(a_0), x(a_1), \cdots, x(a_m)$$

are subject to fluctuating error, we may wish all these entries to be present in A with nonvanishing coefficients $\alpha_0, \cdots, \alpha_m$ in order to diminish the effect of the fluctuating error. Now when S is constantly equal to I, minimizing M is equivalent to minimizing J, since

$$M^2 = |I|J.$$

The special formula in $\mathscr{A}^*$ is important also for the following reason. In our study of broad interpolation in § 100 below, we will see that the best broad formula in $\mathscr{A}^*$ is often inaccessible to us and that the special formula is good for broad interpolation, although perhaps not best.

The special formula is exact at tabular arguments $u = a_0, \cdots, a_m$. For, if

$$Ax = x(a_{i_0}), \qquad u = a_{i_0}, \qquad i_0 = 0, \cdots, m,$$

then J vanishes and therefore is minimal.

§ 95. **Interpolation in a table with regularly spaced arguments.** Suppose that tabular values

$$x(0), x(1), x(2), \cdots$$

of a function x are given; and that m, n are fixed integers, $m \geqq 0$, $n \geqq 1$. Let $\mathscr{A}^*_{m,n}$ be the set of approximations A, where

$$Ax = \alpha_0 x(0) + \alpha_1 x(1) + \cdots + \alpha_m x(m)$$

and $\alpha_0, \alpha_1, \cdots, \alpha_m$ are functions of u such that

$$Ax = x(u) \quad \text{for all real } u,$$

whenever x is a polynomial of degree $n - 1$.

The set $\mathscr{A}^*_{m,n}$ is not empty if $m \geqq n - 1$. If $m = n - 1$, then $\mathscr{A}^*_{m,n}$ consists of precisely one element. If $m < n - 1$, $\mathscr{A}^*_{m,n}$ is empty since the condition

$$Ax = x(u)$$

cannot be satisfied for $u \neq 0, 1, \cdots, m$. We therefore assume henceforth that

$$m \geqq n - 1 \geqq 0.$$

Let A_n^m be the best narrow formula in $\mathscr{A}^*_{m,n}$ and let B_n^m be the special formula in $\mathscr{A}^*_{m,n}$.

We shall state a series of facts about the formulas. The omitted proofs are rather like those of § 27. Cf. [Meyers-Sard 2].

Each coefficient α_i, $i = 0, \cdots, m$, in B_n^m is a broken polynomial in u of degree $2n - 1$, with transitions at $u = 0, 1, \cdots, m$, but with derivatives of order $\leqq 2n - 2$ continuous on $-\infty < u < \infty$.

The formula B_n^m is symmetric in $u = m/2$: that is, B_n^m with u replaced by $m - u$ is precisely B_n^m with α_i replaced by α_{m-i}, $i = 0, \cdots, m$. If we write

$$\alpha_i = \alpha_i(u),$$

then

$$\alpha_i(m - u) = \alpha_{m-i}(u), \qquad i = 0, \cdots, m.$$

For repeated use of B_n^m one could tabulate the coefficients $\alpha_1, \cdots, \alpha_m$ as functions of u.

We denote by J_n^m and M_n^m the quantities (93) and (92) for B_n^m, respectively. Then

$$(M_n^m)^2 = \begin{cases} (m - u)J_n^m & \text{if } u \leqq 0, \\ mJ_n^m & \text{if } 0 \leqq u \leqq m, \\ uJ_n^m & \text{if } m \leqq u. \end{cases}$$

Let us say that we *shift* a formula in $\mathscr{A}^*_{m,n}$ *j times* if we replace u in the formula by $u - j$ and also $x(i)$, $i = 0, \cdots, m$, by $x(i + j)$. The best narrow formula A_n^m is that one of the following finite set of formulas which has the least modulus:

$$(96) \qquad \begin{cases} B_n^p, & n - 1 \leqq p \leqq m; \\ B_n^p \text{ shifted once}, & n - 1 \leqq p \leqq m - 1; \\ B_n^p \text{ shifted twice}, & n - 1 \leqq p \leqq m - 2; \\ \vdots & \\ B_n^p \text{ shifted } m - n + 1 \text{ times}, & p = n - 1. \end{cases}$$

For example, A_3^3 is that one of the three formulas:

$$B_3^3, \ B_3^2, \ B_3^2 \text{ shifted once},$$

which has the least modulus.

We now list certain formulas B_n^m, A_n^m, along with J_n^m, for all u.

§ 97. **The case** $n = 1$.

$$\left.\begin{aligned} B_1^0 x &= x(0) \\ J_1^0 &= |u| \end{aligned}\right\} \quad \text{for all } u.$$

$$\left.\begin{aligned} B_1^m x &= x(0) \\ J_1^m &= -u \end{aligned}\right\} \quad \text{if } u \leqq 0.$$

$$\left.\begin{aligned} B_1^m x &= (i_0 - u)x(i_0 - 1) + (u - i_0 + 1)x(i_0) \\ J_1^m &= (i_0 - u)(u - i_0 + 1) \end{aligned}\right\} \quad \begin{aligned} &\text{if } 0 \leqq i_0 - 1 \leqq u \leqq i_0 \leqq m \\ &i_0 = 1, 2, \cdots, m \geqq 1. \end{aligned}$$

$$\left.\begin{aligned} B_1^m x &= x(m) \\ J_1^m &= u - m \end{aligned}\right\} \quad \text{if } m \leqq u.$$

Also, A_1^m is the conventional formula

$$A_1^m x = x(i_0),$$

where i_0 is the integer among $0, 1, \cdots, m$ which is closest to u (or one of the two such integers if there are two). Thus A_1^m is the formula B_1^0 shifted i_0 times. The modulus of A_1^m is $|u - i_0|$.

§ 98. **The case** $n = 2$. For $m = 1, 2, 3, 4$ the formulas B_2^m are as follows.

$$B_2^1 x = (1 - u)x(0) + ux(1) \quad \text{for all } u.$$

$$J_2^1 = \begin{cases} u^2(1 - u) & \text{if } u \leqq 0, \\ u^2(1 - u)^2 & \text{if } 0 \leqq u \leqq 1, \\ u(1 - u)^2 & \text{if } 1 \leqq u. \end{cases}$$

$$\left.\begin{aligned} 4B_2^2 x &= (-5u + 4)x(0) + 6ux(1) - ux(2), \\ 24J_2^2 &= u^2(-8u + 7) \end{aligned}\right\} \quad \text{if } u \leqq 0.$$

$$\left.\begin{aligned} 4B_2^2 x &= (u - 1)(u^2 + u - 4)x(0) + 2u(3 - u^2)x(1) \\ &\qquad + u(u - 1)(u + 1)x(2), \\ 24J_2^2 &= u^2(1 - u)^2(-u)^2(-u^2 - 2u + 7) \end{aligned}\right\} \quad \text{if } 0 \leqq u \leqq 1.$$

$$\left.\begin{aligned} 4B_2^2 x &= (u - 1)(u - 2)(3 - u)x(0) + 2(u - 2) \\ &\qquad \times (u^2 - 4u + 1)x(1) + (u - 1) \\ &\qquad \times (-u^2 + 5u - 2)x(2), \\ 24J_2^2 &= (u - 1)^2(2 - u)^2(-u^2 + 6u - 1) \end{aligned}\right\} \quad \text{if } 1 \leqq u \leqq 2.$$

$$\left.\begin{aligned} 4B_2^2 x &= (u - 2)x(0) - 6(u - 2)x(1) + (5u - 6)x(2), \\ 24J_2^2 &= (2 - u)^2(8u - 9) \end{aligned}\right\} \quad \text{if } 2 \leqq u.$$

Since $m = 2$ here, the results for $1 \leqq u \leqq 2$ may be obtained from those for $0 \leqq u \leqq 1$ by reflection in $u = m/2 = 1$. Likewise the results for $2 \leqq u$ may be obtained from those for $u \leqq 0$.

The coefficients $\alpha_0, \alpha_1, \alpha_2$ above are indeed piecewise polynomials of degree (at most) $2n - 1 = 3$, with derivatives of order $2n - 2 = 2$ continuous everywhere.

$$\left.\begin{aligned} 15B_2^3x &= (-19u + 15)x(0) + 24ux(1) - 6ux(2) + ux(3), \\ 45J_2^3 &= u^2(-15u + 13) \end{aligned}\right\} \text{ if } u \leqq 0.$$

$$\left.\begin{aligned} 15B_2^3x &= (u - 1)(2u + 5)(2u - 3)x(0) + 3u(-3u^2 + 8) \\ &\quad \times x(1) + 6u(u - 1)(u + 1)x(2) - u(u - 1) \\ &\quad \times (u + 1)x(3), \\ 45J_2^3 &= u^2(1 - u)^2(-2u^2 - 4u + 13) \end{aligned}\right\} \text{ if } 0 \leqq u \leqq 1.$$

$$\left.\begin{aligned} 15B_2^3x &= (u - 1)(u - 2)(-5u + 12)x(0) + 3(u - 2) \\ &\quad \times (5u^2 - 14u + 4)x(1) + 3(u - 1) \\ &\quad \times (-5u^2 + 16u - 7)x(2) + (u - 1)(u - 2) \\ &\quad \times (5u - 3)x(3), \\ 45J_2^3 &= (u - 1)^2(2 - u)^2(-5u^2 + 15u - 3) \end{aligned}\right\} \text{ if } 1 \leqq u \leqq 2.$$

$$\left.\begin{aligned} 15B_2^3x &= (u - 2)(u - 3)(u - 4)x(0) - 6(u - 2)(u - 3) \\ &\quad \times (u - 4)x(1) + 3(u - 3)(3u^2 - 18u + 19) \\ &\quad \times x(2) + (u - 2)(2u - 3)(-2u + 11)x(3), \\ 45J_2^3 &= (u - 2)^2(3 - u)^2(-2u^2 + 16u - 17) \end{aligned}\right\} \text{ if } 2 \leqq u \leqq 3.$$

$$\left.\begin{aligned} 15B_2^3x &= -(u - 3)x(0) + 6(u - 3)x(1) - 24(u - 3)x(2) \\ &\quad + (19u - 42)x(3), \\ 45J_2^3 &= (3 - u)^2(15u - 32) \end{aligned}\right\} \text{ if } 3 \leqq u.$$

$$\left.\begin{aligned} 56B_2^4x &= (-71u + 56)x(0) + 90ux(1) - 24ux(2) \\ &\qquad + 6ux(3) - ux(4), \\ 336J_2^4 &= u^2(-112u + 97) \end{aligned}\right\} \text{ if } u \leqq 0.$$

$$\left.\begin{aligned} 56B_2^4x &= (u - 1)(15u^2 + 15u - 56)x(0) + 2u \\ &\quad \times (-17u^2 + 45)x(1) + 24u(u - 1)(u + 1)x(2) \\ &\quad - 6u(u - 1)(u + 1)x(3) + u(u - 1)(u + 1)x(4), \\ 336J_2^4 &= u^2(1 - u)^2(-15u^2 - 30u + 97) \end{aligned}\right\} \text{ if } 0 \leqq u \leqq 1.$$

$$\left.\begin{aligned} 56B_2^4x &= (u - 1)(u - 2)(-19u + 45)x(0) + 2(u - 2) \\ &\quad \times (29u^2 - 80u + 23)x(1) + 8(u - 1) \\ &\quad \times (-8u^2 + 25u - 11)x(2) + 2(u - 1)(u - 2) \\ &\quad \times (15u - 9)x(3) + (u - 1)(u - 2)(-5u + 3)x(4), \\ 336J_2^4 &= (u - 1)^2(2 - u)^2(-39u^2 + 114u - 23) \end{aligned}\right\} \text{ if } 1 \leqq u \leqq 2.$$

$$\left.\begin{aligned} 56B_2^4x &= (u-2)(u-3)(5u-17)x(0) + 2(u-2)(u-3) \\ &\quad \times (-15u+51)x(1) + 8(u-3)(8u^2-39u+39) \\ &\quad \times x(2) + 2(u-2)(-29u^2+152u-167)x(3) \\ &\quad + (u-2)(u-3)(19u-31)x(4), \\ 336J_2^4 &= (u-2)^2(3-u)^2(-39u^2+198u-191) \end{aligned}\right\} \text{ if } 2 \leqq u \leqq 3.$$

$$\left.\begin{aligned} 56B_2^4x &= -(u-3)(u-4)(u-5)x(0) + 6(u-3)(u-4) \\ &\quad \times (u-5)x(1) - 24(u-3)(u-4)(u-5) \\ &\quad \times x(2) + 2(u-4)(17u^2-136u+227)x(3) \\ &\quad + (u-3)(-15u^2+135u-244)x(4), \\ 336J_2^4 &= (u-3)^2(4-u)^2(-15u^2+150u-263) \end{aligned}\right\} \text{ if } 3 \leqq u \leqq 4.$$

$$\left.\begin{aligned} 56B_2^4x &= (u-4)[x(0) - 6x(1) + 24x(2) - 90x(3)] \\ &\qquad + (71u-228)x(4), \\ 336J_2^4 &= (u-4)^2(112u-351) \end{aligned}\right\} \text{ if } 4 \leqq u.$$

Also, for $m = 1, 2, 3, 4$, A_2^m is the conventional formula

$$A_2^m x = (i_0 - u)x(i_0 - 1) + (u - i_0 + 1)x(i_0),$$

where $i_0 - 1$, i_0 are consecutive integers in $[0, m]$ closest to u; that is,

$$\begin{aligned} i_0 &= 1 && \text{if } u \leqq 1, \\ i_0 &= m && \text{if } m - 1 \leqq u, \\ i_0 - 1 \leqq u &\leqq i_0 && \text{otherwise.} \end{aligned}$$

Thus A_2^m is B_2^1 shifted $i_0 - 1$ times. The modulus of the above formula is

$$(i_0 - u)(u - i_0 + 1).$$

I surmise that A_2^m is the above formula for all m.

---

§ 99. **The case** $n = 3$. For $m = 2, 3, 4, 5$ the formulas B_3^m are as follows.

$$2B_3^2x = (u-1)(u-2)x(0) - 2u(u-2)x(1) + u(u-1)x(2) \quad \text{for all } u.$$

$$120J_3^2 = \begin{cases} u^2(u-1)(u-2)(-6u+5) & \text{if } u \leqq 0, \\ u^2(u-1)^2(u-2)(u^2+u-5) & \text{if } 0 \leqq u \leqq 1, \\ u(u-1)^2(u-2)^2(-u^2+5u-1) & \text{if } 1 \leqq u \leqq 2, \\ u(u-1)(u-2)^2(6u-7) & \text{if } 2 \leqq u. \end{cases}$$

$$\left.\begin{aligned} 132B_3^3x &= (93u^2 - 223u + 132)x(0) + 3u(-71u + 113) \\ &\quad \times x(1) + 3u(49u - 47)x(2) + u(-27u + 25) \\ &\quad \times x(3), \\ 31680J_3^3 &= u^2(-1584u^3 + 5343u^2 - 5778u + 2015) \end{aligned}\right\} \text{ if } u \leqq 0.$$

$$\left.\begin{aligned} 132B_3^3x &= (u - 1)(-2u^4 - 2u^3 - 2u^2 + 91u - 132)x(0) \\ &\quad + 3u(2u^4 - 71u + 113)x(1) + 3u(u - 1) \\ &\quad \times (-2u^3 - 2u^2 - 2u + 47)x(2) + u(u - 1) \\ &\quad \times (2u^3 + 2u^2 + 2u - 25)x(3), \\ 31680J_3^3 &= u^2(1 - u)^2(-4u^6 - 8u^5 - 12u^4 + 356u^3 \\ &\quad - 168u^2 - 1748u + 2015) \end{aligned}\right\} \text{ if } 0 \leqq u \leqq 1.$$

$$\left.\begin{aligned} 132B_3^3x &= (u - 1)(u - 2)(4u^3 - 18u^2 - 2u + 63)x(0) \\ &\quad + 3(u - 2)(-4u^4 + 22u^3 - 16u^2 - 43u - 3) \\ &\quad \times x(1) + 3(u - 1)(4u^4 - 26u^3 + 34u^2 \\ &\quad + 23u + 6)x(2) + (u - 1)(u - 2) \\ &\quad \times (-4u^3 + 18u^2 + 2u + 3)x(3), \\ 31680J_3^3 &= (u - 1)^2(2 - u)^2(-16u^6 + 144u^5 - 308u^4 \\ &\quad - 312u^3 + 1208u^2 - 276u - 9) \end{aligned}\right\} \text{ if } 1 \leqq u \leqq 2.$$

$$\left.\begin{aligned} 132B_3^3x &= (u - 2)(u - 3)(-2u^3 + 20u^2 - 68u + 53) \\ &\quad \times x(0) + 3(u - 2)(u - 3)(2u^3 - 20u^2 \\ &\quad + 68u - 31)x(1) + 3(u - 3)(-2u^4 + 24u^3 \\ &\quad - 108u^2 + 145u - 62)x(2) + (u - 2) \\ &\quad \times (2u^4 - 26u^3 + 128u^2 - 191u + 93)x(3), \\ 31680J_3^3 &= (u - 2)^2(3 - u)^2(-4u^6 + 80u^5 - 672u^4 \\ &\quad + 2668u^3 - 4632u^2 + 3512u - 961) \end{aligned}\right\} \text{ if } 2 \leqq u \leqq 3.$$

$$\left.\begin{aligned} 132B_3^3x &= (u - 3)(-27u + 56)x(0) + 3(u - 3) \\ &\quad \times (49u - 100)x(1) + 3(u - 3)(-71u + 100) \\ &\quad \times x(2) + (93u^2 - 335u + 300)x(3), \\ 31680J_3^3 &= (3 - u)^2(1584u^3 - 8913u^2 + 16488u - 10000) \end{aligned}\right\} \text{ if } 3 \leqq u.$$

— — — — — — — — — — — —

$$\left.\begin{aligned} 1840B_3^4x &= (1359u^2 - 3166u + 1840)x(0) + 4u(-829u \\ &\quad + 1261)x(1) + 46u(59u - 56) + 4u(-229u \\ &\quad + 211)x(3) + u(159u - 146)x(4), \\ 220800J_3^4 &= u^2(-11040u^3 + 36473u^2 - 38864u + 13398) \end{aligned}\right\} \text{ if u } \leqq 0.$$

$$\left.\begin{aligned} 1840B_3^4x &= (u - 1)(-33u^4 - 33u^3 - 33u^2 + 1326u \\ &\quad - 1840)x(0) + 4u(28u^4 - 829u + 1261)x(1) \\ &\quad + 46u(u - 1)(-3u^3 - 3u^2 - 3u + 56)x(2) \\ &\quad + 4u(u - 1)(18u^3 + 18u^2 + 18u - 211)x(3) \\ &\quad + u(u - 1)(-13u^3 - 13u^2 - 13u + 146)x(4), \\ 220800J_3^4 &= u^2(1 - u)^2(-33u^6 - 66u^5 - 99u^4 + 2586u^3 \\ &\quad - 1061u^2 - 12068u + 13398) \end{aligned}\right\} \text{ if } 0 \leqq u \leqq 1.$$

$$\left.\begin{aligned}
1840B_3^4x &= (u-1)(u-2)(79u^3-323u^2-7u+864)x(0)\\
&\quad + 4(u-2)(-74u^4+362u^3-296u^2\\
&\quad - 401u-51)x(1)+46(u-1)(9u^4-51u^3\\
&\quad + 69u^2+8u+12)x(2)+4(u-1)(u-2)\\
&\quad \times(-64u^3+218u^2-38u+41)x(3)\\
&\quad + (u-1)(u-2)(59u^3-183u^2+53u-36)\\
&\quad \times x(4),\\
220800J_3^4 &= (u-1)^2(2-u)^2(-217u^6+1658u^5\\
&\quad - 3351u^4-1458u^3+7935u^2-1808u-102)
\end{aligned}\right\}\text{ if } 1 \leqq u \leqq 2.$$

$$\left.\begin{aligned}
1840B_3^4x &= (u-2)(u-3)(-59u^3+525u^2-1421u\\
&\quad +1024)x(0)+4(u-2)(u-3)(64u^3\\
&\quad - 550u^2+1366u-719)x(1)+46(u-3)\\
&\quad \times(-9u^4+93u^3-321u^2+416u-188)x(2)\\
&\quad + 4(u-2)(74u^4-822u^3+3056u^2-4337u\\
&\quad + 2167)x(3)+(u-2)(u-3)(-79u^3\\
&\qquad\qquad + 1020u^2-1201u+724)x(4),\\
220800J_3^4 &= (u-2)^2(3-u)^2(-217u^6+3550u^5\\
&\quad - 22271u^4+67554u^3-103417u^2+77176u\\
&\qquad\qquad - 22582)
\end{aligned}\right\}\text{ if } 2 \leqq u \leqq 3.$$

$$\left.\begin{aligned}
1840B_3^4x &= (u-3)(u-4)(13u^3-169u^2+741u-946)\\
&\quad \times x(0)+4(u-3)(u-4)(-18u^3+234u^2\\
&\quad - 1026u+1301)x(1)+46(u-3)(u-4)\\
&\quad \times(3u^3-39u^2+171u-196)x(2)+4(u-4)\\
&\quad \times(-28u^4+448u^3-2688u^2+6339u\\
&\quad - 5113)x(3)+(u-3)(33u^4-561u^3\\
&\qquad\qquad + 3597u^2-8970u+7624)x(4),\\
220800J_3^4 &= (u-3)^2(4-u)^2(-33u^6+858u^5-9339u^4\\
&\quad + 51798u^3-148493u^2+209004u-11442)
\end{aligned}\right\}\text{ if } 3 \leqq u \leqq 4.$$

$$\left.\begin{aligned}
1840B_3^4x &= (u-4)(159u-490)x(0)+(u-4)(-229u\\
&\quad + 705)x(1)+46(u-4)(59u-180)x(2)\\
&\quad + 4(u-4)(-829u+2055)x(3)\\
&\quad + (1359u^2-7706u+10920)x(4),\\
220800J_3^4 &= (u-4)^2(11040u^3-96007u^2+277000u\\
&\qquad\qquad - 265050)
\end{aligned}\right\}\text{ if } 4 \leqq u.$$

— — — — — — — — — — — —

$$
\left.\begin{aligned}
79820B_3^5x &= 4(14861u^2 - 34448u + 19955)x(0) \\
&\quad + u(-146677u + 221405)x(1) + u(126233u \\
&\quad - 119545)x(2) + u(-53167u + 48935)x(3) \\
&\quad + u(17123u - 15715)x(4) + 4u(-739u \\
&\qquad + 678)x(5), \\
19156800J_3^5 &= u^2(-957840u^3 + 3152557u^2 - 3350090u \\
&\qquad + 1152429)
\end{aligned}\right\} \text{if } u \leqq 0.
$$

$$
\left.\begin{aligned}
79820B_3^5x &= 4(u - 1)(-368u^4 - 368u^3 - 368u^2 + 14493u \\
&\quad - 19955)x(0) + u(5092u^4 - 146677u \\
&\quad + 221405)x(1) + u(u - 1)(-6688u^3 \\
&\quad - 6688u^2 - 6688u + 119545)x(2) \\
&\quad + u(u - 1)(4232u^3 + 4232u^2 + 4232u \\
&\quad - 48935)x(3) + u(u - 1)(-1408u^3 - 1408u^2 \\
&\quad - 1408u + 15715)x(4) \\
&\quad + 4u(u - 1)(61u^3 + 61u^2 + 61u - 678)x(5), \\
19156800J_3^5 &= u^2(1 - u)^2(-2944u^6 - 5888u^5 - 8832u^4 \\
&\quad + 226000u^3 - 90336u^2 - 1045232u \\
&\qquad + 1152429)
\end{aligned}\right\} \text{if } 0 \leqq u \leqq 1.
$$

$$
\left.\begin{aligned}
79820B_3^5x &= 4(u - 1)(u - 2)(905u^3 - 3650u^2 - 30u \\
&\quad + 9341)x(0) + (u - 2)(-13954u^4 + 67322u^3 \\
&\quad - 55816u^2 - 67849u - 9523)x(1) + (u - 1) \\
&\quad \times (21306u^4 - 118664u^3 + 161276u^2 + 7569u \\
&\quad + 27994)x(2) + (u - 1)(u - 2)(-16394u^3 \\
&\quad + 53948u^2 - 11628u + 10313)x(3) + (u - 1) \\
&\quad \times (u - 2)(6586u^3 - 20212u^2 + 6132u \\
&\quad - 3997)x(4) + 4(u - 1)(u - 2)(-291u^3 \\
&\qquad + 887u^2 - 277u + 176)x(5), \\
19156800J_3^5 &= (u - 1)^2(2 - u)^2(-20668u^6 + 155072u^5 \\
&\quad - 311344u^4 - 113588u^3 + 679992u^2 \\
&\qquad - 154744u - 9523)
\end{aligned}\right\} \text{if } 1 \leqq u \leqq 2.
$$

$$
\left.\begin{aligned}
79820B_3^5x &= 4(u - 2)(u - 3)(-767u^3 + 6520u^2 - 16948u \\
&\quad + 12031)x(0) + (u - 2)(u - 3)(14040u^3 \\
&\quad - 114510u^2 + 272510u - 146127)x(1) \\
&\quad + (u - 3)(-26780u^4 + 260550u^3 \\
&\quad - 861850u^2 + 1107623u - 503586)x(2) \\
&\quad + (u - 2)(26780u^4 - 275050u^3 + 970600u^2 \\
&\quad - 1359627u + 680471)x(3) + (u - 2)(u - 3) \\
&\quad \times (-14040u^3 + 96090u^2 - 180410u \\
&\quad + 108673)x(4) + 4(u - 2)(u - 3)(767u^3 \\
&\qquad - 4985u^2 + 9273u - 5584)x(5), \\
19156800J_3^5 &= (u - 2)^2(3 - u)^2(-31616u^6 + 474240u^5 \\
&\quad - 2781708u^4 + 8057080u^3 - 12052136u^2 \\
&\qquad + 8947180u - 2637083)
\end{aligned}\right\} \text{if } 2 \leqq u \leqq 3.
$$

$$\left.\begin{aligned}
79820B_3^5x = {} & 4(u-3)(u-4)(291u^3 - 3478u^2 + 13232u \\
& - 15409)x(0) + (u-3)(u-4)(-6586u^3 \\
& + 78578u^2 - 297962u + 344613)x(1) \\
& + (u-3)(u-4)(16394u^3 - 191962u^2 \\
& + 701698u - 748377)x(2) + (u-4) \\
& \times (-21306u^4 + 307456u^3 - 1577216u^2 \\
& + 3373529u - 2580989)x(3) + (u-3) \\
& \times (13954u^4 - 211758u^3 + 1139086u^2 \\
& - 2553859u + 2050168)x(4) + 4(u-3) \\
& \times (u-4)(-905u^3 + 9925u^2 - 31345u \\
& + 31066)x(5), \\
19156800J_3^5 = {} & (u-3)^2(4-u)^2(-20668u^6 + 464968u^5 \\
& - 4185044u^4 + 19242468u^3 - 47647928u^2 \\
& + 60470924u - 30909143)
\end{aligned}\right\} \text{ if } 3 \leqq u \leqq 4.$$

$$\left.\begin{aligned}
79820B_3^5x = {} & 4(u-4)(u-5)(-61u^3 + 976u^2 - 5246u \\
& + 8777)x(0) + (u-4)(u-5)(1408u^3 \\
& - 22528u^2 + 121088u - 202525)x(1) + (u-4) \\
& \times (u-5)(-4232u^3 + 67712u^2 - 363952u \\
& + 607025)x(2) + (u-4)(u-5)(6688u^3 \\
& - 107008u^2 + 575168u - 917095)x(3) \\
& + (u-5)(-5092u^4 + 101840u^3 - 763800u^2 \\
& + 2399323u - 2670520)x(4) + 4(u-4) \\
& \times (368u^4 - 7728u^3 + 61088u^2 - 200787u \\
& + 232690)x(5), \\
19156800J_3^5 = {} & (u-4)^2(5-u)^2(-2944u^6 + 94208u^5 \\
& - 1260032u^4 + 8782640u^3 - 32985136u^2 \\
& + 63014592u - 48002131)
\end{aligned}\right\} \text{ if } 4 \leqq u \leqq 5.$$

$$\left.\begin{aligned}
79820B_3^5x = {} & 4(u-5)(-739u + 3017)x(0) + (u-5)(17123u \\
& - 69900)x(1) + (u-5)(-53167u \\
& + 216900)x(2) + (u-5)(126233u - 511620) \\
& \times x(3) + (u-5)(-146677u + 511980)x(4) \\
& + 4(14861u^2 - 114162u + 219240)x(5), \\
19156800J_3^5 = {} & (u-5)^2(957840u^3 - 11215043u^2 \\
& + 43662520u - 56514096)
\end{aligned}\right\} \text{ if } 5 \leqq u.$$

— — — — — — — — — — — —

We now consider the best narrow formulas A_3^m, $m = 2, 3, 4, 5$. Since $\mathscr{A}_{2,3}^*$ consists of a single formula, that formula is best. Thus

$$A_3^2 = B_3^2 = \text{the conventional formula, for all } u.$$

For $m = 3, 4, 5$ we compare the moduli of the formulas (96). We find that for extrapolation the conventional practice is best. That is,

$$\begin{array}{ll} A_3^5 = A_3^4 = A_3^3 = B_3^2 & \text{if } u \leqq 0; \\ A_3^5 \text{ is } B_3^2 \text{ shifted 3 times} & \text{if } 5 \leqq u; \\ A_3^4 \text{ is } B_3^2 \text{ shifted twice} & \text{if } 4 \leqq u; \\ A_3^3 \text{ is } B_3^2 \text{ shifted once} & \text{if } 3 \leqq u. \end{array}$$

Now consider strict interpolation, $0 \leqq u \leqq m$. In this case

$$(M_n^m)^2 = mJ_n^m.$$

To facilitate the comparison of the moduli, the following table gives 120 times the square modulus of the formulas (96). The table involves much repetition, since entire columns are repeated after shifting and since M_n^m is symmetric in $u = m/2$. The blank places in the columns refer to extrapolatory cases, hence ones in which the moduli will not be minimal compared to those values that are entered.

Consider the case $m = 3$. The first three columns of the table are pertinent since they refer to elements of $\mathscr{A}_{3,3}^*$: In the first column $\alpha_3 = 0$; in the second column $\alpha_0 = 0$. Because of the symmetry, the facts for $u \leqq 1.5$ are essentially the same as those for $u \geqq 1.5$. From the first three columns, we see that

$$A_3^3 = \begin{cases} B_3^2 & \text{if } u \leqq .55, \\ B_3^3 & \text{if } .56 \leqq u \leqq 2.44, \\ B_3^2 \text{ shifted once} & \text{if } 2.45 \leqq u. \end{cases}$$

We see also that for $0 \leqq u \leqq 3$, the modulus of B_3^3 is never far from the minimal modulus. Indeed M_3^3 is less than 107% of the minimal modulus, $0 \leqq u \leqq 3$. Thus B_3^3 is good in $\mathscr{A}_{3,3}^*$, even for narrow interpolation.

Consider the case $m = 4$. The first six columns of the table are pertinent. Because of symmetry, the facts for $u \leqq 2$ are essentially the same as those for $u \geqq 2$. From the first six columns, we see that

$$A_3^4 = \begin{cases} B_3^2 & \text{if } u \leqq .55, \\ B_3^3 & \text{if } .56 \leqq u \leqq 1.66, \\ B_3^4 & \text{if } 1.67 \leqq u \leqq 2.33, \\ B_3^3 \text{ shifted once} & \text{if } 2.34 \leqq u \leqq 3.44, \\ B_3^2 \text{ shifted twice} & \text{if } 3.45 \leqq u. \end{cases}$$

We see also that M_3^4 is never more than 121% of the minimal modulus, $0 \leqq u \leqq 4$. Thus B_3^4 is good in $\mathscr{A}_{4,3}^*$, even for narrow interpolation.

TABLE 4

120 TIMES THE SQUARE MODULUS OF B_3^m SHIFTED j TIMES

(m, j) / u	(2, 0)	(2, 1)	(3, 0)	(2, 2)	(3, 1)	(4, 0)	(2, 3)	(3, 2)	(4, 1)	(5, 0)
0	0		0			0				0
.1	.1505−		.1693			.2146				.2557
.2	.4388		.4833			.6100				.7549
.3	.6910		.7440			.9349				1.1559
.4	.8185−		.8582			1.0725+				1.3242
.5	.7969		.81125			1.0075				1.2425
.6	.6515−		.6417			.7908				.9740
.7	.4370		.4141			.5063				.6223
.8	.2186		.1987			.2404				.2942
.9	.0586		.0507			.0606				.0742
1.0	0	0	0		0	0			0	0
.1	.0586	.1505−	.0448		.1693	.0519			.2146	.0632
.2	.2186	.4388	.1549		.4833	.1761			.6100	.2135+
.3	.4370	.6910	.2836		.7440	.3158			.9349	.3810
.4	.6515−	.8185−	.3842		.8582	.4170			1.0725+	.5000−
.5	.7969	.7969	.4219		.81125	.4450			1.0075	.5306
.6	.8185−	.6515−	.3842		.6417	.3923			.7908	.4643
.7	.6910	.4370	.2836		.4141	.2787			.5063	.3277
.8	.4388	.2186	.1549		.1987	.1459			.2404	.1697
.9	.1505−	.0586	.0448		.0507	.0402			.0606	.0462
2.0	0	0	0	0	0	0		0	0	0
.1		.0586	.0507	.1505−	.0448	.0402		.1693	.0519	.0448
.2		.2186	.1987	.4388	.1549	.1459		.4833	.1761	.1595−
.3		.4370	.4141	.6910	.2836	.2787		.7440	.3158	.2981
.4		.6515−	.6417	.8185−	.3842	.3923		.8582	.4170	.4090
.5		.7969	.81125	.7969	.4219	.4450		.81125	.4450	.4506
.6		.8185−	.8582	.6515−	.3842	.4170		.6417	.3923	.4090
.7		.6910	.7440	.4370	.2836	.3158		.4141	.2787	.2981
.8		.4388	.4833	.2186	.1549	.1761		.1987	.1459	.1595−
.9		.1505−	.1693	.0586	.0448	.0519		.0507	.0402	.0448
3.0		0	0	0	0	0	0	0	0	0

TABLE 4—*continued*

(m, j) u	(2, 0)	(2, 1)	(3, 0)	(2, 2)	(3, 1)	(4, 0)	(2, 3)	(3, 2)	(4, 1)	(5, 0)
3.0				0	0	0	0	0	0	0
.1				.0586	.0507	.0606	.1505 −	.0448	.0402	.0462
.2				.2186	.1987	.2404	.4388	.1549	.1459	.1697
.3				.4370	.4141	.5063	.6910	.2836	.2787	.3277
.4				.6515 −	.6417	.7908	.8185 −	.3842	.3923	.4643
.5				.7969	.81125	1.0075	.7969	.4219	.4450	.5306
.6				.8185 −	.8582	1.0725 +	.6515 −	.3842	.4170	.5000 −
.7				.6910	.7440	.9349	.4370	.2836	.3158	.3810
.8				.4388	.4833	.6100	.2186	.1549	.1761	.2135 +
.9				.1505 −	.1693	.2146	.0586	.0448	.0519	.0632
4.0				0	0	0	0	0	0	0
.1							.0586	.0507	.0606	.0742
.2							.2186	.1987	.2404	.2942
.3							.4370	.4141	.5063	.6223
.4							.6515 −	.6417	.7908	.9740
.5							.7969	.81125	1.0075	1.2425
.6							.8185 −	.8582	1.0725 +	1.3242
.7							.6910	.7440	.9349	1.1559
.8							.4388	.4833	.6100	.7549
.9							.1505 −	.1693	.2146	.2557
5.0							0	0	0	0

Finally, consider the case $m = 5$. Here all the columns of the table are relevant. We see that

$$A_3^5 = \begin{cases} B_3^2 & \text{if } u \leqq .55, \\ B_3^3 & \text{if } .56 \leqq u \leqq 1.66, \\ B_3^4 & \text{if } 1.67 \leqq u \leqq 2.33, \\ B_3^3 \text{ shifted once} & \text{if } 2.34 \leqq u \leqq 2.66, \\ B_3^4 \text{ shifted once} & \text{if } 2.67 \leqq u \leqq 3.33, \\ B_3^3 \text{ shifted twice} & \text{if } 3.34 \leqq u \leqq 4.44, \\ B_3^2 \text{ shifted three times} & \text{if } 4.45 \leqq u. \end{cases}$$

Thus B_3^5 is never best for narrow interpolation. But M_3^5 is never more than 135% of the minimal modulus, $0 \leqq u \leqq 5$.

§ 100. **Broad interpolation.** Suppose that tabular values

$$x(a_0), \quad x(a_1), \cdots, \quad x(a_m); \qquad a_0 < a_1 < \cdots < a_m,$$

of a function x are given; and that we wish to approximate the value $x(u)$ by

$$Ax = \alpha_0 x(a_0) + \alpha_1 x(a_1) + \cdots + \alpha_m x(a_m),$$

where the coefficients $\alpha_0,, \cdots, \alpha_m$ depend on u. In broad interpolation we are interested in an ensemble U of values of u.

Let

$$Rx = x(u) - Ax.$$

As Rx is a function of u, we write also

$$y(u) = Rx, \qquad u \in U.$$

An appraisal of Rx involves a measurement of overall size of $y(u)$, $u \in U$, and may be given by a *norm* of the function y (cf. § 3 : 2 below). Many norms are reasonable measures of the overall error. For example,

$$\sup_{u \in U} |y(u)|; \tag{101}$$

or

$$\|y\|_{q,\mu} = \left[\int_U |y(u)|^q \, d\mu(u)\right]^{1/q}, \tag{102}$$

where μ is a measure on U such that $d\mu(u)$ indicates the importance of $y(u)$ near u and q is a constant $\geqq 1$. We may and shall admit the value $q = \infty$ by the special definition:

$$\|y\|_{\infty,\mu} = \operatorname{ess\,sup}_{u \in U} |y(u)|,$$

where the essential supremum means the supremum on almost all of U, that is, the infimum, over all sets U_0 whose μ-measure is zero, of

$$\sup_{u \in (U - U_0)} |y(u)|.$$

An investigator is often in a situation in which the choice of norm is at his disposal. It is then natural for him to choose a norm which leads to a relatively simple analysis, among the norms which are suitable to the problem and the data. *The fact that μ may be any measure affords great scope to the investigator.* As regards q, the values $q = 2, 1, \infty$ seem most important. Cf. § 9:1 below.

Suppose that we use the norm $\|y\|_{q,\mu}$ for y.

Let $\mathscr{A}^*$ be the set of approximations A which are exact whenever $x(s)$ is a polynomial in s of degree $n - 1$. We know from Theorem 1:43 that there is a function $\kappa(t, u)$ for each A in $\mathscr{A}^*$ such that

$$(103) \qquad y(u) = Rx = x(u) - Ax = \int_I x_n(t)\kappa(t, u)\,dt, \qquad x \in C_n(I),$$

where I is a fixed interval that contains $a_0, \cdots, a_m$, and U. Suppose that we choose to consider only approximations in $\mathscr{A}^*$ and that we will appraise y in terms of the nth derivative x_n.

We may choose one of many norms with which to measure the function x_n. Suppose that we use

$$\|x_n\|_p = \left[\int_I |x_n(t)|^p\,dt\right]^{1/p}, \qquad p \geqq 1,$$

where p is a constant. We take the measure here as t because the differential in (103) is dt.

We will define the best broad interpolation formula in $\mathscr{A}^*$, relative to the norms $\|y\|_{q,\mu}$ and $\|x_n\|_p$.

Note first that Hölder's inequality applied to (103) shows that

$$|y(u)| \leqq \left[\int_I |x_n(t)|^p\,dt\right]^{1/p}\left[\int_I |\kappa(t, u)|^{p'}\,dt\right]^{1/p'}, \qquad x \in C_n,$$

where

$$\frac{1}{p} + \frac{1}{p'} = 1.$$

Hence

$$\int_U |y(u)|^q\,d\mu(u) \leqq \left[\int_I |x_n(t)|^p\,dt\right]^{q/p}\int_U d\mu(u)\left[\int_I |\kappa(t, u)^{p'}\,dt\right]^{q/p'},$$

$$(104) \qquad \|y\|_{q,\mu} \leqq \|x_n\|_p\left\{\int_U d\mu(u)\left[\int_I |\kappa(t, u)|^{p'}\,dt\right]^{q/p'}\right\}^{1/q}, \qquad x \in C_n.$$

This inequality, though valuable, is not necessarily the best possible. For each A in $\mathscr{A}^*$ there is a *smallest* constant N such that

$$(105) \qquad \|y\|_{q,\mu} \leqq \|x_n\|_p N, \qquad x \in \mathbf{C}_n.$$

Since N is minimal, (104) implies that

$$N \leqq \left\{\int_U d\mu(u)\left[\int_I |\kappa(t, u)|^{p'}\, dt\right]^{q/p'}\right\}^{1/q}.$$

Since

$$\|cy\|_{q,\mu} = c\|y\|_{q,\mu}; \qquad \|cx_n\|_p = c\|x_n\|_p$$

for all real numbers c, we may write

$$(106) \qquad N = \sup \|y\|_{q,\mu},$$

the supremum being taken over all x in $\mathbf{C}_n$ for which $\|x_n\|_p = 1$. The constant N is in fact the norm of the operator R. Cf. § 3 : 8 below.

In terms of the norms $\|y\|_{q,\mu}$ and $\|x_n\|_p$, the *best broad formula* in $\mathscr{A}^*$ is defined as the formula in $\mathscr{A}^*$ which minimizes N. The best broad formula gives us the appraisal (105) with the smallest second member.

There are practical obstacles in the way of determining the best broad formula in $\mathscr{A}^*$. The calculation of N for an individual element A of $\mathscr{A}^*$ is often difficult. Although (106) defines N, it often does not afford a practicable means of calculating N. It is all the more difficult to minimize N over $\mathscr{A}^*$. These difficulties are present for all choices of q and p.

The best broad formula seems inaccessible. So too is the appraisal (105). We may, however, use (104). Let us define the *special formula* $\tilde{B}$ in $\mathscr{A}^*$ as follows: $\tilde{B}$ is that element of $\mathscr{A}^*$ which minimizes

$$(107) \qquad \int_I |\kappa(t, u)|^{p'}\, dt \quad \text{for each } u, \qquad u \in U.$$

Thus if $p' = 2 = p$, the formula $\tilde{B}$ is precisely the special formula B of §§ 86, 95. For, if $p' = 2$, the integral (107) is precisely (93), except for the interval of integration. In (93) the interval is the smallest interval that contains $u, a_0, \cdots, a_m$. Call that interval I_0. In (107) the interval is a fixed interval that contains $a_0, \cdots, a_m$, and U. Thus $I_0 \subset I$. By Theorem 1 : 43, however, $\kappa(t, u)$, for each u, vanishes outside I_0. Thus the part $I - I_0$ does not contribute to (107). The integrals (107) and (93) are therefore equal if $p' = 2$.

Our discussion of the nature of the special formula B in § 86 carries over to $\tilde{B}$.

Now the multiplier of $\|x_n\|_p$ in (104) is a power of an integral over U of a power of (107). Since $\tilde{B}$ minimizes (107) for each u, $\tilde{B}$ a fortiori minimizes the multiplier of $\|x_n\|_p$. Thus *the special formula* $\tilde{B}$ *gives the strongest form of the appraisal* (104). The special formula $\tilde{B}$ is therefore good for broad interpolation.

The same conclusion holds if we use the norm (101) instead of (102).

We conclude with a few remarks about the case

$$p = 2 = p', \qquad q \geqq 1.$$

Here

$$\|x_n\|_2 = \left[\int_I x_n(s)^2\, ds\right]^{1/2}.$$

For each A in $\mathscr{A}^*$, there is a smallest constant N such that

(108) $$\|y\|_{q,\mu} \leqq \|x_n\|_2\, N, \qquad x \in \boldsymbol{C}_n.$$

The inequality (104) becomes

(109) $$\|y\|_{q,\mu} \leqq \|x_n\|_2 \left\{\int_U d\mu(u)\left[\int_I \kappa(t, u)^2\, dt\right]^{q/2}\right\}^{1/q}, \qquad x \in \boldsymbol{C}_n.$$

The best broad formula in $\mathscr{A}^*$ is the formula which minimizes N over $\mathscr{A}^*$.

I have been able to compute the best broad formula only in the case in which, using the notation of § 95, $\mathscr{A}^* = \mathscr{A}^*_{1,1}$. In this case the determination of the best broad formula is feasible because of a known inequality: Number 257 in [Hardy-Pólya-Littlewood 1, p. 185]. It turns out that the best broad formula in $\mathscr{A}^*_{1,1}$ is precisely the special formula B_1^1.

The inequality (108) is often stronger than (109). It may nonetheless be true that the special formula B minimizes N. If so, the special formula would always be the best broad formula. The question is open.

§ 110. **Approximations involving derivatives at tabular values.** Suppose that we are given values of a function x and of its first r derivatives at $s = a_0, a_1, \cdots, a_m$. We may wish to approximate the value $x(u)$ by an expression of the form

$$\begin{aligned} Ax = {} & \alpha_0 x(a_0) + \alpha_1 x(a_1) + \cdots + \alpha_m x(a_m) \\ & + \beta_0 x_1(a_0) + \beta_1 x_1(a_1) + \cdots + \beta_m x_1(a_m) \\ & + \cdots + \lambda_0 x_r(a_0) + \lambda_1 x_r(a_1) + \cdots + \lambda_m x_r(a_m), \end{aligned}$$

where $\alpha_i, \beta_i, \cdots, \lambda_i$ are functions of u, $i = 0, \cdots, m$. Our study of §§ 86, 95, 100 may be extended to this case. We illustrate by one example.

Let $\mathscr{A}^*$ be the set of expressions A, where

$$Ax = ax(-1) + bx(1) + \alpha x_1(-1) + \beta x_1(1)$$

and a, b, α, β are functions of u, which are such that

$$Ax = x(u)$$

for each real u whenever x is a polynomial of degree 1. Put

$$Rx = x(u) - Ax.$$

Since Rx is a sum of simple Stieltjes integrals on x and on x_1,

$$R \in \mathscr{C}_1^*.$$

Hence Theorem 1: 43 applies to R with $n = 2$, for each real u, if $A \in \mathscr{A}^*$. For each A in $\mathscr{A}^*$, a function $\kappa(s) = \kappa(s, u)$ exists such that

$$Rx = \int_I x_2(s)\kappa(s)\,ds, \qquad x \in C_2(I),$$

where I is the smallest interval containing -1, 1, and u. For each u, $-\infty < u < \infty$, put

$$J = \int_I \kappa(s)^2\,ds,$$

$$M^2 = |S| \int_S \kappa(s)^2\,ds = |S|J,$$

where S is the support of $\kappa(s)$, that is, the closure of the set of points at which $\kappa(s) \neq 0$.

We define the *special formula* in $\mathscr{A}^*$ as that element of $\mathscr{A}^*$ which minimizes J for each u, and the *best narrow formula* in $\mathscr{A}^*$ as that element of $\mathscr{A}^*$ which minimizes M for each u. The special formula gives the strongest appraisal

$$|Rx| \leqq J^{1/2}\left[\int_I x_2(s)^2\,ds\right]^{1/2}, \qquad x \in C_2.$$

The best narrow formula gives the strongest appraisal

$$|Rx| \leqq M\left[\frac{\int_S x_2(s)^2\,ds}{|S|}\right]^{1/2}, \qquad x \in C_2.$$

In order that $A \in \mathscr{A}^*$, it is necessary and sufficient that $Rx = 0$ when $x(s) = 1$ and when $x(s) = s$; that is,

$$\begin{aligned} a + b &= 1, \\ -a + b + \alpha + \beta &= u. \end{aligned} \tag{111}$$

For simplicity of exposition we now assume that

$$-1 < u < 1.$$

Then

$$I = [-1, 1].$$

By (1: 45),

$$-\kappa(t) = R[(s - t)\theta(t, s)] = (u - t)\theta(t, u) - [(-1 - t)a + \alpha], \quad -1 < t < 1.$$

Hence

$$-\kappa(t) = \begin{cases} a(1+t) - \alpha & \text{if } -1 < t < u, \\ a(1+t) - \alpha + u - t & \text{if } u < t < 1, \end{cases} \tag{112}$$

and

$$J = \int_{-1}^{1} \kappa(t)^2\, dt = \int_{-1}^{1} [a(1+t) - \alpha]^2\, dt$$

$$+ \int_{u}^{1} \{(u-t)^2 + 2(u-t)[a(1+t) - \alpha]\}\, dt.$$

Put $\tau = u - t$ in the second integral. Then

$$J = \frac{8a^2}{3} - 4a\alpha + 2\alpha^2 + \int_{u-1}^{0} \{(1-2a)\tau^2 + 2[a(1+u) - \alpha]\tau\}\, d\tau,$$

$$J = \frac{8a^2}{3} - 4a\alpha + 2\alpha^2 - \frac{(1-2a)(u-1)^3}{3} - [a(1+u) - \alpha](u-1)^2. \tag{113}$$

For each fixed u, there are four variables a, b, α, β subject to the constraints (111). Let us take a, α as the independent variables. Then

$$b = 1 - a,$$
$$\beta = u + 2a - 1 - \alpha;$$

and J is a function of the independent variables a, α. In order for J to be minimal, it is necessary that

$$\frac{\partial J}{\partial a} = 0, \qquad \frac{\partial J}{\partial \alpha} = 0;$$

that is,

$$16a - 12\alpha = (u-1)^2(u+5),$$
$$4a - 4\alpha = (u-1)^2$$

or

$$4a = (u-1)^2(u+2),$$
$$4\alpha = (u-1)^2(u+1).$$

Then

$$4b = (u+1)^2(-u+2),$$
$$4\beta = (u+1)^2(u-1).$$

The minimal value of J is

$$J = \frac{(1-u^2)^3}{24}.$$

Thus the special formula in $\mathscr{A}^*$ is B, where

$$(114)\qquad \begin{aligned} 4Bx = {} & (u-1)^2[(u+2)x(-1)+(u+1)x_1(-1)] \\ & + (u+1)^2[(-u+2)x(1)+(u-1)x_1(1)]. \end{aligned}$$

To find the best narrow formula in $\mathscr{A}^*$, assume that

$$0 \leqq u < 1.$$

The complementary case will be essentially the same. By (112) the function κ is a piecewise linear function of t. The support S is therefore either the interval $[-1, 1]$ or $[-1, u]$ or $[u, 1]$.

If $a = \alpha = 0$, then S is $[u, 1]$. Also, by (113),

$$J = \frac{(1-u)^3}{3},$$

$$M^2 = |S|J = (1-u)J = \frac{(1-u)^4}{3},$$

and the formula A is the Taylor polynomial

$$(115)\qquad Ax = bx(1) + \beta x_1(1) = x(1) + (u-1)x_1(1).$$

If $a = 1$, $b = \beta = 0$, and $\alpha = u + 1$, then the dual case occurs. The support is $[-1, u]$ and the square modulus is

$$\frac{(1+u)^4}{3} \geqq \frac{(1-u)^4}{3},$$

since $u \geqq 0$. Thus we need not consider this case in our minimization.

In all other cases, S is $[-1, 1]$,

$$M^2 = |S|J = 2J,$$

and the minimal M^2 corresponds to the special formula and is

$$M^2 = \frac{(1-u^2)^3}{12}.$$

Thus the best narrow formula in $\mathscr{A}^*$ is either the special formula or the Taylor formula, according as

$$\frac{(1-u^2)^3}{12} = \frac{(1-u)^3(1+u)^3}{12}$$

is less than or greater than

$$\frac{(1-u)^4}{3}.$$

That is, the best narrow formula is B, given by (114), if

$$u^3 + 3u^2 + 7u - 3 \leqq 0, \qquad 0 \leqq u \leqq 1;$$

and the best narrow formula is A, given by (115), if

$$u^3 + 3u^2 + 7u - 3 \geqq 0, \qquad 0 \leqq u \leqq 1.$$

For the root, there are two best narrow formulas.

PART 3. DERIVATIVES

The methods of Part 2 may be carried over to the approximation of the rth derivative $x_r(u)$ of $x(s)$ at $s = u$. We do not do this in detail, but indicate some of the facts.

§ 116. **Conventional approximate differentiation.** Suppose that we wish to approximate $x_r(u)$ in terms of the values of $x(s)$ and perhaps its derivatives at $s = a_1, \cdots, a_m$. Suppose that the number of coincidences in $a_1, \cdots, a_m$ is $\leqq q$. (That is, any $q + 1$ of these arguments are not identical.) If $x \in C_{q-1}$, we may construct the Newton polynomial

$$p(s) = x(a_1) + (s - a_1)x(a_1, a_2) + \cdots + (s - a_1)\cdots(s - a_{m-1})x(a_1, \cdots, a_m);$$

and we may approximate $x_r(u)$ by $p_r(u)$. The negative error is then

$$Rx = x_r(u) - p_r(u).$$

Put

$$\rho = \max(r + 1, q),$$

and assume that

$$m \geqq \rho.$$

For fixed u, Rx is a linear combination of values of x and its derivatives of order $\leqq \rho - 1$. Hence

$$R \in \mathscr{C}^*_{\rho-1} \subset \mathscr{C}^*_{\rho} \subset \mathscr{C}^*_{\rho+1} \subset \cdots.$$

Furthermore $Rx = 0$ whenever $x(s)$ is a polynomial of degree $m - 1$, since in that case $p(s) = x(s)$ for all s by Newton's divided difference formula. Thus Theorem 1 : 43 applies to R with

$$n = \rho, \rho + 1, \cdots, m.$$

Hence

$$Rx = \int_I x_n(s)\kappa^n(s)\, ds, \qquad x \in C_n(I),$$

where I is the smallest interval containing $a_1, \cdots, a_m$ and u; and κ^n is given by κ in (1 : 45) and (1 : 11).

§ 117. **Best differentiation.** In the conventional procedure of § 116 (based on the Newton polynomial), the approximation of $x_r(u)$ is in fact a particular linear combination of values of x and perhaps its derivatives at tabular arguments. A more powerful procedure is to consider families of such linear combinations, as was done in § 110 in the approximation of $x(u) = x_0(u)$.

The use of any such linear combination is perfectly simple and direct. Since the formal details of obtaining the best formulas are complicated, we consider only one instance.

Suppose that we wish to approximate the first derivative $x_1(u)$ by an expression of the form

$$Ax = \alpha' x(-2) + \beta' x(-1) + \gamma x(0) + \beta x(1) + \alpha x(2),$$

where the coefficients α', β', α, β, γ are functions of u. Let $\mathscr{A}^*$ be the set of those approximations A which are such that

$$Ax = x_1(u)$$

for each real u whenever x is a polynomial of degree 2. Put

$$Rx = x_1(u) - Ax.$$

Then $R \in \mathscr{C}_1^* \subset \mathscr{C}_2^*$. If $A \in \mathscr{A}^*$, then for each fixed u, Theorem 1:43 applies to R with $n = 2$ and with $n = 3$. We choose to take $n = 3$ and to express Rx in terms of the third derivative $x_3(s)$. For each A in $\mathscr{A}^*$, a function $\kappa(s) = \kappa(s, u)$ exists such that

$$Rx = \int_I x_3(s)\kappa(s)\, ds, \qquad x \in \boldsymbol{C}_3(I),$$

where I is the smallest interval containing -2, 2, and u. For each u, $-\infty < u < \infty$, put

$$J = \int_I \kappa(s)^2\, ds,$$

$$M^2 = |S| \int_S \kappa(s)^2\, ds = |S| J,$$

where S is the support of $\kappa(s)$, that is, the closure of the set of points at which $\kappa(s) \neq 0$.

We define the *special formula* in $\mathscr{A}^*$ as that element of $\mathscr{A}^*$ which minimizes J for each u, and the *best narrow formula* in $\mathscr{A}^*$ as that element of $\mathscr{A}^*$ which minimizes M for each u. The special formula gives the strongest appraisal

$$|Rx| \leqq J^{1/2}\left[\int_I x_3(s)^2\, ds\right]^{1/2}, \qquad x \in \boldsymbol{C}_3.$$

The best narrow formula gives the strongest appraisal

$$|Rx| \leqq M\left[\frac{\int_S x_3(s)^2\, ds}{|S|}\right]^{1/2}, \qquad x \in \boldsymbol{C}_3.$$

In order that $A \in \mathscr{A}^*$, it is necessary and sufficient that $Rx = 0$ when $x(s) = 1$ and when $x(s) = s$ and when $x(s) = s^2$; that is,

$$
\begin{aligned}
\alpha' + \beta' + \gamma + \beta + \alpha &= 0,\\
-2\alpha' - \beta' \quad\quad + \beta + 2\alpha &= 1,\\
4\alpha' + \beta' \quad\quad + \beta + 4\alpha &= 2u.
\end{aligned}
\tag{118}
$$

For simplicity of exposition, we now assume that

$$0 \leqq u \leqq 1.$$

Then

$$I = [-2, 2].$$

By (1 : 45),

$$
\left\{
\begin{aligned}
2\kappa(t) &= -R[(s - t)^2\theta(t, s)] \\
&= (-2 - t)^2\alpha' = (2 + t)^2\alpha' && \text{if } -2 < t < -1,\\
2\kappa(t) &= (-2 - t)^2\alpha' + (-1 - t)^2\beta' \\
&= (2 + t)^2\alpha' + (1 + t)^2\beta' && \text{if } -1 < t < 0,\\
-2\kappa(t) &= -R[(s - t)^2\phi(t, s)] \\
&= (2 - t)^2\alpha + (1 - t)^2\beta - 2(u - t) && \text{if } 0 < t < u,\\
-2\kappa(t) &= (2 - t)^2\alpha + (1 - t)^2\beta && \text{if } u < t < 1,\\
-2\kappa(t) &= (2 - t)^2\alpha && \text{if } 1 < t < 2.
\end{aligned}
\right.
\tag{119}
$$

Hence

$$
\begin{aligned}
4J = 4\int_{-2}^{2} \kappa(t)^2\,dt &= (\alpha^2 + \alpha'^2)\int_0^2 (2 - t)^4\,dt \\
&+ (\beta^2 + \beta'^2)\int_0^1 (1 - t)^4\,dt + 2(\alpha\beta + \alpha'\beta')\int_0^1 (2 - t)^2(1 - t)^2\,dt \\
&+ 4\int_0^u (u - t)^2\,dt - 4\int_0^u (u - t)[(2 - t)^2\alpha + (1 - t)^2\beta]\,dt \\
&= \frac{32}{5}(\alpha^2 + \alpha'^2) + \frac{1}{5}(\beta^2 + \beta'^2) + \frac{31}{15}(\alpha\beta + \alpha'\beta') + \frac{4u^3}{3} \\
&+ \frac{\alpha}{3}(-u^4 + 8u^3 - 24u^2) + \frac{\beta}{3}(-u^4 + 4u^3 - 6u^2).
\end{aligned}
$$

For each fixed u, there are five variables α', β', α, β, γ, subject to the constraints (118). Let us take α, α' as the independent variables. Then

$$\beta = -3\alpha - \alpha' + u + \frac{1}{2},$$

$$\beta' = -\alpha - 3\alpha' + u - \frac{1}{2},$$

$$\gamma = 3\alpha + 3\alpha' - 2u.$$

Hence

$$\beta^2 + \beta'^2 = 10(\alpha^2 + \alpha'^2) + 2u^2 + \frac{1}{2}$$

$$+ 12\alpha\alpha'(-8u - 2)\alpha + (-8u + 2)\alpha',$$

$$\alpha\beta + \alpha'\beta' = -3(\alpha^2 + \alpha'^2) - 2\alpha\alpha' + \left(u + \frac{1}{2}\right)\alpha + \left(u - \frac{1}{2}\right)\alpha';$$

and

$$120J = 66(\alpha^2 + \alpha'^2) - 52\alpha\alpha' + p\alpha + p'\alpha' + q, \tag{120}$$

where

$$p = 20u^4 - 40u^3 - 60u^2 + 14u + 19,$$
$$p' = 10u^4 - 40u^3 + 60u^2 + 14u - 19,$$
$$q = -10u^5 + 35u^4 - 18u^2 + 3.$$

Let us change from the independent variables α, α' to v, w, where

$$v = \alpha + \alpha',$$
$$w = \alpha - \alpha'.$$

Then

$$\alpha^2 + \alpha'^2 = \frac{v^2 + w^2}{2}, \qquad \alpha\alpha' = \frac{v^2 - w^2}{4}, \qquad \alpha = \frac{v + w}{2}, \qquad \alpha' = \frac{v - w}{2};$$

$$120J = 33(v^2 + w^2) - 13(v^2 - w^2) + \frac{p(v + w)}{2} + \frac{p'(v - w)}{2} + q,$$

$$120J = 20v^2 + 46w^2 + \frac{p + p'}{2}v + \frac{p - p'}{2}w + q.$$

For a minimum of J, it is necessary that

$$\frac{\partial J}{\partial v} = \frac{\partial J}{\partial w} = 0;$$

that is,

$$v = -\frac{p + p'}{80}, \qquad w = -\frac{p - p'}{184}.$$

Then the minimal J is $J_{\min}$, where

$$120J_{\min} = \frac{p + p'}{4}v + \frac{p - p'}{4}w + q = q - \frac{(p + p')^2}{320} - \frac{(p - p')^2}{736}$$

by Lemma 46. Now

$$p + p' = 30u^4 - 80u^3 + 28u,$$
$$p - p' = 10u^4 - 120u^2 + 38.$$

Hence

$$(121)\quad \begin{aligned} 23\cdot 9600 J_{\min} = &-5425u^8 + 27{,}600u^7 - 30{,}800u^6 - 28{,}060u^5 \\ &+ 52{,}260u^4 - 14{,}828u^2 + 1910. \end{aligned}$$

Also,

$$\begin{aligned} 80\cdot 23\alpha &= -395u^4 + 920u^3 + 600u^2 - 322u - 190, \\ 80\cdot 23\alpha' &= -295u^4 + 920u^3 - 600u^2 - 322u + 190, \\ 80\cdot 23\beta &= 1480u^4 - 3680u^3 - 1200u^2 + 3128u + 1300, \\ 80\cdot 23\beta' &= 1280u^4 - 3680u^3 + 1200u^2 + 3128u - 1300, \\ 80\cdot 23\gamma &= -2070u^4 + 5520u^3 \qquad\qquad - 5612u. \end{aligned}$$

The special formula in $\mathscr{A}^*$ is

$$Bx = \alpha' x(-2) + \beta' x(-1) + \gamma x(0) + \beta x(1) + \alpha x(2),$$

where $\alpha', \cdots, \alpha$ are given by the above formulas, $0 \leqq u \leqq 1$.

For any A in $\mathscr{A}^*$ and for each u in $[0, 1]$, the support S of $\kappa(t)$ is

$$\begin{aligned} &[-2, 2] &&\text{if } \alpha\alpha' \neq 0; \\ &[-1, 2] &&\text{if } \alpha' = 0,\ \alpha\beta' \neq 0; \\ &[0, 2] &&\text{if } \alpha' = \beta' = 0,\ \alpha \neq 0; \\ &[-2, 1] &&\text{if } \alpha = 0,\ \beta\alpha' \neq 0; \\ &[-1, 1] &&\text{if } \alpha = \alpha' = 0,\ \beta' \neq 0; \\ &[0, 1] &&\text{if } \alpha = \alpha' = \beta' = 0; \\ &[-2, u] &&\text{if } \alpha = \beta = 0. \end{aligned}$$

The modulus M of A may be deduced from (120), by the relation

$$M^2 = |S| J.$$

For the special formula, the square modulus is

$$M^2 = 4J_{\min}$$

with two exceptions, where $\alpha = 0$ or $\alpha' = 0$.

The conventional differentiation formula, on the other hand, is given by

$$\alpha = \alpha' = 0, \qquad \beta = u + \frac{1}{2}, \qquad \beta' = u - \frac{1}{2}, \qquad \gamma = -2u.$$

For the conventional formula,

$$120J = q;$$

$$M^2 = \begin{cases} 2J & \text{if } u \neq \dfrac{1}{2}; \\[2ex] J & \text{if } u = \dfrac{1}{2}. \end{cases}$$

We do not carry the detailed study any further. One could minimize J over the subset of $\mathscr{A}^*$ in which $\alpha' = 0$ and that in which $\alpha = 0$. Then, comparing a finite number of formulas, one could determine the best narrow formula in $\mathscr{A}^*$.

PART 4. SUMS

§ 122. **An instance.** The entire treatment of approximate integration in Part 1 may be extended to summation. As an indication we cite one simple example.

Suppose that we wish to approximate the sum

$$\sum = x(-2) + x(-1) + x(0) + x(1) + x(2)$$

by

$$Ax = \alpha x(-2) + \beta x(0) + \gamma x(2),$$

where α, β, γ are constants independent of the function x. Let $\mathscr{A}^*$ be the set of approximations A which are exact for degree 1. For each A in $\mathscr{A}^*$,

$$Rx \underset{\text{def}}{=} \sum - Ax = \int_{-2}^{2} x_2(t)\kappa(t)\, dt, \qquad x \in \boldsymbol{C}_2,$$

where

$$\kappa(t) = -R[(s-t)\theta(t,s)] = R[(s-t)\phi(t,s)],$$

by Theorem 1: 43 with $n = 2$. By Schwarz's inequality,

$$|Rx| \leqq J^{1/2}\left[\int_{-2}^{2} x_2(s)^2\, ds\right]^{1/2}, \qquad x \in \boldsymbol{C}_2,$$

where

$$J = \int_{-2}^{2} \kappa(t)^2\, dt.$$

We shall now determine the formula in $\mathscr{A}^*$ for which J is minimal.

The constraints on the coefficients α, β, γ of A are

$$\begin{aligned} \alpha + \beta + \gamma &= 5 \\ -2\alpha + 2\gamma &= 0, \end{aligned}$$

since $Rx = 0$ when $x(s) = 1$ and when $x(s) = s$. Let us take α as the independent parameter. Then

$$\gamma = \alpha, \qquad \beta = 5 - 2\alpha.$$

Also

$$\kappa(t) = R[(s-t)\phi(t,s)] = (2-t) - \gamma(2-t) = (2-t)(1-\gamma) \text{ if } 1 < t < 2;$$

$$\kappa(t) = (2 - t) + (1 - t) - \gamma(2 - t) = (2 - t)(1 - \gamma) + (1 - t) \qquad \text{if } 0 < t < 1;$$

$$\kappa(t) = -R[(s - t)\theta(t, s)] = -[(-2 - t) + (-1 - t)] + \alpha(-2 - t)$$

$$= (2 + t)(1 - \alpha) + (1 + t) \qquad \text{if } -1 < t < 0;$$

$$\kappa(t) = (2 + t)(1 - \alpha) \qquad \text{if } -2 < t < -1.$$

Take

$$w = 1 - \alpha = 1 - \gamma$$

as the independent variable in our minimization. Then

$$J = \int_0^2 (2 - t)^2 w^2\,dt + \int_0^1 (1 - t)^2\,dt + 2\int_0^1 (2 - t)(1 - t)w\,dt$$

$$+ \int_{-2}^0 (2 + t)^2 w^2\,dt + \int_{-2}^0 (1 + t)^2\,dt + 2\int_{-1}^0 (2 + t)(1 + t)w\,dt.$$

The last three integrals are respectively equal to the first three. Hence

$$\frac{J}{2} = \frac{8}{3}w^2 + \frac{1}{3} + 2\cdot\frac{5}{6}w = \frac{8w^2 + 5w + 1}{3}.$$

For a minimum of J,

$$w = -\frac{5}{16}, \qquad \alpha = \frac{21}{16} = \gamma, \qquad \beta = \frac{38}{16};$$

the minimal J is

$$J = \frac{2}{3}\left(1 + \frac{5}{2}w\right) = \frac{7}{48}.$$

The formula in $\mathscr{A}^*$ for which J is minimal is

$$Ax = \frac{21x(-2) + 38x(0) + 21x(2)}{16}.$$

CHAPTER 3

Linear Continuous Functionals on C_n

§ 1. **Introduction.** In Chapters 1 and 2 we studied functionals which were known to be elements of $\mathscr{C}_n^*$ for suitable n; that is, functionals F for which Fx was given as a sum of integrals on x and derivatives of x. There may be situations in which we deal with a functional F which is defined in some other fashion. It is therefore important to characterize intrinsically those functionals which are equivalent to elements of $\mathscr{C}_n^*$. We shall do this. We shall also give standard formulas for such functionals and explicit direct procedures for obtaining the formulas (Theorem 39 and Corollary 99).

§ 2. **Normed linear spaces.** For use here and in later chapters we start with a consideration of normed linear spaces and their adjoints. Let R denote the real numbers and C the complex numbers. Let N stand for R or C. Either interpretation of N will be allowed so long as it is retained throughout a discussion.

A *linear space* X is defined as a nonempty set of elements, together with operations of addition and scalar multiplication, denoted

$$x + y \quad \text{and} \quad bx, \qquad x, y \in X, \quad b \in \mathsf{N},$$

respectively, with the following properties. For any x, y, z in X and b, c in N,

(0) $x + y \in X$, $bx \in X$.
(1) $x + y = y + x$.
(2) $x + (y + z) = (x + y) + z$.
(3) $x + y = x + z$ iff $y = z$.
(4) $b(x + y) = bx + by$.
(5) $(b + c)x = bx + cx$.
(6) $b(cx) = (bc)x$.
(7) $1x = x$.

We say that the space X is real or complex according as N is R or C. Linear spaces are also called vector spaces [Banach 1, Chapter 1; Zaanen 1, Chapter 6].

3. LEMMA. *A linear space X contains a unique element θ such that*

$$x + \theta = x, \qquad x \in X.$$

Furthermore, for $x \in X$, $b \in \mathsf{N}$,

$$bx = \theta \quad \textit{iff} \quad b = 0 \quad \textit{or} \quad x = \theta.$$

PROOF. Choose a particular element x_0 of X, as is possible since X is not empty. Put

$$\theta = 0x_0.$$

Then

$$x_0 + \theta = 1x_0 + 0x_0 = (1 + 0)x_0 = x_0.$$

For any x in X,

$$x + x_0 = x + (x_0 + \theta) = x + (\theta + x_0) = (x + \theta) + x_0;$$

hence

$$x = x + \theta$$

by (3). From this relation it follows, also by (3), that θ is unique.

Since

$$x + 0x = x = x + \theta, \qquad x \in X,$$

it follows that

$$0x = \theta,$$

by (3). Also

$$b\theta = b(0x_0) = (b0)x_0 = 0x_0 = \theta, \qquad b \in \mathsf{N}.$$

Conversely, suppose that

$$bx = \theta, \qquad 0 \neq b \in \mathsf{N}, \quad x \in X.$$

Then

$$\frac{1}{b}(bx) = \frac{1}{b}\theta = \theta = \left(\frac{1}{b}b\right)x = 1x = x.$$

Thus the lemma is proved.

We now define $-x$ and $x - y$ as follows:

$$-x = (-1)x,$$
$$x - y = x + (-y), \qquad x, y \in X.$$

4. LEMMA. *In a linear space X, the equation*

$$y + z = x, \qquad x, y \in X,$$

always has a unique solution z in X; and

$$z = x - y.$$

Thus X is an Abelian group relative to addition.

PROOF. Suppose that $x, y \in X$. Put

$$z = x - y \in X.$$

Then

$$y + z = y + (x - y) = y + [x + (-y)] = (y + x) + (-y)$$
$$= (x + y) + (-y) = x + (y - y) = x + \theta = x.$$

Also, z is unique, by (3). This completes the proof.

Continuing in this fashion we can establish all the usual rules for addition, subtraction, and scalar multiplication in a linear space X. We omit the details.

Consider a linear space X. By a *norm*

$$\|x\| = \|x\|_X$$

on X we mean a function on X to R with the following properties. For x, y in X and b in N,

(0) $\|x\|$ is defined and $\|x\| \in \mathsf{R}$.
(1) $\|x\| > 0$ if $x \neq \theta$.
(2) $\|bx\| = |b| \, \|x\|$.
(3) $\|x + y\| \leqq \|x\| + \|y\|$.

Then

$$\|-x\| = \|x\|$$

and

$$\|\theta\| = \|0x\| = 0\|x\| = 0.$$

Hence

$$\|x\| = 0 \quad \text{iff} \quad x = \theta.$$

By a *normed linear space* X we mean a linear space X together with a norm on X.

For the rest of this section we assume that X is a normed linear space. We shall sometimes write 0 instead of θ, when the context will indicate whether 0 is to be understood as an element of N or of X.

The *distance* between elements x and y of X is defined as $\|x - y\|$. This is a permissible definition (under which X is a metric space) since

$$\|x - y\| = \|y - x\| \geqq 0 \quad \text{with equality iff} \quad x = y;$$
$$\|x - y\| + \|y - z\| \geqq \|x - z\|; \qquad x, y, z \in X.$$

In terms of distance we define concepts related to limits and continuity. For example we say that a sequence

$$\{x_\nu\}, \qquad x_\nu \in X, \qquad \nu = 1, 2, \cdots,$$

is a *Cauchy sequence* if

$$\|x_\nu - x_{\nu'}\| \to 0 \quad \text{as} \quad \nu, \nu' \to \infty;$$

we say that $x_\nu \to x$ if

$$x \in X \quad \text{and} \quad \|x_\nu - x\| \to 0 \quad \text{as} \quad \nu \to \infty.$$

The operations

$$\|x\|, \quad x + y, \quad cx; \qquad x, y \in X, \quad c \in \mathsf{N};$$

are continuous in x, y, and c.

Suppose that two norms $\|x\|$ and $|||x|||$ are defined on a linear space X. We say that the norms are *equivalent* if constants b and c exist such that

$$\|x\| \leqq b\, |||x|||, \qquad |||x||| \leqq c\|x\|$$

for all x in X. Equivalent norms lead to the same topology on X. For example, $\{x_\nu\}$ is a Cauchy sequence relative to $\|x\|$ iff it is a Cauchy sequence relative to $|||x|||$.

We now cite examples of normed linear spaces.

The space N of numbers, with addition and multiplication defined in the usual way and with $\|x\| = |x|$, $x \in \mathsf{N}$, is a normed linear space.

Euclidean m-space is a normed linear space, if we define addition, scalar multiplication, and norm in the usual way, relative to a distinguished point 0 in the space.

Suppose that S is an arbitrary nonempty set and that X is a set of functions on S, that is, each element x of X is a map of S into N. We define addition and scalar multiplication of elements of X by their corresponding numerical operations on the values of the functions, and we say that X is a *function space*.† If X is a function space, then the space Y of all finite linear combinations of elements of X is a linear space as well as a function space.

We shall consider a number of function spaces. Let

$$I = \{\alpha \leqq s \leqq \tilde{\alpha}\}, \qquad -\infty < \alpha < \tilde{\alpha} < \infty,$$

be a closed interval. We have defined

$$C_0 = C_0(I)$$

in Chapter 1 as the space of continuous functions on I to R. We now define the *norm* in C_0 as

$$\|x\| = \|x\|_{C_0} = \sup_{s \in I} |x(s)|, \qquad x \in C_0. \tag{5}$$

Since x is continuous on the compact set I, the supremum in (5) is actually attained. Thus an alternative form of (5) is

$$\|x\|_{C_0} = \max_{s \in I} |x(s)|.$$

† In Chapters 8, 9, 10 we broaden the meaning of the term function space and admit spaces of equivalence sets of functions (§ 8 : 2; § 9 : 27).

We use (5) because it carries over to certain enlargements of C_0 that we will study later. One may verify directly that C_0 is a normed linear space.

Let a be any fixed element of I. For a positive integer n, we define

$$C_n = C_n(I) = C_n(I; a)$$

as the space of all functions x on I to R which are continuous together with their derivatives of order $\leqq n$; and we define the norm in C_n as

$$(6) \quad \|x\| = \|x\|_{C_n} = \max\,[|x_0(a)|, |x_1(a)|, \cdots, |x_{n-1}(a)|, \sup_{s \in I} |x_n(s)|] \quad x \in C_n,$$

where the subscripts indicate differentiation. One may verify directly that C_n is a normed linear space. It will be convenient to define an alternative norm in C_n as

$$(7) \qquad |||x||| = |||x|||_{C_n} = \max_{i=0,1,\cdots,n} [\sup_{s \in I} |x_i(s)|], \qquad x \in C_n.$$

It is clear from the Taylor formulas (1 : 15) for $x_i(s)$, $i < n$, that for a suitable constant k,

$$\|x\|_{C_n} \leqq |||x|||_{C_n} \leqq k\|x\|_{C_n}, \qquad x \in C_n.$$

Hence the norms $\|x\|_{C_n}$ and $|||x|||_{C_n}$ are equivalent. Since the latter is independent of a, it follows that norms $\|x\|_{C_n}$ corresponding to different values of a are equivalent. The space $C_n(I; a)$ thus does not depend on a in an essential fashion. For the analogous spaces of functions of several variables, there will be dependence (§§ 4 : 2; 4 : 49; and 6 : 2).

A linear space X is *finite dimensional and of dimension n*, if X contains n but not $n + 1$ free (i.e., linearly independent) elements.

It may be of interest to mention Tychonoff's Theorem that any two norms on a finite dimensional linear space are equivalent [1, p. 769; Dunford-Schwartz 1, p. 245]. Thus the dimension alone of a finite dimensional linear space determines that its topology is that of real or complex Euclidean space of the same dimension. If a linear space is not finite dimensional, different norms which can be defined on it are not necessarily equivalent. For example, in $C_n(I)$ the norms

$$\|x\|_{C_n} \quad \text{and} \quad \|x\|_{C_0}, \qquad x \in C_n,$$

are not equivalent.

§ 8. **Additive operators.** Suppose that X and Y are normed linear spaces. By an *operator* (or operation) T on X to Y we mean simply a map of X into Y. For $x \in X$, we denote by Tx the image of x under T.

Consider an operator T on X to Y. We say that T is *additive* if

$$T(x + x') = Tx + Tx', \qquad x, x' \in X.$$

If T is additive, then

$$T0 = 0,$$

since

$$T0 = T(0 + 0) = T0 + T0.$$

Also

$$T(x - x') = Tx - Tx', \qquad x, x' \in X,$$

since

$$T[x' + (x - x')] = Tx.$$

9. THEOREM. *An additive operator which is continuous at one point is uniformly continuous everywhere.*

PROOF. Suppose that T is continuous at $x_0 \in X$. Let $\eta > 0$ be given. We shall show that $\zeta > 0$ exists such that

$$\|Tx - Tx'\|_Y < \eta \quad \text{whenever} \quad \|x - x'\|_X < \zeta, \qquad x, x' \in X.$$

To this end take $\zeta > 0$ so that

$$\|Tx - Tx_0\|_Y < \eta \quad \text{whenever} \quad \|x - x_0\|_X < \zeta, \qquad x \in X,$$

as is possible since T is continuous at x_0.

Now suppose that

$$\|x - x'\|_X < \zeta, \qquad x, x' \in X.$$

Then

$$\|(x - x' + x_0) - x_0\|_X < \zeta,$$
$$\|T(x - x' + x_0) - Tx_0\|_Y < \eta,$$
$$\|Tx - Tx'\|_Y < \eta.$$

Thus the theorem is proved.

In a classical paper Hamel constructed an additive operator on R to R which is nowhere continuous [1].

We say that an operator T is *homogeneous* if

$$T(cx) = c\,Tx, \qquad x \in X, \qquad c \in \mathsf{N}.$$

Also that T is *linear* if T is both additive and homogeneous, that is, if

$$T(bx + cy) = b\,Tx + c\,Ty; \qquad x, y \in X; \quad b, c \in \mathsf{N}.$$

10. THEOREM. *An additive continuous real operator is linear. An additive continuous complex operator T is linear if*

$$T(ix) = i\,Tx, \qquad x \in X, \quad i^2 = -1.$$

PROOF. Consider the real case, $\mathsf{N} = \mathsf{R}$. Suppose that T is additive. Then

$$T(px) = p\,Tx, \qquad x \in X, \quad p = 0, 1, 2, \cdots;$$

hence

$$T\left(\frac{x}{q}\right) = \frac{1}{q}\,Tx, \qquad q = 1, 2, \cdots;$$

and

$$T\left(\frac{px}{q}\right) = \frac{p}{q}\,Tx, \qquad p = 0, \pm 1, \pm 2, \cdots; \quad q = 1, 2, \cdots.$$

Thus

$$T(rx) = r\,Tx, \qquad x \in X,$$

for any rational number r.

Now suppose that T is continuous and that c is any real number. Let $\{r_\nu\}$, $\nu = 1, 2, \cdots$, be a sequence of rational numbers which $\to c$. Then, for each x in X,

$$T(r_\nu x) = r_\nu\,Tx \to c\,Tx,$$

since scalar multiplication is continuous in Y;

$$r_\nu x \to cx,$$

since scalar multiplication is continuous in X; and

$$T(r_\nu x) \to T(cx),$$

since T is continuous. Hence

$$T(cx) = c\,Tx, \qquad x \in X, \quad c \in \mathsf{R};$$

and T is homogeneous. Hence T is linear.

The complex case $\mathsf{N} = \mathsf{C}$ follows from the real case. This completes the proof.

We say that an operator T is *bounded* if a constant M exists such that

$$\|Tx\|_Y \leqq M\|x\|_X \quad \text{for all } x \text{ in } X.$$

By the bound or Banach norm or *norm* $\|T\|$ of T we mean the infimum of all numbers M for which the last relation holds. If T is bounded,

$$\|Tx\|_Y \leqq \|T\|\,\|x\|_X, \qquad x \in X;$$

and this appraisal is sharp: $\|T\|$ cannot be replaced by a smaller number without making the inequality false for some x in X. Thus

$$\|T\| = \sup_{0 \neq x \in X} \frac{\|Tx\|_Y}{\|x\|_X}.$$

If T is homogeneous as well as bounded, we may replace x by $x/\|x\|_X$ in the last relation; hence

$$\|T\| = \sup_{\substack{x \in X, \\ \|x\|_X = 1}} \|Tx\|_Y. \tag{11}$$

12. THEOREM. *A linear operator is continuous iff it is bounded.*

PROOF. Suppose that T is linear and bounded. Then

$$T\theta = 0.$$

Let $\eta > 0$ be given. Put

$$\zeta = \frac{\eta}{\|T\| + 1}.$$

Then $\|x\| < \zeta$, $x \in X$, implies that

$$\|Tx\| \leqq \|T\| \, \|x\| \leqq \frac{\|T\|\eta}{\|T\| + 1} < \eta.$$

Hence T is continuous at $x = 0$, hence everywhere.

Conversely, suppose that T is linear and continuous. If T were not bounded, there would exist a sequence $\{x_\nu\}$, $\nu = 1, 2, \cdots$, of elements of X such that

$$\|Tx_\nu\| > \nu\|x_\nu\|.$$

Then $\|x_\nu\| > 0$, else $Tx_\nu = 0$. Put

$$x'_\nu = \frac{x_\nu}{\nu\|x_\nu\|} \in X.$$

Then

$$Tx'_\nu = \frac{Tx_\nu}{\nu\|x_\nu\|}, \qquad \|Tx'_\nu\| > 1, \qquad \nu = 1, 2, \cdots.$$

Nonetheless

$$\|x'_\nu\| = \frac{\|x_\nu\|}{\nu\|x_\nu\|} = \frac{1}{\nu} \to 0.$$

This contradicts the fact that T is continuous at 0, and completes the proof.

Thus linear continuous operators are bounded. Furthermore, for a linear operator T to be continuous it is sufficient that T be continuous at one point of X; alternatively that T be bounded. These criteria are useful.

§ 13. **The adjoint space.** By a *functional* we mean an operator on a normed linear space X to the numbers N considered as a normed linear space. The set of all linear continuous functionals on X is called the *adjoint* or conjugate space of X and is denoted X^*. Thus $F \in X^*$ means that F is a linear continuous map of X into N. The norm $\|F\|$ of an element F of X^* is

$$\|F\| = \|F\|_{X^*} = \sup_{\substack{x \in X, \\ \|x\|_X = 1}} |Fx|,$$

an instance of the definition of the previous section. Addition and scalar multiplication of elements of X^* are defined by their numerical counterparts. Then X^* is itself a normed linear space, as may be verified directly.

The study of adjoint spaces is often interesting and important. For the approximator the dominant fact is the following: The nature of X determines the form of elements of X^*; and that form is often known, accessible, and appraisable.

To illustrate: if $X = E_m$ = Euclidean m-space and $F \in X^* = E_m^*$, then for each coordinate system in E_m there exist constants $\alpha_1, \alpha_2, \cdots, \alpha_m$ such that

$$Fx = \alpha_1 x_1 + \cdots + \alpha_m x_m, \qquad x = (x_1, \cdots, x_m) \in E_m.$$

To prove this assertion let $u^1, \cdots, u^m$ be the unit-vectors along the coordinate axes. Then

$$\begin{aligned} x &= x_1 u^1 + \cdots + x_m u^m, \\ Fx &= F(x_1 u^1 + \cdots + x_m u^m) = x_1 F u^1 + \cdots + x_m F u^m \\ &= x_1 \alpha_1 + \cdots + x_m \alpha_m, \end{aligned}$$

where

$$\alpha_i = F u^i, \qquad i = 1, \cdots, m.$$

Thus not only is the form of F prescribed, but explicit formulas are also at hand for the parameters α_i which characterize F. We note in passing that alternative norms in E_m^* depend on the norm in E_m as follows.

Alternative norms in E_m *and* E_m^*.

$x \in E_m, \qquad F \in E_m^*$

$\|x\|$	$\|F\|$
$(x_1^2 + \cdots + x_m^2)^{1/2}$	$(\alpha_1^2 + \cdots + \alpha_m^2)^{1/2}$
$\|x_1\| + \cdots + \|x_m\|$	$\max(\|\alpha_1\|, \cdots, \|\alpha_m\|)$
$\max(\|x_1\|, \cdots, \|x_m\|)$	$\|\alpha_1\| + \cdots + \|\alpha_m\|$
$(\|x_1\|^e + \cdots + \|x_m\|^e)^{1/e}$	$(\|\alpha_1\|^{e'} + \cdots + \|\alpha_m\|^{e'})^{1/e'}$,

where

$$\frac{1}{e} + \frac{1}{e'} = 1, \qquad e, e' > 1.$$

We conclude this section with an illuminating and useful lemma. Note that C_n^* is the adjoint of C_n, whereas $\mathscr{C}_n^*$ is the space defined in § 1 : 3. The relationship between C_n^* and $\mathscr{C}_n^*$ will be discussed later.

14. Lemma.

$$C_{n+1} \subset C_n,$$
$$C_{n+1}^* \supset C_n^*.$$

Proof. The first relation is immediate: if $x \in C_{n+1}$, then a fortiori $x \in C_n$.

The second relation involves the topologies on the spaces. If $F \in C_n^*$, then F is a linear bounded functional on C_n. A fortiori F is defined and linear on C_{n+1}. For a suitable constant M,

$$|Fx| \leqq M|||x|||_{C_n}, \qquad x \in C_n,$$

since F is bounded on C_n. Now if $x \in C_{n+1}$,

$$|||x|||_{C_n} \leqq |||x|||_{C_{n+1}},$$

by (7). Hence, for all x in C_{n+1},

$$|Fx| \leqq M|||x|||_{C_{n+1}};$$

that is, F is bounded on C_{n+1}. Hence $F \in C_{n+1}^*$, as was to be shown.

§ 15. **Riesz's Theorem** (1909). Let

$$I = \{\alpha \leqq s \leqq \tilde{\alpha}\}, \qquad -\infty < \alpha < \tilde{\alpha} < \infty,$$

be a compact interval. Consider the space $C_0 = C_0(I)$ of functions x continuous on I, with norm

$$\|x\| = \sup_{s \in I} |x(s)|.$$

Suppose that λ is a function of bounded variation on I. Then the functional F defined by the relation

$$Fx = \int_\alpha^{\tilde{\alpha}} x(s)\, d\lambda(s), \qquad x \in C_0,$$

is clearly linear on C_0. Furthermore F is bounded, since by (12 : 16),

$$|Fx| = \left|\int_\alpha^{\tilde{\alpha}} x(s)\, d\lambda(s)\right| \leqq (\text{var } \lambda) \sup_{s \in I} |x(s)| = (\text{var } \lambda)\|x\|, \qquad x \in C_0,$$

where var λ denotes the variation of λ on I. Thus

$$F \in C_0^*.$$

Riesz's Theorem, as we shall see, implies that conversely every element of C_0^* is of the form of the above F.

Interesting Treatments of Riesz's Theorem are given in [Riesz-Nagy 1, §§ 50–51, 59–60; Reisz 1, 3; Banach 1, pp. 59–61; Lebesgue 1, pp. 262–267], the first of which I follow. The treatment will carry over directly to its analogue for functions of several variables (cf. Theorem 6 : 9, where further references are given).

16. LEMMA. *Suppose that $F \in C_0^*$ and that*

$$\{x^\nu\}, \qquad \nu = 1, 2, \cdots,$$

is a bounded increasing sequence of elements of C_0. Then the sequence

$$\{Fx^\nu\}$$

of real numbers converges.

PROOF. By hypothesis

$$x^\nu \in C_0(I),$$

$$x^\nu(s) \leqq x^{\nu+1}(s),$$

$$|x^\nu(s)| \leqq N < \infty, \qquad s \in I, \qquad \nu = 1, 2, \cdots.$$

We shall prove that the series

$$Fx^1 + (Fx^2 - Fx^1) + (Fx^3 - Fx^2) + \cdots \tag{17}$$

converges absolutely. To this end observe that

$$|Fx^{\nu+1} - Fx^\nu| = \pm(Fx^{\nu+1} - Fx^\nu) = \pm F(x^{\nu+1} - x^\nu),$$

with suitable choice of sign. It follows by finite additivity that the partial sums of the series

$$|Fx^2 - Fx^1| + |Fx^3 - Fx^2| + \cdots \tag{18}$$

are the images under F of the corresponding partial sums of a series

$$\pm(x^2 - x^1) \pm (x^3 - x^2) \pm \cdots. \tag{19}$$

Now the absolute value of each latter partial sum is at most

$$(x^2(s) - x^1(s)) + (x^3(s) - x^2(s)) + \cdots = x(s) - x^1(s) \leqq 2N, \qquad s \in I,$$

since $\{x^\nu\}$ is increasing. Hence the norm in C_0 of each partial sum of (19) is at most $2N$, and the corresponding partial sum of (18) is at most

$$2N\|F\|_{C_0^*} < \infty.$$

Hence (18) converges and (17) converges absolutely. This completes the proof.

Lemma 16 will enable us to construct an extension G of any element F of C_0^*.

Let M denote the space of functions on I which are *limits of bounded increasing sequences* of elements of C_0. Thus $x \in M$ iff a sequence $\{x^\nu\}$ exists such that

$$\begin{aligned} x^\nu &\in C_0, \\ x^\nu(s) &\leqq x^{\nu+1}(s), \\ |x^\nu(s)| &\leqq N < \infty, \\ x(s) &= \lim_\nu x^\nu(s), \qquad s \in I, \quad \nu = 1, 2, \cdots. \end{aligned}$$

If

$$x, y \in M,$$

then

$$x + y \in M$$

but

$$x - y$$

need not be an element of M.

Let $\mathcal{M}$ denote the space of *differences of elements of* M. Thus $z \in \mathcal{M}$ iff there exist bounded increasing sequences $\{x^\nu\}$ and $\{y^\nu\}$ of elements of C_0 such that

$$z(s) = \lim_\nu x^\nu(s) - \lim_\nu y^\nu(s) = \lim_\nu [x^\nu(s) - y^\nu(s)];$$

or, what is the same, iff

$$z = x - y, \qquad x, y \in M.$$

Clearly $\mathcal{M}$ is a linear space. We now define the *norm* on $\mathcal{M}$ as

(20) $$\|z\|_{\mathcal{M}} = \sup_{s \in I} |z(s)|, \qquad z \in \mathcal{M}.$$

Thus if $x \in C_0$, then $x \in M \subset \mathcal{M}$, and

$$\|x\|_{C_0} = \|x\|_{\mathcal{M}}.$$

If x is the limit of a bounded monotone sequence (decreasing or increasing) of elements of C_0, then $x \in \mathcal{M}$.

Consider a functional $F \in C_0^*$. We define its *natural extension* G as follows:

(21) $$Gx = \lim_\nu Fx^\nu, \qquad x \in M,$$

where $\{x^\nu\}$ is a bounded increasing sequence of elements of C_0 which approaches x; and

(22) $$Gz = Gx - Gy, \qquad z \in \mathcal{M},$$

where

$$z = x - y; \qquad x, y \in M.$$

It must be shown that these definitions are unambiguous. The following lemma asserts, among other things, that Gx depends on x only, $x \in \mathscr{M}$. It shows also that the natural extension involves no loss of properties.

23. Lemma. *If $F \in C_0^*$, then the natural extension G of F is well defined, linear, and bounded with norm*

$$\|G\|_{\mathscr{M}^*} = \|F\|_{C_0^*} \tag{24}$$

on $\mathscr{M}$.

Proof. *Part* 1. G is well defined on M. Suppose that $\{x^\nu\}$ and $\{y^\nu\}$ are two bounded increasing sequences of elements of C_0, each of which approaches $x \in M$. The sequences $\{Fx^\nu\}$ and $\{Fy^\nu\}$ are convergent, by Lemma 16. We shall show that their limits are equal.

We suppose that each sequence is strictly increasing:

$$x^\nu(s) < x^{\nu+1}(s), \qquad y^\nu(s) < y^{\nu+1}(s), \qquad s \in I, \quad \nu = 1, 2, \cdots, \tag{25}$$

since, in the contrary case, we could replace the sequences by

$$\left\{x^\nu(s) - \frac{1}{\nu}\right\}, \qquad \left\{y^\nu(s) - \frac{1}{\nu}\right\},$$

respectively, in as much as

$$F\left(x^\nu - \frac{1}{\nu}\right) = Fx^\nu - \frac{1}{\nu} F1 \to \lim_\nu Fx^\nu.$$

Consider a particular element x^{ν_1} of the sequence $\{x^\nu\}$. For all sufficiently large ν,

$$x^{\nu_1}(s) < y^\nu(s), \qquad s \in I.$$

To prove this assertion, assume its contrary. Then the points s in I such that

$$x^{\nu_1}(s) \geqq y^1(s), \qquad x^{\nu_1}(s) \geqq y^2(s), \cdots \tag{26}$$

would constitute a monotone descending sequence of closed nonempty sets whose intersection would therefore be nonempty [Hausdorff 1, p. 129]. There would exist a point s^0 in I such that (26) would hold with $s = s^0$. Then

$$x^{\nu_1}(s^0) \geqq \lim_\nu y^\nu(s^0) = x(s^0),$$

a contradiction of the fact that

$$x^{\nu_1}(s) < x(s), \qquad s \in I.$$

Thus for each ν_1 there exists $\nu_2 > \nu_1$ such that

$$x^{\nu_1}(s) < y^{\nu_2}(s), \qquad s \in I.$$

By the same argument, for each ν_2 there exists $\nu_3 > \nu_2$ such that

$$y^{\nu_2}(s) < x^{\nu_3}(s), \qquad s \in I.$$

We may therefore construct an increasing sequence

$$x^{\nu_1} < y^{\nu_2} < x^{\nu_3} < y^{\nu_4} < \cdots.$$

These functions are elements of C_0 and are uniformly bounded. Hence the sequence

$$Fx^{\nu_1}, \quad Fy^{\nu_2}, \quad Fx^{\nu_3}, \quad Fy^{\nu_4}, \cdots$$

converges, by Lemma 16. The limit must coincide with $\lim_\nu Fx^\nu$ and $\lim_\nu Fy^\nu$, which two quantities must therefore be equal.

Part 2. G is additive on M. If $x, y \in M$, then

$$x + y = \lim_\nu (x^\nu + y^\nu),$$

where $\{x^\nu\}$, $\{y^\nu\}$ are bounded increasing sequences of elements of C_0. It follows that

$$G(x + y) = \lim_\nu F(x^\nu + y^\nu) = Gx + Gy.$$

Part 3. G is an extension of F. If $x \in C_0$, we may take

$$x^\nu = x, \qquad \nu = 1, 2, \cdots.$$

Hence

$$Gx = \lim_\nu Fx^\nu = Fx.$$

Part 4. G is well defined on $\mathscr{M}$. Suppose that $z \in \mathscr{M}$ and that

$$z = x - y = x' - y', \qquad x, y, x', y' \in M.$$

We shall show that

$$Gx - Gy = Gx' - Gy'$$

and hence that the definition (22) is unambiguous, since (21) is unambiguous by Part 1 of the present proof.

Now

$$x + y' = x' + y \in M.$$

Hence

$$G(x + y') = G(x' + y) = Gx + Gy' = Gx' + Gy,$$

by Part 2.

Part 5. G is linear on $\mathscr{M}$. If $x, y \in \mathscr{M}$ and $b, c \in \mathsf{R}$, then

$$bx + cy \in \mathscr{M} \quad \text{and} \quad G(bx + cy) = b\, Gx + c\, Gy.$$

This may be proved by showing that G is additive and homogeneous on $\mathscr{M}$.

Part 6. G is bounded on $\mathscr{M}$, with norm $\|F\|_{C_0^*}$. We shall prove that

$$(27)\qquad |Gx| \leqq \|F\|_{C_0^*}\|x\|_{\mathscr{M}}, \qquad x \in \mathscr{M}.$$

This will imply that

$$\|G\|_{\mathscr{M}^*} \leqq \|F\|_{C_0^*}.$$

The reverse inequality is immediate, since

$$C_0 \subset \mathscr{M}.$$

Thus (27) will imply that

$$\|G\|_{\mathscr{M}^*} = \|F\|_{C_0^*}.$$

The inequality (27) certainly holds for $x \in C_0$ and hence for $x \in M$. Suppose that $x \in \mathscr{M}$. Then

$$x = y - z; \qquad y, z \in M;$$
$$y = \lim_{\nu} y^{\nu}, \qquad z = \lim_{\nu} z^{\nu},$$

where $\{y^{\nu}\}$, $\{z^{\nu}\}$ are bounded increasing sequences of elements of C_0. Put

$$c = \|x\|_{\mathscr{M}} = \sup_{s \in I} |y(s) - z(s)| = \sup_{s \in I} |x(s)|.$$

Define the functions w^{ν} as

$$w^{\nu}(s) = \begin{cases} y^{\nu}(s) & \text{if } |y^{\nu}(s) - z^{\nu}(s)| \leqq c, \\ z^{\nu}(s) + c & \text{if } y^{\nu}(s) - z^{\nu}(s) > c, \\ z^{\nu}(s) - c & \text{if } y^{\nu}(s) - z^{\nu}(s) < -c, \qquad \nu = 1, 2, \cdots. \end{cases}$$

Thus $w^{\nu}(s)$ is the middle quantity algebraically of

$$z^{\nu}(s) - c, \quad y^{\nu}(s), \quad z^{\nu}(s) + c, \qquad s \in I, \quad \nu = 1, 2, \cdots.$$

Now if u, v are functions on an arbitrary space to R, then the functions

$$\min (u, v), \quad \max (u, v)$$

are both continuous if u and v are continuous. If $\{u^{\nu}\}$, $\{v^{\nu}\}$ are increasing sequences, so are $\{\min (u^{\nu}, v^{\nu})\}$, $\{\max (u^{\nu}, v^{\nu})\}$. Furthermore, the middle quantity of a, b, c is

$$\min [\max (a, b), \ \max (b, c), \ \max (c, a)], \qquad a, b, c \in \mathsf{R}.$$

Hence

$$w^{\nu} \in C_0, \qquad \nu = 1, 2, \cdots,$$

and the sequence $\{w^{\nu}\}$ is increasing. Now $\{w^{\nu}\}$ is a bounded sequence; and

$$\lim_{\nu} w^{\nu}(s) = y(s),$$

since $w^\nu(s) - z^\nu(s)$ is the middle quantity of

$$-c, \quad y^\nu(s) - z^\nu(s), \quad c$$

and $\lim_\nu [w^\nu(s) - z^\nu(s)]$ is the middle quantity of

$$-c, \quad x(s), \quad c,$$

that is, $x(s)$. Also

$$|w^\nu(s) - z^\nu(s)| \leqq c, \qquad s \in I, \quad \nu = 1, 2, \cdots.$$

Now

$$Gx = \lim_\nu Fw^\nu - \lim_\nu Fz^\nu = \lim_\nu F(w^\nu - z^\nu),$$

$$|Gx| = \lim_\nu |F(w^\nu - z^\nu)| \leqq \|F\|_{C_0^*}\, c = \|F\|_{C_0^*}\|x\|_{\mathscr{M}}.$$

Thus (27) is established.

This completes the proof of Lemma 23.

The definition (22) of Gz, $z \in \mathscr{M}$ implies the following. If

$$z = \lim_\nu z^\nu,$$

where $\{z^\nu\}$ is a sequence which is the difference of two bounded increasing sequences of elements of C_0, then

$$Gz = \lim_\nu Fz^\nu.$$

The step function θ and the continuous functions θ^ν, $\nu = 1, 2, \cdots$, are defined as follows:

$$\theta(t, s) = \begin{cases} 1 & \text{if } s \leqq t, \\ 0 & \text{if } s > t, \end{cases} \tag{28}$$

$$\theta^\nu(t, s) = \begin{cases} 1 & \text{if } s \leqq t, \\ 0 & \text{if } s \geqq t + 1/\nu, \\ 1 + \nu(t - s) & \text{if } t < s < t + 1/\nu. \end{cases} \tag{29}$$

For each fixed t in R, $\theta^\nu(t, s)$ is continuous in s, $s \in \mathsf{R}$, and

$$0 \leqq \theta^\nu(t, s) \leqq 1, \qquad \nu = 1, 2, \cdots;$$

furthermore $\{\theta^\nu(t, s)\}$ is a decreasing sequence which approaches $\theta(t, s)$, $s \in \mathsf{R}$.

The space of functions f of bounded variation on I will be denoted $V = V(I)$ (cf. § 12: 14). In considering an element f of V, we extend its definition outside $I = [\alpha, \tilde{\alpha}]$ as follows:

$$f(s) = \begin{cases} f(\alpha) & \text{if } s \leqq \alpha, \\ f(\tilde{\alpha}) & \text{if } s \geqq \tilde{\alpha}. \end{cases} \tag{30}$$

If $f \in V$, the limits $f(s - 0)$ and $f(s + 0)$ exist for all s. Furthermore

$$f(s - 0) = f(s) = f(s + 0) \quad \text{with countable exceptions,}$$

since a function of bounded variation has at most countably many discontinuities.

We denote by V^0 the subspace of V consisting of functions which vanish at $s = \alpha$ and which are continuous on the right except possibly at $s = \alpha$. That is, $f \in V^0$ iff

$$f \in V; \qquad f(\alpha) = 0; \qquad f(s + 0) = f(s), \quad s > \alpha.$$

Note that $f(\alpha + 0)$ may differ from $f(\alpha)$. We call V^0 the *space of normalized functions of bounded variation.*

31. Lemma. *Suppose that $F \in C_0^*$. Define the function λ on* R *as follows:*

$$\lambda(\tilde{s}) = \begin{cases} \lim_{\nu \to \infty} F\theta^\nu(\tilde{s}, s) & \text{if } \tilde{s} > \alpha, \\ 0 & \text{otherwise}, \end{cases} \qquad \tilde{s} \in \mathsf{R}. \tag{32}$$

Then $\lambda \in V$, and

$$\operatorname{var} \lambda \leqq \|F\|_{C_0^*}.$$

This lemma is preparatory. We shall show later that $\lambda \in V^0$ and

$$\operatorname{var} \lambda = \|F\|_{C_0^*}.$$

Proof. In the definition (32) of $\lambda(\tilde{s})$, F acts on its argument as a function of s; the variable $\tilde{s}$ is a parameter. The limit in the above definition of $\lambda(\tilde{s})$ certainly exists, by Lemma 16. Indeed another form of (32) is

$$\lambda(\tilde{s}) = \begin{cases} G\theta(\tilde{s}, s) & \text{if } \tilde{s} > \alpha, \\ 0 & \text{otherwise}, \end{cases} \tag{33}$$

where G is the natural extension of F.

If $\tilde{s} \leqq \alpha$, then (32) states that

$$\lambda(\tilde{s}) = 0 = \lambda(\alpha).$$

If $\tilde{s} \geqq \tilde{\alpha}$, then (32) implies that

$$\lambda(\tilde{s}) = \lim_\nu F\theta^\nu(\tilde{s}, s) = \lim_\nu F[1] = F[1] = \lambda(\tilde{\alpha}),$$

since in this case

$$\theta^\nu(\tilde{s}, s) = 1 \quad \text{for all } s \in I.$$

Thus (32) conforms to (30).

Now consider the variation of λ on I. We shall show that for any subdivision

$$\alpha = \tilde{s}_0 < \tilde{s}_1 < \tilde{s}_2 < \cdots < \tilde{s}_m = \tilde{\alpha}$$

of I,

$$c \underset{\text{def}}{=} \sum_{i=1}^m |\lambda(\tilde{s}_i) - \lambda(\tilde{s}_{i-1})| \leqq \|F\|_{C_0^*}.$$

To this end define the function x as

$$x(s) = \theta(\tilde{s}_1, s)\sigma_1 + \sum_{i=2}^{m} [\theta(\tilde{s}_i, s) - \theta(\tilde{s}_{i-1}, s)]\sigma_i,$$

where

$$\sigma_i = \text{signum}\,[\lambda(\tilde{s}_i) - \lambda(\tilde{s}_{i-1})] = \begin{cases} 1, \\ 0, \\ -1. \end{cases}$$

Then

$$x \in \mathscr{M},$$

since x is a finite sum;

$$Gx = c,$$

by (33); and

$$\|x\|_{\mathscr{M}} \leqq 1,$$

since one term in $x(s)$ equals σ_i and all the other terms vanish, for each s in I. Hence, by Lemma 23,

$$|Gx| = |c| = c \leqq \|G\|_{\mathscr{M}^*}\|x\|_{\mathscr{M}} \leqq \|F\|_{C_0^*}.$$

Hence

$$\text{var}\ \lambda \leqq \|F\|_{C_0^*};$$

and the proof is complete.

34. Riesz's Theorem. *Suppose that $F \in C_0^*$. Put*

(35) $$\lambda(\tilde{s}) = \begin{cases} \lim_{\nu \to \infty} F\theta^\nu(\tilde{s}, s) & \text{if } \tilde{s} > \alpha, \\ 0 & \text{otherwise.} \end{cases}$$

Then $\lambda \in V^0$ and

(36) $$Fx = \int_\alpha^{\tilde{\alpha}} x(s)\, d\lambda(s), \qquad x \in C_0.$$

The function λ is the only element of V^0 for which this relation holds. Furthermore

(37) $$\|F\|_{C_0^*} = \text{var}\ \lambda.$$

An alternative form of (35) is (33). The space V^0 is the space of normalized functions of bounded variation, defined before Lemma 31. The functions θ^ν are defined in (29).

PROOF. *Part* 1. We establish (36). Suppose that $x \in C_0$. Consider a partition

$$\alpha = \tilde{s}_0 \leqq s_1 \leqq \tilde{s}_1 \leqq s_2 \leqq \tilde{s}_2 \leqq \cdots \leqq s_m \leqq \tilde{s}_m = \tilde{\alpha}$$

of I. Define the step function y as

$$y(s) = \begin{cases} x(s_i), & \tilde{s}_{i-1} < s \leqq \tilde{s}_i, \quad i = 1, \cdots, m, \\ x(s_1), & s = \tilde{s}_0. \end{cases}$$

Then

$$y(s) = x(s_1)\theta(\tilde{s}_1, s) + \sum_{i=2}^{m} x(s_i)[\theta(\tilde{s}_i, s) - \theta(\tilde{s}_{i-1}, s)].$$

Thus $y \in \mathcal{M}$. Let G be the natural extension of F. Then by (33)

$$\begin{aligned} Gy &= x(s_1)\lambda(\tilde{s}_1) + \sum_{i=2}^{m} x(s_i)[\lambda(\tilde{s}_i) - \lambda(\tilde{s}_{i-1})] \\ &= \sum_{i=1}^{m} x(s_i)[\lambda(\tilde{s}_i) - \lambda(\tilde{s}_{i-1})], \end{aligned}$$

since

$$\lambda(\tilde{s}_0) = \lambda(\alpha) = 0.$$

The last sum is precisely one which enters in the definition, § 12 : 2, of the Stieltjes integral

$$\int_{\alpha}^{\tilde{\alpha}} x(s)\, d\lambda(s).$$

Hence Gy approaches this integral as the maximum $\tilde{s}_i - \tilde{s}_{i-1}$ approaches zero, by Lemma 31 and Theorem 12 : 27.

On the other hand let ω be the maximum of the oscillations of $x(s)$ on the intervals

$$\tilde{s}_{i-1} \leqq s \leqq \tilde{s}_i, \qquad i = 1, \cdots, m.$$

Then

$$|x(s) - y(s)| \leqq \omega, \qquad s \in I;$$
$$\|x - y\|_{\mathcal{M}} \leqq \omega,$$

and

$$|Gx - Gy| = |G(x - y)| \leqq \|G\|_{\mathcal{M}^*}\, \omega = \|F\|_{C_0^*}\, \omega,$$

by Lemma 23. If the maximum $\tilde{s}_i - \tilde{s}_{i-1}$ approaches zero, so does ω, since x is uniformly continuous on I. Hence Gy approaches Gx, and

$$Gx = Fx = \int_{\alpha}^{\tilde{\alpha}} x(s)\, d\lambda(s).$$

Thus (36) holds.

Part 2. We establish (37). By Lemma 31,

$$\|F\|_{C_0^*} \geqq \operatorname{var} \lambda.$$

On the other hand (36) implies that

$$|Fx| \leqq \sup_{s \in I} |x(s)| \operatorname{var} \lambda = \operatorname{var} \lambda \|x\|_{C_0}.$$

Hence

$$\|F\|_{C_0^*} \leqq \operatorname{var} \lambda;$$

and

$$\|F\|_{C_0^*} = \operatorname{var} \lambda.$$

Part 3. We now show that $\lambda \in V^0$. By Lemma 31,

$$\lambda \in V \quad \text{and} \quad \lambda(s) = \begin{cases} 0 & \text{if } s \leqq \alpha, \\ \lambda(\tilde{\alpha}) & \text{if } s \geqq \tilde{\alpha}. \end{cases}$$

It remains to show that

$$\lambda(\tilde{s} + 0) = \lambda(\tilde{s}), \qquad \alpha < \tilde{s} < \tilde{\alpha}.$$

In this case, by (36),

$$\lambda(\tilde{s}) = \lim_{\nu} F\theta^{\nu}(\tilde{s}, s) = \lim_{\nu} \int_{\alpha}^{\tilde{\alpha}} \theta^{\nu}(\tilde{s}, s)\, d\lambda(s)$$

$$= \lim_{\nu} \int_{[\alpha, \tilde{\alpha}]} \theta^{\nu}(\tilde{s}, s)\, d\lambda(s),$$

since λ is so defined below α and above $\tilde{\alpha}$ that the Riemann-Stieltjes integral of a continuous integrand equals the Lebesgue-Stieltjes integral (cf. § 12: 34). Since the sequence $\{\theta^{\nu}\}$ is monotone and approaches θ,

$$\lambda(\tilde{s}) = \int_{[\alpha, \tilde{\alpha}]} \theta(\tilde{s}, s)\, d\lambda(s) = \int_{[\alpha, \tilde{s}]} d\lambda(s) = \lambda(\tilde{s} + 0),$$

by Theorem 12: 39. Hence

$$\lambda \in V^0.$$

Part 4. We now show that λ is the only element of V^0 for which (36) holds. Thus suppose that

$$Fx = \int_{\alpha}^{\tilde{\alpha}} x(s)\, d\kappa(s), \qquad x \in C_0,$$

where $\kappa \in V^0$. By (32) and Part 3,

$$\lambda(\tilde{s}) = \lambda(\tilde{s}+0) = \lim_{\nu} F\theta^{\nu}(\tilde{s}, s) = \lim_{\nu} \int_{\alpha}^{\tilde{\alpha}} \theta^{\nu}(\tilde{s}, s)\, d\kappa(s)$$

$$= \lim_{\nu} \int_{[\alpha, \tilde{\alpha}]} \theta^{\nu}(\tilde{s}, s)\, d\kappa(s) = \int_{[\alpha, \tilde{\alpha}]} \theta(\tilde{s}, s)\, d\kappa(s) = \int_{[\alpha, \tilde{s}]} d\kappa(s)$$

$$= \kappa(\tilde{s}+0) = \kappa(\tilde{s}), \qquad \alpha < \tilde{s} \leqq \tilde{\alpha},$$

since $\kappa, \lambda \in V^0$. Also,

$$\kappa(\alpha) = \lambda(\alpha) = 0.$$

Hence $\kappa = \lambda$ on I and therefore everywhere, by (30).

This completes the proof of Theorem 34.

Consider a functional $F \in C_0^*$. We may define the *Lebesgue extension* of F as the functional H, where

$$Hx = \int_I x(s)\, d\lambda(s)$$

for all functions x which are Lebesgue-Stieltjes integrable on I relative to λ and λ is given by (35). (Thus certain unbounded functions are admitted. Cf. § 12 : 34.) Then

$$Hx = Gx, \qquad x \in \mathscr{M},$$

by the classical theorem on monotone sequences; and H is an extension of the natural extension G of F. Note that H is an element of the space $\mathscr{C}_0^*$ of § 1 : 3.

Thus if $F \in C_0^*$, the Lebesgue extension of F is an element of $\mathscr{C}_0^*$. Conversely if $H \in \mathscr{C}_0^*$, then the restriction of H to C_0 (that is, the functional H considered on C_0 only) is an element of C_0^*. Thus C_0^* and $\mathscr{C}_0^*$ are essentially equivalent.

§ 38. **The space C_n^*.** Riesz's Theorem provides a representation of elements of C_0^*. Theorem 39 of the present section will do the same for C_n^*, $n > 0$.

Let a be a fixed element of the interval

$$I = \{\alpha \leqq s \leqq \tilde{\alpha}\}, \qquad -\infty < \alpha < \tilde{\alpha} < \infty.$$

The space

$$C_n = C_n(I) = C_n(I; a)$$

has been defined in § 2. Of the two equivalent norms

$$\|x\| = \|x\|_{C_n} = \max_{i=0,\cdots,n} [|x_0(a)|, |x_1(a)|, \cdots, |x_{n-1}(a)|, \sup_{s \in I} |x_n(s)|]$$

and

$$|||x||| = |||x|||_{C_n} = \max_{i=0,\cdots,n} [\sup_{s \in I} |x_i(s)|],$$

the former is the one that we will use ordinarily. In particular, then, the norm in C_n^* is to be based on $\|x\|_{C_n}$. That is, if $F \in C_n^*$, the norm

$$\|F\| = \|F\|_{C_n^*}$$

is the infimum of numbers N such that

$$|Fx| \leqq N\|x\|_{C_n}, \qquad x \in C_n.$$

In the following theorem $\{\theta^\nu(t, s)\}$, $\nu = 1, 2, \cdots$, is the bounded monotone sequence of continuous functions (29) which approach the step function $\theta(t, s)$. The normalized powers are defined in § 1 : 2.

39. Mass theorem. *Suppose that*

$$F \in C_n^*, \qquad n \geqq 1.$$

Put

$$c^i = F[(s - a)^{(i)}], \qquad i < n; \tag{40}$$

$$\lambda(t) = \begin{cases} \lim_\nu F\left[\int_a^s (s - \tilde{s})^{(n-1)}\theta^\nu(t, \tilde{s})\, d\tilde{s}\right] & \text{if } t > \alpha, \\ 0 & \text{otherwise.} \end{cases} \tag{41}$$

Then λ is well defined and an element of V^0; and

$$Fx = \sum_{i<n} c^i x_i(a) + \int_\alpha^{\tilde{\alpha}} x_n(s)\, d\lambda(s), \qquad x \in C_n. \tag{42}$$

Furthermore λ is the only element of V^0 and c^i, $i < n$, are the only constants for which the last relation holds. Also

$$\|F\|_{C_n^*} = \sum_{i<n} |c^i| + \operatorname{var} \lambda. \tag{43}$$

An illustration of the use of the theorem is given in § 53.

Proof. *Part* 1. Existence and properties of λ. Define the functional G on C_0 as

$$Gy = F\int_a^s (s - \tilde{s})^{(n-1)} y(\tilde{s})\, d\tilde{s}, \qquad y \in C_0. \tag{44}$$

For $y \in C_0$, the argument of F in (44) is an element of C_n, with norm

$$\left\|\int_a^s (s - \tilde{s})^{(n-1)} y(\tilde{s})\, d\tilde{s}\right\|_{C_n} = \|y\|_{C_0},$$

since the integral and its first $(n - 1)$ derivatives as to s vanish at $s = a$ and since the nth derivative of the integral is $y(s)$. Hence Gy is well defined, and

$$|Gy| \leqq \|F\|_{C_n^*}\|y\|_{C_0}, \qquad y \in C_0.$$

Since G is clearly linear, it follows that

$$G \in C_0^*.$$

By Theorem 34,

$$(45) \qquad Gy = \int_\alpha^{\tilde{a}} y(s)\, d\lambda(s), \qquad y \in C_0,$$

where

$$\lambda \in V^0,$$

$$\lambda(t) = \begin{cases} \lim_\nu G\theta^\nu(t, s) & \text{if } t > \alpha, \\ 0 & \text{otherwise}; \end{cases}$$

$$\|G\|_{C_0^*} = \operatorname{var} \lambda.$$

The function λ just defined is precisely that in (41).

Part 2. We now establish (42) and the fact that c^i, $i < n$, and λ in V^0 are unique. Consider an element x of C_n. The Taylor formula

$$(46) \qquad x(s) = \sum_{i<n} (s - a)^{(i)} x_i(a) + \int_a^s (s - \tilde{s})^{(n-1)} x_n(\tilde{s})\, d\tilde{s}, \qquad s \in I,$$

implies that

$$Fx = \sum_{i<n} x_i(a) F[(s - a)^{(i)}] + Gx_n = \sum_{i<n} c^i x_i(a) + \int_\alpha^{\tilde{a}} x_n(s)\, d\lambda(s),$$

by (40), (44), (45). Thus (42) is established.

Suppose now that

$$(47) \qquad Fx = \sum_{i<n} b^i x_i(a) + \int_\alpha^{\tilde{a}} x_n(s)\, d\kappa(s), \qquad x \in C_n,$$

where $\kappa \in V^0$. Put

$$x(s) = (s - a)^{(i_0)}, \qquad i_0 < n,$$

herein. Then

$$Fx = F[(s - a)^{(i_0)}] = b^{i_0},$$

since

$$x_i(a) = 0, \qquad i \neq i_0; \qquad x_{i_0}(a) = 1; \qquad x_n(s) = 0, \qquad \text{all } s.$$

Hence

$$b^{i_0} = c^{i_0}$$

by (40). The constants c^i, $i < n$, are therefore unique. Next put

$$x(s) = \int_a^s (s - \tilde{s})^{(n-1)} y(\tilde{s})\, d\tilde{s}, \qquad y \in C_0,$$

in (47). Then

$$Fx = \int_a^{\tilde{a}} y(s)\, d\kappa(s) = \int_a^{\tilde{a}} y(s)\, d\lambda(s), \qquad y \in C_0,$$

since

$$x_i(a) = 0, \qquad i < n,$$

$$x_n(s) = y(s), \qquad s \in I.$$

Since κ, $\lambda \in V^0$, it follows that

$$\kappa = \lambda$$

by the fact that the mass in Riesz's Theorem is unique.

Part 3. We now establish (43). Since

$$\left|\sum_{i<n} c^i x_i(a)\right| \leqq \left[\sum_{i<n} |c^i|\right] \max_{j<n} |x_j(a)|,$$

(42) implies that

$$\begin{aligned} |Fx| &\leqq \left[\sum_{i<n} |c^i|\right] \max_{j<n} |x_j(a)| + \sup_{s \in I} |x_n(s)| \operatorname{var} \lambda \\ &\leqq \left[\sum_{i<n} |c^i| + \operatorname{var} \lambda\right] \max\,[|x_0(a)|, \cdots, |x_{n-1}(a)|, \sup_{s \in I} |x_n(s)|] \\ &= \left[\sum_{i<n} |c^i| + \operatorname{var} \lambda\right] \|x\|_{C_n}, \qquad x \in C_n. \end{aligned}$$

Hence

$$\|F\|_{C_n^*} \leqq \sum_{i<n} |c^i| + \operatorname{var} \lambda.$$

To establish the reverse inequality, let $\eta > 0$ be given and let y be a continuous function on I such that

$$Gy = |Gy| > (\operatorname{var} \lambda - \eta), \qquad \|y\|_{C_0} \leqq 1,$$

where G is defined in (44). Such a function y exists, since

$$\|G\|_{C_0^*} = \operatorname{var} \lambda.$$

Put

$$b^i = \operatorname{signum} c^i;$$

and

$$x(s) = \sum_{i<n} b^i (s - a)^{(i)} + \int_a^s (s - \tilde{s})^{(n-1)} y(\tilde{s})\, d\tilde{s}.$$

Then

$$x \in C_n,$$

and

$$x_i(a) = b^i, \qquad i < n;$$
$$x_n(s) = y(s), \qquad s \in I;$$
$$\|x\|_{C_n} = \max [|b^0|, \cdots, |b^{n-1}|, \sup_{s \in I} |y(s)|] \leqq \max [1, \|y\|_{C_0}] = 1.$$

Also, by (42),

$$Fx = \sum_{i<n} b^i c^i + Gy > \sum |c^i| + \text{var}\, \lambda - \eta \geqq \left(\sum |c^i| + \text{var}\, \lambda - \eta\right) \|x\|_{C_n}.$$

Hence

$$\|F\|_{C_n^*} \geqq \sum_{i<n} |c^i| + \text{var}\, \lambda,$$

since $\eta > 0$ was arbitrary.

This completes the proof of Theorem 39.

In the next corollary we consider a functional F which is linear and continuous on C_{n-1}, $n \geqq 1$. The restriction of F to C_n is then linear and continuous on C_n, by Lemma 14. We may therefore apply Theorem 39 to F.

48. Corollary. *If*

$$F \in C_{n-1}^*, \qquad n \geqq 1,$$

then (40), (41), *and* (42) *hold. Alternative formulas for* λ *are*

(49) $$\lambda(t) = F \int_a^s (s - \bar{s})^{(n-1)} \theta(t, \bar{s})\, d\bar{s}, \qquad t \in \mathsf{R},$$

(50) $$\lambda(t) = F[(s - t)^{(n)} \theta(t, s)] - \theta(t, a) \sum_{i<n} c^i (a - t)^{(n-i)}.$$

If, in addition, F *vanishes for degree* $n - 1$, *then*

(51) $$\lambda(t) = F[(s - t)^{(n)} \theta(t, s)].$$

Proof. Put

$$y(s) = \int_a^s (s - \bar{s})^{(n-1)} \theta(t, \bar{s})\, d\bar{s},$$

and

$$y^\nu(s) = \int_a^s (s - \bar{s})^{(n-1)} \theta^\nu(t, \bar{s})\, d\bar{s}, \qquad \nu = 1, 2, \cdots.$$

Then

$$y \in C_{n-1}, \qquad y^\nu \in C_n \subset C_{n-1}.$$

Hence Fy and Fy^ν are defined. Also

$$Fy = \lim_\nu Fy^\nu,$$

since F is continuous on C_{n-1} and

$$\|y - y^\nu\|_{C_{n-1}} = \sup_{s \in I} \left| \int_a^s [\theta(t, \tilde{s}) - \theta^\nu(t, \tilde{s})]\, d\tilde{s} \right| \to 0$$

as $\nu \to \infty$, by the classical theorem on dominated approach or by direct calculation. Thus (41) implies that

$$\lambda(t) = Fy, \qquad t > \alpha;$$

and (49) is established for $t > \alpha$. Now (49) is correct for $t \leqq \alpha$ also, since the argument of F in (49) is 0 when $t \leqq \alpha$.

We now deduce (50) and (51) from (49) by using equation (11 : 15). Thus, since F is linear on C_{n-1},

$$\begin{aligned} \lambda(t) &= F[(s - t)^{(n)}\theta(t, s) + \{(s - a)^{(n)} - (s - t)^{(n)}\}\theta(t, a)] \\ &= F[(s - t)^{(n)}\theta(t, s)] + \theta(t, a)Fz, \end{aligned}$$

where

$$z(s) = (s - a)^{(n)} - (s - t)^{(n)}.$$

Now z is a polynomial of degree $(n - 1)$ in s. Hence (51) is established if F is zero for degree $n - 1$. In any case,

$$z_n(s) = 0, \qquad \text{all } s;$$

$$z_i(a) = [(s - a)^{(n-i)} - (s - t)^{(n-i)}]_{s=a} = -(a - t)^{(n-i)}, \qquad i < n.$$

Hence, by (42),

$$Fz = -\sum_{i<n} c^i (a - t)^{(n-i)};$$

and (50) follows. This completes the proof.

Consider a functional F in C_n^*. Define c^i, $i < n$, and λ by (40) and (41). By the *Lebesgue extension of F* we mean the functional H defined as

$$Hx = \sum_{i<n} c^i x_i(a) + \int_{[\alpha, \tilde{\alpha}]} x_n(s)\, d\lambda(s) \tag{52}$$

for all x in $\mathbf{C}_n$ which are such that x_n is integrable λ. (The space $\mathbf{C}_n$ is defined in § 1 : 2.) By Theorem 39

$$Hx = Fx, \qquad x \in C_n.$$

Thus H reduces to F but is defined on a space larger than C_n.

Now H above is an element of $\mathscr{C}_n^*$ (defined in § 1 : 3), since (52) is an instance of equation (1 : 4). Thus *the Lebesgue extension of an element of* C_n^* *is an element of* $\mathscr{C}_n^*$.

Conversely, suppose that H is an element of $\mathscr{C}_n^*$; that is, that

$$Hx = \sum_{i \leqq n} \int_I x_i(s)\, d\mu^i(s), \qquad \mu^i \in V, \quad i \leqq n,$$

for all x in C_n which are such that x_n is integrable μ^n. In particular Hx is defined for $x \in C_n$. Let us denote by F the restriction of H to C_n:

$$Fx = \sum_{i \leqq n} \int_a^{\bar{a}} x_i(s)\, d\mu^i(s), \qquad x \in C_n.$$

Clearly F is linear on C_n. Furthermore F is bounded on C_n, since

$$|Fx| \leqq \sum_{i \leqq n} \sup_{s \in I} |x_i(s)| \operatorname{var} \mu^i \leqq \left[\sum_{i \leqq n} \operatorname{var} \mu^i\right] |||x|||_{C_n}, \qquad x \in C_n.$$

Hence $F \in C_n^*$. Thus *the restriction to* C_n *of an element of* $\mathscr{C}_n^*$ *is an element of* C_n^*.

In the sense of the two above paragraphs, C_n^* and $\mathscr{C}_n^*$ are equivalent.

§ 53. **An illustration.** Let

$$I = \{0 \leqq s \leqq 1\}, \qquad a = 0.$$

Consider the functional F defined as

$$Fx = x(1) - x(0) - [x_1(1) - x_1(0)], \qquad x \in C_1(I), \tag{54}$$

where $x_1(s)$ denotes the value of the derivative dx/ds at s. Since Fx is the sum of Stieltjes integrals on x and x_1,

$$F \in C_1^*.$$

Hence Theorem 39 applies to F with $n \geqq 1$. Let us take

$$n = 1.$$

By (40) and (41),

$$c^0 = F[1] = 0,$$

$$\lambda(t) = \lim_\nu F \int_0^s \theta^\nu(t, \tilde{s})\, d\tilde{s}, \qquad t > 0, \tag{55}$$

$$\lambda(0) = 0,$$

and

$$Fx = \int_0^1 x_1(s)\, d\lambda(s), \qquad x \in C_1. \tag{56}$$

We shall carry out the calculation of λ as an illustration. In the present case we may obtain the end result (56) by inspection, since (54) implies that

$$(57) \qquad Fx = \int_0^1 x_1(s)\, ds + x_1(0) - x_1(1), \qquad x \in C_1.$$

Suppose that $t > 0$. By (54),

$$F \int_0^s \theta^\nu(t, \tilde{s})\, d\tilde{s} = \int_0^1 \theta^\nu(t, \tilde{s})\, d\tilde{s} - 0 - \theta^\nu(t, 1) + \theta^\nu(t, 0),$$

since θ^ν is continuous and the derivative of the integral is the integrand with $\tilde{s} = s$. Hence, by (55),

$$\begin{aligned}\lambda(t) &= \lim_\nu \left[\int_0^1 \theta^\nu(t, \tilde{s})\, d\tilde{s} - \theta^\nu(t, 1) + \theta^\nu(t, 0)\right] \\ &= \int_0^1 \theta(t, \tilde{s})\, d\tilde{s} - \theta(t, 1) + \theta(t, 0) \\ &= \int_0^t d\tilde{s} - \theta(t, 1) + 1 = 1 + t - \theta(t, 1).\end{aligned}$$

Thus

$$\lambda(t) = \begin{cases} 1 + t - 1 = t = 1 & \text{if } t = 1, \\ 1 + t & \text{if } 0 < t < 1. \end{cases}$$

And, as we know at the start, by (41),

$$\lambda(0) = 0.$$

Thus $\lambda(t)$ has a jump of $+1$ at $t = 0$ and of -1 at $t = 1$; elsewhere

$$d\lambda(t) = dt.$$

Our calculation therefore confirms (57).

Note that the calculation of $\lambda(1)$ was needed, since the value $\lambda(1)$ affects the integral (56).

§ 58. **The spaces Z and Z^*.** In the rest of this chapter we consider topics which will be used principally in later chapters, in connection with the study of functions of several variables. The ensuing theory for functions of one variable is optional; its generalization for functions of several variables will be essential to our treatment.

Suppose that

$$a \in I = \{\alpha \leqq s \leqq \tilde{\alpha}\}, \qquad -\infty < \alpha < \tilde{\alpha} < \infty.$$

We define the space

$$Z = Z(a)$$

as the subspace of $C_0 = C_0(I)$ consisting of functions that vanish † at $s = a$:

(59) $$Z = \{x \in C_0 : x(a) = 0\}.$$

The norm $\|x\|_Z$ of $x \in Z$ is taken as $\|x\|_{C_0}$. Thus Z is a subspace of C_0 with the same topology. Hence

$$Z \subset C_0, \qquad Z^* \supset C_0^*.$$

Consider an element F of Z^*; that is, a functional F which is linear and continuous on Z. By the Hahn-Banach Theorem [Banach 1, p. 55, Theorem 2], there is an extension G of F which is linear and continuous on C_0 and such that

$$\|G\|_{C_0^*} = \|F\|_{Z^*}.$$

There are many such extensions each of which may be represented as a Stieltjes integral, by Riesz's Theorem. We shall deal with one such extension in the next theorem, where we give a unique, accessible, and useful representation of F, $F \in Z^*$.

We continue to denote by V the space of functions of bounded variation on I and by V^0 the subspace of normalized functions:

(60) $$V^0 = \{x \in V : x(\alpha) = 0 \text{ and } x(s + 0) = x(s) \text{ for all } s > \alpha\}.$$

We also introduce a new space $V^{0,0}$ of elements of V^0 that *vanish on the boundary* of I:

(61) $$V^{0,0} = \{x \in V^0 : x(\tilde{\alpha}) = 0\}.$$

It will be convenient to introduce a bounded monotone sequence of continuous functions that approach the step function $\psi(a, \tilde{s}, s)$ of equation (1 : 12) and § 11 : 2. Put

(62) $$\psi^\nu(a, \tilde{s}, s) = \theta^\nu(\tilde{s}, a) - \theta^\nu(\tilde{s}, s); \qquad \nu = 1, 2, \cdots; \quad s, \tilde{s} \in \mathsf{R},$$

where $\{\theta^\nu(\tilde{s}, s)\}$ is the bounded monotone continuous sequence (29) that approaches $\theta(\tilde{s}, s)$. For each fixed $\tilde{s}$ in R, $\psi^\nu(a, \tilde{s}, s)$ is continuous in s and the sequence $\{\psi^\nu(a, \tilde{s}, s)\}$ converges monotonely to $\psi(a, \tilde{s}, s)$.

63. Mass theorem. *Suppose that* $F \in Z^*(a)$. *Put*

(64) $$\lambda(\tilde{s}) = \begin{cases} -\lim_\nu F\psi^\nu(a, \tilde{s}, s) & \text{if } \tilde{s} > \alpha, \\ 0 & \text{otherwise.} \end{cases}$$

Then $\lambda \in V^{0,0}$ *and*

(65) $$Fx = \int_\alpha^{\tilde{\alpha}} x(s)\, d\lambda(s), \qquad x \in Z(a).$$

† The symbol $\{a \in A : \mathscr{P}\}$ stands for the class of objects a which are elements of the class A and which are such that property $\mathscr{P}$ holds. Following Gödel, we distinguish between sets and classes. All sets are classes; some classes, like the class of all sets, are not sets [Gödel 1, Chapters 1, 2]. All classes that we consider in this book are sets. The words family, collection, ensemble are synonyms for set.

At times we will abbreviate $\{a \in A : \mathscr{P}\}$ to $\{a : \mathscr{P}\}$ or $\{\mathscr{P}\}$.

The function λ *is the only element of* $V^{0,0}$ *for which this relation holds. Furthermore*

$$\|F\|_{Z(a)*} = \int_{s \neq a} d|\lambda|(s). \tag{66}$$

Here $|\lambda|$ is an alternative notion for the variation v of λ (cf. (12: 19)).

The interesting part of the above theorem is that λ in $V^{0,0}$ is unique and that (64) and (66) hold. The relation (65) is quite expected.

Before proving the theorem we cite an example. Suppose that

$$\alpha < a < \tilde{\alpha}$$

and consider the particular functional F on Z:

$$Fx \underset{\text{def}}{=} x(\alpha), \qquad x \in Z.$$

Define the function γ as follows:

$$\gamma(s) = \begin{cases} 0, & s \leqq \alpha, \\ 1, & \alpha < s < a, \\ c, & a \leqq s, \end{cases}$$

where c is an arbitrary real constant. Then $\gamma \in V^0$, and

$$\int_{\alpha}^{\tilde{\alpha}} x(s)\, d\gamma(s) = x(\alpha) + (c - 1)x(a) = x(\alpha) = Fx, \qquad x \in Z,$$

since $x(a) = 0$. As c is arbitrary we have here many integral formulas for Fx. If we specify that

$$\gamma \in V^{0,0},$$

then

$$\gamma(\tilde{\alpha}) = 0 = c.$$

According to the above theorem,

$$\gamma = \lambda$$

is then unique. Note also that

$$\|F\|_{Z^*} = 1,$$

by the definition of F. This confirms (66), since

$$\int d|\gamma|(s) = 1 + |c - 1| = 2, \qquad \int_{s \neq a} d|\gamma|(s) = 1.$$

Proof of Theorem 63. *Part* 1. We establish (65) and the fact that $\lambda \in V^{0,0}$. Given the functional F in Z^*, define the functional G on C_0 as follows. For y in C_0, put

$$x(s) = y(s) - y(a),$$

$$Gy = Fx.$$

Then Fx is defined, since $x \in Z$. Hence G is defined on C_0. Clearly G is linear. Now G is bounded on C_0, since

$$|Gy| = |Fx| \leqq \|F\|_{Z^*}\|x\|_Z = \|F\|_{Z^*}\|y(s) - y(a)\|_{C_0} \leqq 2\|F\|_{Z^*}\|y\|_{C_0}.$$

Hence $G \in C_0^*$ and, by Theorem 34,

$$Gy = \int_\alpha^{\tilde{\alpha}} y(s)\, d\lambda(s), \qquad y \in C_0, \tag{67}$$

where

$$\lambda(\tilde{s}) = \begin{cases} \lim\limits_\nu G\theta^\nu(\tilde{s}, s), & \tilde{s} > \alpha, \\ 0, & \tilde{s} \leqq \alpha. \end{cases}$$

It follows that

$$\lambda(\tilde{s}) = \lim_\nu F[\theta^\nu(\tilde{s}, s) - \theta^\nu(\tilde{s}, a)] = \lim_\nu F[-\psi^\nu(a, \tilde{s}, s)], \qquad \tilde{s} > \alpha.$$

This confirms (64). By Theorem 34, λ is well defined and an element of V^0. Furthermore

$$\lambda(\tilde{\alpha}) = \lim_\nu F[-\psi^\nu(a, \tilde{\alpha}, s)] = \lim_\nu F0 = 0,$$

since

$$\psi^\nu(a, \tilde{\alpha}, s) = 0$$

for all s in I, by (62). Hence

$$\lambda \in V^{0,0}.$$

Suppose that $x \in Z$. Put

$$y(s) = x(s), \qquad s \in I.$$

Then $y \in C_0$, and

$$y(s) - y(a) = x(s) - x(a) = x(s);$$

also

$$Fx = Gy = \int_\alpha^{\tilde{\alpha}} x(s)\, d\lambda(s).$$

Thus (65) is established.

Part 2. Uniqueness of λ. Suppose that $\kappa \in V^{0,0}$ and that

$$Fx = \int_\alpha^{\tilde{\alpha}} x(s)\, d\kappa(s), \qquad x \in Z.$$

If $y \in C_0$,

$$Gy = F[y(s) - y(a)] = \int_\alpha^{\tilde{\alpha}} [y(s) - y(a)]\, d\kappa(s) = \int_\alpha^{\tilde{\alpha}} y(s)\, d\kappa(s),$$

since

$$\int_\alpha^{\tilde{\alpha}} d\kappa(s) = \kappa(\tilde{\alpha}) - \kappa(\alpha) = 0 - 0 = 0.$$

Now $\kappa \in V^0$. Hence

$$\kappa = \lambda,$$

since the function λ in (67) is unique in V^0, by Theorem 34. Thus λ is the only element of $V^{0,0}$ for which (65) holds.

Part 3. The norm of F in Z^*. Integrals are to be understood in the sense of Lebesgue-Stieltjes (cf. § 12: 34). The proof will use the fact that $\lambda \in V^0$; it would apply whether $\lambda \in V^{0,0}$ or not.

Because of the vanishing of $x(a)$, (65) implies that

$$Fx = \int_{s \neq a} x(s)\, d\lambda(s), \qquad x \in Z(a).$$

Hence

$$|Fx| \leqq \sup_{s \neq a} |x(s)| \int_{s \neq a} d|\lambda|(s) = \|x\|_Z \int_{s \neq a} d|\lambda|(s), \qquad x \in Z,$$

and

$$\|F\|_{Z^*} \leqq \int_{s \neq a} d|\lambda|(s).$$

To establish (66) it will be sufficient to reverse the last inequality. Assume that

$$\alpha < a < \tilde{\alpha}.$$

(The cases $a = \alpha$ and $a = \tilde{\alpha}$ are treated similarly and more simply.) Let

$$v(\tilde{s}) = |\lambda|\,(\tilde{s}) = \int_{s \leqq \tilde{s}} d|\lambda|(s)$$

be the variation of λ (cf. (12: 19)). Let $\eta > 0$ be given.

Choose numbers α_1 and α_2 such that

$$\alpha < \alpha_1 < a < \alpha_2 < \tilde{\alpha},$$

α_1 and α_2 are points of continuity of $v(\tilde{s})$, and

$$\int_{\substack{\alpha_1 < s < \alpha_2, \\ s \neq a}} d|\lambda|(s) < \eta. \tag{68}$$

This is indeed possible, whether a is a discontinuity of $v(\tilde{s})$ or not, since v is of bounded variation and is continuous except at countably many points and since

$$\int_{\substack{\alpha_1 < s < \alpha_2, \\ s \neq a}} d|\lambda|(s) = \int_{\alpha_1 < s < a} + \int_{a < s < \alpha_2}$$
$$= [v(a - 0) - v(\alpha_1 + 0)] + [v(\alpha_2 - 0) - v(a + 0)],$$

by Theorem 12: 39. For all sufficiently small $\alpha_2 - \alpha_1$ this quantity is surely less than η. Put

$$I^1 = \{\alpha \leqq s \leqq \alpha_1\},$$
$$I^2 = \{\alpha_1 < s < \alpha_2\},$$
$$I^3 = \{\alpha_2 \leqq s \leqq \tilde{\alpha}\}.$$

Then I^1, I^2, I^3 are a subdivision of I into mutually exclusive intervals, I^1, I^3 are closed, and I^2 is open and contains a.

Consider the functionals H^1 and H^3 defined as

$$H^1x = \int_{I^1} x(s)\, d\lambda(s), \qquad H^3x = \int_{I^3} x(s)\, d\lambda(s).$$

The integrals here may equivalently be considered as Riemann or Lebesgue integrals whenever the integrands are continuous, since, by construction, λ behaves appropriately on the boundaries of I^1 and I^3:

$$\lambda(\alpha_1 + 0) = \lambda(\alpha_1),$$
$$\lambda(\alpha - 0) = \lambda(\alpha);$$
$$\lambda(\tilde{\alpha} + 0) = \lambda(\tilde{\alpha}),$$
$$\lambda(\alpha_2 - 0) = \lambda(\alpha_2).$$

The first three relations here follow from the mere fact that $\lambda \in V^0$; the fourth from the fact that α_2 is a continuity of λ.

Now H^1 defines an element of $C_0(I^1)^*$ and λ is normalized relative to I^1, since the lower boundary of I^1 is α. Hence by (37),

$$\|H^1\|_{C_0(I^1)^*} = \int_{I^1} d|\lambda|(s).$$

An alternative form for H^3 is

$$H^3x = \int_{I^3} x(s)\, d[\lambda(s) - \lambda(\alpha_2)],$$

since $\lambda(\alpha_2)$ is a constant. Now H^3 defines an element of $C_0(I^3)^*$ and $\lambda(s) - \lambda(\alpha_2)$ is normalized relative to I^3. Hence by (37) and (12: 17),

$$\|H^3\|_{C_0(I^3)^*} = \int_{I^3} d[|\lambda|(s) - |\lambda|(\alpha_2)] = \int_{I^3} d|\lambda|(s).$$

It follows from the definition (11) of the norm of a functional that functions z^1 and z^3 exist such that

$$\int_{I^j} z^j(s)\, d\lambda(s) > \int_{I^j} d|\lambda|(s) - \eta,$$

$$z^j \in C_0(I^j),$$

$$\|z^j\|_{C_0(I^j)} = 1, \qquad j = 1 \text{ and } 3.$$

Let z be the function on

$$I = I^1 \cup I^2 \cup I^3$$

defined as follows:

$$z(s) = \begin{cases} z^j(s) & \text{if } s \in I^j,\ j = 1 \text{ and } 3, \\ 0 & \text{if } s = a, \\ \text{linear on} & \alpha_1 \leqq s \leqq a, \\ \text{linear on} & a \leqq s \leqq \alpha_2. \end{cases}$$

Then

$$z \in Z(a)$$

and

$$\|z\|_{Z(a)} = \|z\|_{C_0(I)} = 1.$$

Furthermore

$$\begin{aligned} Fz &= \int_{s \neq a} z(s)\, d\lambda(s) = \int_{I^1} + \int_{I^3} + \int_{I^2-\{a\}} \\ &> \int_{I^1} d|\lambda| - \eta + \int_{I^3} d|\lambda| - \eta + \int_{I^2-\{a\}} z\, d\lambda \\ &= \int_{I-\{a\}} d|\lambda| - 2\eta + \int_{I^2-\{a\}} [z\, d\lambda - d|\lambda|] \\ &> \int_{s \neq a} d|\lambda| - 4\eta = \left[\int_{s \neq a} d|\lambda| - 4\eta\right] \|z\|_{Z(a)}, \end{aligned}$$

since, by (68),

$$\left|\int_{I^2-\{a\}} z\, d\lambda\right| \leqq \int_{I^2-\{a\}} d|\lambda| < \eta.$$

As $\eta > 0$ was arbitrary, it follows that

$$\|F\|_{Z(a)*} \geqq \int_{s \neq a} d|\lambda|.$$

This completes the proof of the theorem.

§ 69. **Taylor operators.** In dealing with Taylor formulas it is advantageous to introduce the *Taylor operator*

$$T = T_s$$

defined as follows. Let a be a given fixed real number. For a function x of the real variable s,

$$Tx = T_s x = T_s[x(s)] = \int_a^s x(\tilde{s})\, d\tilde{s}.$$

Thus T acts on its argument as a function of s: s is replaced by $\tilde{s}$ and the result is integrated with respect to $d\tilde{s}$ from a to s. The image Tx is surely defined if $x \in C_0(I)$ and $a, s \in I$.

We define powers of T in the usual way:

$$T^0 = \text{identity};$$

$$T^{i+1} = TT^i, \qquad i = 0, 1, \cdots.$$

70. Lemma. *The operator T is linear. Also*

(71) $$T^i[x(s)] = \int_a^s (s - \tilde{s})^{(i-1)} x(\tilde{s})\, d\tilde{s} \qquad \textit{if } i \geqq 1;$$

(72) $$T^i[x(a)] = (s - a)^{(i)} x(a);$$

(73) $$T^{i+j} = T^i T^j, \qquad i, j = 0, 1, \cdots.$$

Proof. That T is linear is a fundamental property of integration. The relation (73) holds for iterations T^i of any operator T, providing merely that Tx is in the domain of definition of T whenever x is. For example, consider T^3:

$$T^3 x = TT^2 x = Tz,$$

where

$$z = Ty, \qquad y = Tx.$$

Now

$$T^2 Tx = T^2 y = TTy = Tz.$$

Thus

$$TT^2 = T^2 T.$$

To establish (71) one may proceed by induction, in several ways. One way is the following. For $i = 1$, (71) reduces to the definition. Assume (71) for $i = i_0 \geqq 1$. Then, by (73) and integration by parts,

$$\begin{aligned} T^{i_0+1}[x(s)] &= T^{i_0} T[x(s)] = T^{i_0} \int_a^s dt x(t) = \int_a^s du (s - u)^{(i_0 - 1)} \int_a^u dt x(t) \\ &= \left[-(s - u)^{(i_0)} \int_a^u dt x(t) \right]_{u=a}^s + \int_a^s du (s - u)^{(i_0)} x(u) \\ &= \int_a^s du (s - u)^{(i_0)} x(u). \end{aligned}$$

Thus (71) is established for $i = i_0 + 1$.

Finally (72) follows from (71), since

$$\begin{aligned} T^i[x(a)] &= \int_a^s (s - \tilde{s})^{(i-1)} x(a)\, d\tilde{s} = x(a) \int_a^s (s - \tilde{s})^{(i-1)}\, d\tilde{s} \\ &= x(a)(s - a)^{(i)}, \qquad i > 0. \end{aligned}$$

This completes the proof, since (72) is certainly true for $i = 0$.

As is customary,

$$D = D_s$$

will indicate differentiation with respect to s; and

$$\delta^{j,\,i} = \begin{cases} 1 & \text{if } j = i, \\ 0 & \text{otherwise.} \end{cases}$$

74. LEMMA. *Suppose that x is a function of s. If $x(a)$ is defined,*

$$D^j T^i x(a) = \begin{cases} T^{i-j} x(a) & \text{if } j \leqq i, \\ 0 & \text{if } j > i, \end{cases} \tag{75}$$

and

$$[D^j T^i x(a)]_{s=a} = x(a)\delta^{j,\,i}. \tag{76}$$

If $x(s)$ is integrable,

$$[T^i x(s)]_{s=a} = 0, \qquad i > 0. \tag{77}$$

If $x(s)$ is continuous,

$$\begin{aligned} DTx &= x, \\ D^i T^i x &= x. \end{aligned} \tag{78}$$

PROOF. The relations (75) and (76) are immediate consequences of (72). The relation (77) is an immediate consequence of (71). That

$$DTx = x$$

if x is continuous is a fundamental property of integration. Finally

$$D^i T^i = D \cdots D\, T \cdots T, \qquad i > 0,$$

and therefore is the identity. This completes the proof.

As regards Lemma 74, we may say that

$$T^i x(s), \qquad i > 0,$$

is nullified by the substitution $s = a$; that

$$D^j T^i x(a), \qquad j < i,$$

is nullified by the substitution $s = a$; and that

$$D^j T^i x(a), \qquad j > i,$$

is null by overdifferentiation.

79. THEOREM (TAYLOR FORMULA). *If*

$$x \in C_n(I), \qquad n \geqq 0,$$

then

$$x(s) = \sum_{i<n} T^i x_i(a) + T^n x_n(s) = \sum_{i<n} (s - a)^{(i)} x_i(a) + T^n x_n(s), \qquad s \in I. \tag{80}$$

PROOF. The formula is correct for $n = 0$. Also for $n = 1$, since

$$x_0(a) + Tx_1(s) = x_0(a) + \int_a^s x_1(t)\,dt = x(s), \qquad x \in C_1.$$

The formula then follows by iteration:

$$\begin{aligned} x(s) &= x_0(a) + Tx_1(s) = x_0(a) + T[x_1(a) + Tx_2(s)] \\ &= x_0(a) + Tx_1(a) + T^2x_2(s) = x_0(a) + Tx_1(a) + T^2[x_2(a) + Tx_3(s)], \end{aligned}$$

and so on.

REMARK. Thus far it has not been notably simpler to use T than it would have been to avoid T. One minor advantage, which will become important, is that (80) holds for $n \geqq 0$, whereas the integral formula (46) holds only for $n \geqq 1$. Other advantages will appear later.

The definition (41) of λ in Theorem 39 may be written

$$(81) \qquad \lambda(\bar{s}) = \begin{cases} \lim\limits_{\nu} FT^n\theta^\nu(\bar{s}, s) & \textit{if } \bar{s} > \alpha, \\ 0 & \textit{otherwise}; \end{cases}$$

by (71). This permits us to remove the restriction $n \geqq 1$ in Theorem 39, since (81) with $n = 0$ reduces to (35). Thus if (41) is replaced by (81), then n may equal 0 in Theorem 39 and Theorem 39 includes Theorem 34.

§ 82. **The operator** δ. We define the operator

$$\delta = \delta_s$$

as follows. For a function x of the real variable s,

$$(83) \qquad \delta x = \delta_s x = x(s) - x(a).$$

Thus the operator δ like the operator T depends on a. If $x \in C_0(I)$, then

$$(84) \qquad \delta x \in Z(a),$$

since δx vanishes when $s = a$. If $x \in Z(a)$, then

$$\delta x = x.$$

In any case,

$$(85) \qquad \delta^2 = \delta.$$

We have seen that $Tx \in Z(a)$ whenever x is integrable. Hence

$$(86) \qquad \delta T = T.$$

Of course

$$(87) \qquad D\delta = D.$$

Finally, if $x \in C_1$, then

$$TDx = \delta x$$

and

$$(88) \qquad TD = \delta.$$

§ 89. **The spaces B_n and K_n.** These are instances of the spaces B, K, which we shall study later. We assume that

$$a \in I.$$

The *space*

$$B_n = B_n(I\,;a)$$

is defined as precisely $C_n(I\,;a)$; with the same norm. The space $\boldsymbol{B}_n$ is defined as the space $\boldsymbol{C}_n$.

For $n > 1$, the *space*

$$K_n = K_n(I\,;a)$$

is defined as the space $C_{n-1}(I\,;a)$, with the norm

$$(90)\quad \|x\|_{K_n} = \max\left[|x_0(a)|, |x_1(a)|, \cdots, |x_{n-1}(a)|\,; \sup_{s \in I} |\delta x_{n-1}(s)|\right], \qquad x \in K_n = C_{n-1}.$$

Now

$$x_{n-1}(s) = x_{n-1}(a) + \delta x_{n-1}(s),$$

and therefore

$$|x_{n-1}(s)| \leqq |x_{n-1}(a)| + |\delta x_{n-1}(s)|,$$

$$|\delta_{n-1}(s)| \leqq |x_{n-1}(s)| + |x_{n-1}(a)|, \qquad s \in I, \quad x \in K_n.$$

Hence, by (6),

$$\|x\|_{C_{n-1}} \leqq 2\|x\|_{K_n} \leqq 4\|x\|_{C_{n-1}}, \qquad x \in K_n\,;$$

and the norms $\|x\|_{C_{n-1}}$ and $\|x\|_{K_n}$ are equivalent. The space K_n is therefore essentially the same as C_{n-1}.

We assume for the rest of the chapter that

$$n \geqq 1.$$

91. Expansion theorem. *If $x \in K_n$, then*

$$(92)\quad \begin{aligned} x(s) &= \sum_{i<n} T^i x_i(a) + T^{n-1}\,\delta x_{n-1}(s) \\ &= \sum_{i<n} (s-a)^{(i)} x_i(a) + T^{n-1}\,\delta x_{n-1}(s), \qquad s \in I. \end{aligned}$$

Proof. By (80) with n replaced by $n-1$,

$$x(s) = \sum_{i<n-1} T^i x_i(a) + T^{n-1} x_{n-1}(s), \qquad s \in I.$$

Now

$$T^{n-1}\,\delta x_{n-1}(s) = T^{n-1}[x_{n-1}(s) - x_{n-1}(a)],$$

$$T^{n-1}x_{n-1}(s) = T^{n-1}x_{n-1}(a) + T^{n-1}\,\delta x_{n-1}(s).$$

The relation (92) follows, and the proof is complete.

The next theorem provides a representation for elements of K_n^* and their norms. The theorem is in part a repetition of Theorem 39 with n replaced by $n - 1$. Since the norms $\|x\|_{K_n}$ and $\|x\|_{C_{n-1}}$ are not identical, the norms $\|F\|_{K_n^*}$ and $\|F\|_{C_{n-1}^*}$ are not identical. The functions ψ^ν, defined in (62), are a sequence which converges to the step function ψ.

93. Mass theorem. *Suppose that $F \in K_n^*$. Put*

$$c^i = F[(s - a)^{(i)}], \qquad i < n; \tag{94}$$

$$\lambda(\tilde{s}) = \begin{cases} \lim_{\nu} FT^{n-1}\psi^\nu(a, \tilde{s}, s) & \text{if } \tilde{s} > \alpha, \\ 0 & \text{otherwise.} \end{cases} \tag{95}$$

Then λ is well defined and an element of $V^{0,0}$, and

$$Fx = \sum_{i<n} c^i x_i(a) - \int_\alpha^{\tilde{\alpha}} x_{n-1}(s)\,d\lambda(s), \qquad x \in K_n. \tag{96}$$

Furthermore λ is the only element of $V^{0,0}$ and c^i, $i < n$, are the only constants for which the last relation holds. Also

$$\|F\|_{K_n^*} = \sum_{i<n} |c^i| + \int_{s \neq a} d|\lambda|(s). \tag{97}$$

Proof. The proof is similar to that of Theorem 39, with n replaced by $n - 1$, but we use Theorem 63 instead of Theorem 34 and Theorem 91 instead of Theorem 79.

Part 1. Existence and properties of λ. Define the functional G on $Z(a)$ as

$$Gy = FT^{n-1}y(s), \qquad y \in Z(a). \tag{98}$$

For $y \in Z(a)$, the argument of F in (98) is an element of K_n, with norm

$$\|T^{n-1}y(s)\|_{K_n} = \max\,[0, 0, \cdots, 0; \sup_{s \in I} |y(s)|] = \|y\|_Z,$$

by (90), by (77), and the fact that $y(a) = 0$. Hence Gy is defined and

$$|Gy| \leqq \|F\|_{K_n^*}\|y\|_Z.$$

Since G is linear, it follows that

$$G \in Z^*.$$

By Theorem 63,

$$Gy = -\int_\alpha^{\tilde{\alpha}} y(s)\, d\lambda(s),$$

where

$$\lambda \in V^{0,0},$$

$$\lambda(\tilde{s}) = \begin{cases} \lim_\nu G\psi^\nu(a, \tilde{s}, s) = \lim_\nu FT^{n-1}\psi^\nu(a, \tilde{s}, s) & \text{if } \tilde{s} > \alpha, \\ 0 & \text{otherwise;} \end{cases}$$

and

$$\|G\|_{Z^*} = \int_{s \neq a} d|\lambda|(s).$$

Note that for each fixed $\tilde{s}$,

$$\psi^\nu(a, \tilde{s}, s) \in Z(a),$$

by (62). The function λ just defined is precisely that in (95).

Part 2. We establish (96) and the fact that c^i, $i < n$, and λ in $V^{0,0}$ are unique. Consider an element x of K_n. By Theorem 91

$$x(s) = \sum_{i<n} (s - a)^{(i)} x_i(a) + T^{n-1}\delta x_{n-1}(s).$$

Now

$$\delta x_{n-1}(s) \in Z(a),$$

since $x \in K_n$. Hence

$$Fx = \sum_{i<n} x_i(a) F[(s - a)^{(i)}] + G\delta x_{n-1} = \sum_{i<n} c^i x_i(a) + G\delta x_{n-1}.$$

Furthermore

$$G\delta x_{n-1} = -\int_\alpha^{\tilde{\alpha}} \delta x_{n-1}(s)\, d\lambda(s) = -\int_\alpha^{\tilde{\alpha}} x_{n-1}(s)\, d\lambda(s),$$

since

$$\lambda(\tilde{\alpha}) = \lambda(\alpha) = 0$$

because $\lambda \in V^{0,0}$. The minus sign here is due to our use of (95) as written, without the minus sign of (64).

The uniqueness is established as before: the uniqueness of c^i, $i < n$, is immediate; the uniqueness of the present λ is based on that of the λ in Theorem 63.

Part 3. The norm of F in K_n^*. We establish (97) as before, using (66) instead of (37).

This completes our discussion of the proof of the present theorem.

99. Corollary (Kernel theorem). *Suppose that $F \in K_n^*$. Define c^i, $i < n$, by (94) and λ by (95). Then*

$$(100) \qquad Fx = \sum_{i<n} c^i x_i(a) + \int_I x_n(s)\lambda(s)\,ds$$

for all x in $\boldsymbol{B}_n$.

Note that

$$B_n \subset \boldsymbol{B}_n \subset K_n.$$

Hence (100) holds a fortiori for all x in B_n. The relation (100) need not hold for x in K_n, because x_n need not then exist.

Proof of corollary. We merely transform the last term of (96) by integration by parts. Thus if $x \in \boldsymbol{B}_n$,

$$-\int_a^{\tilde{a}} x_{n-1}(s)\,d\lambda(s) = 0 + \int_a^{\tilde{a}} \lambda(s)\,dx_{n-1}(s) = \int_a^{\tilde{a}} x_n(s)\lambda(s)\,ds,$$

since $\lambda \in V^{0,0}$ and x_{n-1} is absolutely continuous on I (cf. Lemma 12: 46). This proves the corollary.

For the present case of functions of one variable, Corollary 99 may alternatively be derived from Theorem 39 with n replaced by $n - 1$.

It is interesting to compare Corollary 99 and Theorem 1: 8 with

$$\kappa = \lambda.$$

The two results include the same formula (100).

Corollary 99 is deeper than Theorem 1: 8 in that its hypothesis

$$(101) \qquad F \in C_{n-1}^* = K_n^*$$

refers to intrinsic properties of F. The hypothesis

$$(102) \qquad F \in \mathscr{C}_{n-1}^* \underset{\text{def}}{=} \mathscr{K}_n^*$$

in Theorem 1: 8 specifies that Fx be given as a sum of Stieltjes integrals on $x_0(s), \cdots, x_{n-1}(s)$. Since the hypothesis (101) is weaker than (102), the formula (95) is more complicated than (1: 11). The fact that (95) is unambiguous whereas (1: 11) has countably many exceptions is of little importance.

Theorem 1: 8 is not obsolete, since its hypothesis is often valid and since it gives κ in as simple a way as possible.

The hypothesis of Theorem 1: 8 implies that we may permute

$$F \quad \text{and} \quad \lim_{\nu}$$

in (95) if

$$\tilde{s} \notin \mathscr{I}_{F,n-1},$$

where $\mathscr{J}_{F,n-1}$ is the jump set of F, since

(103) $$\lim_\nu T^{n-1}\psi^\nu(a, \tilde{s}, s) = (s - \tilde{s})^{(n-1)}\psi(a, \tilde{s}, s).$$

To establish this relation, note that it is immediate if $n = 1$. If $n > 1$, then

$$\begin{aligned}\lim_\nu T^{n-1}\psi^\nu(a, \tilde{s}, s) &= \lim_\nu \int_a^s (s - t)^{(n-2)}\psi^\nu(a, \tilde{s}, t)\,dt \\ &= \int_a^s (s - t)^{(n-2)} \lim_\nu \psi^\nu(a, \tilde{s}, t)\,dt \\ &= \int_a^s (s - t)^{(n-2)}\psi(a, \tilde{s}, t)\,dt = (s - \tilde{s})^{(n-1)}\psi(a, \tilde{s}, s),\end{aligned}$$

by equation (11 : 18) or (11 : 19).

CHAPTER 4

Functionals in Terms of Partial Derivatives

§ 1. **Introduction.** Theorem 8 of Chapter 1 gives a formula for Fx, where $F \in \mathscr{C}_{n-1}^*$ and $x \in \boldsymbol{C}_n$ As we have seen, the formula has many applications in the theory of approximation.

The present chapter establishes the analogous theorem for functions of two variables. The theorem refers to a pair $\mathscr{K}^*$, $\boldsymbol{B}$ of spaces. There are many such pairs. In each, $\mathscr{K}^*$ plays the rôle of $\mathscr{C}_{n-1}^*$ and $\boldsymbol{B}$ the rôle of $\boldsymbol{C}_n$ in Theorem 1 : 8.

It is the definitions of the spaces which provide the key to the analysis. Our theorems and their applications (in Chapter 5) constitute evidence that the spaces are natural and powerful tools. The principal results of the present chapter are Theorems 36 and 84 [Sard 5; 6; 13].

For some applications it is sufficient to consider only a few individual spaces $\mathscr{K}^*$, $\boldsymbol{B}$ and to replace our general proofs by their counterparts for the particular cases.

§ 2. **The space $B_{p,q}$.** The spaces that we consider are related to a given interval I of the s, t-plane and a given point (a, b) of I. We write

$$I = I_s \times I_t; \qquad I_s = \{\alpha \leqq s \leqq \tilde{\alpha}\}, \quad I_t = \{\beta \leqq t \leqq \tilde{\beta}\}.$$

Then

$$a \in I_s, \qquad b \in I_t.$$

We assume that

$$-\infty < \alpha < \tilde{\alpha} < \infty, \qquad -\infty < \beta < \tilde{\beta} < \infty.$$

Let p and q be given nonnegative integers. Put

$$n = p + q.$$

The *space*

$$B_{p,q} = B_{p,q}(a, b) = B_{p,q}(I; a, b)$$

is defined as the space of functions x on I to R such that the derivatives

$$x_{p,q}(s, t), \qquad (s, t) \in I;$$

(3) $$x_{n-j,j}(s, b), \quad s \in I_s; \qquad j < q;$$

$$x_{i,n-i}(a, t), \quad t \in I_t; \qquad i < p;$$

exist and are continuous, where $x_{i,j}$ is understood as

$$(4)\qquad x_{i,j} = D_t^{j-j_0} D_s^i D_t^{j_0} x, \qquad j_0 = \min(j, q),$$

and

$$D_s = \frac{\partial}{\partial s}, \qquad D_t = \frac{\partial}{\partial t}.$$

Thus the differentiations in $x_{i,j}$ with respect to t, if any, are to be executed first up to q times. Then the differentiations with respect to s, if any. Then the remaining differentiations, if any, with respect to t.

We call the derivatives (3) the *core* of x in $B_{r,q}$ and the derivative $x_{p,q}$ the *pivot*. The core consists of one function on I, q functions on I_s, and p functions on I_t. Each element of the core is a derivative of order n. The pivot $x_{p,q}$ is the only derivative of order n which is required to exist everywhere on I, when $x \in B_{p,q}$; the derivatives in the core other than the pivot are required to exist on the segment

$$s = a, \qquad t \in I_t,$$

or its dual.

The space $B_{p,q}$ of functions of two variables is a generalization of the space C_n of functions of one variable.

By the *complete core* ω of x in $B_{p,q}$ we mean the derivatives (3) together with the values

$$(5)\qquad x_{i,j}(a, b), \qquad i + j < n,$$

taken on by the derivatives of x of order $< n$ at (a, b). The derivatives (5) are to be understood according to the rule (4). We shall see later that ω constitutes a set of coordinates for x in $B_{p,q}$. The letter ω, being the last in the Greek alphabet, may suggest completeness.

To illustrate consider $B_{2,1}$. Here $n = 3$. The core is

$$x_{2,1}(s, t) = D_s^2 D_t x, \qquad x_{3,0}(s, b),$$

$$x_{1,2}(a, t) = D_t D_s D_t x, \qquad x_{0,3}(a, t).$$

The complete core ω consists of these derivatives together with

$$x_{0,0}(a, b), \quad x_{1,0}(a, b), \quad x_{0,1}(a, b), \quad x_{2,0}(a, b),$$

$$x_{1,1}(a, b) = D_t D_s x \,|_{(s,t)=(a,b)}, \quad x_{0,2}(a, b).$$

Another example is $B_{2,0}$. Here $n = 2$. The core is

$$x_{2,0}(s, t), \qquad x_{1,1}(a, t) = D_s D_t x \,|_{(s,t)=(a,t)}, \quad x_{0,2}(a, t).$$

The order of differentiation in $x_{1,1}$ is determined by the fact that $q = 0$. The complete core ω consists of the above derivatives together with

$$x_{0,0}(a, b), \quad x_{1,0}(a, b), \quad x_{0,1}(a, b).$$

In considering $B_{p,q}$ it is helpful to construct a diagram of derivatives as follows. Represent $x_{i,j}$ by the point (i,j) of an i,j-plane. Differentiation with respect to s then corresponds to a move of one unit parallel to the i-axis, and similarly for D_t. The origin represents the function $x = x_{0,0}$ itself. The connecting lines in our diagrams (at the end of the chapter) indicate permissible differentiations. We sometimes write the arguments of $x_{i,j}$ at the point (i,j). Figure 1 includes diagrams of ω in $B_{2,3}$, $B_{2,0}$.

Consider $B_{p,q}$. The order of differentiation in each element of the complete core ω has been prescribed by (4). We describe (4) as the *rule of ω in $B_{p,q}$*. We shall see later that other orders of differentiation of elements of $B_{p,q}$ are permissible and equivalent to those of the rule of ω.

In the diagram of $B_{p,q}$, the rule of ω amounts to the following. A differentiation is to be executed by moving first along the j-axis up to q steps, thereafter parallel to the i-axis the appropriate number of steps, thereafter parallel to the j-axis the appropriate number of steps.

The space $B_{p,q}$ is an instance of spaces of type B to be considered in § 49. A reader may prefer to proceed directly to the more general B rather than to continue with $B_{p,q}$ as we now do.

§ 6. **Taylor formulas.** Any element x of $B_{p,q}$ may be expanded in terms of its complete core ω; and the elements of ω are independent of one another and arbitrary except for conditions of continuity. To establish these facts we shall use the *Taylor operators* T_s and T_t. The operator T_s, defined in § 3 : 69, acts on its argument as a function of s. The operator T_t is the dual of T_s, obtained by replacing s by t and a by b. Thus

$$T_t x(s, t) = \int_b^t x(s, \tilde{t}) \, d\tilde{t},$$

$$T_t x(s, b) = \int_b^t x(s, b) \, d\tilde{t} = (t - b)x(s, b),$$

$$T_s T_t x(s, t) = \int_a^s d\tilde{s} \int_b^t x(\tilde{s}, \tilde{t}) \, d\tilde{t}.$$

7. LEMMA. *The operations in*

$$T_s^i T_t^j x(s, t)$$

may be executed in any order, if x is integrable.

PROOF. By Fubini's Theorem,

$$T_s T_t x = T_t T_s x.$$

The lemma follows by iteration. This completes the proof.

Under certain hypotheses, Leibnitz' rule

$$D_s T_t = T_t D_s$$

is valid. We will not use Leibnitz' rule, however.

As some of the following proofs will be long, the reader may prefer to consider the case $B_{2,1}$, which illustrates most of the ideas.

8. THEOREM (TAYLOR FORMULA). *If $x \in B_{p,q}$, then*

$$
\begin{aligned}
x(s,t) &= \sum_{i+j<n} T_s^i T_t^j x_{i,j}(a,b) + \sum_{j<q} T_s^{n-j} T_t^j x_{n-j,j}(s,b) \\
&\quad + \sum_{i<p} T_s^i T_t^{n-i} x_{i,n-i}(a,t) + T_s^p T_t^q x_{p,q}(s,t) \\
&= \sum_{i+j<n} (s-a)^{(i)}(t-b)^{(j)} x_{i,j}(a,b) + \sum_{j<q} (t-b)^{(j)} T_s^{n-j} x_{n-j,j}(s,b) \\
&\quad + \sum_{i<p} (s-a)^{(i)} T_t^{n-i} x_{i,n-i}(a,t) + T_s^p T_t^q x_{p,q}(s,t), \qquad (s,t) \in I.
\end{aligned} \tag{9}
$$

PROOF. Suppose that $x \in B_{p,q}$ and $(s, t) \in I$. By Theorem 3 : 79 and the rule of ω,

$$x(s,t) = \sum_{j<q} T_t^j x_{0,j}(s,b) + T_t^q x_{0,q}(s,t),$$

$$x_{0,q}(s,t) = \sum_{i<p} T_s^i x_{i,q}(a,t) + T_s^p x_{p,q}(s,t).$$

Hence

$$x(s,t) = \sum_{j<q} T_t^j x_{0,j}(s,b) + \sum_{i<p} T_t^q T_s^i x_{i,q}(a,t) + T_t^q T_s^p\, x_{p,q}(s,t).$$

By Theorem 3: 79 and the rule of ω again,

$$x_{0,j}(s,b) = \sum_{i<n-j} T_s^i x_{i,j}(a,b) + T_s^{n-j} x_{n-j,j}(s,b), \qquad j < q;$$

$$x_{i,q}(a,t) = \sum_{q \leqq j < n-i} T_t^{j-q} x_{i,j}(a,b) + T_t^{n-i-q} x_{i,n-i}(a,t), \qquad i < p.$$

Hence

$$
\begin{aligned}
x(s,t) &= \sum_{\substack{j<q,\\ j<n-i}} T_t^j T_s^i x_{i,j}(a,b) + \sum_{j<q} T_t^j T_s^{n-j} x_{n-j,j}(s,b) \\
&\quad + \sum_{\substack{i<p,\\ q \leqq j<n-i}} T_t^q T_s^i T_t^{j-q} x_{i,j}(a,b) \\
&\quad + \sum_{i<p} T_t^q T_s^i T_t^{n-i-q} x_{i,n-i}(a,t) + T_t^q T_s^p x_{p,q}(s,t).
\end{aligned} \tag{10}
$$

Now the operators T_s, T_t commute (Lemma 7). Also the sets

$$\{(i,j) : j < q \quad \text{and} \quad j < n - i\}$$

and

$$\{(i,j) : q \leqq j < n - i \quad \text{and} \quad i < p\}$$

of pairs of indices are nonoverlapping and together constitute the set

$$\{(i, j) : i + j < n\},$$

since indices are understood to be nonnegative integers unless the contrary is stated. Hence (10) reduces to (9) and the proof is complete.

The complete core ω of x in $B_{p,q}$ is of course determined by x. Conversely (9) shows that x is completely determined by ω. Furthermore, as we will show in the following corollary, the elements of ω are independent of one another. Each element of ω is completely arbitrary, except for the condition of being continuous in its variables if any.

11. COROLLARY. *Suppose that*

$$c^{i,j}, \quad i + j < n,$$

are $n(n+1)/2$ *arbitrary constants; that*

$$y^{n-j,j}(s), \quad j < q,$$

are q *arbitrary continuous functions on* I_s; *that*

$$y^{i,n-i}(t), \quad i < p,$$

are p *arbitrary continuous functions on* I_t; *and that* $y^{p,q}(s, t)$ *is an arbitrary continuous function on* I. *Put*

$$\begin{aligned} z(s, t) = &\sum_{i+j<n} T_s^i T_t^j c^{i,j} + \sum_{j<q} T_s^{n-j} T_t^j y^{n-j,j}(s) \\ &+ \sum_{i<p} T_s^i T_t^{n-i} y^{i,n-i}(t) + T_s^p T_t^q y^{p,q}(s, t), \qquad (s, t) \in I. \end{aligned} \tag{12}$$

Then

$$z \in B_{p,q};$$

and the given elements constitute the complete core ω *of* z *in* $B_{p,q}$; *that is,*

$$\begin{aligned} z_{i,j}(a, b) &= c^{i,j} && i + j < n; \\ z_{n-j,j}(s, b) &= y^{n-j,j}(s), && s \in I_s, \quad j < q; \\ z_{i,n-i}(a, t) &= y^{i,n-i}(t), && t \in I_t, \quad i < p; \\ z_{p,q}(s, t) &= y^{p,q}(s, t), && (s, t) \in I. \end{aligned} \tag{13}$$

The superscripts in $c^{i,j}$ and $y^{i,j}$ serve merely to distinguish different entities.

PROOF. We will establish (13) by differentiating (12) according to the rule of ω. It will follow that $z \in B_{p,q}$, because the functions $y^{i,j}$ in (13) are continuous on I_s, I_t, I, respectively, by hypothesis.

We continue to use the notation

$$(14)\qquad (s-a)^{(m)} = \begin{cases} (s-a)^m/m! & \text{if } m = 1, 2, 3, \cdots; \\ 1 & \text{if } m = 0; \\ 0 & \text{if } m = -1, -2, -3, \cdots. \end{cases}$$

The relation (12) for z may be written

$$(15)\qquad \begin{aligned} z(s,t) = {} & \sum_{i+j<n} c^{i,j}(s-a)^{(i)}(t-b)^{(j)} + \sum_{j<q} (t-b)^{(j)} T_s^{n-j} y^{n-j,j}(s) \\ & + \sum_{i<p} (s-a)^{(i)} T_t^{n-i} y^{i,n-i}(t) + T_s^p T_t^q y^{p,q}(s,t), \end{aligned}$$

by (3 : 72). The polynomial in this expansion may be differentiated in any fashion. A term which contains T_s^ν may be differentiated with respect to s up to ν times. The crux of the proof is that whenever such a term is differentiated more than ν times, the differentiation is carried out only after the term has been nullified by some other operation.

We now calculate the complete core of z.

Part 1. Consider the partial derivative

$$z_{i_0,j_0} = D_s^{i_0} D_t^{j_0} z,$$

where

$$i_0 \leqq p, \qquad j_0 \leqq q.$$

We see from (15) that

$$(16)\qquad \begin{aligned} z_{i_0,j_0}(s,t) = {} & \sum_{i+j<n} c^{i,j}(s-a)^{(i-i_0)}(t-b)^{(j-j_0)} \\ & + \sum_{j<q} (t-b)^{(j-j_0)} T_s^{n-j-i_0} y^{n-j,j}(s) \\ & + \sum_{i<p} (s-a)^{(i-i_0)} T_t^{n-i-j_0} y^{i,n-i}(t) + T_s^{p-i_0} T_t^{q-j_0} y^{p,q}(s,t), \end{aligned}$$

since the exponents of T_s and T_t herein are all nonnegative. In the second summation, for example, $j < q$. Hence

$$n - j > n - q = p \geqq i_0 \quad \text{and} \quad n - j - i_0 \geqq 0.$$

In particular, if $i_0 = p$, $j_0 = q$, then

$$z_{p,q}(s,t) = y^{p,q}(s,t),$$

since $(s-a)^{(i-i_0)}$ or $(t-b)^{(j-j_0)}$ or both will vanish and hence all terms in (16) will vanish except

$$T_s^{p-i_0} T_t^{q-j_0} y^{p,q}(s,t) = y^{p,q}(s,t).$$

Also, if $i_0 + j_0 < n$, then

$$z_{i_0,j_0}(a, b) = c^{i_0,j_0},$$

since

$$[(s - a)^{(i-i_0)}]_{s=a} = \delta^{i,i_0} \tag{17}$$

by (14) and since all terms in (16) that contain an operator T_s or T_t will vanish by (3: 77).

Thus the last line of (13) and part of the first line of (13) are established.

Part 2. Suppose that

$$i_0 > p, \qquad i_0 + j_0 \leqq n.$$

Then

$$j_0 \leqq n - i_0 < n - p = q;$$

and

$$z_{i_0,j_0}(s, b) = D_s^{i_0} z_{0,j_0}(s, b)$$

by the rule of ω. Hence, by (16) with $i_0 = 0$, (17), and (3: 77),

$$z_{0,j_0}(s, b) = \sum_{i<n-j_0} c^{i,j_0}(s - a)^{(i)} + T_s^{n-j_0} y^{n-j_0,j_0}(s),$$

since the exponents of T_t in (16) now are positive. Thus $i < p$ implies that

$$n - i - j_0 > n - p - j_0 = q - j_0 > 0.$$

Hence

$$z_{i_0,j_0}(s, b) = \sum_{i<n-j_0} c^{i,j_0}(s - a)^{(i-i_0)} + T_s^{n-i_0-j_0} y^{n-j_0,j_0}(s). \tag{18}$$

Observe that we have made essential use of the rule of ω.

In particular, if $i_0 = n - j_0$,

$$z_{n-j_0,j_0}(s, b) = y^{n-j_0,j_0}(s),$$

since $i < n - j_0$ then implies that

$$i - i_0 = i - n + j_0 < 0$$

in (18).

Also, if $i_0 + j_0 < n$,

$$z_{i_0,j_0}(a, b) = c^{i_0,j_0},$$

by (18) and (3: 77).

Thus the second line of (13) and another part of the first line are established.

Part 3. Suppose that

$$j_0 > q, \qquad i_0 + j_0 \leqq n.$$

Then

$$i_0 \leqq p$$

and

$$z_{i_0,j_0}(a, t) = D_t^{j_0-q} z_{i_0,q}(a, t),$$

according to the rule of ω. The treatment is similar to that of Part 2, but not exactly the same, since the rule of ω is not symmetric vis à vis s and t. We omit the details.

Thus the corollary is proved.

We may think of the complete core ω of x in $B_{p,q}$ as a set of coordinates for x. Since the components of ω enter in (12) in a linear fashion, $B_{p,q}$ is the direct product of:

$n(n+1)/2$ real lines (one for each $c^{i,j}$, $i + j < n$);

$p + q = n$ spaces C_0 of functions of one variable, continuous on a compact linear interval; and

1 space of functions of two variables, continuous on a compact two-dimensional interval.

In addition to the core and the complete core of x in $B_{p,q}$, we now define the full core. The *full core* ϕ of x in $B_{p,q}$ is the set of derivatives

$$(19) \qquad \begin{array}{lll} x_{i,j}(s, t), & (s, t) \in I; & i \leqq p, \ \ j \leqq q; \\ x_{i,j}(s, b), & s \in I_s; & i > p, \ \ i + j \leqq n; \\ x_{i,j}(a, t), & t \in I_t; & j > q, \ \ i + j \leqq n. \end{array}$$

The elements of ϕ are to be understood according to the rule of ω.

We also consider the following rule as regards order of differentiation in $x_{i,j}$. Put

$$\tilde{\imath} = \min(i, p), \qquad \tilde{\jmath} = \min(j, q).$$

Interpret $x_{i,j}$ as

$$(20) \qquad x_{i,j} = D_s^{i-\tilde{\imath}} D_t^{j-\tilde{\jmath}} x_{\tilde{\imath},\tilde{\jmath}} = (x_{\tilde{\imath},\tilde{\jmath}})_{i-\tilde{\imath},j-\tilde{\jmath}},$$

where the first $\tilde{\imath} + \tilde{\jmath}$ differentiations are allowed in any order among themselves and the last $i + j - (\tilde{\imath} + \tilde{\jmath})$ differentiations are allowed in any order. We shall describe (20) as the *rule of* ϕ.

In our diagram in which $x_{i,j}$ is represented by the point (i, j), the rule of ϕ amounts to the following: the route from $(0, 0)$ to (i, j) that describes the differentiations shall stay in the rectangle whose opposite vertices are $(0, 0)$ and (p, q) as long as possible (cf. Figure 1).

The following corollary states among other things that the rule of ϕ may be used for any derivative in ϕ, if $x \in B_{p,q}$. As a consequence, the space $B_{p,q}$ is symmetric vis à vis s and t, since the rule of ϕ treats s, p in exactly the same way that it treats t, q.

21. Corollary. *Suppose that $x \in B_{p,q}$. Then the elements of the full core ϕ of x in $B_{p,q}$ exist and are continuous in their arguments, $(s, t) \in I$. The elements of ϕ are given by the following formulas, for $(s, t) \in I$:*

$$x_{i_0,j_0}(s, t) = \sum_{i+j<n} x_{i,j}(a, b)(s - a)^{(i-i_0)}(t - b)^{(j-j_0)}$$

$$(22) \qquad + \sum_{j<q} (t - b)^{(j-j_0)} T_s^{n-j-i_0} x_{n-j,j}(s, b)$$

$$+ \sum_{i<p} (s - a)^{(i-i_0)} T_t^{n-i-j_0} x_{i,n-i}(a, t)$$

$$+ T_s^{p-i_0} T_t^{q-j_0} x_{p,q}(s, t) \quad \text{if} \quad i_0 \leqq p, j_0 \leqq q;$$

$$(23) \qquad x_{i_0,j_0}(s, b) = D_s^{i_0-p} x_{p,j_0}(s, b) = \sum_{i<n-j_0} x_{i,j_0}(a, b)(s - a)^{(i-i_0)}$$

$$+ T_s^{n-i_0-j_0} x_{n-j_0,j_0}(s, b) \quad \text{if} \quad i_0 > p, i_0 + j_0 \leqq n;$$

$$(24) \qquad x_{i_0,j_0}(a, t) = D_t^{j_0-q} x_{i_0,q}(a, t) = \sum_{j<n-i_0} x_{i_0,j}(a, b)(t - b)^{(j-j_0)}$$

$$+ T_t^{n-i_0-j_0} x_{i_0,n-i_0}(a, t) \quad \text{if} \quad j_0 > q, i_0 + j_0 \leqq n.$$

All interpretations of the elements of ϕ according to the rule of ϕ are permissible and equivalent.

Proof. The essential point here is that (22), (23), (24) follow from the Taylor formula (12) = (15) by differentiation in any order consistent with the rule of ϕ, by Lemmas 7 and 3: 74. The formulas (22), (23), (24) imply that the elements of ϕ are continuous, since the elements of ω are continuous.

The details of the proof are like those of the proof of Corollary 11 and are omitted.

It is interesting to observe that the restriction (20) in the rule of ϕ is necessary. Consider, for example, the space $B_{2,1}$. The full core ϕ of x in $B_{2,1}$ consists of the derivatives.

$$x_{0,0}(s, t), \quad x_{1,0}(s, t), \quad x_{0,1}(s, t), \quad x_{2,0}(s, t),$$

$$x_{11}(s, t) = D_s x_{01}(s, t) = D_t x_{10}(s, t),$$

$$(25) \qquad x_{2,1}(s, t) = D_t x_{2,0}(s, t) = D_s x_{1,1}(s, t);$$

$$x_{3,0}(s, b);$$

$$x_{1,2}(a, t) = D_t x_{1,1}(a, t), \quad x_{0,2}(a, t), \quad x_{0,3}(a, t).$$

There is only one derivative here in which a possible order of differentiation is excluded by the rule of ϕ. It is $x_{1,2}(a, t)$. We cannot in fact interpret $x_{1,2}(a, t)$ as

$$(26) \qquad [D_s x_{0,2}(s, t)]_{s=a}.$$

To see this, let w be a Weierstrass function on R, everywhere continuous and nowhere differentiable. Put

$$x(s, t) = T_s^2 T_t^1 w(t) = (s - a)^{(2)} T_t w(t). \tag{27}$$

By Corollary 11,

$$x \in B_{2,1},$$

since x is the function whose complete core in $B_{2,1}$ consists entirely of zeros except that

$$x_{2,1}(s, t) = w(t), \qquad (s, t) \in I.$$

Without referring to Corollary 11, one may operate directly on (27) and see that all the derivatives (25) exist and are continuous. On the other hand, since

$$x_{0,1}(s, t) = (s - a)^{(2)} w(t),$$

$x_{0,2}(s, t)$ does not exist if $s \neq a$. Thus the derivative (26) does not exist. Nonetheless

$$x_{1,2}(a, t) = D_t x_{1,1}(a, t) = D_t 0 = 0.$$

The working of the rule of differentiation may be observed also in the space $B_{2,0}$. There the rule of ϕ is the same as the rule of ω. The full core ϕ of x in $B_{2,0}$ is

$$\begin{gathered} x_{0,0}(s, t), \quad x_{1,0}(s, t), \quad x_{2,0}(s, t); \\ x_{1,1}(a, t) = D_t x_{1,0}(a, t), \quad x_{0,1}(a, t), \quad x_{0,2}(a, t). \end{gathered} \tag{28}$$

Consider the particular function

$$x(s, t) = (s - a)^{(2)} w(t).$$

Then

$$x \in B_{2,0},$$

all the derivatives (28) exist and are continuous, but

$$[D_s x_{0,1}(s, t)]_{s=a}$$

does not exist. The last is an interpretation of $x_{1,1}(a, t)$ which must be excluded.

29. Corollary. *If $x \in B_{p,q}$ and $i_0 \leqq p$, $j_0 \leqq q$, then*

$$x_{i_0,j_0} \in B_{p-i_0,q-j_0}.$$

Furthermore the rule of ϕ in $B_{p-i_0,q-j_0}$ applied to the derivatives of x_{i_0,j_0} is consistent with the rule of ϕ in $B_{p,q}$ applied to the derivatives of x.

PROOF. The diagram of the full core of x_{i_0,j_0} in $B_{p-i_0,q-j_0}$ is obtained from the diagram of the full core of x in $B_{p,q}$ by translating the origin to (i_0, j_0). This proves the corollary.

A reader interested in linear functionals on $B_{p,q}$ may now turn to Chapter 6. There a topology is introduced in $B_{p,q}$ and a representation is given of Fx, where $F \in B^*_{p,q}$ and $x \in B_{p,q}$, in terms of Stieltjes integrals on the complete core of x.

§ 30. **The spaces $\mathscr{K}^*_{p,q}$ and $\boldsymbol{B}_{p,q}$.** The values $p = 0$ and $q = 0$ are perfectly admissible in the definition of $B_{p,q}$. Indeed $B_{0,0}$ is just the space of functions continuous on I.

In the present section we assume that

$$p \geqq 1, \qquad q \geqq 1.$$

We continue to study $B_{p,q}$, we define a space $\boldsymbol{B}_{p,q}$ which contains $B_{p,q}$, and we define a space $\mathscr{K}^*_{p,q}$ of functionals. Our purpose is to obtain a standard formula for Fx, where

$$F \in \mathscr{K}^*_{p,q}, \qquad x \in \boldsymbol{B}_{p,q}.$$

In Chapter 6 we will define another space $K_{p,q}$ and study the relation between its adjoint $K^*_{p,q}$ and the space $\mathscr{K}^*_{p,q}$ of the present section.

The *covered core* ξ of x in $B_{p,q}$ is defined as the set of derivatives

$$\begin{aligned} &x_{i,j}(s,t), \quad (s,t) \in I; \quad i < p, \quad j < q; \\ &x_{i,j}(s,b), \quad s \in I_s; \qquad i \geqq p, \quad i + j < n; \\ &x_{i,j}(a,t), \quad t \in I_t; \qquad j \geqq q, \quad i + j < n. \end{aligned} \tag{31}$$

The reason for the name will appear later, when we will see that the variables in the expansions of these derivatives are covered. The Greek letters ω, ϕ, ξ stand for the complete, full, and covered cores, respectively. Thus ξ consists of the full core in $B_{p-1,q-1}$ together with the derivatives

$$\begin{aligned} &x_{n-1-j,j}(s,b), \quad s \in I_s; \qquad j < q; \\ &x_{i,n-1-i}(a,t), \quad t \in I_t; \qquad i < p. \end{aligned}$$

If $x \in B_{p,q}$, the elements of ϕ are continuous in their variables, $(s, t) \in I$; and hence a fortiori the elements of ξ are continuous, since each element of (31) is either an element of (19) or obtainable therefrom by a substitution $s = a$ or $t = b$.

We now define $\mathscr{K}^*_{p,q}$, called the *companion space* of $B_{p,q}$, as the space of functionals which are finite sums of Lebesgue-Stieltjes integrals on the elements of ξ, the order of differentiation in each element of ξ being any order consistent with the rule of ϕ in $B_{p-1,q-1}$. We describe the rule of ϕ in $B_{p-1,q-1}$ as the *rule of* ξ in $B_{p,q}$. The latter is consistent with the rule of ϕ in $B_{p,q}$.

For example, simple functionals in $\mathscr{K}^*_{2,3}$ are

$$[D_t D_s D_t x]_{(s,t)=(s^0,t^0)}, \quad [D_s D_t^2 x]_{(s,t)=(s^0,t^0)},$$

where (s^0, t^0) is a fixed element of I. These two functionals are different interpretations of $x_{1,2}(s^0, t^0)$, each consistent with the rule of ξ. For many functions x, but not all, the two functionals have the same value. Any linear combination of the functionals is an element of $\mathscr{K}^*_{2,3}$.

For brevity and for simplicity of notation, we will write formulas for Fx, $F \in \mathscr{K}^*_{p,q}$, as if only one ordering of each element of ξ were present and we shall use the notation $x_{i,j}$ for that element. No loss of idea will be involved, since any discussion of ours pertinent to

$$\iint x_{i,j}\, d\mu \quad \text{or} \quad \int x_{i,j}\, d\mu$$

will apply also to a finite sum of such integrals with different interpretations of $x_{i,j}$, providing that such interpretations all follow the rule of ξ. Orders of differentiation which do not follow the rule of ξ may vitiate our argument.

Thus an element F of $\mathscr{K}^*_{p,q}$ will be taken as a functional of the form

$$\begin{aligned} Fx = &\sum_{\substack{i<p,\\ j<q}} \iint x_{i,j}(s,t)\, d\mu^{i,j}(s,t) + \sum_{\substack{i+j<n,\\ i \geqq p}} \int x_{i,j}(s,b)\, d\mu^{i,j}(s) \\ &+ \sum_{\substack{i+j<n,\\ j \geqq q}} \int x_{i,j}(a,t)\, d\mu^{i,j}(t), \end{aligned} \tag{32}$$

where the functions $\mu^{i,j}$ are of bounded variation on I, I_s, or I_t, as indicated (cf. Chapter 12). Here and elsewhere integrals are to be taken over I or I_s or I_t, as appropriate, unless the contrary is stated. The superscripts i, j merely distinguish different entities. The domain of definition of F consists of all functions x for which the derivatives $x_{i,j}$ in (32) are integrable relative to $\mu^{i,j}$ in the sense of Lebesgue-Stieltjes. The derivatives $x_{i,j}$ are to be understood according to the rule of ξ.

If a functional G is such that Gx is a finite sum of Stieltjes integrals on elements of the full core ϕ instead of the covered core ξ, each such element being interpreted according to the rule of ϕ, then G may be studied by the methods of Chapter 6 (cf. § 6 : 21).

It is clear from (32) that

$$\mathscr{K}^*_{p,q} \subset \mathscr{K}^*_{p',q'} \quad \text{whenever} \quad p' \geqq p, \quad q' \geqq q. \tag{33}$$

Consider an element F of $\mathscr{K}^*_{p,q}$, given by (32). We now define the *jump*†

† As in § 1 : 3, we could use a notation which indicates the dependence of $\mathscr{J}_s$ on $\mathscr{K}^*_{p,q}$, but this would be cumbersome.

sets $\mathscr{J}_s$ and $\mathscr{J}_t$ of F relative to $\mathscr{K}^*_{p,q}$. The set $\mathscr{J}_s$ is the countable set of points in I_s which are either points of discontinuity of

$$|\mu^{n-1-j,j}|(s) \quad \text{for some } j < q,$$

or of

$$|\mu^{p-1,j'}|(s, \tilde{\beta}) \quad \text{for some } j' < q,$$

where the bars indicate total variations and $\tilde{\beta}$ is substituted after the variation relative to (s, t) has been taken. The total variations are designated $v(s)$ in § 12: 14 and $v(s, t)$ in § 12: 100. The functions $\mu^{i,j}$ here do not constitute all of those that appear in (32). If $s^0 \in \mathscr{J}_s$, then the point $s = s^0$ is a point of positive absolute $\mu^{n-1-j,j}$ variation for some $j < q$, or the line $s = s^0, t \in I_t$ is a line of positive absolute $\mu^{p-1,j'}$ variation for some $j' < q$. The set $\mathscr{J}_t$ is the dual set.

We have defined the space $B_{p,q}$ as the space of functions x on I whose core derivatives are continuous in their arguments, $(s, t) \in I$; and we have shown that the Taylor formula (9) holds for each x in $B_{p,q}$. We now define the larger space $\boldsymbol{B}_{p,q}$ (bold $B_{p,q}$) as the space† of functions with Lebesgue integrable core derivatives for which the Taylor formula (9) holds. That is, the *space* $\boldsymbol{B}_{p,q}$ is the space of functions x on I for which the following conditions all hold:

(1) The derivative $x_{p,q}(s, t)$ exists almost everywhere in I and is Lebesgue integrable.

(2) The derivatives $x_{n-j,j}(s, b)$, $j < q$, exist almost everywhere in I_s and are Lebesgue integrable.

(3) The derivatives $x_{i,n-i}(a, t)$, $i < p$, exist almost everywhere in I_t and are Lebesgue integrable.

(4) The derivatives $x_{i,j}(a, b)$, $i + j < n$, exist at (a, b).

(5) The Taylor formula (9) holds for $x(s, t)$, $(s, t) \in I$. The derivatives here are to be understood according to the rule of ξ extended as follows:

$$\begin{aligned} x_{p,q}(s, t) &= D_s D_t x_{p-1,q-1}(s, t) \quad \text{or} \quad D_t D_s x_{p-1,q-1}(s, t); \\ x_{n-j,j}(s, b) &= D_s x_{n-j-1,j}(s, b), \qquad j < q; \\ x_{i,n-i}(a, t) &= D_t x_{i,n-i-1}(a, t), \qquad i < p; \end{aligned}$$

where all the derivatives after D_s, D_t, being elements of ξ, are understood according to the rule of ξ.

Thus

$$B_{p,q} \subset \boldsymbol{B}_{p,q}.$$

This relation is immediate, except perhaps as regards questions of orders of differentiation. But if $x \in B_{p,q}$, then all orders consistent with the rule of ϕ

† A reader wishing to simplify the theory may disregard $\boldsymbol{B}_{p,q}$ and proceed to Theorem 36, replacing the hypothesis $x \in \boldsymbol{B}_{p,q}$ by the more restrictive $x \in B_{p,q}$.

are allowable and equivalent. In particular, then, orders consistent with the rule of ξ are allowable and equivalent.

The spaces $B_{p,q}$ and $\boldsymbol{B}_{p,q}$ are generalizations of C_n and $\boldsymbol{C}_n$, respectively.

34. Lemma. *Suppose that $x \in \boldsymbol{B}_{p,q}$. Then the elements of ϕ understood according to the rule of ξ exist almost everywhere on I, I_s, I_t, are integrable, and are given by the Taylor formulas* (22), (23), (24), *respectively. The elements of ξ exist everywhere on I, I_s, I_t, are continuous, and are given by the Taylor formulas* (22), (23), (24) *in which the exponents of the operators T_s and T_t are strictly positive.*

Proof. The essential point of the proof is that the relation

$$D_s T_s y(s) = y(s)$$

holds for almost all s if $y(s)$ is integrable and for all s if $y(s)$ is continuous; and that the relations

$$D_s T_s T_t y(s, t) = T_t y(s, t),$$

$$D_s D_t T_s T_t y(s, t) = D_t D_s T_s T_t y(s, t) = y(s, t),$$

hold for almost all (s, t) if $y(s, t)$ is integrable and for all (s, t) if $y(s, t)$ is continuous. [Carathéodory 1, pp. 654–661.]

Consider x in $\boldsymbol{B}_{p,q}$. The Taylor formula (9) holds, by the definition of $\boldsymbol{B}_{p,q}$. We may calculate any element of ϕ by differentiation of the right-hand side of (9) according to any order of differentiation that conforms to the rule of ξ and all such orders give the same result, viz., (22) for all or almost all of I, (23) for all or almost all of I_s, and (24) for all or almost all of I_t. The definition (31) of ξ is such that the exponents of T_s and T_t in the formulas (22), (23), (24) for elements of ξ are all strictly positive.

To see the details of the argument and to see why it would have been inadvisable to allow differentiation according to the rule of ϕ or even ω, consider $B_{2,1}$. Put

$$(35)\quad y(s, t) = T_s^3 e(s) + T_s^2 T_t f(s, t) + (s - a) T_t^2 g(t) + T_t^3 h(t), \qquad (s, t) \in I,$$

where $e(s)$, $f(s, t)$, $g(t)$, $h(t)$ are integrable functions. We shall show that $y \in \boldsymbol{B}_{2,1}$.

The full core ϕ of y in $B_{2,1}$, according to the rule of ξ, and particular values of derivatives of y are

$$y_{1,0}(s, t) = T_s^2 e(s) + T_s T_t f(s, t) + T_t^2 g(t) \qquad \text{for all } (s, t);$$

$$y_{1,0}(a, t) = T_t^2 g(t) \qquad \text{for all } t;$$

$$y_{0,1}(s, t) = T_s^2 f(s, t) + (s - a) T_t g(t) + T_t^2 h(t) \qquad \text{for almost all } (s, t);$$

$$y_{0,1}(a, t) = T_t^2 h(t) \qquad \text{for all } t;$$

$$y_{2,0}(s, t) = T_s e(s) + T_t f(s, t) \qquad \text{for almost all } (s, t);$$

$$\begin{aligned}
y_{2,0}(s, b) &= T_s e(s) && \text{for all } s;\\
y_{1,1}(s, t) &= D_t y_{1,0}(s, t) = T_s f(s, t) + T_t g(t) && \text{for almost all } (s, t);\\
y_{1,1}(a, t) &= T_t g(t) && \text{for all } t;\\
y_{2,1}(s, t) &= D_s D_t y_{1,0}(s, t) = D_t D_s y_{1,0}(s, t) &&\\
&= f(s, t) && \text{for almost all } (s, t);\\
y_{3,0}(s, b) &= D_s y_{2,0}(s, b) = e(s) && \text{for almost all } s;\\
y_{0,2}(a, t) &= D_t y_{0,1}(a, t) = T_t h(t) && \text{for all } t;\\
y_{0,3}(a, t) &= h(t) && \text{for almost all } t;\\
y_{1,2}(a, t) &= D_t y_{1,1}(a, t) = g(t) && \text{for almost all } t.
\end{aligned}$$

By the above,

$$\begin{aligned}
y(a, b) &= y_{1,0}(a, b) = y_{0,1}(a, b) = y_{2,0}(a, b) = y_{1,1}(a, b)\\
&= y_{0,2}(a, b) = 0.
\end{aligned}$$

Now the core of y in $B_{2,1}$ is

$$y_{3,0}(s, b), \quad y_{2,1}(s, t), \quad y_{1,2}(a, t), \quad y_{0,3}(a, t).$$

These derivatives exist almost everywhere; and (35) is an instance of (9). Hence $y \in \boldsymbol{B}_{2,1}$ and equations (22), (23), (24) with $(p, q) = (2, 1)$ and $x = y$ are established almost everywhere.

Furthermore the covered core ξ of y in $B_{2,1}$ is

$$y(s, t), \quad y_{1,0}(s, t);$$

$$y_{2,0}(s, b);$$

$$y_{0,1}(a, t), \quad y_{0,2}(a, t), \quad y_{1,1}(a, t).$$

The above formulas for these functions are valid for all s and t. In the formulas the variables are covered by Taylor operators. That is, if $f(s, t)$ is present, it is preceded by $T_s T_t$; if $e(s)$ is present, it is preceded by T_s; if $g(t)$ or $h(t)$ is present, it is preceded by T_t. It follows that the elements of the covered core ξ are continuous in their variables.

It has been essential here that we did not use the rule of ϕ or even ω. Thus consider $y_{1,1}(a, t)$, an element of the covered core ξ of y in $B_{2,1}$. According to the rule of ξ,

$$y_{1,1}(a, t) = D_t y_{1,0}(a, t) = T_t g(t)$$

for all t, as we have seen. On the other hand, according to the rule of ω,

$$y_{1,1}(a, t) = [D_s y_{0,1}(s, t)]_{s=a}.$$

This derivative need not exist. For example, let $m(t)$ be a function of t

which is strictly increasing, discontinuous at all rational t, and continuous at all irrational t. Take

$$y(s, t) = T_s^2 T_t m(t) = (s - a)^{(2)} T_t m(t),$$

an instance of (35). Then $y_{0,1}(s, t)$, $s \neq a$, exists iff t is irrational. Hence $[D_s y_{0,1}(s, t)]_{s=a}$ exists iff t is irrational. As a consequence, $D_t[D_s y_{0,1}(s, t)]_{s=a}$, which is $y_{1,2}(a, t)$ according to the rule of ω, does not exist for any t, even though $y_{1,2}(a, t) \in \omega_{a,t}$.

Thus Lemma 34 is established for $(p, q) = (2,1)$.

A similar argument applies to the general case. We omit the details.

36. Kernel theorem. *Suppose that $F \in \mathscr{K}^*_{p,q}$. Then functions*

$$\kappa^{p,q}(s, t), \quad (s, t) \in I;$$

$$\kappa^{n-j,j}(s), \quad s \in I_s; \qquad j < q;$$

$$\kappa^{i,n-i}(t), \quad t \in I_t; \qquad i < p;$$

all of bounded variation; and constants

$$c^{i,j}, i + j < n,$$

exist such that

$$(37)\quad \begin{aligned} Fx = {} & \sum_{i+j<n} c^{i,j} x_{i,j}(a, b) + \sum_{j<q} \int x_{n-j,j}(s,\ b)\kappa^{n-j,j}(s)\, ds \\ & + \sum_{i<p} \int x_{i,n-i}(a, t)\kappa^{i,n-i}(t)\, dt \\ & + \iint x_{p,q}(s, t)\kappa^{p,q}(s, t)\, ds\, dt \end{aligned}$$

whenever $x \in \boldsymbol{B}_{p,q}$. Furthermore

$$(38)\quad c^{i,j} = F[(s - a)^{(i)}(t - b)^{(j)}], \qquad i + j < n;$$

and the kernels $\kappa^{i,j}$ may be taken so that

$$(39)\quad \kappa^{n-j,j}(\tilde{s}) = F[(s - \tilde{s})^{(n-j-1)}\psi(a, \tilde{s}, s)(t - b)^{(j)}], \qquad \tilde{s} \notin \mathscr{J}_s, \ \ j < q;$$

$$(40)\quad \kappa^{i,n-i}(\tilde{t}) = F[(s - a)^{(i)}(t - \tilde{t})^{(n-i-1)}\psi(b, \tilde{t}, t)], \qquad \tilde{t} \notin \mathscr{J}_t, \ \ i < p;$$

$$(41)\quad \begin{aligned} \kappa^{p,q}(\tilde{s}, \tilde{t}) = {} & F[(s - \tilde{s})^{(p-1)}\psi(a, \tilde{s}, s)(t - \tilde{t})^{(q-1)}\psi(b, \tilde{t}, t)], \\ & \tilde{s} \notin \mathscr{J}_s \ \text{ and } \ \tilde{t} \notin \mathscr{J}_t; \end{aligned}$$

where $\mathscr{J}_s$ and $\mathscr{J}_t$ are the jump sets of F. Conversely if constants $c^{i,j}$ and functions $\kappa^{i,j} \in V$ are given, then the functional F defined by (37) *may be extended so as to become an element of $\mathscr{K}^*_{p,q}$.*

A few comments before the proof may be of interest.

The relations (39)–(41) define the kernels $\kappa^{i,j}$ except possibly for countably many values of s and of t. This knowledge is entirely adequate for the use of (37). In practice, the sets $\mathscr{J}_s$ and $\mathscr{J}_t$ of exceptional values are often finite.

The relation (37) cannot be simplified by combination of any of its terms. This is a consequence of Corollary 11. For, the elements of the complete core of x in $B_{p,q}$ are independent. We can take all of these elements as zero, except any particular one, which if continuous in its variables may be otherwise arbitrary. Thus for certain functions x in $B_{p,q} \subset \boldsymbol{B}_{p,q}$, all terms of (37) except any particular one vanish.

The value of the present theorem rests in the fact that F, which is easily recognizable as an element of $\mathscr{K}^*_{p,q}$, is expressed in a standard way that is accessible and involves ordinary integrals on the core of x rather than Stieltjes integrals.

Applications of the theorem will be given in Chapter 5. The reader, if he wishes, may now turn to Chapter 5 and read the parts that refer to $B_{p,q}$ but omit the parts that refer to $B_{\ulcorner p,q \urcorner}$ or B.

We may express the defining relations (39)–(41) in terms of the step functions θ or ϕ of (11 : 3 and 7), by use of the equalities

$$\psi(a, \tilde{s}, s) = \theta(\tilde{s}, a) - \theta(\tilde{s}, s) = \phi(\tilde{s}, s) - \phi(\tilde{s}, a).$$

This sometimes is advantageous because $\theta(\tilde{s}, a)$ and $\phi(\tilde{s}, a)$ are independent of s. For example, (39) may be written as

$$\begin{aligned}\kappa^{n-j,j}(\tilde{s}) &= \theta(\tilde{s}, a)F[(s - \tilde{s})^{(n-j-1)}(t - b)^{(j)}] \\ &\quad - F[(s - \tilde{s})^{(n-j-1)}\theta(\tilde{s}, s)(t - b)^{(j)}], \qquad \tilde{s} \notin \mathscr{J}_s, \quad j < q.\end{aligned}$$

If F is zero for polynomials of degree $n - 1$, then the first term vanishes and

$$(39') \qquad \begin{aligned}\kappa^{n-j,j}(\tilde{s}) &= -F[(s - \tilde{s})^{(n-j-1)}\theta(\tilde{s}, s)(t - b)^{(j)}] \\ &= F[(s - \tilde{s})^{(n-j-1)}\phi(\tilde{s}, s)(t - b)^{(j)}], \qquad \tilde{s} \notin \mathscr{J}_s.\end{aligned}$$

The dual relation holds for $\kappa^{i,n-i}(\tilde{t})$. As regards $\kappa^{p,q}(\tilde{s}, \tilde{t})$, its alternative forms are no simpler than (41).

PROOF. The proof is similar to that of Theorem 1 : 8. We start with the Taylor formula for x; we operate thereon by (32); and we use the device (1 : 14).

Part 1. Suppose that $x \in \boldsymbol{B}_{p,q}$. By Lemma 34 the elements of the covered core ξ may be expressed by the Taylor formulas (22), (23), (24). In these formulas as will be verified, the variables will be covered; that is, whenever an element of the core appears, its variables will be present and it will be preceded by T_s if it contains an s and by T_t if it contains a t. Now by Lemma 3 : 70 and (1 : 14),

$$T_s^h y(s) = \int_a^s (s - \tilde{s})^{(h-1)} y(\tilde{s})\, d\tilde{s} = \int (s - \tilde{s})^{(h-1)} y(\tilde{s}) \psi(a, \tilde{s}, s)\, d\tilde{s} \quad \text{if } h > 0.$$

Hence the elements of ξ are as follows, by (22), (23), (24), for all (s, t) in I:

$$x_{i_0,j_0}(s, t) = \sum_{i+j<n} x_{i,j}(a, b)(s - a)^{(i-i_0)}(t - b)^{(j-j_0)} + \sum_{j<q} (t - b)^{(j-j_0)}$$

$$\times \int (s - \tilde{s})^{(n-j-i_0-1)}\psi(a, \tilde{s}, s)x_{n-j,j}(\tilde{s}, b)\, d\tilde{s} + \text{dual term}$$

$$+ \iint (s - \tilde{s})^{(p-i_0-1)}(t - \tilde{t})^{(q-j_0-1)}\psi(a, \tilde{s}, s)\psi(b, \tilde{t}, t)x_{p,q}(\tilde{s}, \tilde{t})\, d\tilde{s}\, d\tilde{t}$$

$$\text{if } i_0 < p, j_0 < q;$$

$$x_{i_0,j}(s, b) = \sum_{i<n-j} x_{i,j}(a, b)(s - a)^{(i-i_0)} + \int (s - \tilde{s})^{(n-i_0-j-1)}$$

$$\times \psi(a, \tilde{s}, s)x_{n-j,j}(\tilde{s}, b)\, d\tilde{s} \qquad \text{if } i_0 \geqq p,\ i_0 + j < n;$$

$$x_{i,j_0}(a, t) = \text{dual expression} \qquad \text{if } j_0 \geqq q,\ i + j_0 < n.$$

By (32), then,

$$Fx = \sum_{\substack{i_0<p,\\ j_0<q}} \iint d\mu^{i_0,j_0}(s, t)\Big[\sum_{i+j<n} x_{i,j}(a, b)(s - a)^{(i-i_0)}(t - b)^{(j-j_0)}$$

$$+ \sum_{j<q} (t - b)^{(j-j_0)} \int (s - \tilde{s})^{(n-j-i_0-1)}\psi(a, \tilde{s}, s)$$

$$\times x_{n-j,j}(\tilde{s}, b)\, d\tilde{s} + \text{dual term} + \iint (s - \tilde{s})^{(p-i_0-1)}$$

$$\times (t - \tilde{t})^{(q-j_0-1)}\psi(a, \tilde{s}, s)\psi(b, \tilde{t}, t)\, x_{p,q}(\tilde{s}, \tilde{t})\, d\tilde{s}\, d\tilde{t}\Big]$$

$$+ \sum_{p\leqq i_0<n-j} \int d\mu^{i_0,j}(s)\Big[\sum_{i<n-j} x_{i,j}(a, b)(s - a)^{(i-i_0)} + \int (s - \tilde{s})^{(n-i_0-j-1)}$$

$$\times \psi(a, \tilde{s}, s)x_{n-j,j}(\tilde{s}, b)\, d\tilde{s}\Big] + \text{dual term.}$$

Hence, by Fubini's Theorem,

$$Fx = \sum_{i+j<n} c^{i,j}x_{i,j}(a, b) + \sum_{j<q} \int x_{n-j,j}(\tilde{s}, b)\kappa^{n-j,j}(\tilde{s})\, d\tilde{s} + \text{dual term}$$

$$+ \iint x_{p,q}(\tilde{s}, \tilde{t})\kappa^{p,q}(\tilde{s}, \tilde{t})\, d\tilde{s}\, d\tilde{t},$$

where

$$c^{i,j} = \sum_{\substack{i_0<p,\\ j_0<q}} \iint (s-a)^{(i-i_0)}(t-b)^{(j-j_0)}\, d\mu^{i_0,j_0}(s,t)$$
$$+ \sum_{p \leqq i_0 < n-j} \int (s-a)^{(i-i_0)}\, d\mu^{i_0,j}(s) + \text{dual term}, \qquad i+j<n;$$

(42)
$$\kappa^{n-j,j}(\tilde{s}) = \sum_{\substack{i_0<p,\\ j_0<q}} \iint (t-b)^{(j-j_0)}(s-\tilde{s})^{(n-j-i_0-1)}\psi(a,\tilde{s},s)\, d\mu^{i_0,j_0}(s,t)$$
$$+ \sum_{p \leqq i_0 < n-j} \int (s-\tilde{s})^{(n-i_0-j-1)}\psi(a,\tilde{s},s)\, d\mu^{i_0,j}(s), \qquad j<q;$$

$$\kappa^{i,n-i}(\tilde{t}) = \text{dual expression}, \qquad i<p;$$

(43)
$$\kappa^{p,q}(\tilde{s},\tilde{t}) = \sum_{\substack{i_0<p,\\ j_0<q}} \iint (s-\tilde{s})^{(p-i_0-1)}\psi(a,\tilde{s},s)(t-\tilde{t})^{(q-j_0-1)} \times \psi(b,\tilde{t},t)\, d\mu^{i_0,j_0}(s,t).$$

Thus (37) is established. The kernels are defined by the above relations for all $(\tilde{s},\tilde{t})$. The kernels so defined are elements of V. Consider $\kappa^{p,q}(\tilde{s},\tilde{t})$, for example. The variation of each integrand in (43) as a function of $(\tilde{s},\tilde{t})$ is bounded, uniformly over (s,t). Hence the variation of the integral is bounded. Likewise if either $\tilde{s}$ or $\tilde{t}$ is fixed.

Part 2. The relation (38) for the constants $c^{i,j}$ is an immediate consequence of (37), obtained by putting

$$x(s,t) = (s-a)^{(i_0)}(t-b)^{(j_0)}, \qquad i_0+j_0<n,$$

in (37).

To establish (39), consider the function y defined as

$$y(s,t) = (s-\tilde{s})^{(n-j_0-1)}\psi(a,\tilde{s},s)(t-b)^{(j_0)}, \qquad j_0<q.$$

In preparation for the calculation, when possible, of Fy by (32), we first calculate the covered core ξ of y. Thus

(44) $$y_{i,j}(s,t) = (s-\tilde{s})^{(n-j_0-i-1)}\psi(a,\tilde{s},s)(t-b)^{(j_0-j)} \qquad i<p, j<q.$$

This relation is valid if $n-j_0-i-1>0$, because the jump in ψ at $s=\tilde{s}$ is nullified by the factor $s-\tilde{s}$. But since $j_0<q$,

$$n-j_0>n-q=p.$$

Hence $n-j_0 \geqq p+1$. Also $p \geqq i+1$. Hence $n-j_0 \geqq i+2$ and $n-j_0-i-1 \geqq 1$.

Next, by (44) and the rule of ξ,

$$\begin{aligned} y_{i,j}(s, b) &= D_s^{i-p+1} y_{p-1,j}(s, b) \\ &= D_s^{i-p+1}[(s - \tilde{s})^{(q-j_0)} \psi(a, \tilde{s}, s)\, \delta^{j,j_0}], \qquad i + j < n, \quad i \geqq p. \end{aligned}$$

Hence

$$y_{i,j}(s, b) = 0 \qquad \text{if } j \neq j_0,\ i + j < n,\ i \geqq p.$$

Suppose that $j = j_0$. Then

$$y_{i,j_0}(s, b) = D_s^{i-p+1}[(s - \tilde{s})^{(q-j_0)} \psi(a, \tilde{s}, s)], \qquad p \leqq i < n - j_0.$$

Since

$$q - j_0 - (i - p + 1) = n - i - j_0 - 1 \geqq 0,$$

we distinguish two cases, according as inequality or equality holds. In the first case,

$$y_{i,j_0}(s, b) = (s - \tilde{s})^{(n-j_0-i-1)} \psi(a, \tilde{s}, s), \qquad p \leqq i < n - j_0 - 1.$$

In the second case, the last differentiation with respect to s can be performed iff $s \neq \tilde{s}$, because of the jump in ψ. Thus

$$y_{i,j_0}(s, b) = \psi(a, \tilde{s}, s), \qquad s \neq \tilde{s}, \quad p \leqq i = n - j_0 - 1.$$

Next

$$y_{i,j}(a, t) = D_t^{j-q+1} y_{i,q-1}(a, t) = D_t^{j-q+1} 0 = 0, \qquad i + j < n, \quad j \geqq q,$$

by (44), since $\psi(a, \tilde{s}, a) = 0$.

Thus all the derivatives of y that enter in Fy as given by (32) exist and have been calculated with only the following qualification:

$$y_{n-j_0-1,j_0}(s, b)$$

exists only when $s \neq \tilde{s}$. The missing value of this derivative is material to the value of the corresponding integral in (32) iff $\tilde{s}$ is a point of positive $|\mu^{n-j_0-1,j_0}|$ variation. It follows that if $\tilde{s} \notin \mathscr{J}_s$, the missing value is immaterial. Hence, by (32),

$$\begin{aligned} Fy = \sum_{\substack{i<p,\\ j<q}} \iint (s - \tilde{s})^{(n-j_0-i-1)} \psi(a, \tilde{s}, s)(t - b)^{(j_0-j)}\, d\mu^{i,j}(s, t) \\ + \sum_{p \leqq i < n-j_0} \int (s - \tilde{s})^{(n-j_0-i-1)} \psi(a, \tilde{s}, s)\, d\mu^{i,j_0}(s) + 0, \qquad \tilde{s} \notin \mathscr{J}_s. \end{aligned}$$

Hence, by (42),

$$Fy = \kappa^{n-j_0,j_0}(\tilde{s}), \qquad \tilde{s} \notin J_s, \quad j_0 < q.$$

This establishes (39).

The relation (40) is dual.

To establish (41), consider the function z defined as

$$z(s, t) = (s - \tilde{s})^{(p-1)}\psi(a, \tilde{s}, s)(t - \tilde{t})^{(q-1)}\psi(b, \tilde{t}, t).$$

In preparation for the calculation, when possible, of Fz, we calculate the covered core ξ of z. Thus

$$(45) \quad z_{i,j}(s, t) = (s - \tilde{s})^{(p-i-1)}\psi(a, \tilde{s}, s)(t - \tilde{t})^{(q-j-1)}\psi(b, \tilde{t}, t), \qquad i < p, \quad j < q,$$

except that

$$\text{if} \quad i = p - 1, \quad s \text{ must be different from } \tilde{s};$$
$$\text{if} \quad j = q - 1, \quad t \text{ must be different from } \tilde{t}.$$

Next, by (45) and the rule of ξ,

$$(46) \quad z_{i,j}(s, b) = D_s^{i-p+1}z_{p-1,j}(s, b) = D_s^{i-p+1}0 = 0, \qquad i + j < n, \quad i \geqq p,$$

except possibly in the case $s = \tilde{s}$. Similarly

$$(47) \qquad z_{i,j}(a, t) = 0, \qquad i + j < n, \quad j \geqq q,$$

except possibly in the case $t = \tilde{t}$.

We now evaluate Fz by (32). Let us agree, as is natural, that an integrand which is everywhere zero except at one point at which it is not defined is taken to be zero at that point. Then the exceptional values in (46) and (47) have no effect. By (32), then,

$$Fz = \sum_{\substack{i<p,\\ j<q}} \iint (s - \tilde{s})^{(p-i-1)}\psi(a, \tilde{s}, s)(t - \tilde{t})^{(q-j-1)}\psi(b, \tilde{t}, t)d\mu^{i,j}(s, t),$$

$$\tilde{s} \notin \mathscr{J}_s \quad \text{and} \quad \tilde{t} \notin \mathscr{J}_t,$$

since the missing values of (45) are material only when $s = \tilde{s}$ is a line of positive $|\mu^{p-1,j}|$ variation, $j < q$, or when $t = \tilde{t}$ is a line of positive $|\mu^{i,q-1}|$ variation, $i < p$. Hence, by (43),

$$Fz = \kappa^{p,q}(\tilde{s}, \tilde{t}), \qquad \tilde{s} \notin \mathscr{J}_s \quad \text{and} \quad \tilde{t} \notin \mathscr{J}_t,$$

and (41) is established.

Part 3. Suppose that constants $c^{i,j}$ and functions $\kappa^{i,j}$ in V are given. Consider the functional F defined by (37). Then Fx is defined for $x \in \boldsymbol{B}_{p,q}$. We may readily transform (37) by the use of integration by parts into a formula which defines an extension of F. Thus assume that the kernels $\kappa^{i,j}$ all vanish on the boundary of I:

$$(48) \qquad \begin{aligned} \kappa^{n-j,j}(s) &= 0 \quad \text{if } s = \alpha \text{ or } \tilde{\alpha}, j < q; \\ \kappa^{i,n-i}(t) &= 0 \quad \text{if } t = \beta \text{ or } \tilde{\beta}, i < p; \\ \kappa^{p,q}(s, t) &= 0 \quad \text{if } s = \alpha \text{ or } \tilde{\alpha} \text{ or if } t = \beta \text{ or } \tilde{\beta}. \end{aligned}$$

If a change in the definition of the kernels is here involved, it does not affect the value of Fx, $x \in \boldsymbol{B}_{p,q}$ nor does it alter the fact that $\kappa^{i,j} \in V$. Indeed this change is not necessary to our argument, but has the advantage of making a later equation briefer than it would otherwise be.

For $x \in \boldsymbol{B}_{p,q}$, (37) may be written:

$$Fx = \sum_{i+j<n} c^{i,j} x_{i,j}(a, b) + \sum_{j<q} \int \kappa^{n-j,j}(s)\, dx_{n-j-1,j}(s, b)$$

$$+ \text{ dual term } + \iint \kappa^{p,q}(s, t)\, dx_{p-1,q-1}(s, t).$$

The conditions for integration by parts are satisfied. For example, $\kappa^{p,q} \in V$ and $x_{p-1,q-1}(s, t)$ is absolutely continuous and hence continuous. Hence, for $x \in \boldsymbol{B}_{p,q}$, by (48) and Theorems 12: 56 and 12: 8,

$$Fx = \sum_{i+j<n} c^{i,j} x_{i,j}(a, b) + \sum_{j<q} \int x_{n-j-1,j}(s, b)\, d\kappa^{n-j,j}(s)$$

$$+ \text{ dual term } + \iint x_{p-1,q-1}(s, t)\, d\kappa^{p,q}(s, t).$$

The right-hand member of this formula is an instance of (32) and therefore defines an element of $\mathscr{K}^*_{p,q}$.

This completes the proof of Theorem 36.

§ 49. **The spaces** B. The above theory of the spaces $B_{p,q}$, $\boldsymbol{B}_{p,q}$, and $\mathscr{K}^*_{p,q}$ starts with the definition of the space $B_{p,q}$ and leads to the kernel theorem 36. We now develop a theory of spaces, B, $\boldsymbol{B}$, $\mathscr{K}^*$ of which the previous theory is an instance. The core of x in $B_{p,q}$ contains the derivative $x_{p,q}(s, t)$ and other partial derivatives, each evaluated at either (s, b) or (a, t), and each of order n. We shall define many spaces B whose core contains $x_{p,q}(s, t)$ and n other partial derivatives, each evaluated at either (s, b) or (a, t), but which latter partial derivatives are not necessarily of order n.

Let I be a compact interval of the (s, t)-plane and let (a, b) be a point of I. Write

$$I = I_s \times I_t, \qquad I_s = \{\alpha \leqq s \leqq \tilde{\alpha}\}, \qquad I_t = \{\beta \leqq t \leqq \tilde{\beta}\}.$$

Let p, q be nonnegative integers. Put

$$n = p + q.$$

To define a space B (which we call simply a "space B" or a "space of type B" or a "space with pivot $x_{p,q}$") we first define its pivot and core. The *pivot* is the derivative $x_{p,q}(s, t)$, $(s, t) \in I$, understood according to a specified order of differentiation:

$$(50) \qquad x_{p,q}(s, t) = D_{\zeta_n} D_{\zeta_{n-1}} \cdots D_{\zeta_1} x,$$

where $(\zeta_n, \zeta_{n-1}, \cdots, \zeta_1)$ is a permutation of p letters s and q letters t. Consider the successive derivatives that enter in the definition of the pivot.

These are

$$x, \quad D_{\zeta_1}x, \quad D_{\zeta_2}D_{\zeta_1}x, \cdots, \quad D_{\zeta_{n-1}}D_{\zeta_{n-2}}\cdots D_{\zeta_1}x. \tag{51}$$

Let $r_1, r_2, \cdots, r_n$ be specified nonnegative integers. The *core* of x in B is defined as the pivot and the following derivatives:

$$\begin{aligned}
&D_{\zeta_1'}^{r_1}x \text{ evaluated at } (s, b) \text{ if } \zeta_1' \text{ is } s \text{ or at } (a, t) \text{ if } \zeta_1' \text{ is } t,\\
&D_{\zeta_2'}^{r_2}D_{\zeta_1}x \text{ evaluated at } (s, b) \text{ if } \zeta_2' \text{ is } s \text{ or at } (a, t) \text{ if } \zeta_2' \text{ is } t,\\
&D_{\zeta_3'}^{r_3}D_{\zeta_2}D_{\zeta_1}x \text{ evaluated at } (s, b) \text{ if } \zeta_3' \text{ is } s \text{ or at } (a, t) \text{ if } \zeta_3' \text{ is } t,\\
&\vdots\\
&D_{\zeta_n'}^{r_n}D_{\zeta_{n-1}}D_{\zeta_{n-2}}\cdots D_{\zeta_1}x \text{ evaluated at } (s, b) \text{ if } \zeta_n' \text{ is } s \text{ or at}\\
&\qquad\qquad (a, t) \text{ if } \zeta_n' \text{ is } t;\ (s, t) \in I,
\end{aligned} \tag{52}$$

where ζ_i' is t or s according as ζ_i is s or t, $i = 1, \cdots, n$. Thus the derivatives (52) are obtained by differentiating each of the derivatives (51) a finite number of times with respect to that variable s or t which is not the variable of differentiation in the next differentiation in the pivot.

The space B is defined as the space of those functions $x(s, t)$ for which the core derivatives (50) and (52) exist and are continuous in their variables, $(s, t) \in I$. The space B depends on I, (a, b), (p, q), the permutation $\zeta_n, \cdots, \zeta_1$ of p letters s and q letters t, and $r_1, \cdots, r_n$.

We denote by $\omega_{s,b}$ the set of those derivatives (52) which have argument (s, b) and by $\omega_{a,t}$ the set which have argument (a, t). Thus $\omega_{s,b}$ is a set of q derivatives, and $\omega_{a,t}$ is a set of p derivatives. We denote by $\omega_{s,t}$ the set consisting of the single element $x_{p,q}(s, t)$. The *core* of x in B is

$$\omega_{s,t} \cup \omega_{s,b} \cup \omega_{a,t}.$$

We denote by $\omega_{a,b}$ the set of derivatives of x which are predecessors (in the strict sense) of derivatives in the core, each evaluated at (a, b). The *complete core* of x in B is defined as

$$\omega = \omega_{s,t} \cup \omega_{s,b} \cup \omega_{a,t} \cup \omega_{a,b}.$$

The complete core ω is a set consisting of one function on I, q functions on I_s, p functions on I_t, and

$$r_1 + r_2 + \cdots + r_n$$

constants.

To illustrate consider a first example B^1 of a space B defined as follows (see Figure 2). The space B^1 is the space of functions $x(s, t)$ for which the partial derivatives

$$\begin{aligned}
x_{1,2}(s, t) &= D_tD_sD_tx,\\
x_{2,1}(s, b) &= D_s(D_sD_tx),\\
x_{0,4}(a, t) &= D_t^3(D_tx),\\
x_{1,0}(s, b) &= D_s(x)
\end{aligned} \tag{53}$$

exist and are continuous, $(s, t) \in I$. Here

$$p = 1, \quad q = 2, \quad n = 3, \quad r_1 = 1, \quad r_2 = 3, \quad r_3 = 1.$$

The core $\omega_{s,t} \cup \omega_{s,b} \cup \omega_{a,t}$ of x in B^1 is the set of derivatives (53). The set $\omega_{a,b}$ consists of

$$x_{0,0}(a, b), \quad x_{0,1}(a, b), \quad x_{0,2}(a, b), \quad x_{0,3}(a, b), \quad x_{1,1}(a, b) = D_s D_t x. \tag{54}$$

The complete core ω consists of the derivatives (53) and (54).

Together with the sets of derivatives, it is convenient to consider the corresponding sets of indices defined as follows:

$\bar{\omega}_{s,t} = \{(p, q)\} =$ the set consisting of the single element (p, q);

$\bar{\omega}_{s,b} = \{(i, j) : x_{i,j}(s, b) \in \omega_{s,b}\} =$ the set of pairs (i, j) such that $x_{i,j}(s, b) \in \omega_{s,b}$;

$\bar{\omega}_{a,t} = \{(i, j) : x_{i,j}(a, t) \in \omega_{a,t}\}$;

$\bar{\omega}_{a,b} = \{(i, j) : x_{i,j}(a, b) \in \omega_{a,b}\}$;

and

$$\bar{\omega} = \bar{\omega}_{s,t} \cup \bar{\omega}_{s,b} \cup \bar{\omega}_{a,t} \cup \bar{\omega}_{a,b}.$$

In our diagrams, we may represent the pivot $\omega_{s,t}$ by a polygonal arc of n unit segments from the point $(0, 0)$ to the point (p, q) of which p segments are parallel to the i-axis and q are parallel to the j-axis. We call this arc the *main route*. The main route is to be drawn so that it describes the differentiation (50). We sometimes write (s, t) at the point (p, q) to indicate that the derivative $x_{p,q}$ has arguments (s, t). From each integral point of the main route other than (p, q), we draw a parallel of integral length in the direction not used by the main route, terminating in a point of $\bar{\omega}_{s,b} \cup \bar{\omega}_{a,t}$. We sometimes write (s, b) at the points of $\bar{\omega}_{s,b}$ and (a, t) at the points of $\bar{\omega}_{a,t}$.

The elements of $\bar{\omega}_{s,t} \cup \bar{\omega}_{s,b} \cup \bar{\omega}_{a,t}$ together with the main route afford a complete description of the space B (providing that I and (a, b) are given). In our diagrams and tables we give these elements for a number of spaces. The reader may verify that the spaces labelled B are all of type B. We include also spaces $B_{p,q}$ of the first part of this chapter. If $B = B_{p,q}$,

$$\bar{\omega}_{s,b} = \{(n - j, j) : j < q\} = \{(n, 0), (n - 1, 1), \cdots, (p + 1, q - 1)\},$$

$$\bar{\omega}_{a,t} = \{(i, n - i) : i < p\} = \{(0, n), (1, n - 1), \cdots, (p - 1, q + 1)\},$$

$$\bar{\omega}_{s,t} = \{(p, q)\},$$

$$\bar{\omega}_{a,b} = \{(i, j) : i + j < n\}.$$

The space B is characterized by the sets $\bar{\omega}_{s,t}$, $\bar{\omega}_{s,b}$, $\bar{\omega}_{a,t}$ and by the main route. We shall prove, however, that alternative main routes taken with the same sets $\bar{\omega}_{s,t}$, $\bar{\omega}_{s,b}$, $\bar{\omega}_{a,t}$ characterize the same space. One might therefore use the symbol

$$\{\bar{\omega}_{s,t}; \quad \bar{\omega}_{s,b}; \quad \bar{\omega}_{a,t}\}$$

to describe B. The semicolons here are important. For example, a symbol for B^1 is

$$\{(1, 2); \quad (2, 1), \quad (1, 0); \quad (0, 4)\},$$

or

$$\{(1, 2); \quad (1, 0), \quad (2, 1); \quad (0, 4)\}.$$

An important instance of a space of type B is the *space* $B_{\ulcorner p,q \urcorner}$ (read B corner p, q) defined as follows. Its pivot is

$$x_{p,q}(s, t) = D_s^p D_t^q x.$$

Also

$$\bar{\omega}_{s,b} = \{(p, j) : j < q\},$$

$$\bar{\omega}_{a,t} = \{(i, q) : i < p\},$$

and therefore

$$\bar{\omega}_{a,b} = \{(i, j) : i < p \text{ and } j < q\}.$$

The spaces $B_{\ulcorner p,q \urcorner}$ have been studied by Ezrohi [1].

Other instances of spaces B are given in Figures 1–4 and Tables 1–5.

Consider a space B. The order of differentiation in $x_{i,j}$, for $x \in B$ and $(i, j) \in \bar{\omega}$, has been precisely specified. We describe that order as the *rule of* ω. The rule of ω is the following: The differentiations in $x_{i,j}$ are to follow the main route as long as possible. We shall see later that other orders of differentiation are permissible and equivalent. The rule of ω is indicated in each diagram of ω.

55. THEOREM (TAYLOR FORMULA). *If $x \in B$, then*

$$\begin{aligned} x(s, t) = & \sum_{(i,j) \in \bar{\omega}_{a,t}} (s - a)^{(i)}(t - b)^{(j)} x_{i,j}(a, b) \\ & + \sum_{(i,j) \in \bar{\omega}_{s,b}} (t - b)^{(j)} T_s^i x_{i,j}(s, b) + \sum_{(i,j) \in \bar{\omega}_{a,t}} (s - a)^{(i)} T_t^j x_{i,j}(a, t) \\ & + T_s^p T_t^q x_{p,q}(s, t), \qquad (s, t) \in I. \end{aligned} \tag{56}$$

Thus $x(s, t)$, $(s, t) \in I$, is determined by its complete core ω.

Our tables and diagrams give the complete cores of many spaces. If $B = B^1$, for example,

$$\begin{aligned} x(s, t) &= x(a, b) + (t - b)x_{0,1}(a, b) + (s - a)(t - b)x_{1,1}(a, b) \\ &\quad + (t - b)^{(2)}x_{0,2}(a, b) + (t - b)^{(3)}x_{0,3}(a, b) \\ &\quad + \int_a^s x_{1,0}(\tilde{s}, b)\, d\tilde{s} + (t - b)\int_a^s (s - \tilde{s})x_{2,1}(\tilde{s}, b)\, d\tilde{s} \\ &\quad + \int_b^t (t - \tilde{t})^{(3)}x_{0,4}(a, \tilde{t})\, d\tilde{t} + \int_a^s \int_b^t (t - \tilde{t})x_{1,2}(\tilde{s}, \tilde{t})\, d\tilde{s}\, d\tilde{t}, \end{aligned} \tag{57}$$

$$(s, t) \in I, \quad x \in B^1.$$

Proof. The proof depends on repeated application of the relations

$$\begin{aligned} y(s, t) &= y(a, t) + T_s y_{1,0}(s, t), \\ y(s, t) &= y(s, b) + T_t y_{0,1}(s, t), \end{aligned} \tag{58}$$

where the derivative $y_{1,0}$ is a continuous function of s and $y_{0,1}$ a continuous function of t. We first operate along the main route, starting with $x_{0,0}(s, t)$ and work out to $x_{p,q}(s, t)$, at each step using that relation of (58) which is apt. This gives a formula for $x(s, t)$ in terms of derivatives on the route. We then expand each of the latter derivatives, except the pivot, by operating on it along the side route emanating from it. In this process the rule of ω as regards order of differentiation is followed.

The details are illustrated by the particular case $B = B^1$. If $x \in B^1$, since the derivatives of x in the core are continuous,

$$\begin{aligned} x(s, t) &= x(s, b) + T_t x_{0,1}(s, t) = x(s, b) + T_t[x_{0,1}(a, t) + T_s x_{1,1}(s, t)] \\ &= x(s, b) + T_t x_{0,1}(a, t) + T_t T_s x_{1,1}(s, t) \\ &= x(s, b) + T_t x_{0,1}(a, t) + T_t T_s[x_{1,1}(s, b) + T_t x_{1,2}(s, t)] \\ x(s, t) &= x(s, b) + T_t x_{0,1}(a, t) + T_t T_s x_{1,1}(s, b) + T_s T_t^2 x_{1,2}(s, t). \end{aligned} \tag{59}$$

This is the expansion of $x(s, t)$ in terms of elements of the main route. We leave the last term and use the following relations to expand the earlier terms:

$$\begin{aligned} x(s, b) &= x(a, b) + T_s x_{1,0}(s, b), \\ x_{0,1}(a, t) &= x_{0,1}(a, b) + T_t x_{0,2}(a, b) + T_t^2 x_{0,3}(a, b) + T_t^4 x_{0,4}(a, t), \\ x_{1,1}(s, b) &= x_{1,1}(a, b) + T_s x_{2,1}(s, b). \end{aligned} \tag{60}$$

Each of these relations is an instance of the Taylor formula (3 : 80) or, what is the same, the result of iterations of T_s or T_t.

Substitution of (60) in (59) establishes (57), that is, (56) for $B = B^1$.

The definition of a space B and particularly the definitions of $\omega_{s,b}$ and $\omega_{a,t}$ and the rule of ω are such that the argument just applied to B^1 carries over to B. This completes the proof.

61. COROLLARY. *Consider a space B. Let*

$y^{i,j}$, $(i, j) \in \bar{\omega}_{a,b}$, *be arbitrary constants;*
$y^{i,j}(s)$, $(i, j) \in \bar{\omega}_{s,b}$, *be arbitrary continuous functions on* I_s;
$y^{i,j}(t)$, $(i, j) \in \bar{\omega}_{a,t}$, *be arbitrary continuous functions on* I_t;
$y^{p,q}(s, t)$ *be an arbitrary continuous function on* I.

Put

$$\begin{aligned} z(s, t) = & \sum_{(i,j) \in \bar{\omega}_{a,b}} (s - a)^{(i)}(t - b)^{(j)} y^{i,j} + \sum_{(i,j) \in \bar{\omega}_{s,b}} (t - b)^{(j)} T_s^i y^{i,j}(s) \\ & + \sum_{(i,j) \in \bar{\omega}_{a,t}} (s - a)^{(i)} T_t^j y^{i,j}(t) + T_s^p T_t^q y^{p,q}(s, t), \qquad (s, t) \in I. \end{aligned} \tag{62}$$

Then $z \in B$ *and the given elements* $\{y^{i,j}\}$ *constitute the complete core* ω *of* z.

PROOF. We consider a particular case first. Suppose that B is the space B^2 in which the pivot is

$$x_{2,2}(s, t) = D_s^2 D_t^2 x$$

and

$$\bar{\omega}_{s,b} = \{(1, 1), (3, 0)\}, \qquad \omega_{a,t} = \{(0, 3), (1, 3)\}$$

(see Figure 2).

Let $y^{0,0}, y^{1,0}, y^{0,1}, y^{2,0}, y^{0,2}, y^{1,2}$ be constants; $y^{1,1}(s)$, $y^{3,0}(s)$ be continuous functions on I_s; $y^{0,3}(t)$, $y^{1,3}(t)$ be continuous functions on I_t; and $y^{2,2}(s, t)$ be a continuous function on I. Put

$$\begin{aligned} z(s, t) = & \ y^{0,0} + (s - a)y^{1,0} + (t - b)y^{0,1} + (s - a)^{(2)}y^{2,0} \\ & + (t - b)^{(2)}y^{0,2} + (s - a)(t - b)^{(2)}y^{1,2} \\ & + (t - b)T_s y^{1,1}(s) + T_s^3 y^{3,0}(s) \\ & + (s - a)T_t^3 y^{1,3}(t) + T_t^3 y^{0,3}(t) \\ & + T_s^2 T_t^2 y^{2,2}(s, t), \qquad (s, t) \in I. \end{aligned} \tag{63}$$

We shall show that $z \in B^2$ by calculating the complete core ω of z. We use Lemmas 7 and 3: 74. We first calculate from (63) the derivatives of z on the main route:

$$\begin{aligned} z_{0,1}(s, t) = & \ y^{0,1} + (t - b)y^{0,2} + (s - a)(t - b)y^{1,2} + T_s y^{1,1}(s) \\ & + (s - a)T_t^2 y^{1,3}(t) + T_t^2 y^{0,3}(t) + T_s^2 T_t y^{2,2}(s, t); \end{aligned}$$

$$z_{0,2}(s, t) = y^{0,2} + (s - a)y^{1,2} + (s - a)T_t y^{1,3}(t) + T_t y^{0,3}(t) + T_s^2 y^{2,2}(s, t);$$

$$z_{1,2}(s, t) = D_s z_{0,2} = y^{1,2} + T_t y^{1,3}(t) + T_s y^{2,2}(s, t);$$

$$z_{2,2}(s, t) = D_s z_{1,2} = y^{2,2}(s, t).$$

By substitution in the above,

$$z(s, b) = y^{0,0} + (s - a)y^{1,0} + (s - a)^{(2)}y^{2,0} + T_s^3 y^{3,0}(s),$$
$$z_{0,1}(s, b) = y^{0,1} + T_s y^{1,1}(s),$$
$$z_{0,2}(a, t) = y^{0,2} + T_t y^{0,3}(t),$$
$$z_{1,2}(a, t) = y^{1,2} + T_t y^{1,3}(t).$$

Hence, by differentiation according to the rule of ω,

$$z_{1,0}(s, b) = y^{1,0} + (s - a)y^{2,0} + T_s^2 y^{3,0}(s),$$
$$z_{2,0}(s, b) = y^{2,0} + T_s y^{3,0}(s),$$
$$z_{3,0}(s, b) = y^{3,0}(s),$$
$$z_{1,1}(s, b) = D_s z_{0,1}(s, b) = y^{1,1}(s),$$
$$z_{0,3}(a, t) = y^{0,3}(t),$$
$$z_{1,3}(a, t) = D_t z_{1,2}(a, t) = y^{1,3}(t).$$

Thus the core of z exists and consists of the continuous functions

$$y^{i,j}, \qquad (i, j) \in \bar{\omega}_{s,t} \cup \bar{\omega}_{s,b} \cup \bar{\omega}_{a,t}.$$

Hence $z \in B^2$. Finally, we calculate $\omega_{a,b}$ by substitution in the above formulas:

$$z_{0,0}(a, b) = z(a, b) = y^{0,0}, \qquad z_{1,0}(a, b) = y^{1,0},$$
$$z_{2,0}(a, b) = y^{2,0}, \qquad z_{0,1}(a, b) = y^{0,1},$$
$$z_{0,2}(a, b) = y^{0,2}, \qquad z_{1,2}(a, b) = y^{1,2}.$$

Thus the complete core of z is precisely $\{y^{i,j}\}$ and the corollary is proved for B^2.

Observe that we may not consider $z_{2,2}(s, t)$ as $D_t^2 z_{2,0}$ since $z_{2,0}(s, t)$ need not exist. For example, $y^{1,1}(s)$ may be Weierstrass function, everywhere continuous and nowhere differentiable, and all other $y^{i,j}$ may vanish. Then

$$z(s, t) = (t - b)T_s y^{1,1}(s),$$
$$z_{1,0}(s, t) = (t - b)y^{1,1}(s),$$

and $z_{2,0}(s, t)$ exists only for $t = b$.

We now discuss the proof in the general case. Suppose that z is defined by (62). We shall show that the complete core of z in B is $\{y^{i,j}\}$. We consider the terms in (62) separately.

Part 1. Consider the term

$$v(s, t) = T_s^p T_t^q y^{p,q}(s, t)$$

of (62). We shall show that the complete core of v exists and consists exclusively of zeros except that $v_{p,q}(s, t) = y^{p,q}(s, t)$.

Clearly the derivatives $v_{i,j}(s, t)$ on the main route exist and

$$v_{i,j}(s, t) = T_s^{p-i} T_t^{q-j} y^{p,q}(s, t).$$

Hence

$$v_{p,q}(s, t) = y^{p,q}(s, t).$$

Also if (i, j) is on the main route and before (p, q), the substitution $s = a$ or $t = b$ will yield zero because of the presence of T_s or T_t in $v_{i,j}$. This argument applies even if $(i, j) = (p, j)$ since then the substitution is $t = b$, or if $(i, j) = (i, q)$ since then the substitution is $s = a$. Hence all the elements of $\omega_{s,b} \cup \omega_{a,t}$ are derivatives of zero and themselves zero. The elements of $\omega_{a,b}$ also are zero.

Part 2. Consider a term

$$v(s, t) = (t - b)^{(j_0)} T_s^{i_0} y^{i_0,j_0}(s), \qquad (i_0, j_0) \in \bar{\omega}_{s,b},$$

in (62). We shall show that the complete core of v exists and consists

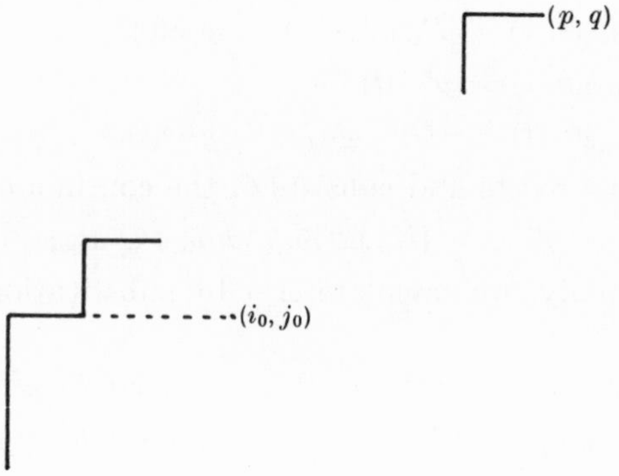

exclusively of zeros except that $v_{i_0,j_0}(s, b) = y^{i_0,j_0}(s)$. Thus

$$v_{i,j}(s, t) = (t - b)^{(j_0 - j)} T_s^{i_0 - i} y^{i_0,j_0}(s)$$

providing that $i \leqq i_0$. Hence

$$v_{i_0,j_0}(s, t) = y^{i_0,j_0}(s) = v_{i_0,j_0}(s, b).$$

Also

$$v_{p,q}(s, t) = 0$$

since, on the main route, any differentiations D_s beyond $D_s^{i_0}$ follow $D_t^{j_0+1}$ and since $D_t^{j_0+1} v = 0$. Also

$$v_{i,j}(s, b) = 0, \qquad (i, j) \in \bar{\omega}_{s,b}, \quad (i, j) \neq (i_0, j_0),$$

because, if $j < j_0$ the substitution $t = b$ nullifies the expression before any differentiations D_s beyond $D_s^{i_0}$; if $j > j_0$ over-differentiation as to t nullifies the expression before any differentiations D_s beyond $D_s^{i_0}$; and j cannot equal j_0 else $(i, j) = (i_0, j_0)$, since $(i, j) \in \bar{\omega}_{s,b}$. Also,

$$v_{i,j}(a, t) = 0, \qquad (i, j) \in \bar{\omega}_{a,t},$$

since the substitution $s = a$ or over-differentiation nullifies the derivative on the main route. Also

$$v_{i,j}(a, b) = 0, \qquad (i, j) \in \bar{\omega}_{a,b}.$$

Part 3. The dual term to that of Part 2 is treated similarly. Finally, the term

$$v = (s - a)^{(i_0)}(t - b)^{(j_0)}y^{i_0,j_0}, \qquad (i_0, j_0) \in \bar{\omega}_{a,b},$$

is a polynomial and may be differentiated in any fashion. Its complete core consists of zeros except that

$$v_{i_0,j_0}(a, b) = y^{i_0,j_0}.$$

This completes the proof of the corollary.

Theorem 55 and Corollary 61 imply that ω is a set of coordinates for x in B, since ω may consist of arbitrary elements continuous in their variables, and since ω determines and is determined by x, $x \in B$.

Suppose that $x \in B$. Then, as we have seen in the above proof, Taylor's formula for x in terms of ω may be differentiated in certain ways. Certain derivatives of x therefore necessarily exist and are expressible in terms of ω.

We now define the full core ϕ of x. In the following the derivatives $x_{i,j}$ are to be understood according to the rule of ω. First, put

$$\bar{\phi}_{s,t} = \{(i, j) : x_{i,j}(s, t) \text{ must exist and be continuous, } (s, t) \in I, \text{ for all functions } x(s, t) \in B\}$$

and

$$\phi_{s,t} = \{x_{i,j}(s, t) : (i, j) \in \bar{\phi}_{s,t}\}.$$

Then put

$$\bar{\phi}_{s,b} = \{(i, j) : (i\, j) \notin \bar{\phi}_{s,t} \text{ and } x_{i,\,j}(s, b) \text{ must exist and be continuous, } s \in I_s, \text{ for all functions } x(s, t) \in B\}$$

and

$$\phi_{s,b} = \{x_{i,j}(s, b) : (i, j) \in \bar{\phi}_{s,b}\}.$$

Define $\bar{\phi}_{a,t}$ and $\phi_{a,t}$ dually. Then the *full core* ϕ is

$$\phi = \phi_{s,t} \cup \phi_{s,b} \cup \phi_{a,t}.$$

The indices in the full core are

$$\bar{\phi} = \bar{\phi}_{s,t} \cup \bar{\phi}_{s,b} \cup \bar{\phi}_{a,t}.$$

The full core consists of derivatives which are continuous on I or I_s or I_t. It might appear that we should define $\bar{\phi}_{a,b}$ as

$$\{(i, j) : (i, j) \notin \bar{\phi}_{s,t} \cup \bar{\phi}_{s,b} \cup \bar{\phi}_{a,t} \text{ and } x_{i,j}(a, b) \text{ must exist for all functions } x(s, t) \text{ in } B\}.$$

This set, however, is empty.

The sets of indices $\bar\phi_{s,t}$, $\bar\phi_{s,b}$, and $\bar\phi_{a,t}$ which describe the full core in particular spaces are given in the figures and tables. In B^1, for example, as we shall see,

$$\begin{aligned}\bar\phi_{s,t} &= \{(0, 0), (1,0), (0, 1), (1, 1), (0, 2), (1, 2)\},\\ \bar\phi_{s,b} &= \{(2, 1)\},\\ \bar\phi_{a,t} &= \{(0, 3), (0, 4)\}.\end{aligned}$$

We define the *rule of* ϕ as the following rule about orders of differentiation. If $(i, j) \in \bar\phi_{s,t}$, the differentiations in $x_{i,j}$ may be executed in any order such that the successive derivatives have indices $(0, 0), \cdots, (i, j)$ all in $\bar\omega$. In the diagram, then, any route may be followed from $(0, 0)$ to (i, j) if all its vertices are in $\bar\omega$. If $(i, j) \in \bar\phi_{s,b}$, then $x_{i,j}(s, b)$ is taken as a derivative as to s alone of $x_{\tilde i,j}(s, b)$ where $(\tilde i, j) \in \bar\phi_{s,t}$. In this case $x_{\tilde i,j}$ may be interpreted according to the above description for elements of $\phi_{s,t}$. If $(i, j) \in \bar\phi_{a,t}$, the dual rule holds.

64. Corollary. *Suppose that* $x \in B$. *Then any element* $x_{i,j}$ *of the full core* ϕ *may be interpreted according to the rule of* ϕ. *Each element of* ϕ *may be expressed in terms of the complete core* ω. *The full core* ϕ *is characterized by the following relations:*

$$\begin{aligned}\bar\phi_{s,t} = \{(i, j) : (i, j) \in \bar\omega,\ &\text{and } i \leqq p, \text{ and } j \leqq q; \text{ and there is no}\\ &(\tilde i, \tilde j) \text{ in } \bar\omega_{s,b} \text{ such that } i > \tilde i, j \leqq \tilde j, \text{ and there is no } (\tilde i, \tilde j) \text{ in}\\ &\bar\omega_{a,t} \text{ such that } j > \tilde j, i \leqq \tilde i\}.\\ \bar\phi_{s,b} = \{(i, j) : (i, j) \in \bar\omega,\ &(i, j) \notin \bar\phi_{s,t}, \text{ and there is an } (\tilde i, j) \text{ in } \bar\omega_{s,b}\\ &\text{such that } i \leqq \tilde i\}.\end{aligned} \tag{65}$$

$\bar\phi_{a,t}$ *is the dual set. Also,*

$$\bar\phi = \bar\omega.$$

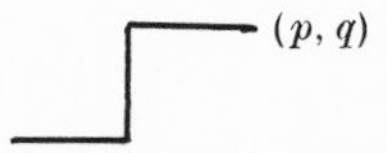

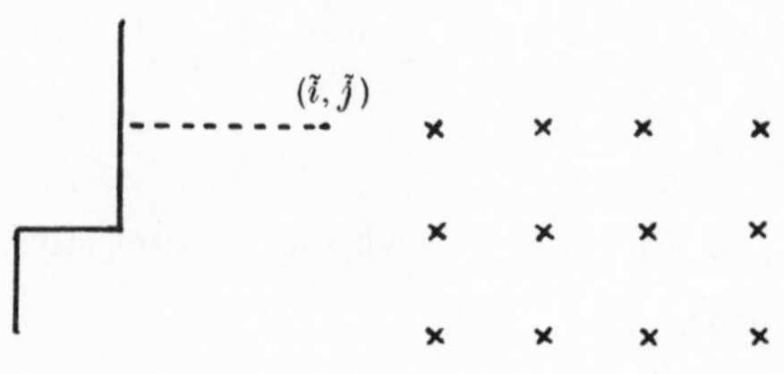

According to (65), $\bar{\phi}_{s,t}$ consists of all (i, j) in $\bar{\omega}$ with $i \leqq p$ and $j \leqq q$ except those, if any, which lie to the right and level with or below points in $\bar{\omega}_{s,b}$ and dually.

Let us introduce the notation

$$\ulcorner p, q \urcorner = \{(i, j) : i \leqq p \quad \text{and} \quad j \leqq q\}. \tag{66}$$

Thus $\ulcorner p, q \urcorner$ (corner p, q) is the set of integral points in the rectangle with opposite vertices (0, 0) and (p, q).

If

$$\bar{\omega} \supset \ulcorner p, q \urcorner, \tag{67}$$

the relations (65) *simplify to the following*:

$$\begin{aligned} \bar{\phi}_{s,t} &= \ulcorner p, q \urcorner, \\ \bar{\phi}_{s,b} &= \{(i, j) : (i, j) \in \bar{\omega} \quad \text{and} \quad i > p\}, \\ \bar{\phi}_{a,t} &= \{(i, j) : (i, j) \in \bar{\omega} \quad \text{and} \quad j > q\}. \end{aligned} \tag{68}$$

The condition (67) holds in $B_{p,q}$, $B_{\ulcorner p,q \urcorner}$, and many other spaces.

Proof of Corollary 64. Consider first the particular case $B = B^2$ (see Figure 2). We shall show that

$$\begin{aligned} \bar{\phi}_{s,t} &= \{(0, 0), (1, 0), (0, 1), (1, 1), (0, 2), (1, 2), (2, 2)\}, \\ \bar{\phi}_{s,b} &= \{(2, 0), (3, 0)\}, \\ \bar{\phi}_{a,t} &= \{(0, 3), (1, 3)\}. \end{aligned} \tag{69}$$

Consider x in B^2. Write the Taylor formula (56) for x. This is in fact (63), where $\{y^{ij}\} = \omega$ consists of elements that are continuous in their variables, $(s, t) \in I$. By differentiation,

$$\begin{aligned} x_{0,0}(s, t) = {} & y^{0,0} + (s - a)y^{1,0} + (t - b)y^{0,1} + (s - a)^{(2)}y^{2,0} \\ & + (t - b)^{(2)}y^{0,2} + (s - a)(t - b)^{(2)}y^{1,2} \\ & + (t - b)T_s y^{1,1}(s) + T_s^3 y^{3,0}(s) + (s - a)T_t^3 y^{1,3}(t) \\ & + T_t^3 y^{0,3}(t) + T_s^2 T_t^2 y^{2,2}(s, t), \end{aligned} \tag{70}$$

$$\begin{aligned} x_{1,0}(s, t) = {} & y^{1,0} + (s - a)y^{2,0} + (t - b)^{(2)}y^{1,2} + (t - b)y^{1,1}(s) \\ & + T_s^2 y^{3,0}(s) + T_t^3 y^{1,3}(t) + T_s T_t^2 y^{2,2}(s, t), \\ x_{0,1}(s, t) = {} & y^{0,1} + (t - b)y^{0,2} + (s - a)(t - b)y^{1,2} + T_s y^{1,1}(s) \\ & + (s - a)T_t^2 y^{1,3}(t) + T_t^2 y^{0,3}(t) + T_s^2 T_t y^{2,2}(s, t), \end{aligned} \tag{71}$$

$$\begin{aligned} x_{1,1}(s, t) &= D_s x_{0,1}(s, t) \\ &= (t - b)y^{1,2} + y^{1,1}(s) + T_t^2 y^{1,3}(t) + T_s T_t y^{2,2}(s, t), \\ x_{1,1}(s, t) &= D_t x_{1,0}(s, t) \quad \text{also.} \end{aligned} \tag{72}$$

$$(73)\qquad \begin{aligned} x_{0,2}(s, t) &= y^{0,2} + (s - a)y^{1,2} + (s - a)T_t y^{1,3}(t) + T_t y^{0,3}(t) \\ &\quad + T_s^2 y^{2,2}(s, t), \\ x_{1,2}(s, t) &= D_s x_{0,2}(s, t) = y^{1,2} + T_t y^{1,3}(t) + T_s y^{2,2}(s, t), \\ x_{1,2}(s, t) &= D_t x_{1,1}(s, t) \quad \text{also}. \end{aligned}$$

$$(74)\qquad x_{2,2}(s, t) = D_s x_{1,2}(s, t) = y^{2,2}(s, t).$$

Furthermore, we have carried the differentiation as far as possible. Thus there are functions x in B for which $x_{2,0}(s, t)$ need not exist, since $x_{1,0}(s, t)$ contains the term $(t - b)y^{1,1}(s)$, and $y^{1,1}(s)$ need not be differentiable. Also for which $x_{2,1}(s, t)$ need not exist. Also for which $x_{1,3}(s, t)$ need not exist, since $x_{1,2}(s, t)$ contains the term $T_s y^{2,2}(s, t)$ which may not be differentiable with respect to t. Also for which $x_{0,3}(s, t)$ need not exist.

Thus relation (69) for $\bar{\phi}_{s,t}$ is established. At the same time the rule of ϕ has been established for $\phi_{s,t}$. Observe that according to the rule of ϕ,

$$x_{2,2}(s, t) = D_s x_{1,2}(s, t).$$

We may not say that $x_{2,2}(s, t)$ is $D_t x_{2,1}(s, t)$, since $(2, 1)$ is not in $\bar{\omega}$. The exclusion is appropriate since, as we have seen, $x_{2,1}(s, t)$ need not exist.

Let us now study $\phi_{s,b}$. We have seen that $x_{2,0}(s, t)$ need not exist. By substitution in (71),

$$x_{1,0}(s, b) = y^{1,0} + (s - a)y^{2,0} + T_s^2 y^{3,0}(s).$$

Hence

$$x_{2,0}(s, b) = y^{2,0} + T_s y^{3,0}(s),$$

$$(75)\qquad x_{3,0}(s, b) = y^{3,0}(s).$$

Thus

$$(2, 0) \in \bar{\phi}_{s,b}, \qquad (3, 0) \in \bar{\phi}_{s,b}.$$

Furthermore, these two elements constitute $\bar{\phi}_{s,b}$. This may easily be seen as follows. Differentiation of (70) cannot be carried beyond $\omega_{s,t} \cup \omega_{s,b} \cup \omega_{a,t}$. Our construction of $\bar{\phi}_{s,t}$ and $\bar{\phi}_{s,b}$ has already comprehended all of $\bar{\omega}$ except $(0, 3)$ and $(1, 3)$. Neither of these is in $\bar{\phi}_{s,b}$.

In a similar fashion, we see that

$$x_{0,2}(a, t) = y^{0,2} + T_t y^{0,3}(t),$$

$$(76)\qquad x_{0,3}(a, t) = y^{0,3}(t),$$

$$(77)\qquad x_{1,2}(a, t) = y^{1,2} + T_t y^{1,3}(t),$$

$$(78)\qquad x_{1,3}(a, t) = D_t x_{1,2}(a, t) = y^{1,3}(t).$$

The relation (69) for $\bar{\phi}_{a,t}$ is correct. The rule of ϕ has applied. No other orders of differentiation are necessarily permissible for all x in B^2.

Proof in the general case. Now let us consider the proof of Corollary 64 for any space B. The most delicate part of the proof is to show that the differentiations according to the rule of ϕ are permissible and equivalent when applied to each term of (62). Let the sets $\bar{\phi}_{s,t}$, $\bar{\phi}_{s,b}$, and $\bar{\phi}_{a,t}$ be defined in relations (65). We shall show that they have the properties specified in the definition of the full core.

Part 1. Consider the term

$$v(s, t) = T_s^p T_t^q y^{p,q}(s, t)$$

in (62) and $v_{i,j}$, where $(i, j) \in \bar{\omega}$.

If $i \leqq p$ and $j \leqq q$, then for all orders of differentiation

$$v_{i,j}(s, t) = T_s^{p-i} T_t^{q-j} y^{p,q}(s, t); \tag{79}$$

hence $v_{i,j}(s, t)$ exists and is continuous. A fortiori, $v_{i,j}(s, t)$ is continuous and independent of the order of its differentiations if $(i, j) \in \bar{\phi}_{s,t}$.

If $i > p$, then surely

$$j < q,$$

and

$$(i, j) \in \bar{\phi}_{s,b},$$

as is clear from the diagram of ω. Hence, according to the rule of ϕ,

$$v_{i,j}(s, b) = D_s^{i-p} v_{p,j}(s, b) = D_s^{i-p} 0 = 0,$$

by (79).

The situation is similar if $j > q$. Also,

$$v_{p,q}(s, t) = y^{p,q}(s, t),$$

and all other elements of the complete core of v vanish.

Part 2. Consider a term

$$v(s, t) = (t - b)^{(j_0)} T_s^{i_0} y^{i_0,j_0}(s), \qquad (i_0, j_0) \in \bar{\omega}_{s,b}$$

in (62). Then surely

$$j_0 < q.$$

We shall study $v_{i,j}$, where $(i, j) \in \bar{\omega}$. If $i \leqq i_0$, then $v_{i,j}(s, t)$ surely exists and is independent of order of differentiation. Suppose then that

$$i > i_0, \qquad (i, j) \in \bar{\omega}.$$

Then $j \neq j_0$. If $j < j_0$, then $(i, j) \in \bar{\phi}_{s,b}$ and, according to the rule of ϕ,

$$v_{i,j}(s, b) = D_s^{i-i_0} v_{i_0,j}(s, b) = D_s^{i-i_0} 0 = 0.$$

If $j > j_0$, then the route from $(0, 0)$ to (i, j) cannot pass through $(i_0 + 1, j_0)$, $(i_0 + 2, j_0), \cdots$. Hence $v_{i,j}(s, b)$ must be of the form $\cdots D_t v_{\bar{i},j_0}$, where $\bar{i} \leqq i_0$. But $v_{\bar{i},j_0}(s, t)$ is independent of t. Hence $v_{i,j}(s, t) = 0$. Also,

$$v_{i_0,j_0}(s, t) = y^{i_0,j_0}(s) = v_{i_0,j_0}(s, b),$$

and all other elements of the complete core of v vanish.

Part 3. The terms in (62) corresponding to (i_0, j_0) in $\bar{\omega}_{a,t}$ are treated dually. Finally, terms

$$v = (s - a)^{(i_0)}(t - b)^{(j_0)}y^{i_0,j_0}, \qquad (i_0, j_0) \in \bar{\omega}_{a,b},$$

are polynomials;

$$v_{i_0,j_0}(s, t) = y^{i_0,j_0} = v_{i_0,j_0}(a, b),$$

and all other elements of the complete core of v vanish.

Part 4. We complete our discussion by indicating that the sets (65) cannot be enlarged. Thus $x_{p+1,j}(s, t), j \leqq q$, need not exist for all x in B, because of the term

$$\underset{s}{T^p}\underset{t}{T^q}y^{p,q}(s, t)$$

in (62). Likewise for $x_{i,q+1}(s, t),\ i \leqq p$. To justify the further exclusions in the characterization (65) of $\bar{\phi}_{s,t}$, suppose that

$$(i_0, j_0) \in \bar{\omega}_{s,b}, \quad i > i_0, \quad j \leqq j_0; \qquad (i, j) \in \bar{\omega}.$$

Consider the term

$$v = (t - b)^{(j_0)}\underset{s}{T^{i_0}}y^{i_0,j_0}(s)$$

in (62). The derivative $v_{i,j}(s, t)$ need not exist for all continuous functions $y^{i_0,j_0}(s)$.

The rule of ϕ, as we have defined it, is as broad as possible. If $(i, j) \in \bar{\phi}_{s,b}$, the last differentiations in $x_{i,j}$ must be differentiations as to s of an element of $\phi_{s,t}$; otherwise the terms $\underset{s}{T^p}\underset{t}{T^q}y^{p,q}(s, t)$ and $(t - b)^{(j_0)}\underset{s}{T^{i_0}}y^{i_0,j_0}(s)$, $i_0 < i$, $(i_0, j_0) \in \bar{\omega}_{s,b}$, could not always be differentiated.

This completes the proof of Corollary 64.

The space B is in fact independent of the main route: any two main routes which lead to the same pivot and are consistent with the same $\bar{\omega}_{s,b}$ and $\bar{\omega}_{a,t}$ and are taken therewith lead to the same space. This is because ϕ and the rule of ϕ would each be the same in the two cases.

A reader who is interested in functionals Fx which are equivalent to finite sums of Stieltjes integrals on the elements of the full core ϕ of x in B may turn to the first part of Chapter 6.

§ 80. **The spaces $\mathscr{K}^*$ and B.** For each space B, with some exceptions, there exists a useful companion space $\mathscr{K}^*$ of functionals. In order to define $\mathscr{K}^*$ we shall first introduce a new core ξ, called the covered core, of x in B.

Consider a space B with pivot $x_{p,q}$. We have defined the complete core ω, the full core ϕ, the rule of ω, and the rule of ϕ.

Let x be an element of B and x_{i_0,j_0} an element of ϕ. Then, as we have seen in Corollary 64, $x_{i_0,j_0}(s, t)$ or $x_{i_0,j_0}(s, b)$ or $x_{i_0,j_0}(a, t)$ may be expanded in terms of elements of ω. The expansion may be obtained by differentiation of and substitution in (56). We shall say that the *variables* in an expansion of x_{i_0,j_0} *are covered* if the following conditions hold:

(1) If $x_{p,q}$ appears in the expansion, it appears only in the form $\cdots T_s \cdots T_t x_{p,q}(s, t)$.

(2) If $x_{i,j}$, $(i, j) \in \bar{\omega}_{s,b}$, appears in the expansion, it appears only in the form $\cdots T_s x_{i,j}(s, b)$.

(3) The dual condition for $x_{i,j}$, $(i, j) \in \bar{\omega}_{a,t}$.

Thus s is covered by T_s and t by T_t.

We now define the covered core ξ as those derivatives of x whose expansion in terms of ω contains only covered variables. The precise definition is as follows:

$$\bar{\xi}_{s,t} = \{(i, j) : (i, j) \in \bar{\phi}_{s,t} \text{ and the variables in the expansion of } x_{i,j}(s, t) \text{ are covered for all } x \in B\};$$

$$\xi_{s,t} = \{x_{i,j}(s, t) : (i, j) \in \bar{\xi}_{s,t}\};$$

$$\bar{\xi}_{s,b} = \{(i, j) : (i, j) \in \bar{\phi}_{s,t} \cup \bar{\phi}_{s,b} \text{ and } (i, j) \notin \bar{\xi}_{s,t} \text{ and the variables in the expansion of } x_{i,j}(s, b) \text{ are covered for all } x \in B\};$$

$$\xi_{s,b} = \{x_{i,j}(s, b) : (i, j) \in \bar{\xi}_{s,b}\}.$$

$\bar{\xi}_{a,t}$ and $\xi_{a,t}$ are defined dually.

The *covered core* is

$$\xi = \xi_{s,t} \cup \xi_{s,b} \cup \xi_{a,t}.$$

Its indices are

$$\bar{\xi} = \bar{\xi}_{s,t} \cup \bar{\xi}_{s,b} \cup \bar{\xi}_{a,t}.$$

It is clear from the definition that

$$\bar{\xi} \subset \bar{\omega}_{a,b}.$$

For if $(i, j) \in \bar{\omega}_{s,t} \cup \bar{\omega}_{s,b} \cup \bar{\omega}_{a,t}$, then the expansion of $x_{i,j}$ is itself and its variables are not covered.

The covered core of B^2 is given in Figure 2. Let us see how it might be determined. We first determine $\bar{\xi}_{s,t}$ by scanning $x_{i,j}(s, t)$, where $(i, j) \in \bar{\phi}_{s,t} \cap \bar{\omega}_{a,b}$. By equations (70) through (78),

$$x_{0,0}(s, t) \in \xi_{s,t},$$

$$x_{1,0}(s, t) \notin \xi_{s,t} \quad \text{because of the term in } y^{1,1}(s),$$

$$x_{0,1}(s, t) \in \xi_{s,t},$$

$$x_{0,2}(s, t) \notin \xi_{s,t} \quad \text{because of the term in } y^{2,2}(s, t),$$

$$x_{1,2}(s, t) \notin \xi_{s,t} \quad \text{because of the term in } y^{2,2}(s, t).$$

Thus

$$\bar{\xi}_{s,t} = \{(0, 0), (0, 1)\},$$

as given in Figure 2. Next consider those of the above derivatives which are not in $\xi_{s,t}$. By substitution in (71) we see that

$$x_{1,0}(s, b) \in \xi_{s,b}, \qquad x_{1,0}(a, t) \notin \xi_{a,t}.$$

The last exclusion is due to the term $y^{1,1}(a)$. Since $y^{1,1}(s)$, an element of $\omega_{s,b}$, appears in the expansion of $x_{1,0}(a, t)$, it must appear in the form $\cdots T_s y^{1,1}(s)$ for $x_{1,0}(a, t)$ to be in $\xi_{a,t}$. Similarly,

$$x_{0,2}(s, b) \notin \xi_{s,b}, \qquad x_{0,2}(a, t) \in \xi_{a,t},$$

$$x_{1,2}(s, b) \notin \xi_{s,b}, \qquad x_{1,2}(a, t) \in \xi_{a,t}.$$

Next consider $x_{i,j}(s, b)$, $(i, j) \in \bar{\phi}_{s,b} \cap \bar{\omega}_{a,b}$. We see that

$$x_{2,0}(s, b) \in \xi_{s,b}.$$

Likewise consider $x_{i,j}(a, t)$, $(i, j) \in \bar{\phi}_{a,t} \cap \bar{\omega}_{a,b}$, which here is the empty set. Thus

$$\bar{\xi}_{s,b} = \{(1, 0), (2, 0)\}, \qquad \bar{\xi}_{a,t} = \{(0, 2), (1, 2)\}.$$

The reader may verify our descriptions of other covered cores in the figures and tables.

For all spaces B,

$$\begin{aligned} \bar{\xi} &= \bar{\omega}_{a,b}, & \bar{\xi}_{s,t} &\subset \bar{\phi}_{s,t}; \\ \bar{\xi}_{s,b} &\subset \bar{\phi}_{s,t} \cup \bar{\xi}_{s,b}, & \bar{\xi}_{a,t} &\subset \bar{\phi}_{s,t} \cup \bar{\phi}_{a,t}, \end{aligned} \tag{81}$$

as is clear from the definition. Furthermore, *if*

$$\bar{\omega} \supset \ulcorner p, q \urcorner,$$

then

$$\begin{aligned} \bar{\xi}_{s,t} &= \{(i, j) : i < p \text{ and } j < q\}, \\ \bar{\xi}_{s,b} &= \{(i, j) : i \geqq p \text{ and, for some } i_0 > i,\ (i_0, j) \in \bar{\omega}_{s,b}\}, \\ &\bar{\xi}_{a,t} \text{ is the dual set.} \end{aligned}$$

In particular, $\bar{\xi}_{s,t}$ is empty if $pq = 0$, and $\bar{\xi}_{s,t} = \ulcorner p - 1, q - 1 \urcorner$ if $pq \geqq 1$, when $\bar{\omega} \supset \ulcorner p, q \urcorner$.

If $B = B_{p,q}$, $pq \geqq 1$, then the covered core as now defined is precisely the set (31); indeed

$$\begin{aligned} \bar{\xi}_{s,t} &= \ulcorner p - 1, q - 1 \urcorner, \\ \bar{\xi}_{s,b} &= \{(i, j) : i \geqq p \text{ and } i + j < n\}, \\ &\bar{\xi}_{a,t} \text{ is the dual set.} \end{aligned}$$

In $B_{\ulcorner p,q \urcorner}$, $\bar{\xi}_{s,b}$ and $\bar{\xi}_{a,t}$ are empty.

We shall say that the covered core ξ of a space B is *well covered* if the following conditions hold:

(1) $\xi_{s,t}$ is not empty.

(2) For each (i, j) in $\bar{\xi}_{s,t}$, $x_{i,j}(s, t)$ may be obtained from $x_{0,0}$ by a sequence of $i + j$ differentiations through derivatives all of which are in $\xi_{s,t}$.

(3) For each (i, j) in $\bar{\xi}_{s,b}$, there exists an $\tilde{i} < i$ such that $(\tilde{i}, j) \in \bar{\xi}_{s,t}$ and $(i', j) \in \bar{\xi}_{s,b}$ for $i' = \tilde{i} + 1, \tilde{i} + 2, \cdots, i$.

(4) For each (i, j) in $\bar{\xi}_{a,t}$, the dual condition holds.

If ξ is well covered, we define the *rule of* ξ as the following rule about orders of differentiation. If $(i, j) \in \bar{\xi}_{s,t}$, the differentiations in $x_{i,j}$ may be executed in any order such that the successive derivatives $x_{0,0}, \cdots, x_{i,j}$ are all in $\xi_{s,t}$. If $(i, j) \in \bar{\xi}_{s,b}$, then $x_{i,j}$ must be a derivative with respect to s alone of an element of $\xi_{s,t}$. If $(i, j) \in \bar{\xi}_{a,t}$, the dual condition holds.

In our figures and tables, we have noted the spaces in which ξ is not well covered. This is the case, for example, in B^2. There $x_{1,2}(a, t)$ is an element of $\xi_{a,t}$ and cannot be obtained by differentiating an element of $\xi_{s,t}$ with respect to t alone. The rule of ξ is indicated in the diagrams wherever ξ is well covered.

The covered core ξ is surely well covered if

$$\tilde{\omega} \supset \ulcorner p, q \urcorner \quad \text{and} \quad pq \geqq 1.$$

For the remainder of this section we will *assume that the space B is such that ξ is well covered.*† We define $\mathscr{K}^*$, called the *companion space* of B, as the space of functionals which are finite sums of Lebesgue-Stieltjes integrals on the elements of the covered core ξ, the order of differentiation in each element of ξ being any order consistent with the rule of ξ.

For brevity and simplicity of notation we write formulas for Fx, $F \in \mathscr{K}^*$, as if only one ordering of differentiation in each x_{i_0, j_0} in ξ actually appears. No essential loss of idea is involved here since any discussion of ours based on properties of

$$\iint x_{i_0,j_0}\, d\mu \quad \text{or} \quad \int x_{i_0,j_0}\, d\mu$$

will apply also to a finite sum of such integrals involving different orders of differentiation in x_{i_0,j_0}, providing that all such orders conform to the rule of ξ.

Thus an element F of $\mathscr{K}^*$ is a functional of the form

$$(82)\qquad \begin{aligned} Fx = &\sum_{(i,j)\in\bar{\xi}_{s,t}} \iint x_{i,j}(s, t)\, d\mu^{i,j}(s, t) + \sum_{(i,j)\in\bar{\xi}_{s,b}} \int x_{i,j}(s, b)\, d\mu^{i,j}(s) \\ &+ \sum_{(i,j)\in\bar{\xi}_{a,t}} \int x_{i,j}(a, t)\, d\mu^{i,j}(t), \end{aligned}$$

† This is analogous to our assumption in § 30 that $pq \geqq 1$.

where $\mu^{i,j}$ are given functions of bounded variation on I, I_s, or I_t, and the integrals are taken over I, I_s, or I_t as appropriate. The superscripts in $\mu^{i,j}$ merely distinguish different entities.

The domain of definition of F consists of all functions x for which the derivatives in the integrands of (82) are integrable relative to the corresponding functions $\mu^{i,j}$ in the sense of Lebesgue-Stieltjes.

Thus if $B = B_{p,q}$, $p, q \geqq 1$, the companion space $\mathscr{K}^*$ just defined is precisely $\mathscr{K}^*_{p,q}$ as previously defined. If $B = B_{\ulcorner p,q \urcorner}$, $p, q \geqq 1$, we denote the companion space by $\mathscr{K}^*_{\ulcorner p,q \urcorner}$. Clearly

$$\mathscr{K}^*_{\ulcorner p,q \urcorner} \subset \mathscr{K}^*_{\ulcorner p',q' \urcorner} \quad \text{if } p' \geqq p,\ q' \geqq q,$$

by (82).

Consider the element F of $\mathscr{K}^*$ given by (82). We define its *jump sets* $\mathscr{J}_s$ and $\mathscr{J}_t$ relative to $\mathscr{K}^*$ as follows. The set $\mathscr{J}_s$ is the countable set of points in I_s which are points of discontinuity of

$$|\mu^{i,j}|(s) \quad \text{for } (i, j), \text{ if any, such that } (i, j) \in \bar{\xi}_{s,b} \text{ and } (i + 1, j) \in \bar{\omega}_{s,b},$$

or of

$$|\mu^{p-1,j}|(s, \tilde{\beta}) \quad \text{for } j, \text{ if any, such that } (p - 1, j) \in \bar{\xi}_{s,t},$$

or of

$$|\mu^{i,j}|(s, \tilde{\beta}) \quad \text{for } (i, j) \text{ if any, such that } (i, j) \in \bar{\xi}_{s,t} \text{ and } (i + 1, \tilde{j}) \in \bar{\omega}_{s,b} \text{ for some } \tilde{j},$$

where the bars indicate total variations and $\tilde{\beta}$ is substituted after the variation relative to (s, t) has been taken; and in addition $\mathscr{J}_s$ includes the point a if $i, j, \tilde{j}$ exist such that $(i, j) \in \bar{\xi}_{a,t}$ and $(i + 1, \tilde{j}) \in \bar{\omega}_{s,b}$.

Thus $\mathscr{J}_s$ is a subset of the following countable set of points in I_s: The set of all points in I_s which are points of discontinuity or lines of discontinuity, as appropriate, of all the total variations of the measures that appear in (82), together with the point a.

The set $\mathscr{J}_t$ is the dual of $\mathscr{J}_s$.

If $B = B_{p,q}$, $p, q \geqq 1$, the jump sets as defined above reduce to those of § 30.

If $B = B_{\ulcorner p,q \urcorner}$, $p, q \geqq 1$, the set $\mathscr{J}_s$ is simply the set of discontinuities of

$$|\mu^{p-1,j}|(s, \tilde{\beta}), \qquad j < q.$$

The set $\mathscr{J}_t$ is the dual.

We have defined B as the space of functions whose core derivatives are continuous in their arguments, $(s, t) \in I$; and we have shown that the Taylor formula (56) holds for each x in B. We shall define a larger† space

† A reader wishing to simplify the theory may disregard $\boldsymbol{B}$ and proceed directly to Theorem 84, replacing the hypothesis $x \in \boldsymbol{B}$ by $x \in B$.

$\boldsymbol{B}$ (bold B) of functions $x(s, t)$ for which the Taylor formula (56) holds and for which the core derivatives are Lebesgue integrable.

Thus far the rule of ξ applies to derivatives $x_{i,j}$ with $(i, j) \in \bar{\xi} = \bar{\omega}_{a,b}$. We need to extend the rule to derivatives in $\omega - \omega_{a,b}$. Assume that

$$pq \geqq 1;$$
$$(p - 1, q - 1) \in \bar{\xi}_{s,t};$$
$$(i - 1, j) \in \bar{\xi}_{s,b} \cup \bar{\xi}_{s,t} \quad \text{whenever } (i, j) \in \bar{\omega}_{s,b};$$
$$(i, j - 1) \in \bar{\xi}_{a,t} \cup \bar{\xi}_{s,t} \quad \text{whenever } (i, j) \in \bar{\omega}_{a,t}.$$

Most spaces B satisfy these conditions, but B^2 and B^5 for example do not. In order that the conditions hold it is sufficient merely that

$$\bar{\omega} \supset \ulcorner p, q \urcorner \quad \text{and} \quad pq \geqq 1.$$

We now define the *rule of* ξ for elements of $\omega - \omega_{a,b}$ as follows:

$$x_{p,q}(s, t) = D_s D_t x_{p-1,q-1}(s, t) \quad \text{or} \quad D_t D_s x_{p-1,q-1}(s, t);$$
$$x_{i,j}(s, b) = D_s x_{i-1,j}(s, b), \qquad (i, j) \in \bar{\omega}_{s,b};$$
$$x_{i,j}(a, t) = D_t x_{i,j-1}(a, t), \qquad (i, j) \in \bar{\omega}_{a,t};$$

where all the derivatives written after D_s, D_t, being elements of ξ, are understood according to the rule of ξ.

The *space* $\boldsymbol{B}$ is defined as the space of functions $x(s, t)$ for which the following conditions all hold:

(1) The derivative $x_{p,q}(s, t)$ exists almost everywhere in I and is Lebesgue integrable there.

(2) The elements of $\omega_{s,b}$ exist almost everywhere in I_s and are Lebesgue integrable there. Dually for $\omega_{a,t}$.

(3) The elements of $\omega_{a,b}$ exist.

(4) The Taylor formula (56) holds for $x(s, t)$, $(s, t) \in I$.

The derivatives are to be understood according to the rule of ξ. Thus

$$B \subset \boldsymbol{B},$$

since the rule of ξ is consistent with the rule of ϕ.

83. Lemma. *Suppose that $x \in \boldsymbol{B}$. Then the elements of $\phi_{s,t}$ are given by Taylor formulas in terms of ω for almost all (s, t) in I; the elements of $\phi_{s,b}$ are given by Taylor formulas in terms of $\omega_{a,b} \cup \omega_{s,b}$ for almost all s in I_s; the elements of $\phi_{a,t}$ are given dually. Each element of ϕ may be interpreted in all fashions consistent with the rule of ξ. The elements of ξ are given by Taylor formulas in terms of ω for all (s, t) in I and are continuous in their variables.*

Proof. This lemma is similar to Lemma 34, and we omit a detailed discussion of the proof. The reader may wish to go over the details for $\boldsymbol{B} = \boldsymbol{B}^1$ or $\boldsymbol{B}^6$, for example.

The lemma would not apply to the space $\boldsymbol{B}^2$, had such a space been defined. The statement that the elements of ξ would be given by Taylor formulas for all (s, t) would be false. To see this, let

$$x(s, t) = T_s^2 T_t^2 y(s, t) + (t - b)T_s z(s),$$

where $y(s, t)$ and $z(s)$ are integrable. This relation is an instance of the Taylor formula (70) on B^2. Conditions (1), $\cdots$, (4) hold with $B = B^2$, and x would be an element of $\boldsymbol{B}^2$ if the latter had been defined. Nonetheless $x_{1,2}(a, t)$, no matter how interpreted, need not exist although it should be an element of $\xi_{a,t}$ in B^2 since the expansion (77) contains only covered variables. To see that $x_{1,2}(a, t)$ need not exist, put

$$z(s) = m(s), \qquad y(s, t) = m(t),$$

where $m(s)$ is a strictly monotone function, discontinuous at rational s and continuous at irrational s. Then

$$\begin{aligned}
x(s, t) &= T_s^2 T_t^2 m(t) + (t - b)T_s m(s);\\
x(s, t) &= (s - a)^{(2)} T_t^2 m(t) + (t - b)T_s m(s);\\
x_{1,0}(s, t) &= (s - a)T_t^2 m(t) + (t - b)m(s) \quad \text{iff } s \text{ is irrational or } t = b;\\
x_{0,1}(s, t) &= (s - a)^{(2)} T_t m(t) + T_s m(s);\\
x_{0,2}(s, t) &= (s - a)^{(2)} m(t) \quad \text{iff } t \text{ is irrational or } s = a;\\
D_s x_{0,1}(s, t) &= (s - a)T_t m(t) + m(s) \quad \text{iff } s \text{ is irrational.}
\end{aligned}$$

If a and t are both rational, then $x_{1,2}(a, t)$ does not exist, for any order of differentiation.

84. Kernel theorem. *Suppose that $F \in \mathscr{K}^*$. Then functions*

$$\begin{aligned}
&\kappa^{p,q}(s, t), \quad (s, t) \in I;\\
&\kappa^{i,j}(s), \quad s \in I_s; \qquad (i, j) \in \bar{\omega}_{s,b};\\
&\kappa^{i,j}(t), \quad t \in I_t; \qquad (i, j) \in \bar{\omega}_{a,t};
\end{aligned}$$

all of bounded variation, and constants

$$c^{i,j}, \qquad (i, j) \in \bar{\omega}_{a,b},$$

exist such that

$$\begin{aligned}
Fx = &\sum_{(i,j)\in\bar{\omega}_{a,b}} c^{i,j} x_{i,j}(a, b) + \sum_{(i,j)\in\bar{\omega}_{s,b}} \int x_{i,j}(s, b)\kappa^{i,j}(s)\, ds\\
&+ \sum_{(i,j)\in\bar{\omega}_{a,t}} \int x_{i,j}(a, t)\kappa^{i,j}(t)\, dt + \iint x_{p,q}(s, t)\kappa^{p,q}(s, t)\, ds\, dt
\end{aligned} \tag{85}$$

whenever $x \in \boldsymbol{B}$. Furthermore

$$c^{i,j} = F[(s - a)^{(i)}(t - b)^{(j)}], \qquad (i, j) \in \bar{\omega}_{a,b}; \tag{86}$$

and the kernels $\kappa^{i,j}$ may be taken so that

$$(87) \qquad \kappa^{i,j}(\tilde{s}) = F[(s - \tilde{s})^{(i-1)}\psi(a, \tilde{s}, s)(t - b)^{(j)}], \qquad \tilde{s} \notin \mathscr{J}_s, \quad (i, j) \in \bar{\omega}_{s,b};$$

$$(88) \qquad \kappa^{i,j}(\tilde{t}) = F[(s - a)^{(i)}(t - \tilde{t})^{(j-1)}\psi(b, \tilde{t}, t)], \qquad \tilde{t} \notin \mathscr{J}_t, \quad (i, j) \in \bar{\omega}_{a,t};$$

$$(89) \qquad \kappa^{p,q}(\tilde{s}, \tilde{t}) = F[(s - \tilde{s})^{(p-1)}\psi(a, \tilde{s}, s)(t - \tilde{t})^{(q-1)}\psi(b, \tilde{t}, t)],$$
$$\tilde{s} \notin \mathscr{J}_s \quad and \quad \tilde{t} \notin \mathscr{J}_t,$$

where $\mathscr{J}_s$ and $\mathscr{J}_t$ are the jump sets of F. Conversely if constants $c^{i,j}$ and functions $\kappa^{i,j} \in V$ are given, then the functional defined by (85) may be extended so as to become an element of $\mathscr{K}^*$.

This theorem includes the earlier Theorem 36. Our comments after the statement of Theorem 36 apply here also.

PROOF. The proof is as before. We start with the Taylor formula for $x(s, t)$ in terms of ω; we operate on x by (82); and we use the device $(1:14)$. Consider x in $\boldsymbol{B}$. By Lemma 83, the elements of the covered core ξ of x will be given for all (s, t) by Taylor formulas based on the complete core ω of x with all variables covered.

It would be uninteresting to repeat the details of the proof, for the most part. Let us consider, however, the rôle of $\mathscr{J}_s$ and $\mathscr{J}_t$ (cf. Part 2 of the proof of Theorem 36).

To establish (87), define the function y as

$$y(s, t) = (s - \tilde{s})^{(i_0-1)}\psi(a, \tilde{s}, s)(t - b)^{(j_0)}, \qquad (i_0, j_0) \in \bar{\omega}_{s,b},$$

and consider Fy. Since $(i_0, j_0) \in \bar{\omega}_{s,b}$, it follows that $(i_0, j_0) \notin \bar{\xi}$.

If $(i, j) \in \bar{\xi}_{s,t}$, then

$$y_{i,j}(s, t) = (s - \tilde{s})^{(i_0-i-1)}\psi(a, \tilde{s}, s)(t - b)^{(j_0-j)},$$

except that if $i = i_0 - 1$, s must be different from $\tilde{s}$. This is true because of the exclusions in (65). For if $i > i_0 - 1$, then $j > j_0$, since $(i, j) \in \bar{\xi}_{s,t}$ and $(i + 1, j) \in \bar{\phi}_{s,t}$ so that $j \leq j_0$ would be excluded. The factor $(t - b)^{(j_0-j)}$ would then annihilate the entire expression, since the path of differentiation must lie in $\bar{\xi}$.

If $(i, j) \in \bar{\xi}_{s,b}$, then for some $(\tilde{i}, j)$ in $\bar{\xi}_{s,t}$,

$$y_{i,j}(s, b) = D_s^{i-\tilde{i}}y_{\tilde{i},j}(s, b) = \begin{cases} 0 & \text{if } j \neq j_0, \\ (s - \tilde{s})^{(i_0-i-1)}\psi(a, \tilde{s}, s) & \text{if } j = j_0, \end{cases}$$

except that if $i = i_0 - 1$, $j = j_0$, then s must be different from $\tilde{s}$.

If $(i, j) \in \bar{\xi}_{a,t}$, then for some $(i, \tilde{j})$ in $\bar{\xi}_{s,t}$,

$$y_{i,j}(a, t) = D_t^{j-\tilde{j}}y_{i,\tilde{j}}(a, t) = 0,$$

except that if $i = i_0 - 1$, a must be different from $\tilde{s}$.

Now all the exceptional values of s noted above are inconsequential in the use of (82) unless $\tilde{s} \in \mathscr{J}_s$. Hence if $\tilde{s} \notin \mathscr{J}_s$, we may evaluate Fy, and furthermore

$$Fy = \kappa^{i,j}(\tilde{s}), \qquad (i, j) \in \bar{\omega}_{s,b}.$$

To establish (89), define the function z as

$$z(s, t) = (s - \tilde{s})^{(p-1)}\psi(a, \tilde{s}, s)(t - \tilde{t})^{(q-1)}\psi(b, \tilde{t}, t),$$

and consider Fz.

If $(i, j) \in \bar{\xi}_{s,t}$,

$$z_{i,j}(s, t) = (s - \tilde{s})^{(p-i-1)}\psi(a, \tilde{s}, s)(t - \tilde{t})^{(q-j-1)}\psi(b, \tilde{t}, t),$$

except that if $i = p - 1$, s must be different from $\tilde{s}$ and if $j = q - 1$, t must be different from $\tilde{t}$.

If $(i, j) \in \bar{\xi}_{s,b}$, then for some $(\tilde{i}, j)$ in $\bar{\xi}_{s,t}$,

$$z_{i,j}(s, b) = D_s^{i-i}z_{\tilde{i},j}(s, b) = 0,$$

except that if $\tilde{i} = p - 1$, then $z_{i,j}(s, b)$ may not be defined if $s = \tilde{s}$. We agree to count the integrand $z_{i,j}(s, b)$ as identically zero in a case like this.

If $(i, j) \in \bar{\xi}_{a,t}$, the dual situation holds.

Now all the exceptional values of s noted above are inconsequential unless $\tilde{s} \in \mathscr{J}_s$ and those of t are inconsequential unless $\tilde{t} \in \mathscr{J}_t$. Hence

$$Fz = \kappa^{p,q}(\tilde{s}, \tilde{t}), \qquad \tilde{s} \notin \mathscr{J}_s \quad \text{and} \quad \tilde{t} \notin \mathscr{J}_t.$$

This completes our discussion of the proof of Theorem 84.

The form of relations (86)–(89) for $c^{i,j}$ and $\kappa^{i,j}$ depends only on (i, j) and whether (i, j) is an element of $\bar{\omega}_{a,b}$, $\bar{\omega}_{s,b}$, $\bar{\omega}_{a,t}$, $\bar{\omega}_{s,t}$, respectively, and not otherwise on the space B. The relations (87)–(89) may be put into alternative forms by the use of the equalities

$$\psi(a, \tilde{s}, s) = \theta(\tilde{s}, a) - \theta(\tilde{s}, s) = \phi(\tilde{s}, s) - \phi(\tilde{s}, a)$$

of § 11 : 2. Thus, for example, (87) implies that

$$\kappa^{i,j}(\tilde{s}) = \theta(\tilde{s}, a)F[(s - \tilde{s})^{(i-1)}(t - b)^{(j)}] - F[(s - \tilde{s})^{(i-1)}\theta(\tilde{s}, s)(t - b)^{(j)}],$$
$$(i, j) \in \bar{\omega}_{s,t},$$

since $\theta(\tilde{s}, a)$ is independent of s. Hence, if *Fx is zero for polynomials of degree $i + j - 1$, then*

$$(90) \quad \kappa^{i,j}(\tilde{s}) = -F[(s - \tilde{s})^{(i-1)}\theta(\tilde{s}, s)(t - b)^{(j)}]$$

$$(91) \qquad\qquad = F[(s - \tilde{s})^{(i-1)}\phi(\tilde{s}, s)(t - b)^{(j)}], \qquad \tilde{s} \notin \mathscr{J}_s, \quad (i, j) \in \bar{\omega}_{s,b}.$$

The dual relation holds: *If Fx is zero for degree $i + j - 1$, then*

$$(92) \quad \kappa^{i,j}(\tilde{t}) = -F[(s - a)^{(i)}(t - \tilde{t})^{(j-1)}\theta(\tilde{t}, t)]$$

$$(93) \qquad\qquad = F[(s - a)^{(i)}(t - \tilde{t})^{(j-1)}\phi(\tilde{t}, t)], \qquad \tilde{t} \notin \mathscr{J}_t, \quad (i, j) \in \bar{\omega}_{a,t}.$$

The formula for $\kappa^{p,q}(\tilde{s}, \tilde{t})$ may be transformed similarly, but comparable simplifications do not occur.

§ 94. **Symmetry.** Suppose that I and (a, b) are symmetric relative to the t-axis; that is, that 0 is the midpoint of I_s and that $a = 0$. Consider $F \in \mathscr{K}^*$.

We say that F is *symmetric in* s if

$$F[x(s, t)] = F[x(-s, t)]$$

whenever $x \in B$. *In this case*

$$c^{i,j} = 0, \qquad i \text{ odd}, \quad (i, j) \in \bar{\omega}_{a,b};$$

and the kernel

$$\kappa^{i,j}, \quad (i, j) \in \bar{\omega}_{s,b} \cup \bar{\omega}_{s,t},$$

is even or odd in s *according as* i *is even or odd.*

We say that F is *skew symmetric in* s if

$$F[x(s, t)] = -F[x(-s, t)]$$

whenever $x \in B$. *In this case*

$$c^{i,j} = 0, \qquad i \text{ even}, \quad (i, j) \in \bar{\omega}_{a,b};$$

and the kernel

$$\kappa^{i,j}, \quad (i, j) \in \bar{\omega}_{s,b} \cup \bar{\omega}_{s,t},$$

is even or odd in s *according as* i *is odd or even.*

These facts are proved by the use of (86)–(89). The proofs are similar to those of Corollaries 1 : 37 and 1 : 41.

§ 95. **Appraisals.** Suppose that $F \in \mathscr{K}^*$. We have established an equality for Fx, $x \in \boldsymbol{B}$. The equality can be the basis for infinitely many sharp appraisals of Fx, $x \in \boldsymbol{B}$. We shall indicate some of these.

For simplicity of notation suppose that $B = B_{p,q}$, $p, q \geqq 1$. Our discussion carries over to all spaces B which have companions $\mathscr{K}^*$. We know that

$$\begin{aligned} Fx = {} & \sum_{i+j<n} c^{i,j} x_{i,j}(a, b) + \sum_{j<q} \int x_{n-j,j}(s, b) f^j(s)\, ds \\ & + \sum_{i<p} \int x_{i,n-i}(a, t) g^i(t)\, dt + \iint x_{p,q}(s, t) h(s, t)\, ds\, dt, \qquad x \in \boldsymbol{B}_{p,q}, \end{aligned} \tag{96}$$

where f^j, g^i, and h are functions of bounded variation. Now the complete core of x consists of independent elements. Hence each term in the expression for Fx may be appraised separately. If the appraisals of the individual terms are sharp, the resulting appraisal for Fx is sharp. Thus

$$|Fx| \leqq \sum_{i+j<n} |c^{i,j}|\, |x_{i,j}(a, b)| + \sum_{j<q} A^j + \sum_{i<p} B^i + C, \tag{97}$$

where A^j is any sharp appraisal of

$$\int x_{n-j,j}(s, b) f^j(s)\, ds,$$

B^i is any sharp appraisal of

$$\int x_{i,n-i}(a, t)g^i(t)\, dt,$$

and C is any sharp appraisal of

$$\iint x_{p,q}(s, t)h(s, t)\, ds\, dt.$$

Alternatively, we may treat the right-hand member of (96) as one integral (on the space which is the union of the s, t-plane, the q s-axes, the p t-axes, and the $n(n + 1)/2$ points (a, b)). Thus, for example,

$$\begin{aligned}|Fx| \leqq L\Big[\sum_{i+j<n} |x_{i,j}(a, b)| &+ \sum_{j<q} \int |x_{n-j,j}(s, b)|\, ds \\ &+ \sum_{i<p} \int |x_{i,n-i}(a, t)|\, dt + \iint |x_{p,q}(s, t)|\, ds\, dt\Big], \qquad x \in \boldsymbol{B}_{p,q},\end{aligned} \tag{98}$$

where

$$L = \max\,[|c^{i,j}|, i + j < n;\ \sup_{s \in I_s} |f^j(s)|, j < q;\ \sup_{t \in I_t} |g^i(t)|, i < p;\ \sup_{(s,t) \in I} |h(s, t)|].$$

The suprema in the expression for L may be replaced by essential suprema; this will make no difference if f^j, g^i, h at each discontinuity lie between their upper and lower limits. Or

$$\begin{aligned}|Fx| \leqq M \max\,[|x_{i,j}(a, b)|, i + j < n;\ &\sup_{s \in I_s} |x_{n-j,j}(s, b)|, j < q; \\ &\sup_{t \in I_t} |x_{i,n-i}(a, t)|, i < p;\ \sup_{(s,t) \in I} |x_{p,q}(s, t)|], \qquad x \in \boldsymbol{B}_{p,q},\end{aligned} \tag{99}$$

where

$$M = \sum_{i+j<n} |c^{i,j}| + \sum_{j<q} \int |f^j(s)|\, ds + \sum_{i<p} \int |g^i(t)|\, dt + \iint |h(s, t)|\, ds\, dt.$$

Here the suprema in the multiplier of M may be replaced by essential suprema.

Finally for $e > 1$ and

$$\frac{1}{e} + \frac{1}{e'} = 1,$$

we may write Hölder's inequality:

$$\begin{aligned}|Fx| \leqq N\Big[\sum_{i+j<n} |x_{i,j}(a, b)|^e &+ \sum_{j<q} \int |x_{n-j,j}(s, b)|^e\, ds \\ &+ \sum_{i<p} \int |x_{i,n-i}(a, t)|^e\, dt + \iint |x_{p,q}(s, t)|^e\, ds\, dt\Big]^{1/e}, \qquad x \in \boldsymbol{B}_{p,q},\end{aligned} \tag{100}$$

where

$$N = \left[\sum_{i+j<n} |c^{i,j}|^{e'} + \sum_{j<q} \int |f^j(s)|^{e'}\,ds + \sum_{i<p} \int |g^i(t)|^{e'}\,dt + \iint |h(s,t)|^{e'}\,ds\,dt\right]^{1/e'}.$$

In particular, for $e = e' = 2$,

$$\begin{aligned} |Fx| \leqq J^{1/2}\Big[\sum_{i+j<n} |x_{i,j}(a,b)|^2 &+ \sum_{j<q} \int |x_{n-j,j}(s,b)|^2\,ds \\ &+ \sum_{i<p} \int |x_{i,n-i}(a,t)|^2\,dt + \iint |x_{p,q}(s,t)|^2\,ds\,dt\Big]^{1/2}, \quad x \in \boldsymbol{B}_{p,q}, \end{aligned} \tag{101}$$

where

$$J = \sum_{i+j<n} |c^{i,j}|^2 + \sum_{j<q} \int |f^j(s)|^2\,ds + \sum_{i<p} \int |g^i(t)|^2\,dt + \iint |h(s,t)|^2\,ds\,dt.$$

There are other appraisals still, for we may introduce weights. Thus let

$w^{i,j}$ be positive constants, $i + j < n$;
$w^j(s)$ be positive measurable functions of s, $j < q$;
$w^i(t)$ be positive measurable functions of t, $i < p$; and
$w^{p,q}(s,t)$ be a positive measurable function of (s,t);

all the functions being bounded away from zero and from ∞. Then, by (96),

$$\begin{aligned} Fx = \sum_{i+j<n} \frac{c^{i,j}}{w^{i,j}}\, x_{i,j}(a,b) w^{i,j} &+ \sum_{j<q} \int x_{n-j,j}(s,b) w^j(s) \frac{f^j(s)}{w^j(s)}\,ds \\ &+ \text{dual term} + \iint x_{p,q}(s,t) w^{p,q}(s,t) \frac{h(s,t)}{w^{p,q}(s,t)}\,ds\,dt, \qquad x \in \boldsymbol{B}_{p,q}. \end{aligned}$$

One may now apply all the earlier techniques to this expression. We note the result only for Schwarz's inequality (101):

$$\begin{aligned} |Fx| \leqq \tilde{J}^{1/2}\Big[\sum_{i+j<n} |w^{i,j} x_{i,j}(a,b)|^2 &+ \sum_{j<q} \int |w^j(s) x_{n-j,j}(s,\ b)|^2\,ds \\ &+ \text{dual term} + \iint |w^{p,q}(s,t) x_{p,q}(s,t)|^2\,ds\,dt\Big]^{1/2}, \quad x \in \boldsymbol{B}_{p,q}, \end{aligned} \tag{102}$$

where

$$\tilde{J} = \sum_{i+j<n} \left|\frac{c^{i,j}}{w^{i,j}}\right|^2 + \sum_{j<q} \int \left|\frac{f^j(s)}{w^j(s)}\right|^2 ds + \text{dual term} + \iint \left|\frac{h(s,t)}{w^{p,q}(s,t)}\right|^2 ds\,dt.$$

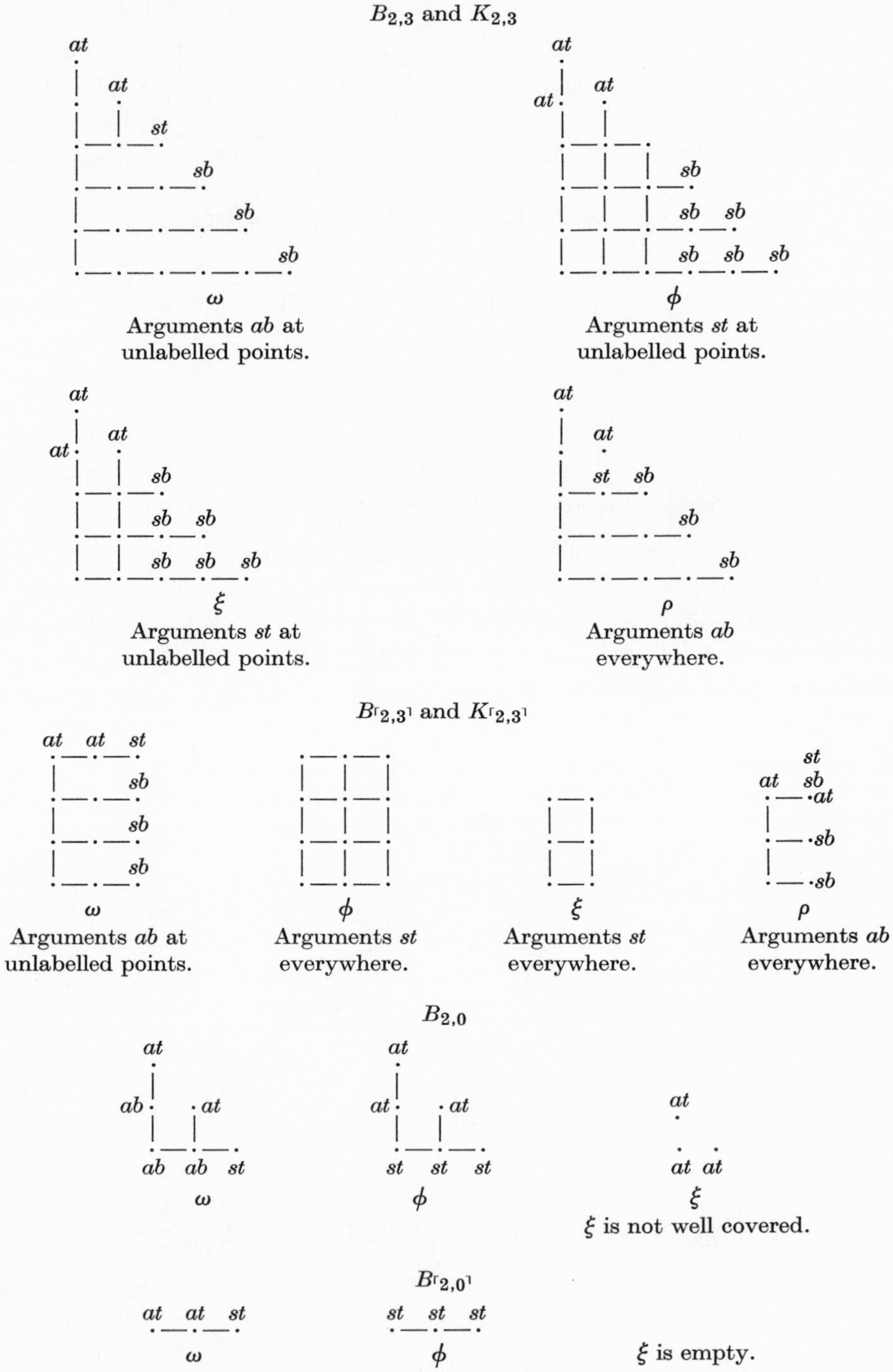

FIGURE 1. Cores and rules of cores.

Table 1

Cores of x in $B_{p,q}$ and, if $pq \geqq 1$, $K_{p,q}$

$$n = p + q$$

$$\omega_{s,t} = \{x_{p,q}(s, t)\}.$$
$$\omega_{s,b} = \{x_{n-j,j}(s, b) : j < q\}.$$
$$\omega_{a,t} = \{x_{i,n-i}(a, t) : i < p\}.$$
$$\omega_{a,b} = \{x_{i,j}(a, b) : i + j < n\}.$$

$$\phi_{s,t} = \{x_{i,j}(s, t) : i \leqq p \quad \text{and} \quad j \leqq q\}.$$
$$\phi_{s,b} = \{x_{i,j}(s, b) : i > p \quad \text{and} \quad i + j \leqq n\}.$$
$$\phi_{a,t} = \{x_{i,j}(a, t) : j > q \quad \text{and} \quad i + j \leqq n\}.$$

$$\xi_{s,t} = \{x_{i,j}(s, t) : i < p \quad \text{and} \quad j < q\}.$$
$$\xi_{s,b} = \{x_{i,j}(s, b) : i \geqq p \quad \text{and} \quad i + j < n\}.$$
$$\xi_{a,t} = \{x_{i,j}(a, t) : j \geqq q \quad \text{and} \quad i + j < n\}.$$

$$\rho_{s,t} = \{\delta_s \delta_t x_{p-1,q-1}(s, t)\}.$$
$$\rho_{s,b} = \{\delta_s x_{n-j-1,j}(s, b) : j < q\}.$$
$$\rho_{a,t} = \{\delta_t x_{i,n-i-1}(a, t) : i < p\}.$$
$$\rho_{a,b} = \omega_{a,b}.$$

Rule of ϕ: For elements of $\phi_{s,t}$, all orders of differentiation. For elements of $\phi_{s,b}$, differentiations as to s alone of an element of $\phi_{s,t}$. For elements of $\phi_{a,t}$, the dual condition.

Rule of ξ: The rule obtained by replacing ϕ by ξ in the above statement.

Table 2

Cores of x in $B_{\ulcorner p,q \urcorner}$ and, if $pq \geqq 1$, $K_{\ulcorner p,q \urcorner}$

$$n = p + q$$

$$\omega_{s,t} = \{x_{p,q}(s, t)\}.$$
$$\omega_{s,b} = \{x_{p,j}(s, b) : j < q\}.$$
$$\omega_{a,t} = \{x_{i,q}(a, t) : i < p\}.$$
$$\omega_{a,b} = \{x_{i,j}(a, b) : i < p \quad \text{and} \quad j < q\}.$$

$$\phi_{s,t} = \{x_{i,j}(s, t) : i \leqq p \quad \text{and} \quad j \leqq q\} = \phi.$$
$\phi_{s,b}$ and $\phi_{a,t}$ are empty.

$$\xi_{s,t} = \{x_{i,j}(s, t) : i < p \quad \text{and} \quad j < q\} = \xi.$$
$\xi_{s,b}$ and $\xi_{a,t}$ are empty.

$$\rho_{s,t} = \{\delta_s \delta_t x_{p-1,q-1}(s, t)\}.$$
$$\rho_{s,b} = \{\delta_s x_{p-1,j}(s, b) : j < q\}.$$
$$\rho_{a,t} = \{\delta_t x_{i,q-1}(a, t) : i < p\}.$$
$$\rho_{a,b} = \omega_{a,b}.$$

The rules of ϕ and ξ permit all orders of differentiation.

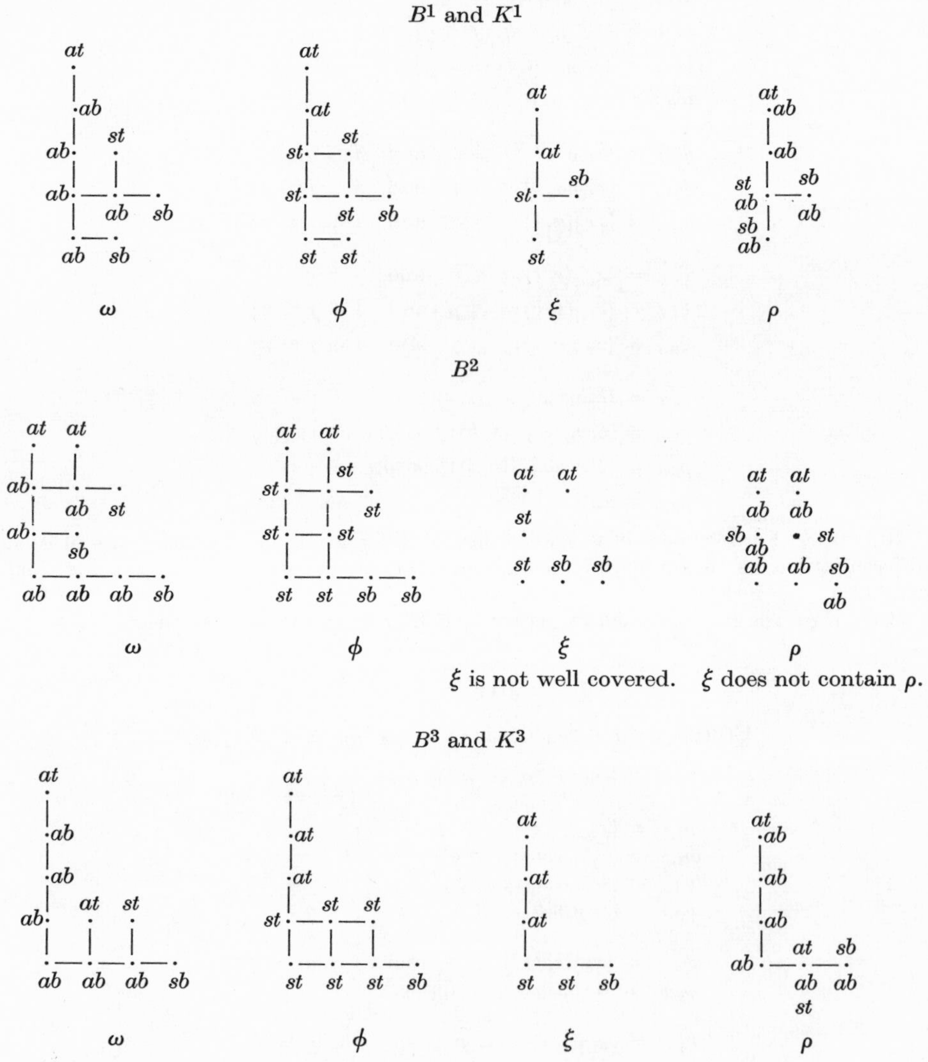

FIGURE 2. Cores and rules of cores.

B^4

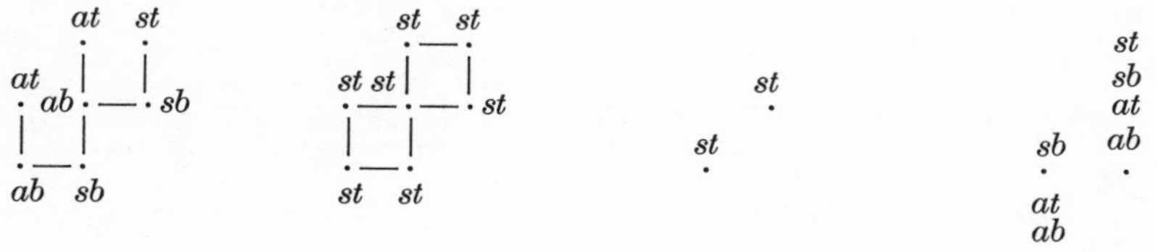

ω φ ξ ρ

ξ is not well covered.

B^5

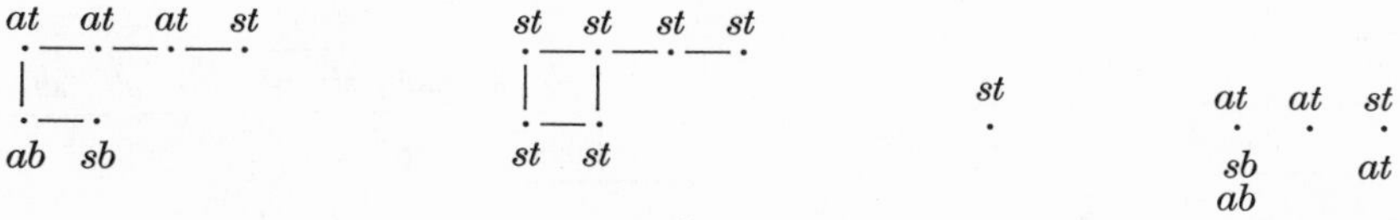

ω φ ξ ρ

Neither ξ nor φ contains ρ.

B^6 and K^6

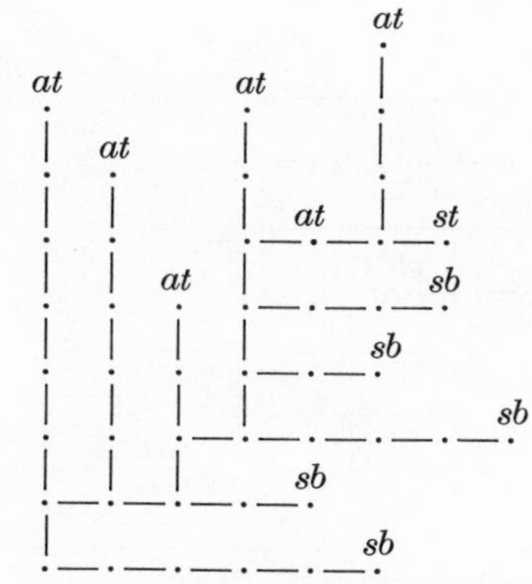

ω

Arguments *ab* at unlabelled points.

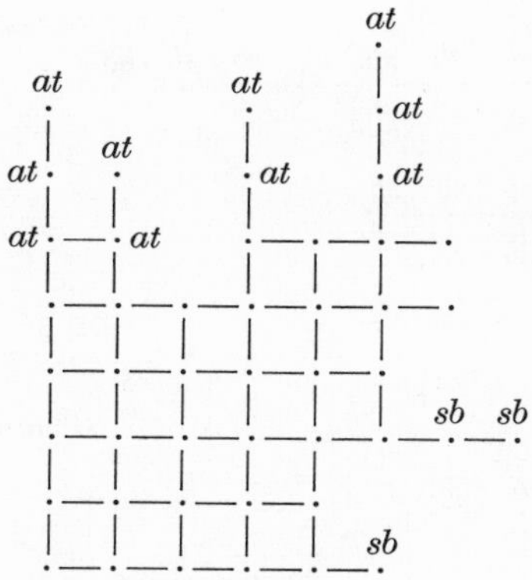

φ

Arguments *st* at unlabelled points.

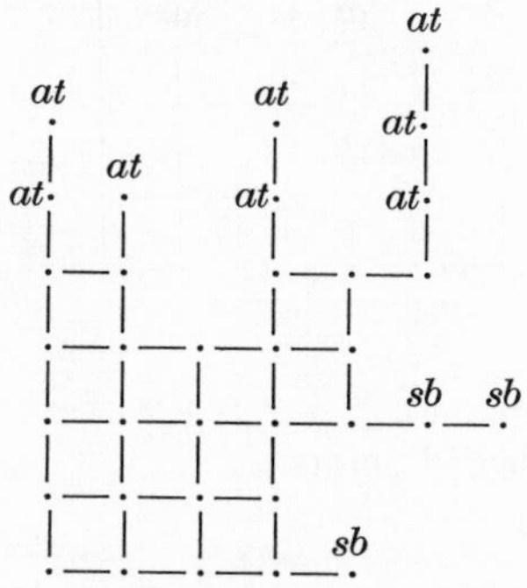

ξ

Arguments *st* at unlabelled points.

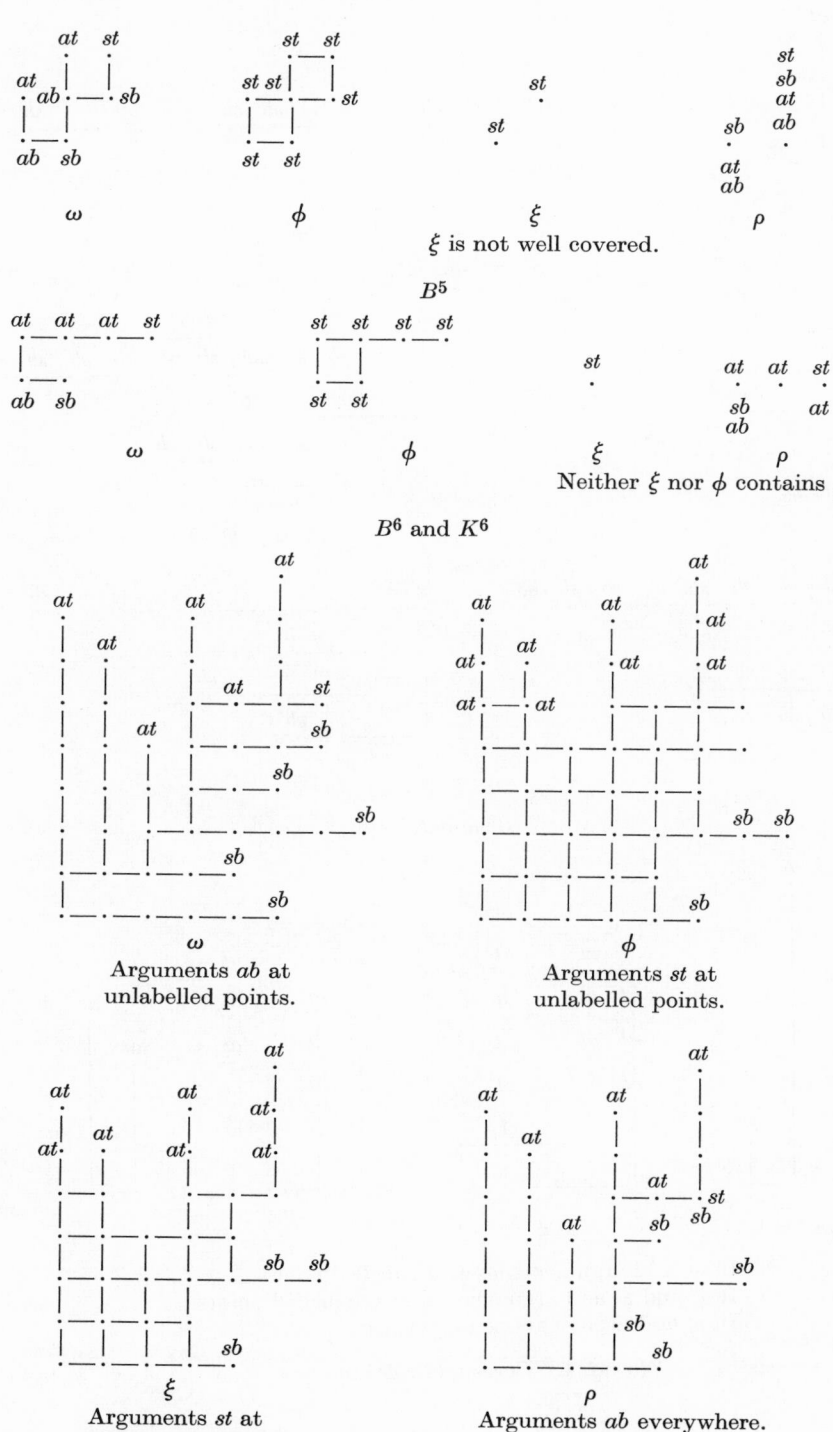

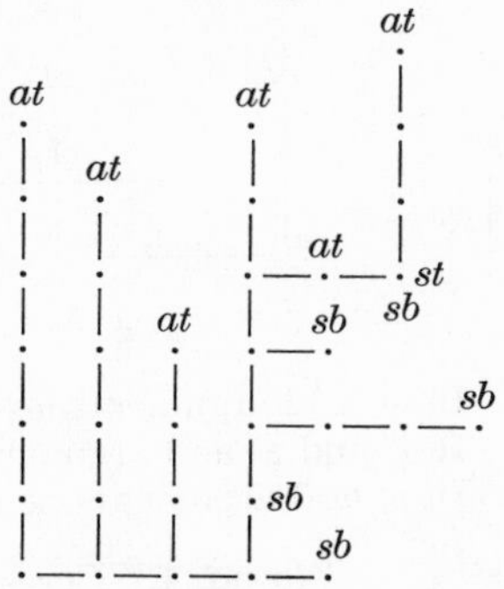

ρ

Arguments *ab* everywhere.

Figure 3. Cores and rules of cores.

B^7 and K^7

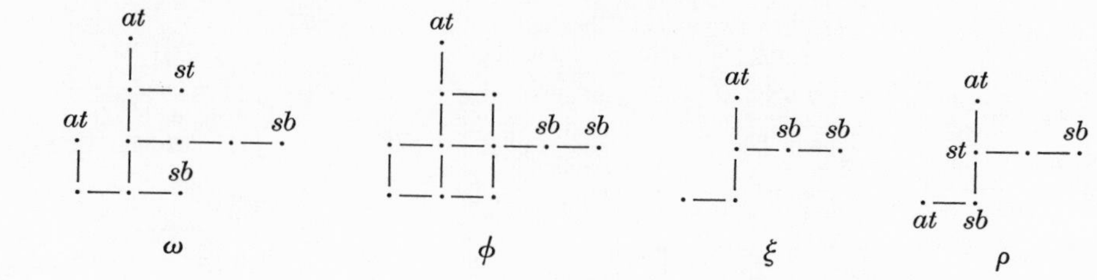

B^8 and K^8.

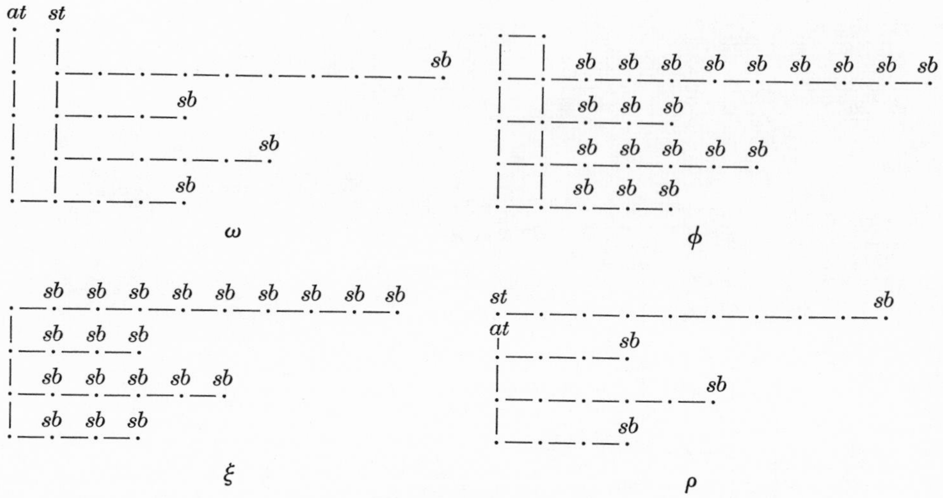

B^9 and K^9

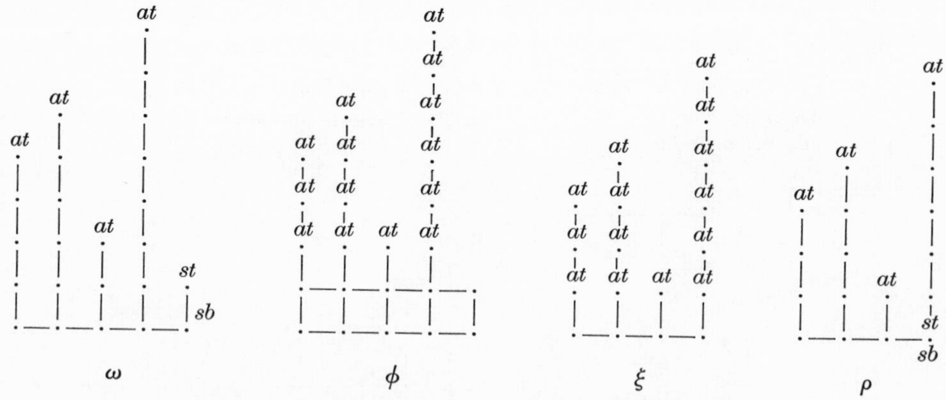

In ω, add arguments *ab* at unlabelled points.
In ϕ and ξ, add arguments *st* at unlabelled points.
In ρ, add arguments *ab* everywhere.

FIGURE 4. Cores and rules of cores.

TABLE 3

CORES OF ALL SPACES B WITH $(p, q) = (1, 1)$

$\bar\omega_{s,t} = \{(1, 1)\}$.			$\bar\phi_{s,t}$	$\bar\phi_{s,b}$	$\bar\phi_{a,t}$	$\bar\xi_{s,t}$	$\bar\xi_{s,b}$	$\bar\xi_{a,t}$	$\bar\rho_{s,t} = \{(0,0)\}$. $\bar\rho_{a,b} = \bar\omega_{a,b}$.		Names; Comment
$\bar\omega_{s,b}$	$\bar\omega_{a,t}$	$\bar\omega_{a,b}$							$\bar\rho_{s,b}$	$\bar\rho_{a,t}$	
20	02	00 10 01	00 10	20	02	00	10	01	10	01	$B_{1,1,}$, $K_{1,1}$
10	01	00	$\bar\omega$			00			00	00	$B_{\ulcorner 1,1\urcorner}$, $K_{\ulcorner 1,1\urcorner}$
$i_0 0$ $i_0, j_0 \geqq 1$.	$0 j_0$	$i0$, $i < i_0$ $0j$, $1 \leqq j < j_0$	00 10 01 11	$i0$, $2 \leqq i \leqq i_0$	$0j$, $2 \leqq j \leqq j_0$	00	$i0$, $1 \leqq i < i_0$	$0j$, $1 \leqq j < j_0$	$i_0 - 1, 0$	$0, j_0 - 1$	B, K
10	00		$\bar\omega$								B. There is no K. ξ is not well covered.
00	01		$\bar\omega$								
$i_0 0$ $i_0 \geqq 1$.	00	$i0$, $1 \leqq i < i_0$	00 10 11	$i0$, $2 \leqq i \leqq i_0$			$i0$, $1 \leqq i < i_0$				
00 $j_0 \geqq 1$.	$0 j_0$	$0j$, $1 \leqq j < j_0$	00 01 11		$0j$, $2 \leqq j \leqq j_0$			$0j$, $1 \leqq j < j_0$			

TABLE 4

CORES OF ALL SPACES B WITH $(p, q) = (2, 1)$ FOR WHICH RETRACTS K EXIST

$\bar{\omega}_{s,t} = \{(2, 1)\}$.			$\bar{\phi}_{s,t}$	$\bar{\phi}_{s,b}$	$\bar{\phi}_{a,t}$	$\bar{\xi}_{s,t}$	$\bar{\xi}_{s,b}$	$\bar{\xi}_{a,t}$	$\bar{\rho}_{s,t} = \{(1, 0)\}$. $\bar{\rho}_{a,b} = \bar{\omega}_{a,b}$.		Names
$\bar{\omega}_{s,b}$	$\bar{\omega}_{a,t}$	$\bar{\omega}_{a,b}$							$\bar{\rho}_{s,b}$	$\bar{\rho}_{a,t}$	
30	12 03	00 10 20 01 11 02	$\ulcorner 2, 1 \urcorner$	30	02 03 12	00 10	20	01 11 02	20	11 02	$B_{2,1}$, $K_{2,1}$
20	01 11	00 10	$\ulcorner 2, 1 \urcorner$			00 10			10	00 10	$B_{\ulcorner 2,1 \urcorner}$, $K_{\ulcorner 2,1 \urcorner}$
$i_0 0$	$0 j_0$ $1 j_1$	$i0, i < i_0$ $0j, 1 \leqq j < j_0$ $1j, 1 \leqq j < j_1$	$\ulcorner 2, 1 \urcorner$	$i0$, $3 \leqq i \leqq i_0$	$0j, 2 \leqq j \leqq j_0$ $1j, 2 \leqq j \leqq j_1$	00 10	$i0$, $2 \leqq i < i_0$	$0j, 1 \leqq j < j_0$ $1j, 1 \leqq j < j_1$	$i_0 - 1, 0$	$0, j_0 - 1$ $1, j_1 - 1$	B, K
$i_0 \geqq 2$; $j_0, j_1 \geqq 1$.											

TABLE 5

CORES OF ALL SPACES B WITH $(p, q) = (2, 2)$ FOR WHICH RETRACTS K EXIST

$\bar{\omega}_{s,t} = \{(2, 2)\}.$			$\bar{\phi}_{s,t}$	$\bar{\phi}_{s,b}$	$\bar{\phi}_{a,t}$	$\bar{\xi}_{s,t}$	$\bar{\xi}_{s,b}$	$\bar{\xi}_{a,t}$	$\bar{\rho}_{s,t} = \{(1, 1)\}.$ $\bar{\rho}_{a,b} = \bar{\omega}_{a,b}.$		Names
$\bar{\omega}_{s,b}$	$\bar{\omega}_{a,t}$	$\bar{\omega}_{a,b}$							$\bar{\rho}_{s,b}$	$\bar{\rho}_{a,t}$	
40 31	04 13	00 10 20 30 11 01 02 03 12 21	$\ulcorner 2, 2 \urcorner$	30 40 31	03 04 13	$\ulcorner 1, 1 \urcorner$	20 30 21	02 03 12	30 21	03 12	$B_{2,2}$, $K_{2,2}$
20 21	02 12	[1, 1]	$\ulcorner 2, 2 \urcorner$			$\ulcorner 1, 1 \urcorner$			10 11	01 11	$B_{\ulcorner 2,2 \urcorner}$, $K_{\ulcorner 2,2 \urcorner}$
$i_0 0$ $i_1 1$	$0 j_0$ $1 j_1$	$i0, i < i_0$ $i1, i < i_1$ $0j, 2 \leqq j < j_0$ $1j, 2 \leqq j < j_1$	$\ulcorner 2, 2 \urcorner$	$i0,$ $3 \leqq i \leqq i_0$ $i1,$ $3 \leqq i \leqq i_1$	$0j,$ $3 \leqq j \leqq j_0$ $1j,$ $3 \leqq j \leqq j_1$	$\ulcorner 1, 1 \urcorner$	$i0,$ $2 \leqq i < i_0$ $i1,$ $2 \leqq i < i_1$	$0j,$ $2 \leqq j < j_0$ $1j,$ $2 \leqq j < j_1$	$i_0 - 1, 0$ $i_1 - 1, 1$	$0, j_0 - 1$ $1, j_1 - 1$	B, K
$i_0, i_1, j_0, j_1 \geqq 2.$											
10 $i_1 1$	$0 j_0$ $1 j_1$	$0j, j < j_0$ $1j, 1 \leqq j < j_1$ $i1, 2 \leqq i < i_1$	00 10 01 11 21 02 12 22	$i1,$ $3 \leqq i \leqq i_1$	$0j,$ $3 \leqq j \leqq j_0$ $1j,$ $3 \leqq j \leqq j_1$	00 01 11	$i1,$ $2 \leqq i < i_1$	$0j,$ $2 \leqq j < j_0$ $1j,$ $2 \leqq j < j_1$	00 $i_1 - 1, 1$	$0, j_0 - 1$ $1, j_1 - 1$	B, K
$i_1, j_0, j_1 \geqq 2.$											
$i_0 0$ $i_1 1$	01 $1 j_1$	$i0, i < i_0$ $i1, 1 \leqq i < i_1$ $1j, 2 \leqq j < j_1$	00 01 10 11 12 20 21 22	$i0,$ $3 \leqq i \leqq i_0$ $i1,$ $3 \leqq i \leqq i_1$	$1j,$ $3 \leqq j \leqq j_1$	00 10 11	$i0,$ $2 \leqq i < i_0$ $i1,$ $2 \leqq i < i_1$	$1j,$ $2 \leqq j < j_1$	$i_0 - 1, 0$ $i_1 - 1, 1$	00 $1, j_1 - 1$	B, K
$i_0, i_1, j_1 \geqq 2$											

Chapter 5

Applications

§ 1. **Introduction.** There are many applications of the kernel theorems in the theory of approximation. In the first place one may be interested in a specific process of approximation in which the remainder R is a functional to which the theorems apply. For suitable spaces B, then, there will be formulas for Rx, $x \in \boldsymbol{B}$, in terms of the complete core ω of x. Each such formula is exact and unambiguous; it gives us a powerful insight into R, since the elements of ω are independent of one another. The fact that there are many such formulas for essentially the same R is interesting. Each formula leads to accessible sharp appraisals.

In the second place one may wish to choose a process of approximation from a set of processes. Then formulas for the remainders in the different processes may be pertinent to the choice.

The complications in the formulas are inherent in the problem. Even to approximate $\int_0^1 x(s)\,ds$ in terms of $x(0)$ and $x(1)$ is bold. To express the error one needs the derivative $x_1(s)$ for almost all s in the interval of integration or some substitute. The approximation of a double integral by a finite combination of values of its integrand is more difficult. To express the error one needs several derivatives, artfully chosen, or some substitute.

§ 2. **Approximation of an integral in terms of its integrand at the center of mass.** As a first illustration, suppose that we approximate

$$\iint_I x(s, t)\,d\mu(s, t)$$

by

$$cx(s^0, t^0),$$

where

$$I = I_s \times I_t, \qquad I_s = \{\alpha \leqq s \leqq \tilde{\alpha}\}, \qquad I_t = \{\beta \leqq t \leqq \tilde{\beta}\};$$

μ is a function of bounded variation on I, and

$$c = \iint_I d\mu(s, t) \neq 0, \qquad cs^0 = \iint_I s\,d\mu(s, t), \qquad ct^0 = \iint_I t\,d\mu(s, t).$$

The remainder in the approximation is

$$Rx = \iint_I x(s, t)\,d\mu(s, t) - cx(s^0, t^0). \tag{3}$$

The approximation amounts to replacing the integrand $x(s, t)$ by its value $x(s^0, t^0)$ at the center of mass. Since we have assumed that $c \neq 0$, the center of mass (s^0, t^0) is well defined. If $d\mu \geqq 0$ for all (s, t), then $(s^0, t^0) \in I$. As we have not required that $d\mu$ be nonnegative, we add the hypothesis:

$$(s^0, t^0) \in I.$$

If (s^0, t^0) were not in I, one could replace I by a larger interval that did contain (s^0, t^0) and one could put $d\mu = 0$ outside the original I.

An important observation is the following. We are here considering a very general double integral since μ may be any function of bounded variation for which $c \neq 0$. In particular $d\mu$ may vanish on a measurable subset of I, so that the integral need not at all have a rectangular character.

Let (a, b) be a fixed point in I. Our spaces will refer to I and (a, b).

Since Rx, defined in (3), is merely a Stieltjes integral on x, it is clear that

$$R \in \mathscr{K}^*_{p,q} \quad \text{for all} \quad p \geqq 1, \quad q \geqq 1.$$

Indeed

$$R \in \mathscr{K}^*,$$

for all companions $\mathscr{K}^*$ (§ 4: 80).

By construction, $Rx = 0$ when $x(s, t) = 1$ or s or t. Hence, by (4: 38),

$$\begin{aligned} c^{0,0} &= R[(1)] = 0, \\ c^{1,0} &= R[(s - a)] = 0, \\ c^{0,1} &= R[(t - b)] = 0. \end{aligned}$$

CASE i. Let us consider R as an element of $\mathscr{K}^*_{1,1}$ and express Rx in terms of the core of x in $B_{1,1}$. The jump set $\mathscr{J}_s$ consists of the single point $s = s^0$; likewise $\mathscr{J}_t = \{t^0\}$. Also

$$(4) \qquad \kappa^{2,0}(\tilde{s}) = R[(s - \tilde{s})\psi(a, \tilde{s}, s)] = - R[(s - \tilde{s})\theta(\tilde{s}, s)] = R[(s - \tilde{s})\phi(\tilde{s}, s)], \quad \tilde{s} \neq s^0;$$

$$(5) \qquad \kappa^{0,2}(\tilde{t}) = \text{the dual expressions;}$$

$$(6) \qquad \kappa^{1,1}(\tilde{s}, \tilde{t}) = R[\psi(a, \tilde{s}, s)\psi(b, \tilde{t}, t)], \qquad \tilde{s} \neq s^0 \quad \text{and} \quad \tilde{t} \neq t^0;$$

by (4: 39–41) and the relation between ψ, θ, and ϕ. Cf. (4: 90–93).

For $x \in \boldsymbol{B}_{1,1}$,

$$(7) \qquad \begin{aligned} Rx = \int_{I_s} x_{2,0}(s, b)\kappa^{2,0}(s)\, ds + \iint_I x_{1,1}(s, t)\kappa^{1,1}(s,t)\, ds\, dt \\ + \int_{I_t} x_{0,2}(a, t)\kappa^{0,2}(t)\, dt. \end{aligned}$$

We have an equality for Rx, which expresses Rx as the sum of three independent terms involving the second partials of x.

CASE ii. Consider R as an element of $\mathscr{K}^*_{p,q}$, $p, q \geqq 1$. Then the jump set $\mathscr{J}_s$ is empty if $p > 1$ and $\mathscr{J}_s = \{s^0\}$ if $p = 1$. Similarly for $\mathscr{J}_t$. The formula (4: 37) for Rx, $x \in \boldsymbol{B}_{p,q}$, may have terms $c^{i,j}x_{i,j}(a, b)$ in which $c^{i,j}$ does not vanish. The terms in (4: 37) will involve independent elements, viz., the elements of the complete core ω of x in $B_{p,q}$.

CASE iii. Consider R as an element of $\mathscr{K}^*_{\ulcorner 1,1 \urcorner}$. Then

$$\mathscr{J}_s = \{s^0\}; \qquad \mathscr{J}_t = \{t^0\}.$$

If $x \in \boldsymbol{B}_{\ulcorner 1,1 \urcorner}$,

$$Rx = \int_{I_s} x_{1,0}(s, b)\kappa^{1,0}(s)\, ds + \iint_I x_{1,1}(s, t)\kappa^{1,1}(s, t)\, ds\, dt + \int_{I_t} x_{0,1}(a, t)\kappa^{0,1}(t)\, dt,$$

where $\kappa^{1,1}$ is as in Case i above and

$$\kappa^{1,0}(\tilde{s}) = R[\psi(a, \tilde{s}, s)] = -R[\theta(\tilde{s}, s)] = R[\phi(\tilde{s}, s)], \qquad \tilde{s} \neq s_0;$$
$$\kappa^{0,1}(\tilde{t}) = \text{the dual expressions};$$

by (4: 90–93).

CASE iv. Consider R as an element of $\mathscr{K}^*_{\ulcorner p,q \urcorner}$, $p, q \geqq 1$. Then $\mathscr{J}_s$ is empty if $p > 1$ and $\mathscr{J}_s = \{s^0\}$ if $p = 1$. Similarly for $\mathscr{J}_t$. The formula (4: 85) for Rx, $x \in \boldsymbol{B}_{\ulcorner p,q \urcorner}$, may have terms $c^{i,j}x_{i,j}(a, b)$ in which $c^{i,j}$ does not vanish.

CASE v. Consider R as an element of $\mathscr{K}^*$, the companion of a space B. The tables of Chapter 4 give a number of such spaces. The formula (4: 85) will express Rx, $x \in \boldsymbol{B}$, in terms of the complete core ω of x in B. The present case includes all the preceding ones.

§ 8. **An instance.** Consider the particular functional obtained from (3) by putting

$$I = \{-1 \leqq s, t \leqq 1\}, \qquad d\mu(s, t) = ds\, dt.$$

Then

$$c = \int_{-1}^{1}\int_{-1}^{1} ds\, dt = 4, \qquad s^0 = 0 = t^0;$$

$$Rx = \int_{-1}^{1}\int_{-1}^{1} x(s, t)\, ds\, dt - 4x(0, 0). \tag{9}$$

CASE i. Let us take

$$(a, b) = (0, 0)$$

and consider R as an element of $\mathscr{K}^*_{1,1}$. This comes under Case i of the preceding section. For x in $\boldsymbol{B}_{1,1}$, equation (7) holds. We now compute the kernels by (4), (5), (6). Thus

$$\kappa^{2,0}(\bar{s}) = R[(s - \bar{s})\psi(0, \bar{s}, s)] = \int_{-1}^{1}\int_{-1}^{1} (s - \bar{s})\psi(0, \bar{s}, s)\, ds\, dt + 4\bar{s}\psi(0, \bar{s}, 0),$$

$$\kappa^{2,0}(\bar{s}) = 2\int_{-1}^{1} (s - \bar{s})\psi(0, \bar{s}, s)\, ds,$$

since $\psi(0, \bar{s}, 0) = 0$. If $0 < \bar{s}$, then $\psi(0, \bar{s}, s) = 1$ for $s > \bar{s}$ and 0 otherwise. Hence

$$\kappa^{2,0}(\bar{s}) = 2\int_{\bar{s}}^{1} (s - \bar{s})\, ds = (1 - \bar{s})^2, \qquad 0 < \bar{s}.$$

If $\bar{s} < 0$, then $\kappa^{2,0}(\bar{s}) = \kappa^{2,0}(-\bar{s})$, by symmetry (§ 4: 94). The fact that $\kappa^{2,0}(\bar{s})$ is an even function may be verified directly: If $\bar{s} < 0$, then $\psi(0, \bar{s}, s) = -1$ for $s \leqq \bar{s}$ and 0 otherwise. Hence

$$\kappa^{2,0}(\bar{s}) = -2\int_{-1}^{\bar{s}} (s - \bar{s})\, ds = (-1 - \bar{s})^2 = (1 + \bar{s})^2, \qquad \bar{s} < 0.$$

Since 0 is in $\mathscr{J}_s$, the formula for $\kappa^{2,0}(\bar{s})$ might fail at $\bar{s} = 0$. Whether $\kappa^{2,0}(\bar{s})$ is defined at $\bar{s} = 0$ or not is immaterial to the evaluation of the term involving $\kappa^{2,0}$ in (7). We may and shall take

$$\kappa^{2,0}(s) = (1 - |s|)^2, \qquad s \in \boldsymbol{I}_s. \tag{10}$$

Interchanging s and t does not affect (9). Hence

$$\kappa^{0,2}(t) = (1 - |t|)^2, \qquad t \in \boldsymbol{I}_t. \tag{11}$$

Finally

$$\kappa^{1,1}(\bar{s}, \bar{t}) = R[\psi(0, \bar{s}, s)\psi(0, \bar{t}, t)] = \int_{-1}^{1}\int_{-1}^{1} \psi(0, \bar{s}, s)\psi(0, \bar{t}, t)\, ds\, dt - 0.$$

If $0 < \bar{s}$ and $0 < \bar{t}$, then

$$\kappa^{1,1}(\bar{s}, \bar{t}) = \int_{\bar{t}}^{1} dt \int_{\bar{s}}^{1} ds = (1 - \bar{s})(1 - \bar{t}).$$

By the rules of symmetry (§ 4: 94), $\kappa^{1,1}$ is odd in each variable. Thus

$$\begin{aligned} \kappa^{1,1}(s, t) &= -\kappa^{1,1}(-s, t) = -\kappa^{1,1}(s, -t) = \kappa^{1,1}(-s, -t) \\ &= (1 - s)(1 - t), \qquad 0 < s, t \leqq 1. \end{aligned}$$

The values of $\kappa^{1,1}(0, t)$ and $\kappa^{1,1}(s, 0)$ are immaterial. We may take

$$\kappa^{1,1}(s, t) = (1 - |s|)(1 - |t|) \text{ signum } st, \qquad (s, t) \in \boldsymbol{I}. \tag{12}$$

Hence

$$\text{(13)}\quad \begin{aligned} Rx = \int_{-1}^{1} x_{2,0}(s, 0)\kappa^{2,0}(s)\, ds + \int_{-1}^{1}\int_{-1}^{1} x_{1,1}(s, t)\kappa^{1,1}(s, t) ds\, dt \\ + \int_{-1}^{1} x_{0,2}(0, t)\kappa^{0,2}(t)\, dt, \qquad x \in \boldsymbol{B}_{1,1}(0, 0), \end{aligned}$$

where the kernels are given by (10), (11), (12).

In the present case the kernels are so simple that one may verify (13) by transforming its right-hand side by elementary integrations into the right-hand side of (9).

Any of the appraisals of § 4: 95 may be applied to (13). For example

$$\text{(14)}\quad \begin{aligned} |Rx| \leqq \left[J^{2,0}\int_{-1}^{1} |x_{2,0}(s, 0)|^2\, ds\right]^{1/2} + \left[J^{1,1}\int_{-1}^{1}\int_{-1}^{1} |x_{1,1}(s, t)|^2\, ds\, dt\right]^{1/2} \\ + \left[J^{0,2}\int_{-1}^{1} |x_{0,2}(0, t)|^2\, dt\right]^{1/2}, \qquad x \in \boldsymbol{B}_{1,1}(0, 0), \end{aligned}$$

where

$$J^{2,0} = \int_{-1}^{1} |\kappa^{2,0}(s)|^2\, ds = 2\int_{0}^{1} (1 - s)^4\, ds = \frac{2}{5},$$

$$J^{0,2} = \frac{2}{5};$$

$$J^{1,1} = \int_{-1}^{1}\int_{-1}^{1} |\kappa^{1,1}(s, t)|^2\, ds\, dt = 4\int_{0}^{1}\int_{0}^{1} (1 - s)^2(1 - t)^2\, ds\, dt = \frac{4}{9}.$$

The derivatives $x_{2,0}(s, 0)$, $x_{1,1}(s, t)$, $x_{0,2}(0, t)$ are independent of one another (Corollary 4: 11). Consequently the threefold use of Schwarz's inequality above has given us a sharp appraisal of Rx: If $J^{2,0}$ or $J^{1,1}$ or $J^{0,2}$ were replaced in (14) by a smaller quantity, the inequality would become false, even if x were restricted to be a polynomial instead of an element of $\boldsymbol{B}_{1,1}(0, 0)$.

There are infinitely many other sharp inequalities on Rx. We cite (4: 101):

$$\begin{aligned} |Rx| \leqq J^{1/2}\Bigg[\int_{-1}^{1} |x_{2,0}(s, 0)|^2\, ds + \int_{-1}^{1}\int_{-1}^{1} |x_{1,1}(s, t)|^2\, ds\, dt \\ + \int_{-1}^{1} |x_{0,2}(0, t)|^2\, dt\Bigg]^{1/2}, \qquad x \in \boldsymbol{B}_{1,1}(0, 0), \end{aligned}$$

where

$$J = J^{2,0} + J^{1,1} + J^{0,2} = \frac{56}{45}.$$

Case ii. Still considering the functional (9), we may take (a, b) anywhere in I and obtain a formula for Rx, $x \in \boldsymbol{B}_{1,1}(a, b)$. This formula will be different from (13), since

$$\boldsymbol{B}_{1,1}(a, b) \neq \boldsymbol{B}_{1,1}(0, 0) \qquad \text{if } (a, b) \neq (0, 0).$$

It is true, however, that a function x which has all three second partials all continuous everywhere in I is an element of $B_{1,1}(a, b)$ for all (a, b) in I.

Let us obtain the formula for Rx, $x \in \boldsymbol{B}_{1,1}(a, b)$. Here

$$\kappa^{2,0}(\tilde{s}) = -R[(s - \tilde{s})\theta(\tilde{s}, s)] = -\int_{-1}^{1}\int_{-1}^{1} (s - \tilde{s})\theta(\tilde{s}, s)\, ds\, dt - 4\tilde{s}\theta(\tilde{s},0).$$

Now $\theta(\tilde{s}, s) = 1$ if $\tilde{s} \geqq s$ and 0 otherwise. Hence

$$\kappa^{2,0}(\tilde{s}) = -2\int_{-1}^{\tilde{s}} (s - \tilde{s})\, ds - 4\tilde{s}\theta(\tilde{s}, 0) = (1 - |\tilde{s}|)^2,$$

since $\theta(\tilde{s}, 0) = 1$ or 0 according as $\tilde{s} \geqq 0$ or $\tilde{s} < 0$. Thus $\kappa^{2,0}(s)$ and similarly $\kappa^{0,2}(t)$ are precisely the functions (10), (11) of Case i and are independent of (a, b). Also

$$\kappa^{1,1}(\tilde{s}, \tilde{t}) = R[\psi(a, \tilde{s}, s)\psi(b, \tilde{t}, t)].$$

One may calculate $\kappa^{1,1}$ from this relation by considering successively the nine alternative cases corresponding to different orders of a, $\tilde{s}$, and 0, and b, $\tilde{t}$, and 0. Alternatively, by (11 : 4),

$$\begin{aligned}\kappa^{1,1}(\tilde{s}, \tilde{t}) &= R[\theta(\tilde{s}, a) - \theta(\tilde{s}, s)][\theta(\tilde{t}, b) - \theta(\tilde{t}, t)] \\ &= \theta(\tilde{s}, a)\theta(\tilde{t}, b)R[1] - \theta(\tilde{t}, b)R[\theta(\tilde{s}, s)] \\ &\quad - \theta(\tilde{s}, a)R[\theta(\tilde{t}, t)] + R[\theta(\tilde{s}, s)\theta(\tilde{t}, t)].\end{aligned}$$

Now

$$R[1] = 0,$$

$$\begin{aligned}R[\theta(\tilde{s}, s)] &= 2\int_{-1}^{1} \theta(\tilde{s}, s)\, ds - 4\theta(\tilde{s}, 0) \\ &= 2\int_{-1}^{\tilde{s}} ds - 4\theta(\tilde{s}, 0) = 2(1 + \tilde{s}) - 4\theta(\tilde{s}, 0),\end{aligned}$$

$$R[\theta(\tilde{t}, t)] = 2(1 + \tilde{t}) - 4\theta(\tilde{t}, 0) \tag{15}$$

$$\begin{aligned}R[\theta(\tilde{s}, s)\theta(\tilde{t}, t)] &= \int_{-1}^{1}\int_{-1}^{1} \theta(\tilde{s}, s)\theta(\tilde{t}, t)\, ds\, dt - 4\theta(\tilde{s}, 0)\theta(\tilde{t}, 0) \\ &= (1 + \tilde{s})(1 + \tilde{t}) - 4\theta(\tilde{s}, 0)\theta(\tilde{t}, 0).\end{aligned}$$

Hence

$$\begin{aligned}\kappa^{1,1}(s, t) &= -\theta(t, b)[2(1 + s) - 4\theta(s, 0)] - \theta(s, a)[2(1 + t) - 4\theta(t, 0)] \\ &\quad + (1 + s)(1 + t) - 4\theta(s, 0)\theta(t, 0), \qquad s \neq 0 \neq t.\end{aligned} \tag{16}$$

One may verify that this expression for $\kappa^{1,1}$ reduces to (12) if $a = b = 0$.

Alternatively we might have used the function $\phi = 1 - \theta$ in the calculation.

Thus we have established that

$$Rx = \int_{-1}^{1} x_{2,0}(s, b)\kappa^{2,0}(s)\, ds + \int_{-1}^{1}\int_{-1}^{1} x_{1,1}(s, t)\kappa^{1,1}(s, t)\, ds\, dt$$
$$+ \int_{-1}^{1} x_{0,2}(a, t)\kappa^{0,2}(t)\, dt, \qquad x \in \boldsymbol{B}_{1,1}(a, b),$$

where $\kappa^{2,0}$, $\kappa^{1,1}$, $\kappa^{0,2}$ are given by (10), (16), (11).

Case iii. Still referring to the functional (9), we may consider R as an element of $\mathscr{K}^*_{\ulcorner 1,1 \urcorner}$ and obtain a formula for Rx, $x \in \boldsymbol{B}_{\ulcorner 1,1 \urcorner}(a, b)$. Here

$$Rx = \int_{-1}^{1} x_{1,0}(s, b)\kappa^{1,0}(s)\, ds + \int_{-1}^{1}\int_{-1}^{1} x_{1,1}(s, t)\kappa^{1,1}(s, t)\, ds\, dt$$
$$+ \int_{-1}^{1} x_{0,1}(a, t)\kappa^{0,1}(t)\, dt, \qquad x \in \boldsymbol{B}_{\ulcorner 1,1 \urcorner},$$

where, by (15),

$$\kappa^{1,0}(\tilde{s}) = R[\psi(a, \tilde{s}, s)] = -R[\theta(\tilde{s}, s)] = -2(1 + \tilde{s}) + 4\theta(\tilde{s}, 0), \qquad \tilde{s} \neq 0,$$
$$\kappa^{0,1}(\tilde{t}) = \kappa^{1,0}(\tilde{t}),$$
$$\kappa^{1,1}(\tilde{s}, \tilde{t}) = R[\psi(a, \tilde{s}, s)\psi(b, \tilde{t}, t)], \qquad \tilde{s} \neq 0 \neq \tilde{t},$$

and $\kappa^{1,1}$ is therefore given by (16).

Case iv. Still referring to the functional (9), we may consider R as an element of any space $\mathscr{K}^*$ and obtain a formula for Rx, $x \in \boldsymbol{B}$.

Let us take $(a, b) = (0, 0)$. Then

$$c^{i,j} = R[s^{(i)}t^{(j)}].$$

Hence

$$c^{0,0} = 0,$$

as we have seen; and, if $i + j > 0$,

$$c^{i,j} = \begin{cases} \dfrac{4}{(i + 1)!(j + 1)!} & \text{if } i \text{ and } j \text{ are both even,} \\ 0 & \text{otherwise.} \end{cases} \tag{17}$$

Consider, for example, the formula for Rx, $x \in \boldsymbol{B}_{1,2}(0, 0)$. Here

$$c^{2,0} = c^{0,2} = \frac{2}{3}, \qquad c^{i,j} = 0 \quad \text{otherwise, } i + j < 3;$$

$$\kappa^{3,0}(\tilde{s}) = -\kappa^{3,0}(-\tilde{s}) = R[(s - \tilde{s})^{(2)}\psi(0, \tilde{s}, s)] = 2\int_{\tilde{s}}^{1} (s - \tilde{s})^{(2)}\, ds - 0$$
$$= \frac{(1 - \tilde{s})^3}{3}, \qquad \tilde{s} > 0;$$

$$\kappa^{2,1}(\tilde{s}) = \kappa^{2,1}(-\tilde{s}) = R[(s - \tilde{s})\psi(0, \tilde{s}, s)t] = 0;$$

$$\kappa^{1,2}(\tilde{s}, \tilde{t}) = -\kappa^{1,2}(-\tilde{s}, \tilde{t}) = \kappa^{1,2}(\tilde{s}, -\tilde{t}) = -\kappa^{1,2}(-\tilde{s}, -\tilde{t})$$

$$= R[\psi(0, \tilde{s}, s)(t - \tilde{t})\psi(0, \tilde{t}, t)] = \int_{\tilde{s}}^{1} ds \int_{\tilde{t}}^{1} (t - \tilde{t})\, dt - 0$$

$$= \frac{(1 - \tilde{s})(1 - \tilde{t})^2}{2}, \qquad \tilde{s} > 0, \quad \tilde{t} > 0;$$

and

$$\kappa^{0,3}(\tilde{t}) = -\kappa^{0,3}(-\tilde{t}) = R[(t - \tilde{t})^{(2)}\psi(0, \tilde{t}, t)] = \kappa^{3,0}(\tilde{t}) = \frac{(1 - \tilde{t})^3}{3}, \quad \tilde{t} > 0.$$

The formula for Rx, $x \in \boldsymbol{B}_{1,2}(0, 0)$, is

$$Rx = \frac{2}{3} x_{2,0}(0, 0) + \frac{2}{3} x_{0,2}(0, 0) + \int_{-1}^{1} x_{3,0}(s, 0)\kappa^{3,0}(s)\, ds + 0$$

$$+ \int_{-1}^{1}\int_{-1}^{1} x_{1,2}(s, t)\kappa^{1,2}(s, t)\, ds\, dt + \int_{-1}^{1} x_{0,3}(0, t)\, \kappa^{0,3}(t)\, dt.$$

CASE V. We may be interested in formulas for Rx, $x \in \boldsymbol{B}$, which are free of terms $c^{i,j}x_{i,j}(a, b)$. For such a formula to be valid, it is necessary that

$$c^{i,j} = R[(s - a)^{(i)}(t - b)^{(j)}] = 0 \quad \text{for all } (i, j) \text{ in } \bar{\omega}_{a,b}.$$

Let us take $a = b = 0$. Then, by (17), $c^{i,j} \neq 0$ iff i and j are both even and $i + j > 0$.

Thus any space B which has a companion will afford a formula for Rx, $x \in \boldsymbol{B}$, in terms of the core of x in B but free of terms $c^{i,j}x_{i,j}(0, 0)$ iff $\bar{\omega}_{a,b}$ excludes the points $(2h, 2k)$ other than the origin, where h and k are integers. For example, B may be the space B^7 for which

$$\bar{\omega}_{s,t} = \{(2, 2)\},\ \bar{\omega}_{s,b} = \{(4, 1), (2, 0)\},\ \bar{\omega}_{a,t} = \{(1, 3), (0, 1)\};$$

since here

$$\bar{\omega}_{a,b} = \{(0, 0), (1, 0), (1, 1), (2, 1), (3, 1), (1, 2)\}.$$

Cf. Figure 4 : 4.

§ 18. **An example with circular domain of integration.** Consider the particular functional obtained from (3) by putting

$$d\mu(s, t) = \begin{cases} ds\, dt & \text{if } s^2 + t^2 < 1 \\ 0 & \text{otherwise,} \end{cases}$$

and

$$I = \{-1 \leqq s, t \leqq 1\}.$$

Here

$$\iint_I x(s, t)\, d\mu(s, t) = \iint\limits_{s^2+t^2<1} x(s, t)\, ds\, dt,$$

$$c = \iint\limits_{s^2+t^2<1} ds\, dt = \pi, \qquad s^0 = 0 = t^0,$$

and

(19) $$Rx = \iint\limits_{s^2+t^2<1} x(s, t)\, ds\, dt - \pi x(0, 0).$$

CASE i. Let us take $(a, b) = (0, 0)$ and consider R as an element of $\mathscr{K}^*_{1,1}$. For x in $\boldsymbol{B}_{1,1}(0, 0)$,

(20) $$Rx = \int_{-1}^{1} x_{2,0}(s, 0) f(s)\, ds + \int_{-1}^{1}\int_{-1}^{1} x_{1,1}(s, t) g(s, t)\, ds\, dt + \int_{-1}^{1} x_{0,2}(0, t) h(t)\, dt,$$

where the kernels f, g, h are as follows. By symmetry (§ 4: 94),

$$f(s) = f(-s),$$

$$g(s, t) = -g(-s, t) = -g(s, -t) = g(-s, -t);$$

also

$$h(t) = f(t).$$

By (19),

$$f(\tilde{s}) = R[(s - \tilde{s})\psi(0, \tilde{s}, s)] = \iint\limits_{s^2+t^2<1} (s - \tilde{s})\psi(0, \tilde{s}, s)\, ds\, dt + \pi\tilde{s}\psi(0, \tilde{s}, 0);$$

hence

$$f(\tilde{s}) = \iint\limits_{\substack{s^2+t^2<1,\\ s>\tilde{s}}} (s - \tilde{s})\, ds\, dt = \int_{\tilde{s}}^{1} ds(s - \tilde{s})\, 2\int_0^{\sqrt{1-s^2}} dt$$

$$= 2\int_{\tilde{s}}^{1} (s - \tilde{s})\sqrt{1 - s^2}\, ds$$

$$= 2\int_{\tilde{s}}^{1} (u - \tilde{s})\sqrt{1 - u^2}\, du \quad \text{if } 0 < \tilde{s}.$$

The reader may, if he wishes, carry out the integration. For many purposes the last integral as it stands is the most useful expression for $f(\tilde{s})$.

Next

$$g(\tilde{s}, \tilde{t}) = R[\psi(0, \tilde{s}, s)\psi(0, \tilde{t}, t)] = \iint\limits_{s^2+t^2<1} \psi(0, \tilde{s}, s)\psi(0, \tilde{t}, t)\, ds\, dt.$$

Hence

$$g(\tilde{s}, \tilde{t}) = 0 \quad \text{if} \quad \tilde{s}^2 + \tilde{t}^2 \geqq 1;$$

and

$$g(\tilde{s}, \tilde{t}) = \iint\limits_{\substack{s^2+t^2<1,\\ s>\tilde{s},\, t>\tilde{t}}} ds\, dt = \int_{\tilde{s}}^{\sqrt{1-\tilde{t}^2}} du \int_{\tilde{t}}^{\sqrt{1-u^2}} dv = g(\tilde{t}, \tilde{s})$$

$$\text{if } \tilde{s}^2 + \tilde{t}^2 < 1,\ 0 < \tilde{s}, \tilde{t}.$$

Alternative expressions for $g(\tilde{s}, \tilde{t})$ may be deduced by further calculation but the forms just written are perhaps the most useful. When $(\tilde{s}, \tilde{t})$ is within the unit circle and in the first quadrant, $g(\tilde{s}, \tilde{t})$ is the shaded area in Figure 1.

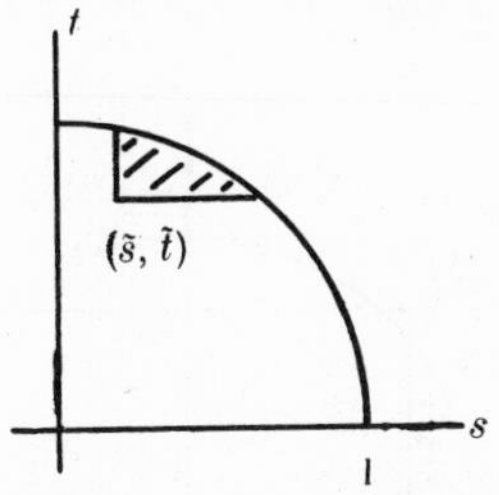

FIGURE 1.

Now that the kernels, f, g, h are known, one could start with the right side of (20) and deduce (19).

CASE ii. Consider the same funtional (19) as an element of $\mathscr{K}^*_{1,1}(a, b)$. The present case reduces to the preceding one if $(a, b) = (0, 0)$. For $x \in \boldsymbol{B}_{1,1}(a, b)$,

$$(21)\qquad Rx = \int_{-1}^{1} x_{2,0}(s, b)\kappa^{2,0}(s)\, ds + \int_{-1}^{1}\int_{-1}^{1} x_{1,1}(s, t)\kappa^{1,1}(s, t)\, ds\, dt + \int_{-1}^{1} x_{0,2}(a, t)\kappa^{0,2}(t)\, dt.$$

The functional (19) is perfectly symmetric. The space $B_{1,1}(a,b)$, however, is not symmetric if $(a, b) \neq (0, 0)$. Although Rx in (19) involves only values of x within the unit circle, the kernel $\kappa^{1,1}(s, t)$ in (21) may be different from zero outside the unit circle.

For example, suppose that

$$(a, b) = (.6, .8).$$

Consider

$$\kappa^{1,1}(\tilde{s}, \tilde{t}) = R[\psi(a, \tilde{s}, s)\psi(b, \tilde{t}, t)].$$

Take $(\tilde{s}, \tilde{t})$ near $(-.75, .75)$. Then

$$\psi(a, \tilde{s}, s) = \begin{cases} -1 & \text{if } s \leqq \tilde{s}, \\ 0 & \text{otherwise,} \end{cases}$$

since $-.75 < a = .6$. Also

$$\psi(b, \tilde{t}, t) = \begin{cases} -1 & \text{if } t \leqq \tilde{t}, \\ 0 & \text{otherwise,} \end{cases}$$

since $.75 < b = .8$. Hence the argument of R vanishes unless $s \leqq \tilde{s}$ and $t \leqq \tilde{t}$ in which case it equals unity. Hence $\kappa^{1,1}(\tilde{s}, \tilde{t})$ equals the shaded area in Figure 2 and is not zero, when $(\tilde{s}, \tilde{t})$ is near $(-.75, .75)$.

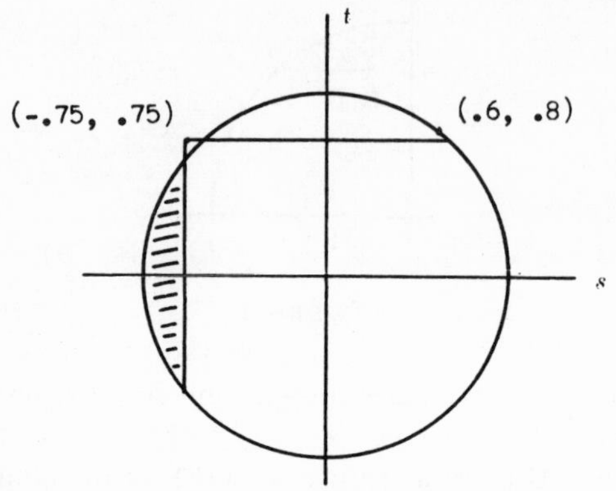

FIGURE 2.

§ 22. **Approximation of an integral in terms of several values of the integrand.** The considerations of the preceding sections extend to any approximation of

$$\iint_I x(s, t)\, d\mu(s, t)$$

by a finite linear combination of values of the integrand $x(s, t)$, since the remainder in such an approximation is still a Stieltjes integral on x and therefore an element of $\mathscr{K}^*$ for all spaces $\mathscr{K}^*$.

For example, let us study

$$Rx = \int_{-1}^{1}\int_{-1}^{1} x(s, t)\, ds\, dt$$
$$- \frac{1}{3}[8x(0, 0) + x(1, 1) + x(-1, 1) + x(1, -1) + x(-1, -1)].$$

Here

$$c^{i,j} = R[(s - a)^{(i)}(t - b)^{(j)}] = 0 \quad \text{if } i + j \leqq 3,$$

since $Rx = 0$ when

$$x(s, t) = 1, s, t, s^2, st, t^2, s^3, s^2t, st^2, t^3.$$

Put

$$(a, b) = (0, 0).$$

Then

$$c^{i,j} = \begin{cases} \dfrac{4}{(i+1)!(j+1)!} - \dfrac{4}{3i!j!} & \text{if } i \text{ and } j \text{ are even and not both zero,} \\ 0 & \text{otherwise.} \end{cases}$$

Thus

$$c^{4,0} = c^{0,4} \neq 0, \qquad c^{2,2} \neq 0.$$

Indeed $c^{2i,2j} \neq 0$ if $2i + 2j \geqq 4$.

By Theorem 4: 36 we may write formulas for Rx, $x \in \boldsymbol{B}_{p,q}$, where $p \geqq 1$, $q \geqq 1$, in terms of the complete core ω of x. For the following cases the formula will consist exclusively of integrals on partial derivatives of x of order $n = p + q$:

$$B_{1,1}, \quad B_{1,2}, \quad B_{2,1}, \quad B_{1,3}, \quad B_{2,2}, \quad B_{3,1}.$$

Likewise we may write formulas for Rx, $x \in \boldsymbol{B}_{\ulcorner p,q \urcorner}$, where $p \geqq 1$, $q \geqq 1$. If $p \leqq 2$ and $q \leqq 4$ or vice versa, the formula will consist exclusively of integrals on partial derivatives of x of order (i, q), $i \leqq p$, and (p, j), $j \leqq q$.

Likewise we may write formulas for Rx, $x \in \boldsymbol{B}$, where B is any space which has a companion. One instance is the space $B = B^8$ for which

$$\bar{\omega}_{s,t} = \{(1, 4)\}, \qquad \bar{\omega}_{s,b} = \{(4, 0), (6, 1), (4, 2), (10, 3)\}, \qquad \bar{\omega}_{a,t} = \{(0,4)\}.$$

The formula for Rx, $x \in \boldsymbol{B}^8$, will consist exclusively of integrals on the derivatives in $\omega_{s,t} \cup \omega_{s,b} \cup \omega_{a,t}$, except for one term in $x_{2,2}(0, 0)$.

We conclude this section by citing the actual formula for Rx, $x \in \boldsymbol{B}_{1,3}(0, 0)$. It is

$$\begin{aligned} Rx = &\int_{-1}^{1} x_{4,0}(s, 0)\kappa^{4,0}(s)\, ds + \int_{-1}^{1} x_{3,1}(s, 0)\kappa^{3,1}(s)\, ds \\ &+ \int_{-1}^{1} x_{2,2}(s, 0)\kappa^{2,2}(s)\, ds + \int_{-1}^{1}\int_{-1}^{1} x_{1,3}(s, t)\kappa^{1,3}(s, t)\, ds\, dt \\ &+ \int_{-1}^{1} x_{0,4}(0, t)\kappa^{0,4}(t)\, dt, \qquad x \in \boldsymbol{B}_{1,3}(0, 0), \end{aligned}$$

where

$$\kappa^{4,0}(s) = \frac{(|s|-1)^3(3|s|+1)}{36},$$
$$\kappa^{3,1}(s) = 0,$$
$$\kappa^{2,2}(s) = \frac{s^2-1}{6},$$
$$\kappa^{1,3}(s, t) = -\kappa^{1,3}(-s, t) = -\kappa^{1,3}(s, -t) = \kappa^{1,3}(-s, -t)$$
$$= \frac{(t-1)^2(st-s-t)}{6}, \qquad 0 < s, t \leqq 1,$$
$$\kappa^{0,4}(t) = \kappa^{4,0}(t).$$

§ 23. **An approximation that involves derivatives of the integrand.** One may approximate

$$\iint_I x(s, t)\, d\mu(s, t)$$

by a linear combination of values of the integrand and its derivatives. The remainder is then an element of many but not all spaces $\mathscr{K}^*$.

An example is the functional

$$(24)\quad \begin{aligned} Rx = \int_{-1}^{1}\int_{-1}^{1} x(s, t)\, ds\, dt - \frac{1}{3}[12x(0, 0) \\ + x_{1,0}(1, 0) - x_{1,0}(-1, 0) + x_{0,1}(0, 1) - x_{0,1}(0, -1)]. \end{aligned}$$

Here Rx is a sum of Stieltjes integrals on $x_{0,0}$, $x_{1,0}$, and $x_{0,1}$. In order that a space $\mathscr{K}^*$ include R it is necessary and sufficient that the covered core ξ of B include $x_{1,0}(\pm 1, 0)$, $x_{0,1}(0, \pm 1)$, and $x_{0,0}(s, t)$, $(s, t) \in I$. Let us take

$$I = \{-1 \leqq s, t \leqq 1\}.$$

Then the condition as regards $x_{0,0}$ is satisfied since the covered core ξ in B is well covered. The condition as regards $x_{1,0}$ will be satisfied iff either $(1, 0) \in \bar{\xi}_{s,t}$ or else $(1, 0) \in \bar{\xi}_{s,b}$ and $b = 0$. Dually for $x_{0,1}$.

In considering spaces B we may consult the tables and figures of Chapter 4.

Let us consider the spaces $B_{p,q}(a, b)$ first.

The covered core ξ of $B_{1,1}(a, b)$ is

$$x_{0,0}(s, t); \qquad x_{1,0}(s, b); \qquad x_{0,1}(a, t).$$

Hence $R \in \mathscr{K}^*_{1,1}(a, b)$ iff $a = b = 0$.

The covered core of $B_{2,1}(a, b)$ is

$$x_{1,0}(s, t),\ \ x_{0,0}(s, t); \qquad x_{2,0}(s, b); \qquad x_{1,1}(a, t),\ \ x_{0,2}(a, t),\ \ x_{0,1}(a, t).$$

Hence $R \in \mathscr{K}^*_{2,1}(a, b)$ iff $a = 0$.

Similarly $R \in \mathscr{K}^*_{1,2}(a, b)$ iff $b = 0$.

The covered core of $B_{3,1}(a, b)$ is

$$x_{2,0}(s, t), \quad x_{1,0}(s, t), \quad x_{0,0}(s, t); \qquad x_{3,0}(s, b); \qquad x_{2,1}(a, t), \quad x_{1,2}(a, t),$$
$$x_{1,1}(a, t), \quad x_{0,3}(a, t), \quad x_{0,2}(a, t), \quad x_{0,1}(a, t).$$

Hence $R \in \mathscr{K}^*_{3,1}(a, b)$ iff $a = 0$.

Similarly $R \in \mathscr{K}^*_{1,3}(a, b)$ iff $b = 0$.

The covered core of $B_{2,2}(a, b)$ includes

$$\xi_{s,t} = \{x_{1,1}(s, t), x_{1,0}(s, t), x_{0,1}(s, t), x_{0,0}(s, t)\}.$$

Hence $R \in \mathscr{K}^*_{2,2}(a, b)$ for all (a, b) in I.

By increasing subscripts (4: 33), we see that R is an element of the following spaces and of no other spaces $\mathscr{K}^*_{p,q}(a, b)$:

$$\begin{aligned}
&\mathscr{K}^*_{p,q}(a, b), \qquad p \geqq 2, \quad q \geqq 2;\\
&\mathscr{K}^*_{p,q}(a, 0), \qquad p \geqq 1, \quad q \geqq 2;\\
&\mathscr{K}^*_{p,q}(0, b), \qquad p \geqq 2, \quad q \geqq 1;\\
&\mathscr{K}^*_{p,q}(0, 0), \qquad p \geqq 1, \quad q \geqq 1.
\end{aligned}$$

Next let us consider the spaces $B_{\ulcorner p,q \urcorner}(a, b)$. Here the covered core ξ is $\xi_{s,t}$ and does not depend on (a, b). Furthermore,

$$R \in \mathscr{K}^*_{\ulcorner p,q \urcorner} \quad \text{iff} \quad p \geqq 2, \quad q \geqq 2.$$

As regards general spaces $\mathscr{K}^*$, we may say that

$$R \in \mathscr{K}^* \quad \text{if} \quad (1, 0) \in \bar{\xi}_{s,t} \quad \text{and} \quad (0, 1) \in \bar{\xi}_{s,t}.$$

In this case no condition is imposed on (a, b). Also

$$R \in \mathscr{K}^* \quad \text{if} \quad (1, 0) \in \bar{\xi}_{s,t} \quad \text{and} \quad (0, 1) \in \bar{\xi}_{a,t} \quad \text{and} \quad a = 0,$$

since (24) involves both $x_{0,1}(0, 1)$ and $x_{0,1}(0, -1)$. Also

$$R \in \mathscr{K}^* \quad \text{if} \quad (0, 1) \in \bar{\xi}_{s,t} \quad \text{and} \quad (1, 0) \in \bar{\xi}_{s,b} \quad \text{and} \quad b = 0.$$

Also

$$R \in \mathscr{K}^* \quad \text{if} \quad (1, 0) \in \bar{\xi}_{s,b} \quad \text{and} \quad (0, 1) \in \bar{\xi}_{a,t} \quad \text{and} \quad a = b = 0.$$

Observe that $Rx = 0$ whenever $x(s, t)$ is a polynomial in (s, t) of degree 3, since $Rx = 0$ when

$$x(s, t) = 1, s, t, \cdots, st^2, t^3.$$

Hence

$$c^{i,j} = R[(s - a)^{(i)}(t - b)^{(j)}] = 0 \quad \text{if } i + j \leqq 3.$$

The formula on $\boldsymbol{B}_{1,1}(0, 0)$ is

$$\begin{aligned}
Rx = \int_{-1}^{1} x_{2,0}(s, 0)f(s)\, ds + \int_{-1}^{1}\int_{-1}^{1} x_{1,1}(s, t)g(s, t)\, ds\, dt&\\
+ \int_{-1}^{1} x_{0,2}(0, t)h(t)\, dt, \qquad x \in \boldsymbol{B}_{1,1}(0, 0);&
\end{aligned}$$

where

$$f(s) = f(-s); \qquad h(t) = f(t);$$

$$g(s, t) = -g(-s, t) = -g(s, -t) = g(-s, -t);$$

and

$$f(s) = (1 - s)^2 - \frac{1}{3}, \qquad 0 < s;$$

$$g(s, t) = (1 - s)(1 - t), \qquad 0 < s, t.$$

We conclude this section with a few remarks about the formulas for Rx, $x \in \boldsymbol{B}$. Take

$$(a, b) = (0, 0).$$

Then

$$c^{i,j} = R[s^{(i)}t^{(j)}].$$

We have already seen that $c^{i,j} = 0$ if $i + j \leqq 3$. Also, by (24),

$$c^{1,j} = c^{i,1} = 0,$$

$$c^{0,i} = c^{i,0} = \begin{cases} \dfrac{4}{(i+1)!} - \dfrac{2}{3(i-1)!} & \text{if } i \text{ is even and positive,} \\ 0 & \text{otherwise.} \end{cases}$$

Also, if $i \geqq 2$, $j \geqq 2$,

$$c^{i,j} = \int_{-1}^{1}\int_{-1}^{1} s^{(i)}t^{(j)}\, ds\, dt = \begin{cases} \dfrac{4}{(i+1)!(j+1)!} & \text{if } i, j \text{ are even,} \\ 0 & \text{otherwise.} \end{cases}$$

Thus the formula for Rx, $x \in \boldsymbol{B}$, in terms of the complete core ω of x will have only integral terms if the covered core ξ excludes

$$x_{i,j}, \quad i \geqq 2, \qquad j \geqq 2, \qquad i \text{ and } j \text{ both even.}$$

Of the many possibilities we cite only the space $B = B^9$ for which

$$\bar{\omega}_{s,t} = \{(4, 1)\},\ \bar{\omega}_{s,b} = \{(4, 0)\},\ \bar{\omega}_{a,t} = \{(0, 4), (1, 5), (2, 2), (3, 7)\}.$$

There is a formula

$$\begin{aligned} Rx = &\int_{-1}^{1}\int_{-1}^{1} x_{4,1}(s, t)\kappa^{4,1}(s, t)\, ds\, dt + \int_{-1}^{1} x_{4,0}(s, 0)\kappa^{4,0}(s)\, ds \\ &+ \int_{-1}^{1} x_{0,4}(0, t)\kappa^{0,4}(t)\, dt + \int_{-1}^{1} x_{1,5}(0, t)\kappa^{1,5}(t)\, dt \\ &+ \int_{-1}^{1} x_{2,2}(0, t)\kappa^{2,2}(t)\, dt + \int_{-1}^{1} x_{3,7}(0, t)\kappa^{3,7}(t)\, dt, \qquad x \in \boldsymbol{B}^9. \end{aligned}$$

The kernels are given by the usual formulas (4: 87–89). Indeed

$$\kappa^{1,5}(t) = 0 = \kappa^{3,7}(t),$$
$$\kappa^{4,0}(s) = \kappa^{0,4}(s).$$

§ 25. A functional which is not an element of $\mathscr{K}^*$ unless n is relatively large. Consider a functional Fx which is defined as a sum of Stieltjes integrals on derivatives $x_{i,j}$ of x. Suppose that the derivative $x_{i^0,j^0}(s, t)$ appears in the expression for Fx in such a way that at least two distinct values of s and at least two distinct values of t are involved. Then in order for F to be an element of $\mathscr{K}^*$, it is necessary that $(i^0, j^0) \in \xi_{s,t}$, because the elements of $\xi - \xi_{s,t}$ are derivatives evaluated at one value of s, viz., $s = a$; or at one value of t, viz., $t = b$.

To illustrate, take

$$I = \{0 \leqq s, t \leqq 1\}.$$

Consider

$$Fx = x_{1,0}(1, 1) - x_{1,0}(0, 0) + x_{0,1}(0, 1) - x_{0,1}(1, 0).$$

In order that $F \in \mathscr{K}^*$, it is necessary that both $x_{1,0}$ and $x_{0,1}$ be in $\xi_{s,t}$. This implies that $p \geqq 2$, $q \geqq 2$, and hence $n \geqq 4$. For example, $F \in \mathscr{K}^*_{2,2}$ and $F \in \mathscr{K}^*_{\ulcorner 2,2 \urcorner}$.

One may consider $n = 4$ as large, since only derivatives of order 1 are involved in the definition of F. Now it is possible to express Fx as a sum of ordinary integrals on derivatives of order < 4 as follows. Consider the functionals

$$Gx = x_{1,0}(1, 1) - x_{1,0}(0, 0),$$
$$Hx = x_{0,1}(0, 1) - x_{0,1}(1, 0).$$

Then, for all (a, b) in I,

$$G \in \mathscr{K}^*_{2,1}(a, b) \cap \mathscr{K}^*_{\ulcorner 2,1 \urcorner}(a, b),$$
$$H \in \mathscr{K}^*_{1,2}(a, b) \cap \mathscr{K}^*_{\ulcorner 1,2 \urcorner}(a, b),$$

and

$$Fx = Gx + Hx.$$

We may express Gx in terms of the complete core of x in $B_{2,1}$ and Hx in terms of the complete core of x in $B_{1,2}$. The two complete cores are largely but not entirely the same. Thus for $x \in \boldsymbol{B}_{2,1} \cap \boldsymbol{B}_{1,2}$, we may write an expression for Fx in terms of ordinary integrals on

$$x_{3,0}(s, b),\ x_{2,1}(s, t) \text{ and } x_{2,1}(s, b), \quad x_{1,2}(s, t) \text{ and } x_{1,2}(a, t), \quad x_{0,3}(a, t)$$

and terms

$$c^{i,j}x_{i,j}(a, b), \qquad i + j < 3.$$

The formula, however, *would not give Fx in terms of independent elements.* It would be difficult to obtain a sharp appraisal from the formula. Similarly for $x \in \boldsymbol{B}_{\ulcorner 2,1 \urcorner} \cap \boldsymbol{B}_{\ulcorner 1,2 \urcorner}$.

In considering any functional, one may always study the possible advantages and disadvantages of decomposing the functional into a sum of other functionals. As regards the above illustration, we could also write

$$Fx = \tilde{G}x + \tilde{H}x,$$

where

$$\tilde{G}x = x_{1,0}(1, 1) - x_{0,1}(1, 0),$$
$$\tilde{H}x = x_{0,1}(0, 1) - x_{1,0}(0, 0).$$

There are many ways to study $\tilde{G}$ and $\tilde{H}$. For example,

$$\tilde{G} \in \mathscr{K}^*_{1,1}(1, 1), \qquad \tilde{H} \in \mathscr{K}^*_{1,1}(0, 0).$$

We may therefore write a formula for Fx, $x \in \boldsymbol{B}_{1,1}(1, 1) \cap \boldsymbol{B}_{1,1}(0, 0)$, in terms of ordinary integrals on

$$x_{2,0}(s, 0) \text{ and } x_{2,0}(s, 1), \quad x_{1,1}(s, t), \quad x_{0,2}(0, t) \text{ and } x_{0,2}(1, t)$$

and terms

$$c^{i,j}x_{i,j}(a, b), \qquad i + j < 2.$$

These elements are not independent of one another.

§ 26. **An example involving a circular domain and partial derivatives.** Consider the functional

$$Rx = \iint\limits_{s^2+t^2<1} x(s, t)\, ds\, dt - \frac{\pi}{8}[8x(0, 0) + x_{2,0}(0, 0) + x_{0,2}(0, 0)],$$

which is the remainder in the indicated approximation of the integral. Here $Rx = 0$ whenever x is a polynomial in (s, t) of degree 3. Take

$$I = \{-1 \leqq s, t \leqq 1\}.$$

In order that $R \in \mathscr{K}^*$ it is necessary and sufficient that the covered core include $x_{2,0}(0, 0)$ and $x_{0,2}(0, 0)$. It follows that

$$\begin{aligned} R &\in \mathscr{K}^*_{p,q}(0, 0) && \text{if } p \geqq 1 \text{ and } q \geqq 2, \text{ or if } p \geqq 2 \text{ and } q \geqq 1, \\ R &\in \mathscr{K}^*_{p,q}(a, 0) && \text{if } p \geqq 1 \text{ and } q \geqq 3, \\ R &\in \mathscr{K}^*_{p,q}(0, b) && \text{if } p \geqq 3 \text{ and } q \geqq 1, \\ R &\in \mathscr{K}^*_{p,q}(a, b) && \text{if } p \geqq 3 \text{ and } q \geqq 3. \end{aligned}$$

Also

$$R \in \mathscr{K}^*_{\ulcorner p,q \urcorner}(a, b) \quad \text{if } p \geqq 3 \text{ and } q \geqq 3.$$

Let us take

$$(a, b) = (0, 0).$$

Then

$$c^{i,j} = R[s^{(i)}t^{(j)}] = \begin{cases} 4 \displaystyle\iint\limits_{\substack{s^2+t^2<1,\\ s>0,t>0}} s^{(i)}t^{(j)}\, ds\, dt & \text{if } i \text{ and } j \text{ are even and } i + j > 3, \\ 0 & \text{otherwise.} \end{cases}$$

In particular

$$c^{2,2} = \frac{\pi}{96}.$$

CASE i. Consider R as an element of $\mathscr{K}^*_{1,2}(0, 0)$. By Theorem 4 : 36,

$$Rx = \int_{-1}^{1} x_{3,0}(s, 0)f(s)\,ds + \int_{-1}^{1}\int_{-1}^{1} x_{1,2}(s, t)g(s, t)\,ds\,dt + \int_{-1}^{1} x_{0,3}(0, t)f(t)\,dt, \qquad x \in \boldsymbol{B}_{1,2}(0, 0);$$

where

$$f(\tilde{s}) = -f(-\tilde{s}) = \iint\limits_{\substack{u^2+v^2<1,\\ u>\tilde{s}}} (u - \tilde{s})^{(2)}\,du\,dv, \qquad 0 < \tilde{s};$$

$$g(\tilde{s}, \tilde{t}) = -g(-\tilde{s}, \tilde{t}) = g(\tilde{s}, -\tilde{t}) = -g(-\tilde{s}, -\tilde{t}) = \iint\limits_{\substack{u^2+v^2<1,\\ u>\tilde{s},v>\tilde{t}}} (v - \tilde{t})\,du\,dv, \qquad 0 < \tilde{s}, \tilde{t}.$$

The function $g(s, t)$ vanishes if $s^2 + t^2 \geqq 1$. The derivative $x_{2,1}(s, 0)$ does not enter in the formula for Rx because the kernel $\kappa^{2,1}$ vanishes. The reverse calculation seems impracticable.

CASE ii. In similar fashion, we may consider R as an element of $\mathscr{K}^*_{p,q}(0, 0)$, $p + q = n \geqq 3$. The formula for Rx, $x \in \boldsymbol{B}_{p,q}(0, 0)$, will be free of terms $c^{i,j}x_{i,j}(0, 0)$ iff $p = 1$, $q = 2$ or $p = 2$, $q = 1$.

CASE iii. Consider R as an element of $\mathscr{K}^*_{\ulcorner 3,3 \urcorner}(0, 0)$. By Theorem 4 : 84,

$$Rx = \frac{\pi}{96} x_{2,2}(0, 0) + \int_{-1}^{1} x_{3,0}(s, 0)f(s)\,ds + \int_{-1}^{1} x_{3,2}(s, 0)g(s)\,ds + \int_{-1}^{1}\int_{-1}^{1} x_{3,3}(s, t)h(s, t)\,ds\,dt + \int_{-1}^{1} x_{2,3}(0, t)g(t)\,dt + \int_{-1}^{1} x_{0,3}(0, t)f(t)\,dt, \qquad x \in \boldsymbol{B}_{\ulcorner 3,3 \urcorner}(0, 0),$$

where

$$f(s) = -f(-s) = \iint\limits_{\substack{u^2+v^2<1,\\ u>s}} (u - s)^{(2)}\,du\,dv, \qquad s > 0;$$

$$g(s) = -g(-s) = \iint\limits_{\substack{u^2+v^2<1,\\ u>s}} (u - s)^{(2)}v^{(2)}\,du\,dv, \qquad s > 0;$$

$$h(s, t) = -h(-s, t) = -h(s, -t) = h(-s, -t) = \iint\limits_{\substack{u^2+v^2<1,\\ u>s,v>t}} (u - s)^{(2)}(v - t)^{(2)}\,du\,dv, \qquad s, t > 0.$$

§ 27. **An interpolation.** Consider the approximation of $x(0, 0)$ in terms of $x(1, 1)$, $x(-1, 1)$, $x(0, -1)$ for which the remainder is

$$Rx = x(0, 0) - \frac{1}{4}[x(1, 1) + x(-1, 1) + 2x(0, -1)].$$

Here $Rx = 0$ whenever x is a polynomial in (s, t) of degree 1 and

$$R[s^2] \neq 0 \neq R[t^2].$$

Take

$$I = \{-1 \leqq s, t \leqq 1\}.$$

The functional R is an element of all spaces $\mathscr{K}^*$, since Rx is a Stieltjes integral on $x(s, t)$.

Consider R as an element of $\mathscr{K}^*_{1,1}(0, 1)$. By Theorem 4: 36,

$$Rx = \int_{-1}^{1} x_{2,0}(s, 1)f(s)\,ds + \int_{-1}^{1} x_{0,2}(0, t)h(t)\,dt \qquad x \in \boldsymbol{B}_{1,1}(0, 1),$$

where

$$f(s) = -\frac{1 - |s|}{4}, \qquad h(t) = -\frac{1 - |t|}{2}.$$

This result may easily be verified by the reverse calculation.

§ 28. **Double linear interpolation.** We now study conventional linear interpolation in a two-way table. By a translation of axes we may arrange that the interpolation for $x(u, v)$ be based on the tabular entries

$$x(0, 0), \quad x(\alpha, 0), \quad x(0, \beta), \quad x(\alpha, \beta); \qquad \alpha > 0, \quad \beta > 0.$$

Conventional double linear interpolation is the approximation of $x(u, v)$ for which the remainder is

$$Rx = x(u, v) - \frac{1}{\alpha\beta}[(\alpha - u)(\beta - v)x(0, 0) + u(\beta - v)x(\alpha, 0) + v(\alpha - u)x(0, \beta) + uvx(\alpha, \beta)].$$

Here α, β are fixed, and we consider u, v to be fixed. Take

$$I = \{0 \leqq s \leqq \alpha, \quad 0 \leqq t \leqq \beta\}; \qquad (u, v) \in I.$$

The functional R is a Stieltjes integral on x and therefore an element of all spaces $\mathscr{K}^*$. Also $Rx = 0$ when

$$x(s, t) = 1,\ s,\ t, \text{ or } st.$$

Consider R as an element of $\mathscr{K}^*_{1,1}(0, 0)$. By Theorem 4: 36,

$$Rx = \int_0^{\alpha} x_{2,0}(s, 0)f(s)\,ds + \int_0^{\alpha} ds \int_0^{\beta} x_{1,1}(s, t)g(s, t)\,dt + \int_0^{\beta} x_{0,2}(0, t)h(t)\,dt, \qquad x \in \boldsymbol{B}_{1,1}(0, 0), \tag{29}$$

where

$$\begin{aligned} f(\tilde{s}) &= R[(s - \tilde{s})\psi(0, \tilde{s}, s)], \\ g(\tilde{s}, \tilde{t}) &= R[\psi(0, \tilde{s}, s)\psi(0, \tilde{t}, t)], \\ h(\tilde{t}) &= R[(t - \tilde{t})\psi(0, \tilde{t}, t)], \end{aligned} \qquad \begin{aligned} &\tilde{s} \neq 0, u, \alpha \\ &\text{and} \quad \tilde{t} \neq 0, v, \beta. \end{aligned}$$

The excluded values are the jump sets $\mathscr{J}_s$ and $\mathscr{J}_t$ and are immaterial.

Take

$$0 < \tilde{s} < \alpha, \qquad 0 < \tilde{t} < \beta.$$

Then

$$\psi(0, \tilde{s}, s) = \begin{cases} 1 & \text{if } s > \tilde{s}, \\ 0 & \text{otherwise.} \end{cases}$$

Likewise for $\psi(0, \tilde{t}, t)$. Hence

$$\begin{aligned} f(\tilde{s}) &= (u - \tilde{s})\psi(0, \tilde{s}, u) - \frac{1}{\alpha\beta}[u(\beta - v)(\alpha - \tilde{s}) + uv(\alpha - \tilde{s})] \\ &= (u - \tilde{s})\psi(0, \tilde{s}, u) - \frac{u(\alpha - \tilde{s})}{\alpha}; \end{aligned}$$

$$f(\tilde{s}) = \begin{cases} \dfrac{-u(\alpha - \tilde{s})}{\alpha} & \text{if } u < \tilde{s}, \\ u - \tilde{s} - \dfrac{u(\alpha - \tilde{s})}{\alpha} = \dfrac{-\tilde{s}(\alpha - u)}{\alpha} & \text{if } u > \tilde{s}. \end{cases}$$

By interchange of letters, $h(\tilde{t})$ is the function $f(\tilde{s})$ with $u, \alpha, \tilde{s}$ replaced by $v, \beta, \tilde{t}$, respectively.

Finally

$$g(\tilde{s}, \tilde{t}) = \psi(0, \tilde{s}, u)\psi(0, \tilde{t}, v) - \frac{1}{\alpha\beta}uv,$$

$$g(\tilde{s}, \tilde{t}) = \begin{cases} \dfrac{-uv}{\alpha\beta} & \text{if } u < \tilde{s} \text{ or if } v < \tilde{t}, \\ 1 - \dfrac{uv}{\alpha\beta} & \text{if } u > \tilde{s} \text{ and } v > \tilde{t}. \end{cases}$$

§ 30. **An approximate differentiation.** Consider the approximation of the derivative $x_{1,0}(0, 0)$ for which the remainder is

$$Rx = x_{1,0}(0, 0) - \frac{1}{4}[x(1, 1) - x(-1, 1) + x(1, -1) - x(-1, -1)].$$

Here $Rx = 0$ whenever x is a polynomial in (s, t) of degree 2.

Take

$$I = \{-1 \leqq s, t \leqq 1\}.$$

Now Rx is the sum of Stieltjes integrals on $x_{1,0}$ and $x_{0,0}$; and R is an element of $\mathscr{K}^*$ if the covered core ξ of x includes $x_{1,0}(0, 0)$. In particular,

$$R \in \mathscr{K}^*_{2,1}(a, b), \qquad R \in \mathscr{K}^*_{1,1}(a, 0), \qquad R \in \mathscr{K}^*_{\ulcorner 2,1 \urcorner}(a, b);$$

and hence

$$\begin{aligned} &R \in \mathscr{K}^*_{p,q}(a, b) &&\text{if } p \geqq 2,\ q \geqq 1,\\ &R \in \mathscr{K}^*_{p,q}(a, 0) &&\text{if } p \geqq 1,\ q \geqq 1,\\ &R \in \mathscr{K}^*_{\ulcorner p,q \urcorner}(a, b) &&\text{if } p \geqq 2,\ q \geqq 1. \end{aligned}$$

CASE i. Consider R as an element of $\mathscr{K}^*_{1,1}(0, 0)$. By Theorem 4 : 36,

$$Rx = \int_{-1}^{1} x_{2,0}(s, 0)f(s)\,ds + \int_{-1}^{1}\int_{-1}^{1} x_{1,1}(s, t)g(s, t)\,ds\,dt, \quad x \in \boldsymbol{B}_{1,1}(0, 0),$$

where

$$f(s) = -f(-s) = -\frac{1-s}{2}, \qquad 0 < s,$$

$$g(s, t) = -\frac{1}{4}\text{ signum } t.$$

The derivative $x_{0,2}(0, t)$ does not appear since the kernel $\kappa^{0,2}$ vanishes. As regards the rules of symmetry (§ 4 : 94) note that R is skew-symmetric in s and symmetric in t.

CASE ii. Consider R as an element of $\mathscr{K}^*_{2,1}(a, b)$. Then

$$\begin{aligned} Rx = {}& \int_{-1}^{1} x_{3,0}(s, b)f(s)\,ds + \int_{-1}^{1}\int_{-1}^{1} x_{2,1}(s, t)g(s, t)\,ds\,dt \\ &+ \int_{-1}^{1} x_{1,2}(a, t)h(t)\,dt, \qquad x \in \boldsymbol{B}_{2,1}(a, b), \end{aligned}$$

where, with possible finite exceptions,

$$f(\tilde{s}) = R[(s - \tilde{s})^{(2)}\psi(a, \tilde{s}, s)] = \frac{-(1 - |\tilde{s}|)^2}{4},$$

$$h(\tilde{t}) = R[(s - a)(t - \tilde{t})\psi(b, \tilde{t}, t)] = \frac{-(1 - |\tilde{t}|)}{2},$$

for all (a, b); and

$$g(\tilde{s}, \tilde{t}) = R[(s - \tilde{s})\psi(a, \tilde{s}, s)\psi(b, \tilde{t}, t)] = \begin{cases} \dfrac{-(1 - |\tilde{s}|)\text{ signum }(\tilde{s}\,\tilde{t})}{4} & \text{if } a = b = 0,\\[2ex] \dfrac{4\lambda - 1 + \tilde{s}}{4} & \text{if } a = b = -1, \end{cases}$$

where

$$\lambda = \begin{cases} 1 & \text{if } \tilde{s} < 0 \text{ and } \tilde{t} < 0,\\ 0 & \text{otherwise.} \end{cases}$$

The derivative $x_{0,3}(a, t)$ does not enter in the formula, since the kernel $\kappa^{0,3}$ vanishes.

§ 31. **Another approximate differentiation.** Let

$$Rx = x_{1,1}(0, 0) - \frac{1}{4}[x(1, 1) - x(-1, 1) - x(1, -1) + x(-1, -1)].$$

Then Rx is the remainder in the indicated approximation of the cross-derivative $x_{1,1}(0, 0)$ in terms of the corner values. Take

$$I = \{-1 \leqq s, t \leqq 1\}.$$

Here $Rx = 0$ whenever x is a polynomial in (s, t) of degree 3. Also R is an element of $\mathscr{K}^*$ if the covered core ξ of x includes $x_{1,1}(0, 0)$. Hence

$$R \in \mathscr{K}^*_{2,2}(a, b), \quad R \in \mathscr{K}^*_{2,1}(0, b), \quad R \in \mathscr{K}^*_{1,2}(a, 0), \quad R \in \mathscr{K}^*_{\lceil 2,2 \rceil}(a, b).$$

One may increase subscripts in the above relations.

§ 32. **Best integration formulas.** In each section thus far we have considered one approximation, without discussing why that approximation was studied or where it came from.

There are situations in which we may wish to consider a set of approximations and decide on the choice of one approximation from the set. The decision will depend on the given set and on the criterion of choice. The situation is similar to ones considered in Chapter 2, but the relations among the elements of the problem are now more complicated.

To fix our ideas suppose that we wish to approximate

$$\int_{-1}^{1} \int_{-1}^{1} x(s, t)\, ds\, dt$$

by a linear combination of values of the integrand $x(s, t)$ at

$$(s, t) = (0, 0), \quad (\pm 1, 0), \quad (0, \pm 1), \quad (\pm 1, \pm 1).$$

Suppose also that we choose to consider only such linear combinations which treat similar positions similarly. Each approximation will then be determined by three real numbers α, β, and γ; and the remainder in the approximation will be

$$\begin{aligned} Rx = & \int_{-1}^{1} \int_{-1}^{1} x(s, t)\, ds\, dt - \alpha x(0, 0) \\ & -\beta[x(1, 1) + x(-1, 1) + x(1, -1) + x(-1, -1)] \\ & -\gamma[x(1, 0) + x(-1, 0) + x(0, 1) + x(0, -1)]. \end{aligned} \tag{33}$$

Then

$$R[1] = 0 \quad \text{iff} \quad \alpha + 4\beta + 4\gamma = 4;$$

$$0 = R[s] = R[t] = R[st] = R[s^3] = R[s^2t] = R[st^2] = R[t^3];$$

$$R[s^2] = R[t^2] = 0 \quad \text{iff} \quad 4\beta + 2\gamma = \frac{4}{3}.$$

Take

$$I = \{-1 \leqq s, t \leqq 1\}.$$

Then R is an element of all spaces $\mathscr{K}^*$.

CASE i. Suppose that we choose to consider only approximations which are exact for degree 1. That is, we consider functionals R, defined by (33), in which the three parameters α, β, γ are subject to one condition

$$\alpha + 4\beta + 4\gamma = 4. \tag{34}$$

Suppose also that we choose to consider functions x in $\boldsymbol{B}_{1,1}(0, 0)$ and to express Rx in terms of the core of x in $B_{1,1}$. Then

$$\begin{aligned} Rx = &\int_{-1}^{1} x_{2,0}(s, 0) f(s)\, ds + \int_{-1}^{1}\int_{-1}^{1} x_{1,1}(s, t) g(s, t)\, ds\, dt \\ &+ \int_{-1}^{1} x_{0,2}(0, t) f(t)\, dt, \qquad x \in \boldsymbol{B}_{1,1}(0, 0), \end{aligned} \tag{35}$$

where

$$\begin{aligned} f(\tilde{s}) &= f(-\tilde{s}) = R[(s - \tilde{s})\psi(0, \tilde{s}, s)] \\ &= \int_{-1}^{1} dt \int_{\tilde{s}}^{1} (s - \tilde{s})\, ds - 0 - 2(1 - \tilde{s})\beta - (1 - \tilde{s})\gamma \\ &= (1 - \tilde{s})^2 - (1 - \tilde{s})(2\beta + \gamma), \qquad 0 < \tilde{s}; \end{aligned} \tag{36}$$

$$\begin{aligned} g(\tilde{s}, \tilde{t}) &= -g(-\tilde{s}, \tilde{t}) = -g(\tilde{s}, -\tilde{t}) = g(-\tilde{s}, -\tilde{t}) = R[\psi(0, \tilde{s}, s)\psi(0, \tilde{t}, t)] \\ &= \int_{\tilde{t}}^{1} dt \int_{\tilde{s}}^{1} ds - \beta = (1 - \tilde{s})(1 - \tilde{t}) - \beta, \qquad 0 < \tilde{s}, \tilde{t}. \end{aligned}$$

Suppose that we choose to use the sharp appraisal

$$\begin{aligned} |Rx| \leqq J^{1/2}\bigg[&\int_{-1}^{1} |x_{2,0}(s, 0)|^2\, ds + \int_{-1}^{1}\int_{-1}^{1} |x_{1,1}(s, t)|^2\, ds\, dt \\ &+ \int_{-1}^{1} |x_{0,2}(0, t)|^2\, dt\bigg]^{1/2}, \qquad x \in \boldsymbol{B}_{1,1}, \end{aligned}$$

where

$$J = \int_{-1}^{1} |f(s)|^2\, ds + \int_{-1}^{1}\int_{-1}^{1} |g(s, t)|^2\, ds\, dt + \int_{-1}^{1} |f(t)|^2\, dt.$$

In this case it is reasonable to minimize J. We may call the formula that minimizes J the *best formula relative to*

$$\int_{-1}^{1} |x_{2,0}(s, 0)|^2\, ds + \int_{-1}^{1}\int_{-1}^{1} |x_{1,1}(s, t)|^2\, ds\, dt + \int_{-1}^{1} |x_{0,2}(0, t)|^2\, dt$$

among the formulas related to (33) which are exact for degree 1. The calculation of this best formula is as follows.

$$J = 4\int_0^1 f(s)^2\, ds + 4\int_0^1\int_0^1 g(s, t)^2\, ds\, dt.$$

$$\frac{1}{4}J = \int_0^1 [(1 - s)^2 - (2\beta + \gamma)(1 - s)]^2\, ds + \int_0^1\int_0^1 [(1 - t)(1 - s) - \beta]^2\, ds\, dt.$$

Change the variables of integration, and for convenience put

$$\tilde{\gamma} = 2\beta + \gamma.$$

Then

$$\frac{1}{4}J = \int_0^1 [s^2 - \tilde{\gamma}s]^2\, ds + \int_0^1\int_0^1 [st - \beta]\, ds\, dt.$$

$$\frac{1}{4}J = \frac{1}{5} - \frac{\tilde{\gamma}}{2} + \frac{\tilde{\gamma}^2}{3} + \frac{1}{9} - \frac{\beta}{2} + \beta^2.$$

Let us take β, $\tilde{\gamma}$ as independent variables, as is permissible. We see that J is minimal iff

$$\tilde{\gamma} = \frac{3}{4}, \qquad \beta = \frac{1}{4}$$

and that the minimal J is

$$J_{\min} = 4\left(\frac{1}{5} - \frac{\tilde{\gamma}}{4} + \frac{1}{9} - \frac{\beta}{4}\right) = \frac{11}{45}.$$

Then

$$\gamma = \tilde{\gamma} - 2\beta = \frac{1}{4}$$

$$\alpha = 4 - 4\beta - 4\gamma = 2.$$

Thus the linear combination which assigns the weight 2 to the integrand at $(0, 0)$ and the weights $1/4$ to the integrand at $(\pm 1, 0)$, $(0, \pm 1)$, $(\pm 1, \pm 1)$ is best in the sense described.

If the formula is iterated over a lattice of squares, the weights assigned to integrands at lattice points away from the boundary will be 2, 1/2, and 1.

CASE ii. Alternatively we may choose to consider approximations which are exact for degree 3. That is, we consider functionals R, defined by (33), in which the three parameters α, β, γ are subject to the constraints

$$\begin{aligned} \alpha + 4\beta + 4\gamma &= 4, \\ 2\beta + \gamma &= \frac{2}{3}. \end{aligned} \tag{37}$$

Suppose that we choose to consider functions x in $\boldsymbol{B}_{2,2}(0, 0)$ and to express Rx in terms of the core of x in $B_{2,2}$. Then

$$\begin{aligned} Rx = &\int_{-1}^{1} x_{4,0}(s, 0)f(s)\,ds + \int_{-1}^{1} x_{3,1}(s, 0)g(s)\,ds \\ &+ \int_{-1}^{1}\int_{-1}^{1} x_{2,2}(s, t)h(s, t)\,ds\,dt + \int_{-1}^{1} x_{1,3}(0, t)g(t)\,dt \\ &+ \int_{-1}^{1} x_{0,4}(0, t)f(t)\,dt, \qquad x \in \boldsymbol{B}_{2,2}, \end{aligned}$$

where, by the constraints,

$$\begin{aligned} f(\tilde{s}) &= f(-\tilde{s}) = R[(s - \tilde{s})^{(3)}\psi(0, \tilde{s}, s)] \\ &= \int_{-1}^{1} dt \int_{\tilde{s}}^{1} (s - \tilde{s})^{(3)}\,ds - 2(1 - \tilde{s})^{(3)}\beta - (1 - \tilde{s})^{(3)}\gamma \\ &= 2(1 - \tilde{s})^{(4)} - (2\beta + \gamma)(1 - \tilde{s})^{(3)} \\ &= \frac{(1 - \tilde{s})^4}{12} - \frac{2}{3}\frac{(1 - \tilde{s})^3}{6}, \qquad 0 < \tilde{s}; \\ g(\tilde{s}) &= -g(-\tilde{s}) = R[(s - \tilde{s})^{(2)}\psi(0, \tilde{s}, s)\,t] = 0 - 0 = 0; \\ h(\tilde{s}, \tilde{t}) &= h(-\tilde{s}, \tilde{t}) = h(\tilde{s}, -\tilde{t}) = h(-\tilde{s}, -\tilde{t}) \\ &= R[(s - \tilde{s})\psi(0, \tilde{s}, s)(t - \tilde{t})\psi(0, \tilde{t}, t)] \\ &= \int_{\tilde{t}}^{1} (t - \tilde{t})\,dt \int_{\tilde{s}}^{1} (s - \tilde{s})\,ds - (1 - \tilde{s})(1 - \tilde{t})\beta \\ &= \frac{(1 - \tilde{s})^2(1 - \tilde{t})^2}{4} - (1 - \tilde{s})(1 - \tilde{t})\beta, \qquad 0 < \tilde{s}, \tilde{t}. \end{aligned}$$

Note that the kernels f and g are independent of α, β, γ.

The formula for Rx reduces to

$$\begin{aligned} Rx = &\int_{-1}^{1} x_{4,0}(s, 0)f(s)\,ds + \int_{-1}^{1}\int_{-1}^{1} x_{2,2}(s, t)h(s, t)\,ds\,dt \\ &+ \int_{-1}^{1} x_{0,4}(0, t)f(t)\,dt, \qquad x \in \boldsymbol{B}_{2,2}. \end{aligned}$$

Suppose that we choose to use the sharp appraisal

$$|Rx| \leqq J^{1/2}\left[\int_{-1}^{1}|x_{4,0}(s,0)|^2\,ds + \int_{-1}^{1}\int_{-1}^{1}|x_{2,2}(s,t)|^2\,ds\,dt + \int_{-1}^{1}|x_{0,4}(0,t)|^2\,dt\right]^{1/2}, \qquad x \in \boldsymbol{B}_{2,2},$$

where

$$J = \int_{-1}^{1}|f(s)|^2\,ds + \int_{-1}^{1}\int_{-1}^{1}|h(s,t)|^2\,ds\,dt + \int_{-1}^{1}|f(t)|^2\,dt.$$

We may then say that the best formula is the one which minimizes J. Since f is independent of the parameters, it is sufficient to minimize

$$\begin{aligned}\tilde{J} &= \int_{-1}^{1}\int_{-1}^{1}|h(s,t)|^2\,ds\,dt\\ &= 4\int_{0}^{1}\int_{0}^{1}\left[\frac{(1-s)^2(1-t)^2}{4} - (1-s)(1-t)\beta\right]^2 ds\,dt\\ &= 4\int_{0}^{1}\int_{0}^{1}\left[\frac{s^2t^2}{4} - st\beta\right]^2 ds\,dt.\end{aligned}$$

Take β as the independent variable. The unique minimum occurs when

$$\frac{d\tilde{J}}{d\beta} = -8\int_{0}^{1}\int_{0}^{1}\left[\frac{s^2t^2}{4} - st\beta\right] st\,ds\,dt = 0.$$

Hence

$$\frac{1}{64} - \frac{\beta}{9} = 0, \qquad \beta = \frac{9}{64}.$$

Hence, by (37),

$$\gamma = \frac{37}{96}, \qquad \alpha = \frac{91}{48}.$$

Thus the *best formula relative to*

$$\int_{-1}^{1}|x_{4,0}(s,0)|^2\,ds + \int_{-1}^{1}\int_{-1}^{1}|x_{2,2}(s,t)|^2\,ds\,dt + \int_{-1}^{1}|x_{0,4}(0,t)|^2\,dt$$

among the formulas related to (33) which are exact for degree 3 is the formula in which

$$\alpha = \frac{91}{48}, \qquad \beta = \frac{9}{64}, \qquad \gamma = \frac{37}{96}.$$

It is interesting to compare this result with Case i where

$$\alpha = 2 = \frac{96}{48}, \qquad \beta = \frac{1}{4} = \frac{16}{64}, \qquad \gamma = \frac{1}{4} = \frac{24}{96}.$$

One may profitably study other cases pertinent to (33).

Chapter 6

Linear Continuous Functionals on B, Z, K

§ 1. **Introduction.** After introducing a norm in the space B, we study the space B^* of linear continuous functionals on B. Theorem 14 below gives a formula for Fx, $x \in B$, as a sum of Stieltjes integrals on the elements of the complete core ω of x, where $F \in B^*$. The formula is accessible and unique. The functions of bounded variation that enter in the formula may be absolutely continuous. If so, and only then, the integrals reduce to ordinary integrals.

Next we define a new space K, the retract of B. We study the adjoint space K^*. Theorem 48 provides a representation of elements of K^* and leads to an intrinsic characterization of the space $\mathscr{K}^*$ of Chapters 4 and 5. If $F \in K^*$, then the formula for Fx, $x \in B$, of the preceding paragraph is such that the Stieltjes integrals on the elements of the core $\omega - \omega_{a,b}$ of x reduce to ordinary integrals. Furthermore the kernels that enter in the latter integrals may be calculated directly (Theorem 58).

In order to establish Theorem 48 we study still another space $Z = Z(a, b)$ and its adjoint Z^*. The space Z is interesting in itself; it consists of functions $x(s, t)$ which are continuous and which vanish whenever $s = a$ or $t = b$, $(s, t) \in I$. Theorem 33 provides a representation of elements of Z^*.

The present chapter is concerned with functions of two variables. The analogous theory for functions of one variable is in Chapter 3, and m variables in Chapter 7. The spaces B, Z, K are due to Sard [5, 6, 13].

§ 2. **The norm in B.** Let I be a compact interval of the s, t-plane and (a, b) a point of I. Write

$$I = I_s \times I_t; \qquad I_s = \{\alpha \leqq s \leqq \tilde{\alpha}\}; \qquad I_t = \{\beta \leqq t \leqq \tilde{\beta}\}.$$

Consider a space B, based on I and (a, b), with complete core ω and full core ϕ. The space B consists of functions $x(s, t)$ for which the elements of ω are continuous in their variables, $(s, t) \in I$ (cf. § 4 : 49).

If $x \in B$, then the elements of ϕ are continuous in their variables and indeed are given by Taylor formulas based on the elements of ω (Corollary 4 : 64). There is an expansion of each element of ϕ in terms of ω.

We now define the *norm* $\|x\|_B$ of $x \in B$ as the maximum of the suprema of the absolute values of the elements of ω, $(s, t) \in I$:

$$\|x\|_B = \max\,[|x_{i,j}(a, b)|,\ (i, j) \in \bar{\omega}_{a,b};\ \sup_{s \in I_s} |x_{i,j}(s, b)|,\ (i, j) \in \bar{\omega}_{s,b};$$
$$\sup_{t \in I_t} |x_{i,j}(a, t)|,\ (i, j) \in \bar{\omega}_{a,t};\ \sup_{(s,t) \in I} |x_{p,q}(s, t)|].$$

We define also an *alternative norm* $|||x|||_B$ as the maximum of the suprema of the absolute values of the elements of ϕ, $(s, t) \in I$:

$$|||x|||_B = \max [\sup_{s \in I_s} |x_{i,j}(s, b)|, (i, j) \in \bar{\phi}_{s,b};$$
$$\sup_{t \in I_t} |x_{i,j}(a, t)|, (i, j) \in \bar{\phi}_{a,t}; \sup_{(s,t) \in I} |x_{i,j}(s, t)|, (i, j) \in \bar{\phi}_{s,t}].$$

For example, if $B = B_{p,q}$ (cf. § 4: 49),

$$\|x\|_{B_{p,q}} = \max [|x_{i,j}(a, b)|, i + j < n; \sup |x_{n-j,j}(s, b)|, j < q;$$
$$\sup |x_{i,n-i}(a, t)|, i < p; \sup |x_{p,q}(s, t)|]$$

and

$$|||x|||_{B_{p,q}} = \max [\sup |x_{i,j}(s, b)|, i > p, i + j \leqq n;$$
$$\sup |x_{i,j}(a, t)|, j > q, i + j \leqq n;$$
$$\sup |x_{i,j}(s, t)|, i \leqq p, j \leqq q].$$

Here and elsewhere suprema are to be taken over I, I_s, or I_t, as appropriate.

If $B = B_{\ulcorner p,q \urcorner}$,

$$\|x\|_{B_{\ulcorner p,q \urcorner}} = \max [|x_{i,j}(a, b)|, i < p, j < q; \sup |x_{p,j}(s, b)|, j < q;$$
$$\sup |x_{i,q}(a, t)|, i < p; \sup |x_{p,q}(s, t)|]$$

and

$$|||x|||_{B_{\ulcorner p,q \urcorner}} = \max [\sup |x_{i,j}(s, t)|, i \leqq p, j \leqq q].$$

If $B = B^1$ (cf. Figure 4: 2),

$$\|x\|_{B^1} = \max [|x(a, b)|, |x_{0,1}(a, b)|, |x_{0,2}(a, b)|, |x_{0,3}(a, b)|,$$
$$|x_{1,1}(a, b)|, \sup |x_{1,0}(s, b)|, \sup |x_{2,1}(s, b)|,$$
$$\sup |x_{0,4}(a, t)|, \sup |x_{1,2}(s, t)|]$$

and

$$|||x|||_{B^1} = \max [\sup |x_{2,1}(s, b)|, \sup |x_{0,3}(a, t)|, \sup |x_{0,4}(a, t)|,$$
$$\sup |x(s, t)|, \sup |x_{1,0}(s, t)|, \sup |x_{0,1}(s, t)|, \sup |x_{1,1}(s, t)|,$$
$$\sup |x_{0,2}(s, t)|, \sup |x_{1,2}(s, t)|].$$

For any space B *the norms* $\|x\|_B$ *and* $|||x|||_B$ *are equivalent.* Thus, the definitions are such that

$$\|x\|_B \leqq |||x|||_B, \qquad x \in B.$$

In the opposite direction, the Taylor formulas for the elements of ϕ in terms of ω imply that a constant M exists such that

$$|||x|||_B \leqq M\|x\|_B, \qquad x \in B.$$

By the norm in B we will ordinarily mean $\|x\|_B$. In particular the norm in the adjoint space B^* is based on $\|x\|_B$:

$$\|F\|_{B^*} = \inf \{N : |Fx| \leqq N\|x\|_B \text{ whenever } x \in B\}, \qquad F \in B^*.$$

The space B is now a normed linear space. Indeed B is complete and separable—facts which we do not use.

The space $B_{0,0}$, that is, $B_{p,q}$ with $p = q = 0$, is merely the space of continuous functions x on I, with the customary norm

$$\|x\|_{B_{0,0}} = |||x|||_{B_{0,0}} = \sup_{(s,t) \in I} |x(s, t)|.$$

Thus $B_{0,0}$ does not depend on (a, b).

A space B with pivot $x_{p,q}$ depends on (a, b) in an essential way if

$$n = p + q \geqq 1.$$

§ 3. **Riesz's Theorem.** Suppose that λ is a function of bounded variation on I. Then the integral

$$Fx = \iint_I x(s, t)\, d\lambda(s, t)$$

defines a functional F. Clearly F is linear and bounded on $B_{0,0}$, since by (12 : 92),

$$|Fx| \leqq \sup |x(s, t)| \text{ var } \lambda = \|x\|_{B_{0,0}} \text{ var } \lambda,$$

where var λ denotes the variation of λ on I. Thus

$$F \in B^*_{0,0}.$$

The Theorem of F. Riesz will reverse and amplify this observation.

Our discussion will run parallel to that of Chapter 3.

4. Lemma. *Suppose that $F \in B^*_{0,0}$ and that*

$$\{x^\nu\}, \qquad \nu = 1, 2, \cdots,$$

is a bounded increasing sequence of elements of $B_{0,0}$. Then the sequence

$$\{Fx^\nu\}$$

of real numbers converges.

The proof is exactly like that of Lemma 3 : 16 and is omitted.

As in § 3 : 15 we define spaces M and $\mathscr{M}$,

$$B_{0,0} \subset M \subset \mathscr{M},$$

as follows: M is the space of functions which are limits of bounded increasing sequences of elements of $B_{0,0}$; $\mathscr{M}$ is the space of differences of elements of M. The norm in $\mathscr{M}$ is

$$\|x\|_{\mathscr{M}} = \sup_{(s,t) \in I} |x(s, t)|, \qquad x \in \mathscr{M}.$$

Then $\mathscr{M}$ is a linear space and an enlargement of $B_{0,0}$ that preserves norm.

Consider a functional F in $B^*_{0,0}$. We define the *natural extension* G *of* F as follows. If $x \in M$,

$$Gx = \lim_{\nu} Fx^{\nu},$$

where $\{x^{\nu}\}$ is a bounded increasing sequence of elements of $B_{0,0}$ that approaches x. If $x \in \mathscr{M}$, then

$$Gx = Gy - Gz,$$

where y and z are elements of M and

$$x = y - z.$$

5. Lemma. *If* $F \in B^*_{0,0}$, *then the natural extension* G *of* F *is well defined, linear, and bounded with norm*

$$\|G\|_{\mathscr{M}^*} = \|F\|_{B^*_{0,0}}$$

on $\mathscr{M}$.

The proof is exactly like that of Lemma 3: 23 and is omitted.

The definition of G implies that

$$Gx = \lim_{\nu} Fx^{\nu},$$

if $\{x^{\nu}\}$ is a difference of two bounded increasing sequences of elements of $B_{0,0}$. In particular $\{x^{\nu}\}$ may be any bounded decreasing sequence of elements of $B_{0,0}$.

We continue to denote by V the space of functions of bounded variation. The context will indicate whether a particular element of V is a function on I or on I_s or on I_t (cf. §§ 12: 11, 14, 72, 90).

We denote by V^0 the subspace of V consisting of elements of V which vanish on the lower boundary and are continuous from above except possibly on the lower boundary of I, I_s, or I_t, as appropriate. For example $f(s, t) \in V^0$ iff

$$f \in V; \qquad f(\alpha, t) = f(s, \beta) = 0, \quad s \in I_s, \quad t \in I_t;$$
$$f(s + 0, t + 0) = f(s, t), \quad s > \alpha, \quad t > \beta, \quad (s, t) \in I.$$

The elements of V^0 are *normalized* functions of bounded variation.

We continue to denote by

$$\{\theta^{\nu}(\tilde{s}, s)\}, \quad \tilde{s}, s \in \mathsf{R}, \quad \nu = 1, 2, \cdots,$$

the bounded decreasing sequence (3: 29) of continuous functions of s which approaches the step function $\theta(\tilde{s}, s)$ as $\nu \to \infty$.

6. Lemma. *Suppose that* $F \in B^*_{0,0}$. *Define the function* λ *on* $\mathsf{R} \times \mathsf{R}$ *as follows:*

$$\lambda(\tilde{s}, \tilde{t}) = \begin{cases} \lim\limits_{(\nu, \nu') \to (\infty, \infty)} F[\theta^{\nu}(\tilde{s}, s)\theta^{\nu'}(\tilde{t}, t)] & \textit{if } \tilde{s} > \alpha \textit{ and } \tilde{t} > \beta, \\ 0 & \textit{otherwise}. \end{cases} \tag{7}$$

Then

$$\lambda \in V$$

and

$$\text{var } \lambda \leqq \|F\|_{B^*_{0,0}}.$$

This lemma, which is analogous to Lemma 3: 31, is preparatory. Riesz's Theorem will assert that

$$\lambda \in V^0, \qquad \text{var } \lambda = \|F\|_{B^*_{0,0}}.$$

An equivalent form of (7) is

$$(8) \qquad \lambda(\tilde{s}, \tilde{t}) = \begin{cases} G[\theta(\tilde{s}, s)\theta(\tilde{t}, t)] & \text{if } \tilde{s} > \alpha \text{ and } \tilde{t} > \beta, \\ 0 & \text{otherwise,} \end{cases}$$

where G is the natural extension of F.

The relation (7) implies that

$$\lambda(\tilde{s}, \tilde{t}) = \lambda(\tilde{\alpha}, \tilde{t}) \quad \text{if } \tilde{s} \geqq \tilde{\alpha}, \tilde{t} > \beta;$$
$$\lambda(\tilde{s},\tilde{t}) = \lambda(\tilde{s}, \tilde{\beta}) \quad \text{if } \tilde{s} > \alpha, \tilde{t} \geqq \tilde{\beta};$$

since Fx depends only on values $x(s, t)$ corresponding to $(s, t) \in I$ and since $\theta^\nu(\tilde{s}, s) = 1$ for all s in I_s if $\tilde{s} \geqq \tilde{\alpha}$. Furthermore

$$\lambda(\tilde{s}, \tilde{t}) = 0 \quad \text{if } \tilde{s} \leqq \alpha \text{ or } \tilde{t} \leqq \beta.$$

Thus λ *vanishes on the lower boundary of* I.

The proof of Lemma 6 is like that of Lemma 3: 31. We omit the details except to note that the step function which enters in the proof is

$$x(s, t) = \sum_{\substack{i=1,\cdots,m;\\ j=1,\cdots,m'}}{}' [\theta(\tilde{s}_i, s) - \theta(\tilde{s}_{i-1}, s)][\theta(\tilde{t}_j, t) - \theta(\tilde{t}_{j-1}, t)]\sigma_{i,j},$$

where the subdivision of I is

$$\alpha = \tilde{s}_0 < \tilde{s}_1 < \tilde{s}_2 < \cdots < \tilde{s}_m = \tilde{\alpha},$$
$$\beta = \tilde{t}_0 < \tilde{t}_1 < \tilde{t}_2 < \cdots < \tilde{t}_{m'} = \tilde{\beta};$$

$$\sigma_{i,j} = \text{signum}\,[\lambda(\tilde{s}_i, \tilde{t}_j) - \lambda(\tilde{s}_{i-1}, \tilde{t}_j) - \lambda(\tilde{s}_i, \tilde{t}_{j-1}) + \lambda(\tilde{s}_{i-1}, \tilde{t}_{j-1})],$$

and the $'$ after $\sum$ indicates that $\theta(\tilde{s}_0, s)$ and $\theta(\tilde{t}_0, t)$ are to be replaced by zero.

9. Riesz's Theorem. *Suppose that* $F \in B^*_{0,0}$. *Put*

$$(10) \qquad \lambda(\tilde{s}, \tilde{t}) = \begin{cases} \lim\limits_{\nu,\nu'} F[\theta^\nu(\tilde{s}, s)\theta^{\nu'}(\tilde{t}, t)] & \textit{if } \tilde{s} > \alpha \textit{ and } \tilde{t} > \beta, \\ 0 & \textit{otherwise.} \end{cases}$$

Then $\lambda \in V^0$ *and*

$$(11) \qquad Fx = \iint_I x(s, t)\, d\lambda(s, t), \qquad x \in B_{0,0}.$$

The function λ *is the only element of* V^0 *for which this relation holds. Furthermore*

$$(12) \qquad \|F\|_{B^*_{0,0}} = \operatorname{var} \lambda = \iint_I d|\lambda|(s, t).$$

The proof of this theorem is just like that of Theorem 3 : 34 and is omitted. An alternative form of (10) is (8).

It may be of interest to compare the above theorem with other similar results. Suppose that A is an arbitrary set, not necessarily compact, of the s, t-plane, that $C(A)$ is a space of functions x continuous on A with norm

$$\|x\|_{C(A)} = \sup_{(s,t)\in A} |x(s, t)|;$$

and that $C(A)^*$ is the adjoint space. Under certain hypotheses relations analogous to (11) hold for $F \in C(A)^*$. Formulas for the analogues of λ are however not as simple as (10), even when A is compact [Bourbaki 1, Chapter III, §§ 1, 2, 3; Dunford-Schwartz 1, pp. 262–265; Radon 1, III, § 1; L. Schwartz 1, pp. 24–25; Sard 2].

In the theory of approximation we often use (10) or (8) to calculate λ. We thereby take advantage of the hypothesis in Theorem 9 that the set A is a compact interval I. Furthermore the seemingly more general case in which A is an arbitrary compact set of the s, t-plane is essentially no deeper than Theorem 9. For, consider a compact set A. Let I be a compact interval containing A. If $F \in C(A)^*$, then a fortiori $F \in B_{0,0}(I)^*$ and (10), (11), (12) hold. Furthermore it can be shown that

$$\iint_{I-A} d|\lambda|(s, t) = 0;$$

$$Fx = \iint_A x(s, t)\, d\lambda(s, t), \qquad x \in C(A);$$

and

$$\|F\|_{C(A)^*} = \iint_A d|\lambda|(s, t).$$

Thus the analogue of Theorem 9 is established, together with the explicit formula (10) for λ.

In the next section we will consider a theorem similar to Theorem 9 for elements of B^*, where B is a space with pivot $x_{p,q}(s, t)$. If $n = p + q \geqq 1$, we will make essential use of the fact that B is a space of functions defined on a compact interval I. Analogous theorems with I replaced by a general compact set A are for the most part not known in the case $n \geqq 1$ (cf. § 8 of the Introduction). It is only when $p = q = 0$ that an easy transition can be made from compact I to compact A, as above.

§ 13. **The space B^*.** Consider a space B with pivot $x_{p,q}$. For example, B may be $B_{p,q}$ or $B_{\ulcorner p,q \urcorner}$ or neither. We shall deduce from Riesz's Theorem the representation of linear continuous functions on B, that is, of elements of the adjoint space B^*.

The operators T_s, T_t which appear in the next theorem are Taylor operators (§ 4 : 6).

14. MASS THEOREM. *Suppose that $F \in B^*$. Put*

$$(15) \qquad c^{i,j} = F[(s-a)^{(i)}(t-b)^{(j)}], \qquad (i,j) \in \bar{\omega}_{a,b};$$

$$\lambda^{i,j}(\tilde{s}) = \begin{cases} \lim_{\nu} F[(t-b)^{(j)} T^i_s \theta^\nu(\tilde{s}, s)] & \text{if } \tilde{s} > \alpha, \\ 0 & \text{otherwise}, \end{cases} \qquad (i,j) \in \bar{\omega}_{s,b};$$

$$(16) \qquad \lambda^{i,j}(\tilde{t}) = \text{dual expression}, \qquad (i,j) \in \bar{\omega}_{a,t};$$

$$\lambda^{p,q}(\tilde{s}, \tilde{t}) = \begin{cases} \lim_{\nu,\nu'} F[T^p_s T^q_t \theta^\nu(\tilde{s}, s)\theta^{\nu'}(\tilde{t}, t)] & \text{if } \tilde{s} > \alpha \text{ and } \tilde{t} > \beta, \\ 0 & \text{otherwise}. \end{cases}$$

The functions $\lambda^{i,j}$, $(i,j) \in \bar{\omega} - \bar{\omega}_{a,b}$, are well defined and are elements of V^0. Also

$$(17) \qquad \begin{aligned} Fx = &\sum_{(i,j)\in\bar{\omega}_{a,b}} c^{i,j} x_{i,j}(a,b) + \sum_{(i,j)\in\bar{\omega}_{s,b}} \int x_{i,j}(s,b)\, d\lambda^{i,j}(s) \\ &+ \text{dual sum} + \iint x_{p,q}(s,t)\, d\lambda^{p,q}(s,t), \qquad x \in B. \end{aligned}$$

The functions $\lambda^{i,j}$ are the only elements of V^0 and the constants $c^{i,j}$ are the only numbers for which the last relation holds. Furthermore

$$(18) \qquad \|F\|_{B^*} = \sum_{\bar{\omega}_{a,b}} |c^{i,j}| + \sum_{\bar{\omega}_{s,b}} \int d|\lambda^{i,j}|(s) + \text{dual sum} + \iint d|\lambda^{p,q}|(s,t).$$

Here and elsewhere integrals are to be taken over I_s, I_t, I, as appropriate, subject to any explicit conditions that may be indicated. An illustration of the use of the theorem is given in § 27.

PROOF. The proof is like that of Theorem 3 : 39. We expand x by the Taylor formula in terms of ω, operate on x with F, and study each resulting term.

Part 1. We establish (17). Suppose that $x \in B$. Then by Theorem 4: 55.

$$\begin{aligned} x(s,t) = &\sum_{\bar{\omega}_{a,b}} (s-a)^{(i)}(t-b)^{(j)} x_{i,j}(a,b) + \sum_{\bar{\omega}_{s,b}} (t-b)^{(j)} T^i_s x_{i,j}(s,b) \\ &+ \text{dual sum} + T^p_s T^q_t x_{p,q}(s,t), \qquad (s,t) \in I. \end{aligned}$$

Hence

$$(19)\qquad \begin{aligned} Fx = \sum_{\bar{\omega}_{a,b}} c^{i,j} x_{i,j}(a, b) + \sum_{\bar{\omega}_{s,b}} F[(t-b)^{(j)} T_s^i x_{i,j}(s, b)] \\ + \text{dual sum} + F[T_s^p T_t^q x_{p,q}(s, t)], \end{aligned}$$

where $c^{i,j}$ are given by (15).

Consider the terms of (19) separately.

The last term may be evaluated as follows. Let the functional G be defined as

$$Gy = G[y(s, t)] = F[T_s^p T_t^q y(s, t)], \qquad y \in B_{0,0}.$$

For each y in $B_{0,0}$, the function

$$z(s, t) = T_s^p T_t^q y(s, t)$$

is an element of B whose complete core consists entirely of zeros except that

$$z_{p,q}(s, t) = y(s, t)$$

(Corollary 4: 61). Hence $Gy = Fz$ is well defined and linear. Furthermore

$$\|z\|_B = \max\,[0, 0, \cdots, 0, \sup_{(s,t)\in I} |y(s, t)|] = \|y\|_{B_{0,0}}.$$

Hence

$$|Gy| \leqq \|F\|_{B*}\|z\|_B = \|F\|_{B*}\|y\|_{B_{0,0}}, \qquad y \in B_{0,0};$$

and G is bounded and so an element of $B^*_{0,0}$. By Theorem 9,

$$Gy = \iint y(s, t)\, d\lambda^{p,q}(s, t), \quad y \in B_{0,0},$$

where

$$\lambda^{p,q}(\tilde{s}, \tilde{t}) = \begin{cases} \lim_{\nu,\nu'} G[\theta^\nu(\tilde{s}, s)\theta^{\nu'}(\tilde{t}, t)], & \text{if } \tilde{s} > \alpha \text{ and } \tilde{t} > \beta, \\ 0 & \text{otherwise.} \end{cases}$$

Hence the last term of (19) is

$$F[T_s^p T_t^q x_{p,q}(s, t)] = Gx_{p,q} = \iint_I x_{p,q}(s, t)\, d\lambda^{p,q}(s, t),$$

where $\lambda^{p,q}$ is given by (16).

The other terms of (19) are treated similarly, by using Theorem 3: 34 for functionals in C_0^*.

Thus (17) is established.

Part 2. Uniqueness of $\lambda^{i,j}$ in V^0 and $c^{i,j}$. We proceed as in Part 2 of the proof of Theorem 3: 39. Thus suppose that

$$\begin{aligned} Fx = \sum_{\bar{\omega}_{a,b}} b^{i,j} x_{i,j}(a, b) + \sum_{\bar{\omega}_{s,b}} \int x_{i,j}(s, b)\, d\kappa^{i,j}(s) + \text{dual sum} \\ + \iint x_{p,q}(s, t)\, d\kappa^{p,q}(s, t), \qquad x \in B, \end{aligned}$$

where $\kappa^{i,j}$ are elements of V^0 and $b^{i,j}$ are constants. By appropriate substitutions for x we may now show that $b^{i,j} = c^{i,j}$ and $\kappa^{i,j} = \lambda^{i,j}$. For example, put

$$x(s, t) = (t - b)^{(j_0)} T_s^{i_0} y(s), \qquad y \in C_0(I_s), \quad (i_0, j_0) \in \bar{\omega}_{s,b}.$$

The complete core of x in B then consists entirely of zeros except that

$$x_{i_0,j_0}(s, b) = y(s).$$

Hence

$$Fx = \int y(s)\, d\kappa^{i_0,j_0}(s) = \int y(s)\, d\lambda^{i_0,j_0}(s).$$

Since this relation holds for all y in C_0 and since κ^{i_0,j_0} and λ^{i_0,j_0} are both elements of V^0, it follows that

$$\kappa^{i_0,j_0}(s) = \lambda^{i_0,j_0}(s), \qquad s \in \mathsf{R}_s,$$

by Theorem 3 : 34.

Part 3. The relation (18) is established just as was (3 : 43). Thus (17) implies that

$$\begin{aligned} |Fx| \leqq \Big[\sum_{\bar{\omega}_{a,b}} |c^{i,j}| + \sum_{\bar{\omega}_{s,b}} \int d|\lambda^{i,j}|(s) + \text{dual sum} + \iint d|\lambda^{p,q}|(s, t) \Big] \\ \times \max\,[|x_{i,j}(a, b)|,\ (i, j) \in \bar{\omega}_{a,b}\,;\ \sup |x_{i,j}(s, b)|, \\ (i, j) \in \bar{\omega}_{s,b};\ \text{dual terms}\,;\ \sup |x_{p,q}(s, t)|], \qquad x \in B. \end{aligned}$$

Since the second factor is precisely $\|x\|_B$,

$$\|F\|_{B^*} \leqq \sum_{\bar{\omega}_{a,b}} |c^{i,j}| + \sum_{\bar{\omega}_{s,b}} \int d|\lambda^{i,j}|(s) + \text{dual sum} + \iint d|\lambda^{p,q}|(s, t).$$

To establish the reverse inequality, let $\eta > 0$ be given. By Theorems 9 and 3 : 34 we know that functions $y^{i,j}$, $(i, j) \in \bar{\omega} - \bar{\omega}_{a,b}$, exist such that

$$\int y^{i,j}(s)\, d\lambda^{i,j}(s) > \int d|\lambda^{i,j}|(s) - \eta, \qquad y^{i,j} \in C_0(I_s), \quad \|y\|_{C_0(I_s)} = 1, \quad (i, j) \in \bar{\omega}_{s,b};$$

$$\text{dual relations}, \quad (i, j) \in \bar{\omega}_{a,t};$$

$$\iint y^{p,q}(s, t)\, d\lambda^{p,q}(s, t) > \iint d|\lambda|(s, t) - \eta, \qquad y^{p,q} \in B_{0,0}, \quad \|y\|_{B_{0,0}} = 1.$$

Put

$$\begin{aligned} x(s, t) = \sum_{\bar{\omega}_{a,b}} (s - a)^{(i)}(t - b)^{(j)} \operatorname{signum} c^{i,j} + \sum_{\bar{\omega}_{s,b}} (t - b)^{(j)} T_s^i y^{i,j}(s) \\ + \text{dual sum} + T_s^p T_t^q y^{p,q}(s, t). \end{aligned}$$

Then $x \in B$, and

$$\begin{aligned} \|x\|_B = \max\,[\operatorname{signum} c^{i,j},\ (i, j) \in \bar{\omega}_{a,b}\,;\ \sup |y^{i,j}(s)|,\ (i, j) \in \bar{\omega}_{s,b}; \\ \text{dual terms}\,;\ \sup |y^{p,q}(s, t)|] = 1. \end{aligned}$$

On the other hand

$$Fx = \sum_{\bar{\omega}_{a,b}} |c^{i,j}| + \sum_{\bar{\omega}_{s,b}} \int y^{i,j}(s)\, d\lambda^{i,j}(s) + \text{dual sum}$$
$$+ \iint y^{p,q}(s,t)\, d\lambda^{p,q}(s,t)$$
$$\geqq \sum_{\bar{\omega}_{a,b}} |c^{i,j}| + \sum_{\bar{\omega}_{s,b}} \int d|\lambda^{i,j}|(s) + \text{dual sum}$$
$$+ \iint d|\lambda^{p,q}|(s,t) - k\eta,$$

where k is the number of elements in $\bar{\omega} - \bar{\omega}_{a,b}$. Since k is a fixed constant and η is arbitrarily small, (18) follows.

This completes the proof of the theorem.

Consider a functional $F \in B^*$. We define the *Lebesgue extension* G of F as follows:

$$Gx = \sum_{\bar{\omega}_{a,b}} c^{i,j} x_{i,j}(a,b) + \sum_{\bar{\omega}_{s,b}} \int_{I_s} x_{i,j}(s,b)\, d\lambda^{i,j}(s) + \text{dual sum} + \iint_I x_{p,q}(s,t)\, d\lambda^{p,q}(s,t), \tag{20}$$

where $c^{i,j}$, $\lambda^{i,j}$ are defined by (15), (16). Thus Gx is defined whenever x is a function whose core in B consists of elements $x_{i,j}$ which are integrable in the sense of Lebesgue-Stieltjes relative to the corresponding $\lambda^{i,j}$. For $x \in B$,

$$Gx = Fx;$$

and G is defined on a space larger than B.

One may use the last theorem to analyze a given functional F, without any consideration of kernel theorems like Theorem 58 below or Theorem 4: 84. For a particular $F \in B^*$, the masses $\lambda^{i,j}$ may or may not be absolutely continuous. Each mass $\lambda^{i,j}$ may be calculated by (16). If a mass is absolutely continuous, it may be differentiated and the Stieltjes integral in which it enters in (17) may be replaced by an ordinary integral (cf. Lemma 12: 130). Thus formulas for Fx in terms of ordinary integrals, if existent, may be obtained from (17). In any case, Fx, $x \in B$, may be studied by (17).

The kernel theorems 58 and 4: 84, where applicable, lead more directly to formulas for Fx, $x \in B$, in terms of ordinary integrals on elements of ω. The theorems, however, require the theory of the space K^* (considered in § 38, § 47) or $\mathscr{K}^*$ (considered in § 4: 80).

§ 21. **The space $\mathscr{B}^*$.** It may be of interest to study a space similar to $\mathscr{K}^*$ of § 4 : 80.

Consider a space B with complete core ω and full core ϕ. We define $\mathscr{B}^*$ as the space of functionals which are finite sums of Lebesgue-Stieltjes integrals relative to functions of bounded variation of the elements of the full core ϕ of the function operated on. The elements of ϕ are understood in any way consistent with the rule of ϕ.

For brevity and simplicity of notation, we will write formulas for

$$Fx, \qquad F \in \mathscr{B}^*,$$

as if only one ordering of differentiation appears in each x_{i_0,j_0} in ϕ. As in § 4: 80, this involves no essential loss of idea. Thus an element F of $\mathscr{B}^*$ is a functional of the form

$$\begin{aligned} Fx = & \sum_{(i,j)\in\bar{\phi}_{s,t}} \iint x_{i,j}(s,t)\,d\mu^{i,j}(s,t) + \sum_{(i,j)\in\bar{\phi}_{s,b}} \int x_{i,j}(s,b)\,d\mu^{i,j}(s) \\ & + \sum_{(i,j)\in\bar{\phi}_{a,t}} \int x_{i,j}(a,t)\,d\mu^{i,j}(t), \end{aligned} \tag{22}$$

where the functions $\mu^{i,j}$ are given and are of bounded variation on I, I_s, or I_t as appropriate. The domain of definition of F consists of all functions x for which the integrands in (22) are Lebesgue-Stieltjes integrable relative to the corresponding functions $\mu^{i,j}$.

Consider $F \in \mathscr{B}^*$. The jump set $\mathscr{J}_s$ of F may be defined as the countable set of points other than $s = \tilde{\alpha}$ in I_s which are points of discontinuity of

$$|\mu^{i,j}|(s, \tilde{\beta}), \qquad (i,j) \in \bar{\phi}_{s,t},$$

or

$$|\mu^{i,j}|(s), \qquad (i,j) \in \bar{\phi}_{s,b},$$

where the bars indicate total variations and $\tilde{\beta}$ is substituted after the variation relative to (s, t) has been taken. Thus

$$\tilde{\alpha} \notin \mathscr{J}_s \subset I_s.$$

The set $\mathscr{J}_t$ is the dual.

The sets $\mathscr{J}_s$ and $\mathscr{J}_t$ as just defined are larger than they need be.

If $F \in B^*$, the Lebesgue extension (20) of F is an element of $\mathscr{B}^*$. The next theorem includes the converse statement.

23. Theorem. *If $F \in \mathscr{B}^*$, then the restriction of F to B is an element of B^*. The functions $\lambda^{i,j} \in V^0$ which enter in the standard form* (17) *for Fx satisfy the following relations:*

$$\begin{aligned} \lambda^{i,j}(\tilde{s}) &= F[(t-b)^{(j)} T_s^i \theta(\tilde{s}, s)], && \alpha < \tilde{s} \notin \mathscr{J}_s, \quad (i,j) \in \bar{\omega}_{s,b}; \\ \lambda^{i,j}(\tilde{t}) &= \textit{dual expression}, && (i,j) \in \bar{\omega}_{a,t}; \\ \lambda^{p,q}(\tilde{s}, \tilde{t}) &= F[T_s^p \theta(\tilde{s}, s) T_t^q \theta(\tilde{t}, t)], && \alpha < \tilde{s} \notin \mathscr{J}_s \quad \textit{and} \quad \beta < \tilde{t} \notin \mathscr{J}_t. \end{aligned} \tag{24}$$

The present theorem affords a simpler calculation of the functions $\lambda^{i,j}$ than does Theorem 14. Thus, consider $\lambda^{p,q}$, for preciseness. We know that $\lambda^{p,q}(\tilde{s}, \tilde{t})$ vanishes if $\tilde{s} = \alpha$ or if $\tilde{t} = \beta$, since $\lambda^{p,q} \in V^0$. The corner value $\lambda^{p,q}(\tilde{\alpha}, \tilde{\beta})$ is given by (24), since

$$\tilde{\alpha} \notin \mathscr{J}_s, \qquad \tilde{\beta} \notin \mathscr{J}_t.$$

The value of $\lambda^{p,q}(\tilde{s}, \tilde{t})$ at all other points $(\tilde{s}, \tilde{t}) \in I$, if needed, can be derived from the values which are given by (24), by the use of the relation

$$\lambda^{p,q}(\tilde{s} + 0, \tilde{t} + 0) = \lambda^{p,q}(\tilde{s}, \tilde{t}), \qquad \alpha < \tilde{s} \text{ and } \beta < \tilde{t},$$

a relation which is a consequence of the fact that $\lambda^{p,q} \in V^0$.

Proof. Suppose the $F \in \mathscr{B}^*$. If $x \in B$, the integrals in (22) certainly exist, because the integrands are continuous. Clearly F is linear on B. Furthermore (22) implies that

$$|Fx| \leqq \sum_{\phi_{s,t}} \sup |x_{i,j}(s,t)| \iint d|\mu^{i,j}|(s,t)$$

$$+ \sum_{\phi_{s,b}} \sup |x_{i,j}(s,b)| \int d|\mu^{i,j}|(s) + \text{dual sum}$$

$$\leqq |||x|||_B \Big[\sum_{\phi_{s,t}} \iint d|\mu^{i,j}|(s,t)$$

$$+ \sum_{\phi_{s,b}} \int d|\mu^{i,j}|(s) + \text{dual sum} \Big], \qquad x \in B.$$

Thus the restriction of F to B is bounded on B and therefore is an element of B^*.

It remains to establish (24). The idea of the proof is that we may interchange lim and F in (16), when

$$\tilde{s} \notin \mathscr{J}_s \text{ and } \tilde{t} \notin \mathscr{J}_t.$$

Consider one of the functions defined in (16), say $\lambda^{p,q}$, to focus our thoughts. Take

$$\alpha < \tilde{s}, \qquad \beta < \tilde{t}.$$

Then

$$\lambda^{p,q}(\tilde{s}, \tilde{t}) = \lim_{\nu,\nu'} F[T_{\tilde{s}}^p \theta^\nu(\tilde{s}, s) T_{\tilde{t}}^q \theta^{\nu'}(\tilde{t}, t)].$$

Since the functions θ^ν are continuous, the argument of F here is an element of B. Differentiations of the argument leading to elements of the full core ϕ may be carried out using the relations

$$D_s T_s = \text{identity},$$
$$D_t T_t = \text{identity},$$

without exception. By (22), $\lambda^{p,q}(\tilde{s}, \tilde{t})$ is the limit of a sum of integrals in which the integrands are of the form

$$\cdots T_s^g \theta^\nu(\tilde{s}, s) T_t^h \theta^{\nu'}(\tilde{t}, t), \qquad g, h \geqq 0.$$

By the classical theorem on monotone approach, the limit sign may be moved across the integral signs and across T_s, T_t. Hence $\lambda^{p,q}(\tilde{s}, \tilde{t})$ is a sum of integrals in which the integrands are of the form

$$\cdots T_s^g \theta(\tilde{s}, s) T_t^h \theta(\tilde{t}, t), \qquad g, h \geqq 0. \tag{25}$$

This sum, however, is that given by (24), if

$$\tilde{s} \notin \mathscr{J}_s \quad \text{and} \quad \tilde{t} \notin \mathscr{J}_t. \tag{26}$$

For, the argument of F in (24), although not an element of B, is such that all the derivatives in its full core exist and are of the form (25), with only the following qualification:

$$s \neq \tilde{s} \quad \text{if } g = 0,$$
$$t \neq \tilde{t} \quad \text{if } h = 0.$$

The case $s = \tilde{\alpha}$ is not exceptional, because $\theta^\nu(\tilde{s}, s) = \theta(\tilde{s}, s) = 1$ for all s in I_s and all ν, when $\tilde{s} = \tilde{\alpha}$. Likewise for $t = \tilde{\beta}$. Now the missing values $s = \tilde{s}$ and $t = \tilde{t}$ are immaterial to the use of (22) if (26) holds, since the missing values are then sets of absolute $\mu^{i,j}$ variation zero for the pertinent (i, j). Thus (26) implies that the expression in (24) for $\lambda^{p,q}(\tilde{s}, \tilde{t})$ may be evaluated and equals exactly the value given by (16).

This completes the proof.

§ 27. **Illustration.** Consider the particular functional

$$Rx = \int_{-1}^{1}\int_{-1}^{1} x(s, t)\, ds\, dt - \alpha x(0, 0)$$
$$- \beta[x(1, 1) + x(1, -1) + x(-1, 1) + x(-1, -1)],$$

which is in fact the functional (5: 33) with $\gamma = 0$. If $x(s, t) = 1$, then $Rx = 0$ iff

$$\alpha + 4\beta = 4.$$

Let us specify that this condition hold. We shall think of β as the independent parameter; α is determined by β.

Let I be the interval $-1 \leqq s, t \leqq 1$. Take $(a, b) = (0, 0)$.

Since Rx is a Stieltjes integral on x, $R \in \mathscr{B}^*$ and the restriction of R to B is an element of B^*, for all spaces B. Using Theorem 14, we shall study R as an element of $B_{0,1}^*$. Alternatively we could use Theorem 23. We cannot use a theory of a space $\mathscr{K}_{0,1}^*$, since the latter is not defined: for a space $\mathscr{K}^*$ to exist it is necessary that $pq \geqq 1$.

In the space $B_{0,1}$,

$$\bar{\omega}_{a,b} = \{(0, 0)\};\ \bar{\omega}_{s,b} = \{(1, 0)\};\ \bar{\omega}_{a,t} \text{ is empty};\ \bar{\omega}_{s,t} = \{(0, 1)\}.$$

By Theorem 14,

$$(28)\quad Rx = \int_{-1}^{1}\int_{-1}^{1} x_{0,1}(s, t)\, d\lambda(s, t) + \int_{-1}^{1} x_{1,0}(s, 0)\, d\mu(s), \qquad x \in B_{0,1},$$

where λ, μ vanish on the lower boundaries and

$$\lambda(\tilde{s}, \tilde{t}) = \lim_{\nu,\nu'} R[\theta^{\nu}(\tilde{s}, s)T_t\theta^{\nu'}(\tilde{t}, t)], \qquad \tilde{s} > -1 \text{ and } \tilde{t} > -1;$$

$$\mu(\tilde{s}) = \lim_{\nu} R[T_s\theta^{\nu}(\tilde{s}, s)], \qquad \tilde{s} > -1;$$

since

$$c^{0,0} = R[1] = 0.$$

Now Rx is a Stieltjes integral on x. Hence, by the classical theorem on monotone approach,

$$\lambda(\tilde{s}, \tilde{t}) = R[\theta(\tilde{s}, s)T_t\theta(\tilde{t}, t)], \qquad \tilde{s} > -1 \text{ and } \tilde{t} > -1;$$

$$\mu(\tilde{s}) = R[T_s\theta(\tilde{s}, s)], \qquad \tilde{s} > -1.$$

Furthermore

$$T_s\theta(\tilde{s}, s) = \int_a^s \theta(\tilde{s}, u)\, du = (s - \tilde{s})\theta(\tilde{s}, s) + (\tilde{s} - a)\theta(\tilde{s}, a)$$
$$= (s - \tilde{s})\theta(\tilde{s}, s) + \tilde{s}\theta(\tilde{s}, 0),$$

by (11: 15). Likewise

$$T_t\theta(\tilde{t}, t) = (t - \tilde{t})\theta(\tilde{t}, t) + \tilde{t}\theta(\tilde{t}, 0).$$

Hence

$$(29)\quad \begin{aligned} \lambda(\tilde{s}, \tilde{t}) &= R\{\theta(\tilde{s}, s)[(t - \tilde{t})\theta(\tilde{t}, t) + \tilde{t}\theta(\tilde{t}, 0)], \qquad \tilde{s} > -1,\ \tilde{t} > -1;\\ \mu(\tilde{s}) &= R[(s - \tilde{s})\theta(\tilde{s}, s)], \qquad \tilde{s} > -1; \end{aligned}$$

as $\tilde{s}\theta(\tilde{s}, 0)$ is a constant.

For $-1 < \tilde{s} \leqq 1$,

$$\mu(\tilde{s}) = \int_{-1}^{1}\int_{-1}^{1} (s - \tilde{s})\theta(\tilde{s}, s)\, ds\, dt + \alpha\tilde{s}\theta(\tilde{s}, 0)$$
$$- \beta[2(1 - \tilde{s})\theta(\tilde{s}, 1) + 2(-1 - \tilde{s})\theta(\tilde{s}, -1)]$$
$$= 2\int_{-1}^{\tilde{s}} (s - \tilde{s})\, ds + \alpha\tilde{s}\theta(\tilde{s}, 0) + 2\beta(1 + \tilde{s})\theta(\tilde{s}, -1)$$
$$= -(1 + \tilde{s})^2 + \alpha\tilde{s}\theta(\tilde{s}, 0) + 2\beta(1 + \tilde{s}),$$

since $(1 - \tilde{s})\theta(\tilde{s}, 1) = 0$ both when $\tilde{s} < 1$ and $\tilde{s} = 1$. Hence

$$\mu(\tilde{s}) = \begin{cases} -(1 + \tilde{s})^2 + 2\beta(1 + \tilde{s}) & \text{if } -1 < \tilde{s} < 0,\\ -(1 + \tilde{s})^2 + \alpha\tilde{s} + 2\beta(1 + \tilde{s}) & \\ \qquad = -(1 - \tilde{s})^2 + 2\beta(1 - \tilde{s}) & \text{if } 0 \leqq \tilde{s} \leqq 1. \end{cases}$$

As $\mu(-1) = 0$, the first line here is valid if $\tilde{s} = -1$ also. Indeed for $-1 \leqq \tilde{s} \leqq 1$,

$$\mu(\tilde{s}) = -(1 - |\tilde{s}|)^2 + 2\beta(1 - |\tilde{s}|).$$

Thus μ is absolutely continuous, and

$$\begin{aligned} d\mu(s) &= 2[1 - |s| - \beta] \text{ signum } s\, ds \\ &= 2[(1 - \beta) \text{ signum } s - s]\, ds, \quad s \neq 0, \end{aligned}$$

since

$$\frac{d}{ds}|s| = \text{signum } s, \qquad s \neq 0.$$

The value of $d\mu(s)$ at $s = 0$ is immaterial.

We now calculate $\lambda(\tilde{s}, \tilde{t})$ by (29). Suppose that $-1 < \tilde{s}, \tilde{t} \leqq 1$. Then

$$\begin{aligned} &\int_{-1}^{1}\int_{-1}^{1} \theta(\tilde{s}, s)[(t - \tilde{t})\theta(\tilde{t}, t) + \tilde{t}\theta(\tilde{t}, 0)]\, ds\, dt \\ &\qquad = \int_{-1}^{\tilde{s}} ds \left[\int_{-1}^{\tilde{t}} (t - \tilde{t})\, dt + 2\tilde{t}\theta(\tilde{t}, 0)\right] \\ &\qquad = (1 + \tilde{s})\left[\frac{-(1 + \tilde{t})^2}{2} + 2\tilde{t}\theta(\tilde{t}, 0)\right] \\ &\qquad = \begin{cases} \dfrac{-(1 + \tilde{s})(1 + \tilde{t})^2}{2} & \text{if } \tilde{t} < 0, \\ \dfrac{-(1 + \tilde{s})(1 - \tilde{t})^2}{2} & \text{if } 0 \leqq \tilde{t} \end{cases} \\ &\qquad = \frac{-(1 + \tilde{s})(1 - |\tilde{t}|)^2}{2}. \end{aligned}$$

Hence

$$\begin{aligned} \lambda(\tilde{s}, \tilde{t}) &= \frac{-(1 + \tilde{s})(1 - |\tilde{t}|)^2}{2} - \alpha\theta(\tilde{s}, 0)[-\tilde{t}\theta(\tilde{t}, 0) + \tilde{t}\theta(\tilde{t}, 0)] \\ &\quad - \beta\theta(\tilde{s}, 1)[(1 - \tilde{t})\theta(\tilde{t}, 1) + \tilde{t}\theta(\tilde{t}, 0) + (-1 - \tilde{t}) + \tilde{t}\theta(\tilde{t}, 0)] \\ &\quad - \beta[(1 - \tilde{t})\theta(\tilde{t}, 1) + \tilde{t}\theta(\tilde{t}, 0) + (-1 - \tilde{t}) + \tilde{t}\theta(\tilde{t}, 0)] \\ &= \frac{-(1 + \tilde{s})(1 - |\tilde{t}|)^2}{2} - \beta[1 + \theta(\tilde{s}, 1)][(-1 - \tilde{t}) + 2\tilde{t}\theta(\tilde{t}, 0) \\ &\qquad\qquad + (1 - \tilde{t})\theta(\tilde{t}, 1)]. \end{aligned}$$

Now

$$\begin{aligned} -1 - \tilde{t} + 2\tilde{t}\theta(\tilde{t}, 0) &= -1 + |\tilde{t}|, \\ (1 - \tilde{t})\theta(\tilde{t}, 1) &= 0. \end{aligned}$$

Hence

$$\lambda(s,t) = \begin{cases} \dfrac{-(1+s)(1-|t|)^2}{2} + \beta(1-|t|) & \text{if } -1 < s < 1,\ -1 < t \leqq 1; \\ \dfrac{-(1+s)(1-|t|)^2}{2} + 2\beta(1-|t|) = -(1-|t|)^2 + 2\beta(1-|t|) & \\ \qquad \text{if } s = 1,\quad -1 < t \leqq 1. & \end{cases}$$

We know also that $\lambda(s, t) = 0$ if $s = -1$ or if $t = -1$. Thus $\lambda(s, t)$ has discontinuities at $s = 1$ and at $s = -1$;

$$\lambda(1, t) - \lambda(1 - 0, t) = \beta(1 - |t|);$$
$$\lambda(-1 + 0, t) - \lambda(-1, t) = \beta(1 - |t|);$$

and $\lambda(s, t)$ is absolutely continuous on $-1 < s < 1$, $-1 \leqq t \leqq 1$, with

$$\lambda(s,t) = \frac{-(1+s)(1-|t|)^2}{2} + \beta(1-|t|),$$

$$d_{s,t}\lambda(s,t) = (1-|t|)\,(\text{signum } t)\, ds\, dt, \qquad t \neq 0.$$

Hence, for any function $y(s, t)$ continuous on I,

$$\begin{aligned} \int_{-1}^{1}\int_{-1}^{1} y(s,t)\, d\lambda(s,t) &= \beta \int_{t=-1}^{1} y(1,t)\, d(1-|t|) + \beta \int_{-1}^{1} y(-1,t)\, d(1-|t|) \\ &\quad + \int_{-1}^{1}\int_{-1}^{1} y(s,t)(1-|t|)\,(\text{signum } t)\, ds\, dt \\ &= \int_{-1}^{1}\int_{-1}^{1} y(s,t)(1-|t|)\,(\text{signum } t)\, ds\, dt \\ &\quad - \beta \int_{-1}^{1} y(1,t)\,(\text{signum } t)\, dt \\ &\quad - \beta \int_{-1}^{1} y(-1,t)\,(\text{signum } t)\, dt. \end{aligned}$$

Thus an explicit form of (28) is

$$\begin{aligned} Rx = {} & \int_{-1}^{1}\int_{-1}^{1} x_{0,1}(s,t)(1-|t|)\,(\text{signum } t)\, ds\, dt - \beta \int_{-1}^{1} x_{0,1}(1,t)\,(\text{signum } t)\, dt \\ & - \beta \int_{-1}^{1} x_{0,1}(-1,t)\,(\text{signum } t)\, dt \\ & + 2 \int_{-1}^{1} x_{1,0}(s,0)(-s + (1-\beta)\,\text{signum } s)\, ds, \qquad x \in B_{0,1}. \end{aligned}$$

One may check this relation by direct evaluation of the right member. The parameter β is arbitrary and determines α.

We note in conclusion that Rx may be appraised by a sharp Schwarzian inequality:

$$|Rx| \leqq J^{1/2}\left[\int_{-1}^{1}\int_{-1}^{1} x_{0,1}(s,t)^2\,ds\,dt + \int_{-1}^{1} x_{0,1}(1,t)^2\,dt + \int_{-1}^{1} x_{0,1}(-1,t)^2\,dt + \int_{-1}^{1} x_{1,0}(s,0)^2\,ds\right]^{1/2}, \qquad x \in B_{0,1},$$

where

$$J = \int_{-1}^{1}\int_{-1}^{1}(1-|t|)^2\,ds\,dt + 4\beta^2 + 4\int_{-1}^{1}[(1-\beta)\,\text{signum}\,s - s]^2\,ds.$$

The minimal J occurs for

$$\beta = \frac{1}{5},$$

in which case

$$\alpha = \frac{16}{5}.$$

(Details omitted.)

§ 30. **The operators δ_s and δ_t.** In addition to the operator δ_s defined in § 3 : 82, we shall use its dual operator δ_t. Thus if x is a function on I,

$$\delta_s x(s,t) = x(s,t) - x(a,t),$$
$$\delta_t x(s,t) = x(s,t) - x(s,b),$$
$$\delta_s\delta_t x(s,t) = \delta_t\delta_s x(s,t) = x(s,t) - x(s,b) - x(a,t) + x(a,b).$$

§ 31. **The spaces Z and Z^*.** This section is similar to § 3 : 58. Let

$$I = I_s \times I_t; \qquad I_s = \{\alpha \leqq s \leqq \tilde{\alpha}\}; \qquad I_t = \{\beta \leqq t \leqq \tilde{\beta}\};$$

and let (a, b) be a given fixed element of I. We define the space $Z = Z(a, b)$ as the subspace of $B_{0,0} = B_{0,0}(I; a, b)$ which consists of functions $x(s, t)$ that vanish on $s = a$ and on $t = b$:

$$Z = Z(a,b) = \{x \in B_{0,0} : x(a,t) = 0 \text{ for all } t \in I_t \text{ and } x(s,b) = 0 \text{ for all } s \in I_s\}.$$

The norm $\|x\|_Z$ of x in Z is taken as $\|x\|_{B_{0,0}}$. Thus Z is a subspace of $B_{0,0}$ with the same topology. Hence

$$Z \subset B_{0,0}, \qquad Z^* \supset B_{0,0}^*.$$

Theorem 33 gives a unique, accessible, and useful representation of F, $F \in Z^*$.

We continue to denote by V^0 the space of normalized functions of bounded variation, defined before Lemma 6. We denote by $V^{0,0}$ the subspace of V^0

consisting of functions that vanish everywhere on the boundary of I, I_s or I_t, as appropriate. For example, $f(s, t) \in V^{0,0}$ iff

$$f \in V; \qquad f(s + 0, t + 0) = f(s, t), \quad s > \alpha, \quad t > \beta;$$
$$f(s, t) = 0 \qquad \text{if } s = \alpha \text{ or } s = \tilde{\alpha} \text{ or } t = \beta \text{ or } t = \tilde{\beta}.$$

In the following theorem,

$$\psi^\nu(a, \tilde{s}, s) = \theta^\nu(\tilde{s}, a) - \theta^\nu(\tilde{s}, s), \quad \nu = 1, 2, \cdots; \qquad s, \tilde{s} \in \mathsf{R}, \tag{32}$$

where $\{\theta^\nu(\tilde{s}, s)\}$ is the bounded decreasing sequence of continuous functions (3 : 29) which approach $\theta(\tilde{s}, s)$.

33. Mass theorem. *Suppose that $F \in Z(a, b)^*$. Put*

$$\lambda(\tilde{s}, \tilde{t}) = \begin{cases} \lim\limits_{\nu,\nu'} F[\psi^\nu(a, \tilde{s}, s)\psi^{\nu'}(b, \tilde{t}, t)] & \text{if } \tilde{s} > \alpha \text{ and } \tilde{t} > \beta, \\ 0 & \text{otherwise.} \end{cases} \tag{34}$$

Then $\lambda \in V^{0,0}$, and

$$Fx = \iint_I x(s, t)\, d\lambda(s, t), \qquad x \in Z(a, b). \tag{35}$$

The function λ is the only element of $V^{0,0}$ for which this relation holds. Furthermore

$$\|F\|_{Z(a,b)^*} = \iint_{\substack{s \neq a, \\ t \neq b}} d|\lambda|(s, t). \tag{36}$$

This theorem is the two-dimensional analogue of Theorem 3 : 63. The interesting facts here are that λ in $V^{0,0}$ is unique and that (36) holds. The relation (35) is quite expected.

Proof. The proof is like that of Theorem 3 : 63.

Part 1. We establish (35). Given the functional $F \in Z(a, b)^*$, define the functional G on $B_{0,0}$ as follows. For $y \in B_{0,0}$, put

$$Gy = F\delta_s\delta_t y.$$

Since

$$\delta_s\delta_t y = y(s, t) - y(s, b) - y(a, t) + y(a, b) \in Z(a, b),$$

$F\delta_s\delta_t y$ is defined. Hence G is defined on $B_{0,0}$. Clearly G is additive. Now G is bounded on $B_{0,0}$, because

$$\begin{aligned} |Gy| &= |F\delta_s\delta_t y| \leqq \|F\|_{Z^*}\|\delta_s\delta_t y\|_Z \\ &= \|F\|_{Z^*}\|y(s, t) - y(s, b) - y(a, t) + y(a, b)\|_{B_{0,0}} \\ &\leqq \|F\|_{Z^*}4\|y\|_{B_{0,0}}. \end{aligned}$$

Hence $G \in B^*_{0,0}$, and by Theorem 9,

$$Gy = \iint y(s, t)d\lambda(s, t), \qquad y \in B_{0,0},$$

where

$$\lambda(\tilde{s}, \tilde{t}) = \begin{cases} \lim\limits_{\nu, \nu'} G[\theta^{\nu}(\tilde{s}, s)\theta^{\nu'}(\tilde{t}, t)], & \tilde{s} > \alpha \text{ and } \tilde{t} > \beta, \\ 0 & \text{otherwise.} \end{cases}$$

By (32),

$$\begin{aligned} \lambda(\tilde{s}, \tilde{t}) &= \lim_{\nu, \nu'} F[\theta^{\nu}(\tilde{s}, s)\theta^{\nu'}(\tilde{t}, t) - \theta^{\nu}(\tilde{s}, a)\theta^{\nu'}(\tilde{t}, t) \\ &\qquad - \theta^{\nu}(\tilde{s}, s)\theta^{\nu'}(\tilde{t}, b) + \theta^{\nu}(\tilde{s}, a)\theta^{\nu'}(\tilde{t}, b)] \\ &= \lim_{\nu, \nu'} F[\psi^{\nu}(a, \tilde{s}, s)\psi^{\nu'}(b, \tilde{t}, t)], \qquad \tilde{s} > \alpha, \quad \tilde{t} > \beta. \end{aligned}$$

This confirms (34). The last limit exists, since the middle one does. We know that $\lambda \in V^0$, by Theorem 9. Furthermore,

$$\lambda(\tilde{\alpha}, \tilde{t}) = \lim_{\nu} F[\psi^{\nu}(a, \tilde{\alpha}, s)\psi^{\nu}(b, \tilde{t}, t)] = \lim_{\nu} F0 = 0, \qquad \tilde{t} \in I_t,$$

$$\lambda(\tilde{s}, \tilde{\beta}) = 0, \qquad \tilde{s} \in I_s,$$

since $\psi^{\nu}(a, \tilde{\alpha}, s) = 0$ for $s \in I_s$. Thus

$$\lambda \in V^{0,0}.$$

Suppose that $x \in Z(a, b)$. Put

$$y(s, t) = x(s, t).$$

Then $y \in B_{0,0}$, and

$$\delta_s\delta_t y = x(s, t) - 0 - 0 + 0 = x(s, t);$$

also

$$Fx = F\delta_s\delta_t y = Gy = \iint_I x(s, t)\, d\lambda(s, t).$$

Thus (35) is established.

Part 2. Uniqueness of λ. This is established as in the proof of Theorem 3:63.

Part 3. The norm of G in Z^*. Although the proof here is similar to Part 3 of the proof of Theorem 3: 63, it is sufficiently different to merit our giving the details.

Integrals are to be understood in the sense of Lebesgue-Stieltjes. The proof will use the fact that $\lambda \in V^0$; it would apply whether $\lambda \in V^{0,0}$ or not.

Because of the vanishing of $x(a, t)$ and $x(s, b)$, (35) implies that

$$Fx = \iint\limits_{\substack{s \neq a,\\ t \neq b}} x(s, t)\, d\lambda(s, t), \qquad x \in Z(a, b).$$

Hence

$$\|F\|_{Z^*} \leqq \iint\limits_{\substack{s \neq a,\\ t \neq b}} d|\lambda|(s, t).$$

To establish (36), it will be sufficient to reverse the last inequality. Assume that

$$\alpha < a < \tilde{\alpha}, \qquad \beta < b < \tilde{\beta}.$$

(The cases in which (a, b) is on the boundary of I are treated similarly and more simply.) Let

$$v(\tilde{s}, \tilde{t}) = |\lambda|(\tilde{s}, \tilde{t}) = \iint\limits_{\substack{s \leqq \tilde{s},\\ t \leqq \tilde{t}}} d|\lambda|(s, t)$$

be the variation of λ (cf. (12: 101)).

Let $\eta > 0$ be given.

Choose numbers $\alpha_1, \alpha_2, \beta_1, \beta_2$, such that

$$\alpha < \alpha_1 < a < \alpha_2 < \tilde{\alpha}; \qquad \beta < \beta_1 < b < \beta_2 < \tilde{\beta};$$

the lines

$$\tilde{s} = \alpha_1, \qquad \tilde{s} = \alpha_2, \qquad \tilde{t} = \beta_1, \qquad \tilde{t} = \beta_2$$

consist entirely of points of continuity of $v(\tilde{s}, \tilde{t})$; and

$$\iint\limits_{A} d|\lambda|(s, t) < \eta, \tag{37}$$

where

$$\begin{aligned}
A &= \{(s, t) : \alpha_1 < s < \alpha_2 \text{ and } s \neq a \text{ and } \beta_1 < t < \beta_2 \text{ and } t \neq b\}\\
&= (I^2 \cup I^4 \cup I^6 \cup I^8 \cup I^5) \cap \{s \neq a\} \cap \{t \neq b\}\\
&= I - (\{s = \alpha\} \cup \{t = b\} \cup I^1 \cup I^3 \cup I^7 \cup I^9),\\
I^1 &= \{\alpha \leqq s \leqq \alpha_1, \beta \leqq t \leqq \beta_1\},\\
I^2 &= \{\alpha_1 < s < \alpha_2, \beta \leqq t \leqq \beta_1\},\\
I^3 &= \{\alpha_2 \leqq s \leqq \tilde{\alpha}, \beta \leqq t \leqq \beta_1\},\\
I^4 &= \{\alpha \leqq s \leqq \alpha_1, \beta_1 < t < \beta_2\},\\
I^5 &= \{\alpha_1 < s < \alpha_2, \beta_1 < t < \beta_2\},\\
I^6 &= \{\alpha_2 \leqq s \leqq \tilde{\alpha}, \beta_1 < t < \beta_2\},\\
I^7 &= \{\alpha \leqq s \leqq \alpha_1, \beta_2 \leqq t \leqq \tilde{\beta}\},\\
I^8 &= \{\alpha_1 < s < \alpha_2, \beta_2 \leqq t \leqq \tilde{\beta}\},\\
I^9 &= \{\alpha_2 \leqq s \leqq \tilde{\alpha}, \beta_2 \leqq t \leqq \tilde{\beta}\}.
\end{aligned}$$

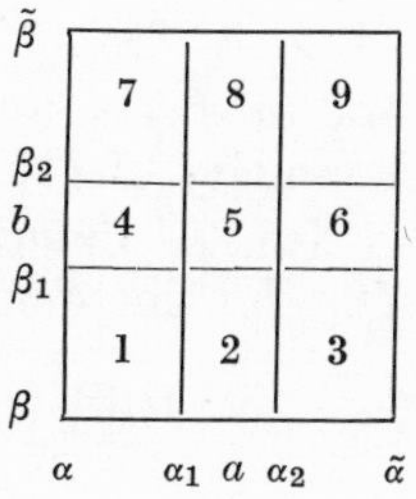

This construction is indeed possible because all discontinuities of v lie on countably many line segments parallel to the axes (Theorems 12: 110 and 88), and because

$$\iint_A d|\lambda|(s, t) \leqq [v(\alpha_2 - 0, \tilde{\beta}) - v(a + 0, \tilde{\beta}) + v(a - 0, \tilde{\beta}) - v(\alpha_1 + 0, \tilde{\beta})]$$
$$+ [v(\tilde{\alpha}, \beta_2 - 0) - v(\tilde{\alpha}, b + 0) + v(\tilde{\alpha}, b - 0) - v(\tilde{\alpha}, \beta_1 + 0)],$$

inequality being due to counting part of I^5 twice. For all sufficiently small $\alpha_2 - \alpha_1$ and $\beta_2 - \beta_1$, the right member is surely less than η. Whether $v(\tilde{s}, \tilde{t})$ has discontinuities on $\tilde{s} = a$ or $\tilde{t} = b$ is immaterial.

Note that $I^1, I^2, \cdots, I^9$ is a subdivision of I into mutually exclusive intervals some not closed; that I^1, I^3, I^7, I^9 are closed; and that I^5 is open and contains (a, b).

Consider the functionals H^1, H^3, H^7, H^9 defined as follows:

$$H^j x = \iint_{I^j} x(s, t)\, d\lambda(s, t), \qquad j = 1, 3, 7, 9.$$

The integrals here may equivalently be considered as Riemann or Lebesgue integrals whenever the integrands are continuous, since by construction λ behaves appropriately on the boundaries of $I^j, j = 1, 3, 7, 9$. As regards I^1, for example, the conditions that insure the equality of Riemann and Lebesgue integrals are (§§ 12: 127, 72)

$$\begin{aligned} \lambda(\alpha_1 + 0, t) &= \lambda(\alpha_1, t), \\ \lambda(\alpha - 0, t) &= \lambda(\alpha, t), \qquad t \in I_t, \\ \lambda(s, \beta_1 + 0) &= \lambda(s, \beta_1), \\ \lambda(s, \beta - 0) &= \lambda(s, \beta), \qquad s \in I_s. \end{aligned}$$

These equalities hold because λ is everywhere continuous on $s = \alpha_1$ and on $t = \beta_1$ and because $\lambda \in V^0$.

By § 12: 66,

$$H^j x = \iint_{I^j} x(s, t)\, d\lambda(s, t) = \iint_{I^j} x(s, t)\, d\mu^j(s, t), \qquad j = 1, 3, 7, 9,$$

where

$$\mu^j(s, t) = \lambda(s, t) - \lambda(\alpha^j, t) - \lambda(s, \beta^j) + \lambda(\alpha^j, \beta^j)$$

and (α^j, β^j) is the lower left corner of I^j. Then $\mu^j(s, t)$ vanishes on the lower boundary of I^j and is continuous from above elsewhere.

Now H^j defines an element of $B_{0,0}(I^j)^*$ and μ^j is normalized relative to I^j. By Theorem 9,

$$\|H^j\|_{B_{0,0}(I^j)^*} = \iint_{I^j} d|\mu^j|(s, t) = \iint_{I^j} d|\lambda|(s, t), \qquad j = 1, 3, 7, 9.$$

Hence functions z^j exist such that

$$\iint_{I^j} z^j(s, t)\, d\lambda(s, t) > \iint_{I^j} d|\lambda|(s, t) - \eta,$$

$$z^j \in B_{0,0}(I^j), \quad \|z^j\|_{B_{0,0}(I^j)} = 1; \qquad j = 1, 3, 7, 9.$$

Let z be a continuous function on I defined as follows:

$$z(s, t) = \begin{cases} z^j(s, t) & \text{if } (s, t) \in I^j,\ j = 1, 3, 7, 9; \\ 0 & \text{if } s = a \text{ or if } t = b; \\ \text{a continuous function of } (s, t) \text{ on} \\ \text{the closure of } A, \text{ always } \leqq 1 \\ \text{numerically.} \end{cases}$$

A definition of z can be given explicitly in elementary fashion. Then by construction

$$z \in Z(a, b), \qquad \|z\|_{Z(a,b)} = 1.$$

Furthermore

$$Fz = \iint_{\substack{s \neq a, \\ t \neq b}} z(s, t)\, d\lambda(s, t) = \iint_{I^1 \cup I^3 \cup I^7 \cup I^9} z\, d\lambda + \iint_A z\, d\lambda$$

$$\geqq \iint_{I^1 \cup I^3 \cup I^7 \cup I^9} d|\lambda| - 4\eta + \iint_A z\, d\lambda$$

$$= \iint_{\substack{s \neq a, \\ t \neq b}} d|\lambda| - 4\eta + \iint_A z\, d\lambda - \iint_A d|\lambda|$$

$$\geqq \iint_{\substack{s \neq a, \\ t \neq b}} d|\lambda| - 6\eta = \left[\iint_{\substack{s \neq a, \\ t \neq b}} d|\lambda| - 6\eta\right] \|z\|_{Z(a,b)},$$

since, by (37),

$$\left|\iint_A z\, d\lambda\right| \leqq \iint_A d|\lambda| < \eta.$$

As $\eta > 0$ was arbitrary, it follows that

$$\|F\|_{Z(a,b)^*} \geqq \iint_{\substack{s \neq a, \\ t \neq b}} d|\lambda|.$$

This completes the proof.

§ 38. **The space K.** Let $I = I_s \times I_t$ be a compact interval of the s, t-plane and let (a, b) be a fixed point of I. Consider a space B with pivot $x_{p,q}(s, t)$. For example B might be $B_{p,q}$ or $B_{\ulcorner p,q \urcorner}$ or neither.

We have defined the complete core ω, the full core ϕ and the covered core ξ of x in B (§§ 4: 49, 80). We have defined the equivalent norms

$$\|x\|_B = \max [|x_{i,j}(a, b)|, (i, j) \in \bar{\omega}_{a,b}; \sup_{s \in I_s} |x_{i,j}(s, b)|,$$

$$(i, j) \in \bar{\omega}_{s,b}; \text{ dual terms}; \sup_{(s,t) \in I} |x_{p,q}(s, t)|]$$

and

$$|||x|||_B = \max [\sup_{s \in I_s} |x_{i,j}(s, b)|, (i, j) \in \bar{\phi}_{s,b}; \text{ dual terms};$$

$$\sup_{(s,t) \in I} |x_{i,j}(s, b)|, (i, j) \in \bar{\phi}_{s,t}].$$

In this section we shall define a space K which we call the retract of B. Most spaces B, but not all, have retracts.

Suppose that B is such that

$$\text{(39)} \qquad \begin{aligned} &\text{if } (i, j) \in \bar{\omega}_{s,b}, \quad \text{then } i \geqq 1; \\ &\text{if } (i, j) \in \bar{\omega}_{a,t}, \quad \text{then } j \geqq 1; \\ &p \geqq 1, q \geqq 1. \end{aligned}$$

Thus the complete core ω has the following property: whenever $x_{i,j}$ in ω contains the variable s, then $i \geqq 1$; and dually.

Put

$$\begin{aligned} \rho_{a,b} &= \omega_{a,b} = \{x_{i,j}(a, b) : (i, j) \in \bar{\omega}_{a,b}\}, \\ \rho_{s,b} &= \{\delta_s x_{i-1,j}(s, b) : (i, j) \in \bar{\omega}_{s,b}\}, \\ \rho_{a,t} &= \{\delta_t x_{i,j-1}(a, t) : (i, j) \in \bar{\omega}_{a,t}\}, \\ \rho_{s,t} &= \{\delta_s \delta_t x_{p-1,q-1}(s, t)\}; \end{aligned}$$

and

$$\rho = \rho_{a,b} \cup \rho_{s,b} \cup \rho_{a,t} \cup \rho_{s,t}.$$

We call ρ the *retracted core*; ρ is defined iff condition (39) holds.

In connection with the tables and figures it is convenient to put

$$\begin{aligned} \bar{\rho}_{a,b} &= \bar{\omega}_{a,b}, \\ \bar{\rho}_{s,b} &= \{(i - 1, j) : (i, j) \in \bar{\omega}_{s,b}\}, \\ \bar{\rho}_{a,t} &= \text{dual}, \\ \bar{\rho}_{s,t} &= \{(p - 1, q - 1)\}; \\ \bar{\rho} &= \bar{\rho}_{a,b} \cup \bar{\rho}_{s,b} \cup \bar{\rho}_{a,t} \cup \bar{\rho}_{s,t}. \end{aligned}$$

In the diagrams, $\bar{\rho}$ is obtained from $\bar{\omega}$ by retaining certain points and retracting others. The same point may appear several times in $\bar{\rho}$.

The retracted core ρ is similar to the complete core ω, but the last differentiation as to s in $x_{i,j}$ is replaced by δ_s, if $x_{i,j} \in \omega_{s,t} \cup \omega_{s,b}$; and dually.

We shall say that the covered core ξ *contains* ρ if the following conditions hold:

$$\begin{aligned} &(p - 1, q - 1) \in \bar{\xi}_{s,t}, \\ &(i - 1, j) \in \bar{\xi}_{s,t} \cup \bar{\xi}_{s,b} \quad \text{whenever } (i, j) \in \bar{\omega}_{s,b}, \\ &(i, j - 1) \in \bar{\xi}_{s,t} \cup \bar{\xi}_{a,t} \quad \text{whenever } (i, j) \in \bar{\omega}_{a,t}. \end{aligned}$$

Thus ξ contains ρ iff each derivative that enters in ρ is either in ξ or may be obtained from a derivative in ξ by the substitution $s = a$ or $t = b$.

We *assume* for the rest of this chapter that ρ *exists* and that ξ *is well covered* (§ 4 : 80) *and contains* ρ. For all of this *it is sufficient that*

$$\bar{\omega} \supset \ulcorner p, q \urcorner, \qquad pq \geqq 1. \tag{40}$$

We now define the rule of ρ as regards order of differentiation. Our procedure is analogous to that in the definition of the space B itself, where we defined ω and the rule of ω. We specify a main route in ρ, that is, an order of differentiation

$$(0, 0), \cdots, (p - 1, q - 1)$$

in $x_{p-1,q-1}$ all of whose vertices lie in $\bar{\xi}_{s,t}$. Such a main route exists, since ξ is well covered and contains ρ. Alternative main routes may exist, but which alternative is chosen will in the end be immaterial (Corollary 45 below). The *rule of* ρ is defined as that order of differentiation which follows the main route in ρ as long as possible. Thus if (i, j) is on the main route, the differentiations in $x_{i,j}$ are to be taken along the route; if (i, j) is off the main route, the differentiations in $x_{i,j}$ are to be those of the beginning of the main route followed by differentiations as to one variable only. For any (i, j) in $\bar{\rho}$, the rule of ρ can be executed in one and only one way.

In $B_{p,q}$ and $B_{\ulcorner p,q \urcorner}$, $pq \geqq 1$, we take the main route in ρ to be that specified by

$$D_s^{p-1} D_t^{q-1} x.$$

The cores ω, ϕ, ξ, and ρ and their rules for particular spaces B are given in the figures and tables, Chapter 4. The lines in the diagrams indicate differentiations conforming to the rule of the core in question. A differentiation according to the rule of ω surely conforms to the rule of ϕ; one according to the rule of ρ surely conforms to the rule of ξ.

The reader may consider B^1, B^3, B^6, $B_{2,3}$, $B_{\ulcorner 2,3 \urcorner}$, for example.

The *retract* K is defined as the space of functions $x(s, t)$ for which the elements of ρ interpreted according to the rule of ρ exist and are continuous in their variables, if any, $(s, t) \in I$. Note that

$$B \subset K.$$

The study of the space K now runs parallel to that of B.

41. EXPANSION THEOREM. *If $x \in K$, then*

$$\begin{aligned} x(s, t) = &\sum_{(i,j) \in \bar{\omega}_{a,b}} (s - a)^{(i)}(t - b)^{(j)} x_{i,j}(a, b) \\ &+ \sum_{(i,j) \in \bar{\omega}_{s,b}} (t - b)^{(j)} T_s^{i-1} \delta_s x_{i-1,j}(s, b) \\ &+ \textit{dual sum} + T_s^{p-1} T_t^{q-1} \delta_s \delta_t x_{p-1,q-1}(s, t), \qquad (s, t) \in I. \end{aligned} \tag{42}$$

Thus $x(s, t)$, $(s, t) \in I$, is determined by its retracted core ρ.

PROOF. Perhaps the simplest proof is based on an argument of permanence of form. Suppose first that $x \in B$. Then the Taylor formula (4: 56) implies (42), since

$$\begin{aligned} \delta_s x_{i-1,j}(s, b) &= T_s x_{i,j}(s, b), && (i, j) \in \bar{\omega}_{s,b}; \\ \delta_t x_{i,j-1}(a, t) &= T_t x_{i,j}(a, t), && (i, j) \in \bar{\omega}_{a,t}; \\ \delta_s \delta_t x_{p-1,q-1}(s, t) &= T_s T_t x_{p,q}(s, t). \end{aligned}$$

Thus (42) is established for $x \in B$. The right side of (42) can therefore be transformed following the rule of ρ by elementary integrations into the left side, when $x \in B$. The same transformations however apply when $x \in K$. Thus the theorem is established.

Alternatively one may prove the theorem by repeated use of the Taylor relations (4: 58) and the elementary relations

$$\begin{aligned} y(s, t) &= y(a, t) + \delta_s y(s, t), \\ y(s, t) &= y(s, b) + \delta_t y(s, t), \end{aligned}$$

starting with $x(s, t)$ and conforming to the rule of ρ. This proof would be like that of Theorem 4: 55.

43. COROLLARY. *Consider a space K. Let*
$y^{i,j}$, $(i, j) \in \bar{\omega}_{a,b}$, be arbitrary constants;
$y^{i,j}(s)$, $(i, j) \in \bar{\omega}_{s,b}$, be arbitrary continuous functions of s that vanish at $s = a$, that is, arbitrary elements of $Z(a)$;
$y^{i,j}(t)$, $(i, j) \in \bar{\omega}_{a,t}$, be arbitrary elements of $Z(b)$;
$y^{p,q}(s, t)$ be an arbitrary element of $Z(a, b)$.
Put

$$\begin{aligned} z(s, t) = &\sum_{\bar{\omega}_{a,b}} (s - a)^{(i)}(t - b)^{(j)} y^{i,j} + \sum_{\bar{\omega}_{s,b}} (t - b)^{(j)} T_s^{i-1} y^{i,j}(s) \\ &+ \textit{dual sum} + T_s^{p-1} T_t^{q-1} y^{p,q}(s, t). \end{aligned} \tag{44}$$

Then $z \in K$, and the given elements $\{y^{i,j}\}$ constitute the retracted core ρ of z:

$$\begin{aligned} z_{i,j}(a, b) &= y^{i,j}, && (i, j) \in \bar{\omega}_{a,b}; \\ \delta_s z_{i-1,j}(s, b) &= y^{i,j}(s), && (i, j) \in \bar{\omega}_{s,b}; \\ \delta_t z_{i,j-1}(a, t) &= y^{i,j}(t), && (i, j) \in \bar{\omega}_{a,t}; \\ \delta_s \delta_t z_{p-1,q-1}(s, t) &= y^{p,q}(s, t); && (s, t) \in I. \end{aligned}$$

45. COROLLARY. *Suppose that* $x \in K$. *Then the derivatives of* x *which are elements of* ξ *exist, are continuous,* $(s, t) \in I$, *and are given in terms of* ρ *by formulas obtained from the expansion formula* (42) *by differentiation in any way consistent with the rule of* ξ.

PROOFS. Corollaries 43, 45 are similar to Corollaries 4 : 61, 64. We shall discuss the proofs together. One operates on the right sides of (44) and (42) by differentiation and differencing. The hypothesis that ξ is well covered and contains ρ enters in the following way. Consider x in B. The elements of ξ can be obtained by differentiation of the Taylor formula (4: 56) in any order consistent with the rule of ξ, in particular according to the rule of ρ. In the successive equations the variables are always covered. If we replace $\cdots T_s D_s$ by $\cdots \delta_s$ and $\cdots T_t D_t$ by $\cdots \delta_t$ in the successive equations, we have expressions for the elements of ξ in terms of ρ, valid not merely for $x \in B$ but for $x \in K$.

The idea is illustrated by considering the space B^4 (see Figure 4: 3) for which

$$x_{p,q} = x_{2,2} = D_t D_s D_t D_s x, \quad \bar{\omega}_{s,b} = \{(1, 0), (2, 1)\}, \quad \bar{\omega}_{a,t} = \{(0, 1), (1, 2)\}.$$

Here ξ contains ρ but ξ is not well covered. The present corollaries do not apply. The space K^4 is not defined. For x in B^4, the analogue of (42) is

$$\begin{aligned} x(s, t) = x(a, b) + (s - a)x_{1,1}(a, b) + \delta_s x(s, b) + (t - b)T_s \delta_s x_{1,1}(s, b) \\ + \delta_t x(a, t) + (s - a)T_t \delta_t x_{1,1}(a, t) + T_s T_t \delta_s \delta_t x_{1,1}(s, t), \quad (s, t) \in I. \end{aligned}$$

This formula is perfectly valid. Now suppose that we replace the elements of ρ herein by arbitrary elements of $Z(a, b)$, $Z(a)$, $Z(b)$, and constants, as appropriate. The right side will then not necessarily define a function whose retracted core is the substituted elements, because the term corresponding to $\delta_s x(s, b)$ will be an arbitrary element of $Z(a)$ and therefore not necessarily differentiable as to s and the term corresponding to $\delta_t x(a, t)$ will be not necessarily differentiable as to t.

Similarly, Corollaries 43, 45 do not apply to B^5, the space for which (cf. Figure 4 : 3)

$$x_{p,q} = x_{3,1} = D_s^3 D_t x, \qquad \bar{\omega}_{s,b} = \{(1, 0)\}, \qquad \bar{\omega}_{a,t} = \{(0, 1), (1, 1), (2, 1)\}.$$

Here ξ is well covered but does not contain ρ. Indeed ϕ does not contain ρ.

Corollary 45 implies that K depends on B alone and not on the particular main route in ρ chosen to determine the rule of ρ. Theorem 41 and Corollary 43 imply that ρ is a set of coordinates for x in K, since ρ may consist of arbitrary elements of $Z(a, b)$, $Z(a)$, $Z(b)$, and constants, as appropriate, and since ρ determines and is determined by x, $x \in K$.

§ 46. **The norm in** K. The space K consists of functions $x(s, t)$ for which the elements of ρ are continuous in their variables, if any, $(s, t) \in I$. We have seen that if $x \in K$, then the elements of ξ are continuous in their variables and that there is an expansion, obtained by differentiation of (42), of each element of ξ in terms of ρ.

The *norm* $\|x\|_K$ of x in K is defined as the maximum of the suprema of the absolute values of the elements of ρ, $(s, t) \in I$:

$$\|x\|_K = \max [|x_{i,j}(a, b)|, (i, j) \in \bar{\omega}_{a,b}; \sup_{s \in I_s} |\delta_s x_{i-1,j}(s, b)|, (i, j) \in \bar{\omega}_{s,b};$$
$$\sup_{t \in I_t} |\delta_t x_{i,j-1}(a, t)|, (i, j) \in \bar{\omega}_{a,t}; \sup_{(s,t) \in I} |\delta_s \delta_t x_{p-1,q-1}(s, t)|].$$

The alternative norm $|||x|||_K$ is defined as the maximum of the suprema of the absolute values of the elements of ξ, $(s, t) \in I$:

$$|||x|||_K = \max [\sup_{s \in I_s} |x_{i,j}(s, b)|, (i, j) \in \bar{\xi}_{s,b}; \sup_{t \in I_t} |x_{i,j}(a, t)|,$$
$$(i, j) \in \bar{\xi}_{a,t}; \sup_{(s,t) \in I} |x_{i,j}(s, t)|, (i, j) \in \bar{\xi}_{s,t}].$$

For any space K, *the norms* $\|x\|_K$ *and* $|||x|||_K$ *are equivalent.* Thus the expansion formulas for elements of ξ in terms of ρ imply that a constant M exists such that

$$|||x|||_K \leqq M\|x\|_K, \qquad x \in K.$$

In the opposite direction,

$$\|x\|_K \leqq 4|||x|||_K, \qquad x \in K,$$

since ξ contains ρ and since

$$|\delta_s \delta_t y(s, t)| \leqq 4 \sup |y(s, t)|.$$

By the norm in K we will ordinarily mean $\|x\|_K$. In particular, the norm in the adjoint space K^* is based on $\|x\|_K$.

§ 47. **The space K^*.** Consider a space K and its adjoint space K^*.

48. MASS THEOREM. *Suppose that* $F \in K^*$. *Put*

$$(49) \qquad c^{i,j} = F[(s-a)^{(i)}(t-b)^{(j)}], \qquad (i, j) \in \bar{\omega}_{a,b};$$

$$\lambda^{i,j}(\tilde{s}) = \begin{cases} \lim_{\nu} F[(t-b)^{(j)} T_s^{i-1} \psi^{\nu}(a, \tilde{s}, s)] & \text{if } \tilde{s} > \alpha, \\ 0 & \text{otherwise}, \quad (i, j) \in \bar{\omega}_{s,b}; \end{cases}$$

$$(50) \quad \lambda^{i,j}(\tilde{t}) = \textit{dual relation}, \qquad (i, j) \in \bar{\omega}_{a,t};$$

$$\lambda^{p,q}(\tilde{s}, \tilde{t}) = \begin{cases} \lim_{\nu,\nu'} F[T_s^{p-1} T_t^{q-1} \psi^{\nu}(a, \tilde{s}, s) \psi^{\nu'}(b, \tilde{t}, t)] & \text{if } \tilde{s} > \alpha \text{ and } \tilde{t} > \beta, \\ 0 & \text{otherwise}. \end{cases}$$

Then the functions $\lambda^{i,j}$, $(i, j) \in \bar{\omega} - \bar{\omega}_{a,b}$, *are well defined and are elements of* $V^{0,0}$. *Also*

$$(51) \quad \begin{aligned} Fx = {} & \sum_{\bar{\omega}_{a,b}} c^{i,j} x_{i,j}(a, b) - \sum_{\bar{\omega}_{s,b}} \int x_{i-1,j}(s, b)\, d\lambda^{i,j}(s) \\ & - \sum_{\bar{\omega}_{a,t}} \int x_{i,j-1}(a, t)\, d\lambda^{i,j}(t) + \iint x_{p-1,q-1}(s, t)\, d\lambda^{p,q}(s, t), \qquad x \in K. \end{aligned}$$

The functions $\lambda^{i,j}$ *are the only elements of* $V^{0,0}$ *and the constants* $c^{i,j}$ *are the only numbers for which the last relation holds. Furthermore*

$$\|F\|_{K^*} = \sum_{\bar{\omega}_{a,b}} |c^{i,j}| + \sum_{\bar{\omega}_{s,b}} \int_{s \neq a} d|\lambda^{i,j}|(s) + \sum_{\bar{\omega}_{a,t}} \int_{t \neq b} d|\lambda^{i,j}|(t) + \iint_{\substack{s \neq a, \\ t \neq b}} d|\lambda^{p,q}|(s, t). \tag{52}$$

Part of the interest in this theorem lies in the fact that the masses $\lambda^{i,j}$ are in $V^{0,0}$ (vanish everywhere on the boundary of I_s, I_t, or I, as appropriate, and are normalized) and are unique; and in the formula for $\|F\|_{K^*}$.

Proof. An alternative form of (51) is

$$Fx = \sum_{\bar{\omega}_{a,b}} c^{i,j} x_{i,j}(a, b) - \sum_{\bar{\omega}_{s,b}} \int \delta_s x_{i-1,j}(s, b)\, d\lambda^{i,j}(s) - \text{dual sum} + \iint \delta_s \delta_t x_{p-1,q-1}(s, t)\, d\lambda^{p,q}(s, t), \qquad x \in K. \tag{53}$$

The relations (51) and (53) are equivalent because the masses $\lambda^{i,j}$ are elements of $V^{0,0}$. Consider the last term of (53), for example.

$$\begin{aligned}\iint \delta_s \delta_t x_{p-1,q-1}(s, t)\, d\lambda^{p,q}(s, t) &= \iint x_{p-1,q-1}(s, t)\, d\lambda^{p,q}(s, t) \\ &\quad - \iint x_{p-1,q-1}(a, t)\, d\lambda^{p,q}(s, t) \\ &\quad - \iint x_{p-1,q-1}(s, b)\, d\lambda^{p,q}(s, t) \\ &\quad + \iint x_{p-1,q-1}(a, b)\, d\lambda^{p,q}(s, t) \\ &= \iint x_{p-1,q-1}(s, t)\, d\lambda^{p,q}(s, t), \quad x \in K,\end{aligned}$$

since the integrals in which the integrand is a constant or a function of one variable vanish (Lemma 12 : 64).

The proof of the theorem is similar to that of Theorem 14. We expand x in terms of ρ, operate on each term, and use the mass theorems for $Z(a)^*$, $Z(a, b)^*$.

Part 1. We establish (53) and the fact that $\lambda^{i,j} \in V^{0,0}$. Suppose that $x \in K$. Then by (42),

$$x(s, t) = \sum_{\bar{\omega}_{a,b}} x_{i,j}(a, b)(s - a)^{(i)}(t - b)^{(j)} + \sum_{\bar{\omega}_{s,b}} (t - b)^{(j)} T_s^{i-1} \delta_s x_{i-1,j}(s, b) + \text{dual sum} + T_s^{p-1} T_t^{q-1} \delta_s \delta_t x_{p-1,q-1}(s, t), \qquad (s, t) \in I.$$

Hence

$$(54)\quad \begin{aligned} Fx = & \sum_{\bar{\omega}_{a,b}} c^{i,j} x_{i,j}(a, b) + \sum_{\bar{\omega}_{s,b}} F[(t-b)^{(j)} T_s^{i-1} \delta_s x_{i-1,j}(s, b)] \\ & + \text{dual sum} + F[T_s^{p-1} T_t^{q-1} \delta_s \delta_t x_{p-1,q-1}(s, t)], \end{aligned}$$

where $c^{i,j}$ are given by (49).

The last term may be evaluated as follows. Consider the functional G defined as

$$Gz = G[z(s, t)] = F[T_s^{p-1} T_t^{q-1} z(s, t)], \qquad z \in Z(a, b).$$

For each z in $Z(a, b)$, the function

$$y(s, t) = T_s^{p-1} T_t^{q-1} z(s, t)$$

is an element of K whose retracted core ρ consists entirely of zeros except that

$$\delta_s \delta_t y_{p-1,q-1}(s, t) = z(s, t),$$

by Corollary 43. It follows that $Gz = Fy$ is well defined and linear on $Z(a, b)$. Furthermore

$$\|y\|_K = \max\,[0, \cdots, 0, \sup_{(s,t) \in I} |z(s, t)|] = \|z\|_{Z(a,b)}.$$

Hence

$$|Gz| = |Fy| \leqq \|F\|_{K^*} \|y\|_K = \|F\|_{K^*} \|z\|_{Z(a,b)}, \qquad z \in Z(a, b).$$

Hence G is bounded on $Z(a, b)$ and an element of $Z(a, b)^*$. By Theorem 33,

$$Gz = \iint z(s, t)\, d\lambda^{p,q}(s, t), \qquad z \in Z(a, b),$$

where

$$\lambda^{p,q}(\tilde{s}, \tilde{t}) = \begin{cases} \lim_{\nu,\nu'} G[\psi^{\nu}(a, \tilde{s}, s) \psi^{\nu'}(b, \tilde{t}, t)], & \tilde{s} > \alpha \text{ and } \tilde{t} > \beta, \\ 0 & \text{otherwise.} \end{cases}$$

Thus $\lambda^{p,q}$ satisfies (50); and

$$\begin{aligned} F[T_s^{p-1} T_t^{q-1} \delta_s \delta_t x_{p-1,q-1}(s, t)] &= G[\delta_s \delta_t x_{p-1,q-1}(s, t)] \\ &= \iint \delta_s \delta_t x_{p-1,q-1}(s, t)\, d\lambda^{p,q}(s, t), \qquad x \in K. \end{aligned}$$

By Theorem 33, $\lambda^{p,q} \in V^{0,0}$.

The other terms in (54) are treated similarly. The minus signs in (53) are due to our change in (50) of the sign in (3 : 64). Thus (53) and hence (51) are established.

Part 2. The uniqueness of $\lambda^{i,j} \in V^{0,0}$ and $c^{i,j}$ is established as in Part 2 of the proof of Theorem 14. One uses (53).

Part 3. The formula for $\|F\|_{K^*}$ is established as was that for $\|F\|_{B^*}$ in Theorem 14.

This completes the proof.

Consider a functional $F \in K^*$. We define its *Lebesgue extension* by the right hand member of equation (51). The Lebesgue extension is thus a functional defined for all functions x for which the Lebesgue-Stieltjes integrals in (51) exist. Since the covered core ξ contains the retracted core ρ, it follows that the Lebesgue extension of F is an element of $\mathscr{K}^*$, the space defined in § 4 : 80. The next theorem includes the converse statement.

55. THEOREM. *If $F \in \mathscr{K}^*$, then the restriction of F to K is an element of K^*. The functions $\lambda^{i,j} \in V^{0,0}$ which enter in the standard form* (51) *for Fx satisfy the following relations:*

$$\lambda^{i,j}(\tilde{s}) = F[(t-b)^{(j)}(s-\tilde{s})^{(i-1)}\psi(a,\tilde{s},s)], \quad \alpha < \tilde{s} \notin \mathscr{J}_s, \quad (i,j) \in \bar{\omega}_{s,b};$$

$$(56) \qquad \lambda^{i,j}(\tilde{t}) = \textit{dual expression}, \qquad (i,j) \in \bar{\omega}_{a,t};$$

$$\lambda^{p,q}(\tilde{s},\tilde{t}) = F[(s-\tilde{s})^{(p-1)}\psi(a,\tilde{s},s)(t-\tilde{t})^{(q-1)}\psi(b,\tilde{t},t)], \quad \alpha < \tilde{s} \notin \mathscr{J}_s \text{ and } \beta < \tilde{t} \notin \mathscr{J}_t;$$

where $\mathscr{J}_s$, $\mathscr{J}_t$ are the jump sets of F.

The present theorem affords a simpler calculation of the functions $\lambda^{i,j}$ than does Theorem 48. The functions $\lambda^{i,j}$ vanish everywhere on the boundary of I_s, I_t, or I, as appropriate. The formulas (56) confirm this fact for $\tilde{s} = \tilde{\alpha}$ and for $\tilde{t} = \tilde{\beta}$, since

$$\psi(a, \tilde{\alpha}, s) = 0 \quad \text{for all } s \in I_s.$$

The values of $\lambda^{i,j}$ at interior points are either given by (56) or, if needed, are deducible from values given by (56) by replacing $\tilde{s}$ by $\tilde{s} + 0$ and $\tilde{t}$ by $\tilde{t} + 0$. This use of limits from above is valid because

$$\lambda^{i,j} \in V^{0,0} \subset V^0.$$

The proof of Theorem 55 is like that of Theorem 23 and is omitted, except for the following remark. One uses the equality

$$T_s^m\psi(a,\tilde{s},s) = (s-\tilde{s})^{(m)}\psi(a,\tilde{s},s),$$

which is (11 : 19), at the end of the argument.

§ 57. **K^* as a subspace of B^*.** We have seen that

$$B \subset K.$$

Furthermore

$$|||x|||_B \geqq |||x|||_K, \qquad x \in B,$$

since the full core ϕ contains the covered core ξ. It follows that a functional bounded relative to the norm in K will be bounded relative to the norm in B. Hence

$$K^* \subset B^*.$$

Thus the hypothesis $F \in K^*$ of Theorem 48 is more restrictive than the hypothesis $F \in B^*$ of Theorem 14. It is natural therefore that the conclusion of Theorem 48 be stronger than that of Theorem 14. This is indeed the case. We now establish a stronger relation than (17), valid if $F \in K^*$.

58. Kernel theorem. *Suppose that* $F \in K^*$. *Define* $c^{i,j}$ *by* (49) *and* $\lambda^{i,j} \in V^{0,0}$ *by* (50). *Then*

$$\begin{aligned} Fx &= \sum_{\bar{\omega}_{a,b}} c^{i,j} x_{i,j}(a, b) + \sum_{\bar{\omega}_{s,b}} \int x_{i,j}(s, b) \lambda^{i,j}(s)\, ds \\ &\quad + \textit{dual sum} + \iint x_{p,q}(s, t) \lambda^{p,q}(s, t)\, ds\, dt \end{aligned} \tag{59}$$

for all x *in* $\boldsymbol{B}$.

Proof. The space $\boldsymbol{B}$ is defined in § 4 : 80, just before Lemma 4 : 83. Note that the conditions for the definition of $\boldsymbol{B}$ (§ 4 : 80) are precisely those for K (§ 38); and that

$$B \subset \boldsymbol{B} \subset K.$$

To establish (59) we evaluate each integral in (51) by parts, making use of the fact that

$$\lambda^{i,j} \in V^{0,0}, \qquad (i, j) \in \bar{\omega} - \bar{\omega}_{a,b}.$$

For example, by Corollary 12 : 59 and Lemma 12 : 130,

$$\begin{aligned} \iint x_{p-1,q-1}(s, t)\, d\lambda^{p,q}(s, t) &= \iint \lambda^{p,q}(s, t)\, dx_{p-1,q-1}(s, t) \\ &= \iint \lambda^{p,q}(s, t) x_{p,q}(s, t)\, ds\, dt, \qquad x \in \boldsymbol{B}. \end{aligned}$$

This completes the proof.

Theorems 55 and 58 provide a new proof of Theorem 4 : 84, since relations (56) are essentially the same as (4 : 87–89).

It is interesting to compare Theorems 58 and 4 : 84. Theorem 58 is deeper, in that its hypothesis $F \in K^*$ refers to intrinsic and essential properties of F (linearity and continuity relative to the norm in K). The hypothesis $F \in \mathscr{K}^*$ of Theorem 4 : 84 specifies that Fx be given as a sum of Stieltjes integrals on the elements of the covered core ξ. Since $F \in K^*$ is weaker than $F \in \mathscr{K}^*$, the formulas (50) are more complicated than (56). Theorems 58 and 4 : 84 are evidence that the spaces B, K are important.

CHAPTER 7

Functions of m Variables

§ 1. **Introduction.** It is clear that the results of our earlier chapters for functions of one and two variables generalize to functions of m variables.

A function of m variables is a complicated object. It may have

$$\frac{(n+1)(n+2)\cdots(n+m-1)}{(m-1)!}$$

different partial derivatives of order n, if $m > 1$. Thus an analysis that involves derivatives often requires long descriptions.

Our later chapters will in part consider methods of study of approximation by means other than derivatives. The present chapter continues the work of its predecessors.

§ 2. **The space B.** For clarity of exposition, we take $m = 3$. The ideas apply to any m.

Let I be a compact interval of s, t, u-space and (a, b, c) a given fixed point of I (interior or not). Write

$$I = I_s \times I_t \times I_u,$$

$$I_s = \{\alpha \leqq s \leqq \tilde{\alpha}\}, \qquad I_t = \{\beta \leqq t \leqq \tilde{\beta}\}, \qquad I_u = \{\gamma \leqq u \leqq \tilde{\gamma}\}.$$

Let p, q, r be nonnegative integers. Put

$$n = p + q + r.$$

We shall define a space B, which we call a space of type B or a space with pivot $x_{p,q,r}$. To define B, we first define its pivot and core.

The *pivot* is the derivative $x_{p,q,r}(s, t, u)$ understood according to a specified order of differentiation

$$x_{p,q,r}(s, t, u) = D_{\zeta_n} D_{\zeta_{n-1}} \cdots D_{\zeta_1} x, \tag{3}$$

where $(\zeta_n, \cdots, \zeta_1)$ is a permutation of p letters s, q letters t, and r letters u; and

$$D_s = \frac{\partial}{\partial s}, \qquad D_t = \frac{\partial}{\partial t}, \qquad D_u = \frac{\partial}{\partial u}.$$

Consider the derivatives

$$x,\ D_{\zeta_1} x,\ D_{\zeta_2} D_{\zeta_1} x, \cdots,\ D_{\zeta_{n-1}} \cdots D_{\zeta_1} x \tag{4}$$

which enter in the definition of the pivot $x_{p,q,r}$. These together with the pivot we call the *main route*. Each of the derivatives (4) is a function of s, t, u. Reduce each to a function of two variables by putting

$$s = a \quad \text{or} \quad t = b \quad \text{or} \quad u = c,$$

according as the differentiation which produces the next element in the main route is D_s or D_t or D_u. Let there now be given for each element y of (4), a space of type B on functions of two variables in which the derivative y plays the rôle of x. We shall call this space the *cross-section* at y and denote it by

$$B^y. \tag{5}$$

If $(p, q, r) = (0, 0, 0)$, the set of derivatives (4) is empty. In this case the main route consists of the pivot $x_{0,0,0}(s, t, u)$ alone.

The *complete core* ω of x in B is defined as the set consisting of the pivot $x_{p,q,r}(s, t, u)$ and the complete cores of the n cross-sections B^y. We subdivide ω into mutually exclusive parts

$$\omega_{s,t,u}; \quad \omega_{a,t,u}, \quad \omega_{s,b,u}, \quad \omega_{s,t,c}; \quad \omega_{s,b,c}, \quad \omega_{a,t,c}, \quad \omega_{a,b,u}; \quad \omega_{a,b,c};$$

where the subscript indicates the argument of the derivatives. For example, $\omega_{a,t,u}$ consists of those elements of ω whose arguments are (a, t, u). Thus $\omega_{s,t,u}$ consists of the pivot alone.

The *rule of* ω regarding order of differentiation is the following: any derivative (in ω) is understood as being obtained by a sequence of differentiations that follow the main route as long as possible and thereafter follow the main route of the appropriate cross-section as long as possible. Thus if $x_{i,j,k} \in \omega$ and if $x_{i,j,k}$ is understood according to the rule of ω, the order of differentiations in $x_{i,j,k}$ is uniquely specified.

The *space* B is defined as the space of those functions $x(s, t, u)$ for which the elements of the complete core ω, understood according to the rule of ω, exist and are continuous in their variables, if any, for $(s, t, u) \in I$.

It will be convenient to denote by $\bar{\omega}$, $\bar{\omega}_{s,t,u}$, $\bar{\omega}_{a,t,u}$, $\cdots$ the sets of indices (i, j, k) that occur in the elements $x_{i,j,k}$ of ω, $\omega_{s,t,u}$, $\omega_{a,t,u}$, $\cdots$, respectively. Thus $\bar{\omega}_{s,t,u}$ is the set consisting of the single element (p, q, r).

To illustrate, we cite an example $B = B^{10}$ of a space with pivot $x_{1,1,1}$. The diagram of ω and its rule may illuminate the formal description (cf. Figure 1). In the diagram, the point (i, j, k) represents the derivative $x_{i,j,k}$; the arguments of the derivative are marked at the point; and the permissible differentiations are indicated by lines joining points. The space B^{10} is characterized by the following relations:

$$x_{1,1,1}(s, t, u) = D_u D_s D_t x = \text{pivot of } B^{10}.$$

$$x_{2,2,0}(s, t, c) = D_t D_s (D_s D_t x) = \text{pivot in the cross-section at } x_{1,1,0}.$$

$$x_{0,1,1}(a, t, u) = D_u (D_t x) = \text{pivot in the cross-section at } x_{0,1,0}.$$

$$
\begin{aligned}
&x_{2,0,1}(s, b, u) = D_u D_s^2(x) = \text{pivot in the cross-section at } x.\\
&\left.\begin{aligned} x_{3,1,0}(s, b, c) &= D_s(D_s^2 D_t x)\\ x_{2,0,0}(s, b, c) &= D_s^2 x \end{aligned}\right\} = \text{the elements of } \omega_{s,b,c}.\\
&\left.\begin{aligned} x_{1,2,0}(a, t, c) &= D_t(D_s D_t x)\\ x_{0,2,0}(a, t, c) &= D_t(D_t x) \end{aligned}\right\} = \text{the elements of } \omega_{a,t,c}.\\
(6)\quad &\left.\begin{aligned} x_{1,0,2}(a, b, u) &= D_u^2(D_s x)\\ x_{0,0,2}(a, b, u) &= D_u^2 x \end{aligned}\right\} = \text{the elements of } \omega_{a,b,u}.\\
&\left.\begin{aligned} x_{2,1,0}(a, b, c) &= D_s^2 D_t x\\ x_{1,1,0}(a, b, c) &= D_s D_t x\\ x_{0,1,0}(a, b, c) &= D_t x\\ x_{1,0,1}(a, b, c) &= D_u D_s x\\ x_{1,0,0}(a, b, c) &= D_s x\\ x_{0,0,1}(a, b, c) &= D_u x\\ x_{0,0,0}(a, b, c)& \end{aligned}\right\} = \text{the elements of } \omega_{a,b,c}.
\end{aligned}
$$

Thus there is 1 element in $\omega_{s,t,u}$; there are p elements in $\omega_{a,t,u}$, q elements in $\omega_{s,b,u}$, r elements in $\omega_{s,t,c}$, and a number of elements in the remaining part of ω that depends on the space B.

The seventeen derivatives (6) constitute the complete core ω in B^{10}. The rule of ω is written out in (6) for each element of ω. The space B^{10} is the space of functions $x(s, t, u)$ for which the derivatives (6) exist and are continuous in their variables, if any, $(s, t, u) \in I$. The space B^{10} is, in the end, completely determined by the sets

$$
(7)\quad
\begin{aligned}
\bar\omega_{s,t,u} &= \{(1, 1, 1)\},\\
\bar\omega_{a,t,u} &= \{(0, 1, 1)\},\\
\bar\omega_{s,b,u} &= \{(2, 0, 1)\},\\
\bar\omega_{s,t,c} &= \{(2, 2, 0)\},\\
\bar\omega_{s,b,c} &= \{(3, 1, 0), (2, 0, 0)\},\\
\bar\omega_{a,t,c} &= \{(1, 2, 0), (0, 2, 0)\},\\
\bar\omega_{a,b,u} &= \{(0, 0, 2), (1, 0, 2)\},\\
\bar\omega_{a,b,c} &= \{(2, 1, 0), (1, 1, 0), (0, 1, 0), (1, 0, 1), (1, 0, 0), (0, 0, 1), (0, 0, 0)\},
\end{aligned}
$$

in the sense that any choice of main route and cross-sections that leads to the sets (7) defines a space B which is the same as B^{10}. This is because ϕ and the rule of ϕ will be the same, whatever the choice of main route and cross-sections.

Other illustrations are the spaces B^{11}, B^{12}, $B^{\ulcorner 3,2,1 \urcorner}$ indicated in Figures 2, 3 and Tables 1, 2. The definition of $B_{\ulcorner p,q,r \urcorner}$ is indicated in its table. As regards $B_{p,q,r}$, there are a number of different ways in which the space $B_{p,q}$ of Chapter 4 may be generalized to a space of functions of three variables [Sard 5, (9: 15)]. We indicate one possibility in Table 1. The space

$B_{0,0,0} = B^{\ulcorner}{}_{0,0,0}{}^{\urcorner}$ is the familiar space of functions $x(s, t, u)$ continuous on I. Thus $B_{0,0,0}$ is independent of (a, b, c). If $n > 0$, the space B depends on (a, b, c) in an essential way.

8. THEOREM (TAYLOR FORMULA). *If $x \in B$, then*

$$
\begin{aligned}
x(s, t, u) &= \sum_{(i,j,k) \in \bar{\omega}} T_s^i T_t^j T_u^k x_{i,j,k} \\
&= \sum_{(i,j,k) \in \bar{\omega}_{a,b,c}} (s - a)^{(i)}(t - b)^{(j)}(u - c)^{(k)} x_{i,j,k}(a, b, c) \\
&\quad + \sum_{\bar{\omega}_{s,b,c}} (t - b)^{(j)}(u - c)^{(k)} T_s^i x_{i,j,k}(s, b, c) + \textit{similar sums} \\
&\quad + \sum_{\bar{\omega}_{a,t,u}} (s - a)^{(i)} T_t^j T_u^k x_{i,j,k}(a, t, u) + \textit{similar sums} \\
&\quad + T_s^p T_t^q T_u^r x_{p,q,r}(s, t, u), \qquad (s, t, u) \in I.
\end{aligned} \tag{9}
$$

For proof see Theorem 4: 55.

10. COROLLARY. *Consider a space B. Let*

$y^{i,j,k}$, $(i, j, k) \in \bar{\omega}_{a,b,c}$,	*be arbitrary constants,*
$y^{i,j,k}(s)$, $(i, j, k) \in \bar{\omega}_{s,b,c}$,	*be arbitrary continuous functions of s, that is, arbitrary elements of $C_0(I_s)$;*
$y^{i,j,k}(t)$, $(i, j, k) \in \bar{\omega}_{a,t,c}$,	*be arbitrary elements of $C_0(I_t)$;*
$y^{i,j,k}(u)$, $(i, j, k) \in \bar{\omega}_{a,b,u}$,	*be arbitrary elements of $C_0(I_u)$;*
$y^{i,j,k}(t, u)$, $(i, j, k) \in \bar{\omega}_{a,t,u}$,	*be arbitrary elements of $B_{0,0}(I_t \times I_u)$,*
$y^{i,j,k}(s, u)$, $(i, j, k) \in \bar{\omega}_{s,b,u}$,	*be arbitrary elements of $B_{0,0}(I_s \times I_u)$,*
$y^{i,j,k}(s, t)$, $(i, j, k) \in \bar{\omega}_{s,t,c}$,	*be arbitrary elements of $B_{0,0}(I_s \times I_t)$,*
$y^{p,q,r}(s, t, u)$	*be an arbitrary element of $B_{0,0,0}(I)$.*

Put

$$z(s, t, u) = \sum_{\bar{\omega}} T_s^i T_t^j T_u^k y^{i,j,k}. \tag{11}$$

Then $z \in B$, and the given elements $\{y^{i,j,k}\}$ constitute the complete core ω of B.

For proof see Corollary 4: 61.

Thus ω is a set of coordinates for x in B; and B is the direct product of $B_{0,0,0}(I)$, p spaces $B_{0,0}(I_t \times I_u)$, q spaces $B_{0,0}(I_s \times I_u)$, r spaces $B_{0,0}(I_s \times I_t)$, a number of spaces $C_0(I_s)$, $C_0(I_t)$, $C_0(I_u)$, and a number of Euclidean lines.

§ 12. **The full core ϕ.** Consider an element x of a space B. A consequence of the Taylor expansion (9) of x is that certain derivatives of x necessarily exist and are expressible in terms of the complete core ω of x.

In the following definition, interpret the derivative $x_{i,j,k}$ according to the rule of ω. Put

$$\bar{\phi}_{s,t,u} = \{(i, j, k) : x_{i,j,k}(s, t, u) \text{ is continuous, } (s, t, u) \in I, \text{ whenever } x \in B\}$$

and

$$\phi_{s,t,u} = \{x_{i,j,k}(s, t, u) : (i, j, k) \in \bar{\phi}_{s,t,u}\}.$$

Also

$$\bar{\phi}_{a,t,u} = \{(i, j, k) : (i, j, k) \notin \bar{\phi}_{s,t,u} \text{ and } x_{i,j,k}(a, t, u) \text{ is continuous, } (t, u) \in I_t \times I_u, \text{ whenever } x \in B\}$$

and

$$\phi_{a,t,u} = \{x_{i,j,k}(a, t, u) : (i, j, k) \in \bar{\phi}_{a,t,u}\}.$$

$\phi_{s,b,u}$ and $\phi_{s,t,c}$ are defined similarly. Note that the sets $\bar{\phi}_{a,t,u}$, $\bar{\phi}_{s,b,u}$, $\bar{\phi}_{s,t,c}$ may overlap. Also,

$$\bar{\phi}_{s,b,c} = \{(i, j, k) : (i, j, k) \notin \bar{\phi}_{s,t,u} \cup \bar{\phi}_{s,b,u} \cup \bar{\phi}_{s,t,c} \text{ and } x_{i,j,k}(s, b, c) \text{ is continuous, } s \in I_s, \text{ whenever } x \in B\}$$

and

$$\phi_{s,b,c} = \{x_{i,j,k}(s, b, c) : (i, j, k) \in \bar{\phi}_{s,b,c}\}.$$

$\phi_{a,t,c}$ and $\phi_{a,b,u}$ are defined similarly.

The *full core* of x in B is

$$\phi = \phi_{s,t,u} \cup \phi_{a,t,u} \cup \phi_{s,b,u} \cup \phi_{s,t,c} \cup \phi_{s,b,c} \cup \phi_{a,t,c} \cup \phi_{a,b,u};$$

its indices are

$$\bar{\phi} = \bar{\phi}_{s,t,u} \cup \bar{\phi}_{a,t,u} \cup \bar{\phi}_{s,b,u} \cup \bar{\phi}_{s,t,c} \cup \bar{\phi}_{s,b,c} \cup \bar{\phi}_{a,t,c} \cup \bar{\phi}_{a,b,u}.$$

By the *rule of* ϕ we mean the description of those orders of differentiation in $x_{i,j,k}$, $(i, j, k) \in \bar{\phi}$, which for all x in B are permissible and equivalent to the rule of ω.

For any space B, one may determine ϕ and the rule of ϕ by study of the Taylor formula (9). We will illustrate the ideas by considering B^{10}. Let us denote by $\wp$ a polynomial in s, t, u. Since polynomials may be differentiated in any way whatever, the parts of the expansions of the elements of ϕ that are polynomials are immaterial to the definition of ϕ or its rule. The symbol $\wp$ in different equations below may stand for different polynomials.

Consider an arbitrary element x of B^{10}. By (9), for $(s, t, u) \in I$,

$$\begin{aligned} x_{0,0,0}(s, t, u) = {} & T_sT_tT_ux_{1,1,1}(s, t, u) + T_s^2T_t^2x_{2,2,0}(s, t, c) \\ & + T_tT_ux_{0,1,1}(a, t, u) + T_s^2T_ux_{2,0,1}(s, b, u) \\ & + (t - b)T_s^3x_{3,1,0}(s, b, c) + T_s^2x_{2,0,0}(s, b, c) \\ & + (s - a)T_t^2x_{1,2,0}(a, t, c) + T_t^2x_{0,2,0}(a, t, c) \\ & + (s - a)T_u^2x_{1,0,2}(a, b, u) + T_u^2x_{0,0,2}(a, b, u) + \wp. \end{aligned} \tag{13}$$

We now proceed as in the proof of Corollary 4 : 64. By differentiation, since the elements of ω are continuous,

$$\begin{aligned} x_{1,0,0}(s,t,u) &= T_tT_ux_{1,1,1}(s,t,u) + T_sT_t^2x_{2,2,0}(s,t,c) \\ &\quad + T_sT_ux_{2,0,1}(s,b,u) + (t-b)T_s^2x_{3,1,0}(s,b,c) \\ &\quad + T_sx_{2,0,0}(s,b,c) + T_t^2x_{1,2,0}(a,t,c) \\ &\quad + T_u^2x_{1,0,2}(a,b,u) + \wp, \end{aligned} \tag{14}$$

$$\begin{aligned} x_{0,1,0}(s,t,u) &= T_sT_ux_{1,1,1}(s,t,u) + T_s^2T_tx_{2,2,0}(s,t,c) \\ &\quad + T_ux_{0,1,1}(a,t,u) + T_s^3x_{3,1,0}(s,b,c) \\ &\quad + (s-a)T_tx_{1,2,0}(a,t,c) + T_tx_{0,2,0}(a,t,c) + \wp, \end{aligned} \tag{15}$$

$$\begin{aligned} x_{0,0,1}(s,t,u) &= T_sT_tx_{1,1,1}(s,t,u) + T_tx_{0,1,1}(a,t,u) + T_s^2x_{2,0,1}(s,b,u) \\ &\quad + (s-a)T_ux_{1,0,2}(a,t,u) + T_ux_{0,0,2}(a,b,u) + \wp. \end{aligned} \tag{16}$$

Now consider $x_{2,0,0}$. If the element $x_{1,1,1}(s,t,u)$ of ω, which is an arbitrary continuous function of (s,t,u), is not differentiable as to s, the first term of the right member of (14) may not be differentiable as to s. Thus $x_{2,0,0}(s,t,u)$ need not exist, and

$$(2,0,0) \notin \bar{\phi}_{s,t,u}.$$

If we put $u = c$ or $t = b$ in (14), the term becomes zero. Thus

$$\begin{aligned} x_{2,0,0}(s,t,c) &= T_t^2x_{2,2,0}(s,t,c) + (t-b)T_sx_{3,1,0}(s,b,c) \\ &\quad + x_{2,0,0}(s,b,c) + \wp, \end{aligned} \tag{17}$$

$$x_{2,0,0}(s,b,u) = T_ux_{2,0,1}(s,b,u) + x_{2,0,0}(s,b,c) + \wp. \tag{18}$$

Likewise

$$(0,2,0) \notin \bar{\phi}_{s,t,u}, \qquad (0,2,0) \notin \bar{\phi}_{a,t,u},$$

because of the term $T_ux_{0,1,1}(a,t,u)$ in (15). However, by (15),

$$\begin{aligned} x_{0,2,0}(s,t,c) &= T_s^2x_{2,2,0}(s,t,c) + (s-a)x_{1,2,0}(a,t,c) \\ &\quad + x_{0,2,0}(a,t,c) + \wp. \end{aligned} \tag{19}$$

Likewise

$$(0,0,2) \notin \bar{\phi}_{s,t,u} \cup \bar{\phi}_{a,t,u} \cup \bar{\phi}_{s,b,u} \cup \bar{\phi}_{s,t,c},$$

because of the terms $T_tx_{0,1,1}(a,t,u)$ and $T_s^2x_{2,0,1}(s,b,u)$ in (16). These terms are not necessarily differentiable with respect to u. If we put $s = a$ and $t = b$, however, these terms vanish. Thus, by (16),

$$x_{0,0,2}(a,b,u) = x_{0,0,2}(a,b,u). \tag{20}$$

By (14) and (15),

$$\begin{aligned} x_{1,1,0}(s,t,u) = D_tx_{1,0,0} &= T_ux_{1,1,1}(s,t,u) + T_sT_tx_{2,2,0}(s,t,c) \\ &\quad + T_s^2x_{3,1,0}(s,b,c) + T_tx_{1,2,0}(a,t,c) + \wp \\ &= D_sx_{0,1,0}. \end{aligned} \tag{21}$$

Thus not only is (1, 1, 0) in $\bar{\phi}_{s,t,u}$, but the alternative orders of differentiation are equivalent. The rule of ϕ therefore permits either order in $x_{1,1,0}$.

By (14) and (16),

$$(22)\quad \begin{aligned} x_{1,0,1}(s, t, u) &= D_u x_{1,0,0} = D_s x_{0,0,1} \\ &= T_t x_{1,1,1}(s, t, u) + T_s x_{2,0,1}(s, b, u) + T_u x_{1,0,2}(a, b, u) + \wp. \end{aligned}$$

By (15) and (16),

$$(23)\quad \begin{aligned} x_{0,1,1}(s, t, u) &= D_u x_{0,1,0} = D_t x_{0,0,1} \\ &= T_s x_{1,1,1}(s, t, u) + x_{0,1,1}(a, t, u) + \wp. \end{aligned}$$

By (17), $x_{3,0,0}$ need not exist, even if its arguments are a, b, c, because s may not be put equal to a until after the differentiation and because of the term $x_{2,0,0}(s, b, c)$, which need not be differentiable.

Likewise $x_{0,3,0}$ and $x_{0,0,3}$ need not exist; that is,

$$(0, 3, 0) \notin \bar{\phi}, \qquad (0, 0, 3) \notin \bar{\phi}.$$

By (17) and (21),

$$(24)\quad \begin{aligned} x_{2,1,0}(s, t, c) &= D_t x_{2,0,0} = D_s x_{1,1,0} \\ &= T_t x_{2,2,0}(s, t, c) + T_s x_{3,1,0}(s, b, c) + \wp; \end{aligned}$$

however $D_s x_{1,1,0}(s, t, u)$ need not exist.

By (21) and (19),

$$(25)\quad \begin{aligned} x_{1,2,0}(s, t, c) &= D_t x_{1,1,0} = D_s x_{0,2,0} \\ &= T_s x_{2,2,0}(s, t, c) + x_{1,2,0}(a, t, c) + \wp; \end{aligned}$$

however $D_t x_{1,1,0}(s, t, u)$ need not exist.

By (22) and (18),

$$(26)\quad x_{2,0,1}(s, b, u) = D_s x_{1,0,1} = D_u x_{2,0,0} = x_{2,0,1}(s, b, u);$$

however $D_s x_{1,0,1}(s, t, u)$ need not exist.

By (22),

$$(27)\quad x_{1,0,2}(a, b, u) = D_u x_{1,0,1} = x_{1,0,2}(a, b, u).$$

However $D_s x_{0,0,2}$ need not exist, because $x_{0,0,2}(s, b, c)$ need not exist.

It is clear that $x_{0,2,1}$ and $x_{0,1,2}$ need not exist, since $(0, 2, 1) \notin \bar{\omega}$, $(0, 1, 2) \notin \bar{\omega}$.

By (21), (22), and (23),

$$(28)\quad x_{1,1,1}(s, t, u) = D_u x_{1,1,0} = D_t x_{1,0,1} = D_s x_{0,1,1} = x_{1,1,1}(s, t, u).$$

By (24 and (25),

$$(29)\quad x_{2,2,0}(s, t, c) = D_t x_{2,1,0} = D_s x_{1,2,0} = x_{2,2,0}(s, t, c).$$

By (24),

$$x_{3,1,0}(s, b, c) = D_s x_{2,1,0} = x_{3,1,0}(s, b, c). \tag{30}$$

We have now completed our direct study of $x_{i,j,k}$, where $(i, j, k) \in \bar{\omega}$. We have shown that

$$\begin{aligned}
\bar{\phi}_{s,t,u} &= \{(0, 0, 0), (1, 0, 0), (0, 1, 0), (0, 0, 1), (1, 1, 0), (1, 0, 1), \\
&\qquad\qquad (0, 1, 1), (1, 1, 1)\}, \\
\bar{\phi}_{a,t,u} &= 0, \\
\bar{\phi}_{s,b,u} &= \{(2, 0, 0), (2, 0, 1)\}, \\
\bar{\phi}_{s,t,c} &= \{(2, 0, 0), (0, 2, 0), (2, 1, 0), (1, 2, 0), (2, 2, 0)\}, \\
\bar{\phi}_{s,b,c} &= \{(3, 1, 0)\}, \\
\bar{\phi}_{a,t,c} &= 0, \\
\bar{\phi}_{a,b,u} &= \{(0, 0, 2), (1, 0, 2)\}.
\end{aligned}$$

All orders of differentiation according to the rule of ϕ are indicated in (14)–(30). Both ϕ and the rule of ϕ are described in our diagram of B^{10}. Solid lines in the diagram of ϕ indicate differentiations that conform to the rule of ϕ.

In a similar fashion the reader may establish the results given in the diagrams of ϕ of the other spaces.

We shall not generalize Corollary 4 : 64. Note however that

$$\bar{\phi} = \bar{\omega}.$$

Also that *if* $\bar{\omega} \supset \ulcorner p, q, r \urcorner$, *then* $\bar{\phi}_{s,t,u} = \ulcorner p, q, r \urcorner$ *and all orders of differentiation in elements of* $\phi_{s,t,u}$ *are permissible*, where

$$\ulcorner p, q, r \urcorner = \{(i, j, k) : i \leqq p \text{ and } j \leqq q \text{ and } k \leqq r\}.$$

§ 31. **The norm in B.** Consider a space B with complete core ω and full core ϕ. The space B consists of functions $x(s, t, u)$ for which the elements of ω are continuous in their variables, if any, $(s, t, u) \in I$. If $x \in B$, there is an expansion of each element of ϕ in terms of ω. The elements of ϕ therefore exist and are continuous in their variables, $(s, t, u) \in I$.

The norm in B is defined precisely as in § 6 : 2:

$$\|x\|_B = \max_{(i,j,k) \in \bar{\omega}} [\sup |x_{i,j,k}|, (s, t, u) \in I];$$

the arguments of $x_{i,j,k}$ here are $(a, b, c), \cdots, (s, t, u)$ according as (i, j, k) is in $\bar{\omega}_{a,b,c}, \cdots, \bar{\omega}_{s,t,u}$. The alternative norm is

$$|||x|||_B = \max_{(i,j,k) \in \bar{\phi}} [\sup |x_{i,j,k}|, (s, t, u) \in I];$$

the arguments of $x_{j,j,k}$ here are $(s, b, c), \cdots, (s, t, u)$ according as (i, j, k) is in $\bar{\phi}_{s,b,c}, \cdots, \bar{\phi}_{s,t,u}$.

The norms $\|x\|_B$ *and* $|||x|||_B$ *are equivalent.* By the norm in B we ordinarily mean $\|x\|_B$. The norm in the space B^* adjoint to B will be based on $\|x\|_B$.

§ 32. **Functions of bounded variation.** We continue to denote by V, V^0, and $V^{0,0}$ the spaces of functions of bounded variation, normalized functions of bounded variation, and normalized functions of bounded variation that vanish on the entire boundary. Thus, for example, $\lambda(s, t, u) \in V^0$ iff

$$\lambda(s, t, u) \in V,$$
$$\lambda(\alpha, t, u) = \lambda(s, \beta, u) = \lambda(s, t, \gamma) = 0, \qquad (s, t, u) \in I,$$
$$\lambda(s + 0, t + 0, u + 0) = \lambda(s, t, u), \quad \alpha < s, \beta < t, \gamma < u.$$

The definition of λ outside I is governed by the analogue of § 12:72. Also $\lambda(s, t, u) \in V^{0,0}$ iff

$$\lambda(s, t, u) \in V^0,$$
$$\lambda(\tilde{\alpha}, t, u) = \lambda(s, \tilde{\beta}, u) = \lambda(s, t, \tilde{\gamma}) = 0, \qquad (s, t, u) \in I.$$

§ 33. **The space B^*.** Consider a space B with pivot $x_{p,q,r}$ and the adjoint space B^*.

34. Mass theorem. *Suppose that $F \in B^*$. Put*

(35) $$c^{i,j,k} = F[(s - a)^{(i)}(t - b)^{(j)}(u - c)^{(k)}], \qquad (i, j, k) \in \bar{\omega}_{a,b,c};$$

$$\lambda^{i,j,k}(\tilde{s}) = \begin{cases} \lim\limits_{\nu} F[(t - b)^{(j)}(u - c)^{(k)} T_s^i \theta^\nu(\tilde{s}, s)], \ \tilde{s} > \alpha, \\ 0 \qquad \textit{otherwise}, \ (i, j, k) \in \bar{\omega}_{s,b,c}; \end{cases}$$

similarly for $\bar{\omega}_{a,t,c}$ and $\bar{\omega}_{a,b,u}$;

(36) $$\lambda^{i,j,k}(\tilde{t}, \tilde{u}) = \begin{cases} \lim\limits_{\nu,\nu'} F[(s - a)^{(i)} T_t^j \theta^\nu(\tilde{t}, t) T_u^k \theta^{\nu'}(\tilde{u}, u)], \ \tilde{t} > \beta, \ \tilde{u} > \gamma, \\ 0 \qquad \textit{otherwise}, \ (i, j, k) \in \bar{\omega}_{a,t,u}; \end{cases}$$

similarly for $\bar{\omega}_{s,b,u}$ and $\bar{\omega}_{s,t,c}$;

$$\lambda^{p,q,r}(\tilde{s}, \tilde{t}, \tilde{u}) = \begin{cases} \lim\limits_{\nu,\nu',\nu''} F[T_s^p \theta^\nu(\tilde{s}, s) T_t^q \theta^{\nu'}(\tilde{t}, t) T_u^r \theta^{\nu''}(\tilde{u}, u)], \quad \tilde{s} > \alpha, \tilde{t} > \beta, \tilde{u} > \gamma, \\ 0 \qquad \textit{otherwise}. \end{cases}$$

Then the functions $\lambda^{i,j,k}$, $(i, j, k) \in \bar{\omega} - \bar{\omega}_{a,b,c}$, are well defined and are elements of V^0. Also

$$Fx = \sum_{\bar{\omega}_{a,b,c}} c^{i,j,k} x_{i,j,k}(a, b, c) + \sum_{\bar{\omega}_{s,b,c}} \int x_{i,j,k}(s, b, c)\, d\lambda^{i,j,k}(s) + \textit{similar sums}$$

(37) $$+ \sum_{\bar{\omega}_{a,t,u}} \iint x_{i,j,k}(a, t, u)\, d\lambda^{i,j,k}(t, u) + \textit{similar sums}$$

$$+ \iiint x_{p,q,r}(s, t, u)\, d\lambda^{p,q,r}(s, t, u), \qquad x \in B.$$

The functions $\lambda^{i,j,k}$ *are the only elements of* V^0 *and the constants* $c^{i,j,k}$ *are the only numbers for which the last relation holds. Furthermore*

$$\|F\|_{B^*} = \sum_{\bar{\omega}_{a,b,c}} |c^{i,j,k}| + \sum_{\bar{\omega}_{s,b,c}} \int d|\lambda^{i,j,k}|(s) + \textit{similar sums}$$

$$+ \sum_{\bar{\omega}_{a,t,u}} \iint d|\lambda^{i,j,k}|(t, u) + \textit{similar sums} \tag{38}$$

$$+ \iiint d|\lambda^{p,q,r}|(s, t, u).$$

The proof is just like that of Theorem 6 : 14.

§ 39. **The space $\mathscr{B}^*$.** All of § 6 : 21 generalizes in a direct fashion. The space $\mathscr{B}^*$ is the space of functionals which are finite sums of Lebesgue-Stieltjes integrals relative to functions of bounded variation of the elements of the full core of the function operated on. Thus an element F of $\mathscr{B}^*$ is a functional of the form

$$Fx = \sum_{(i,j,k)\in\bar{\phi}_{s,t,u}} \iiint x_{i,j,k}(s, t, u)\, d\mu^{i,j,k}(s, t, u)$$

$$+ \sum_{(i,j,k)\in\bar{\phi}_{a,t,u}} \iint x_{i,j,k}(a, t, u)\, d\mu^{i,j,k}(t, u) + \textit{similar sums} \tag{40}$$

$$+ \sum_{(i,j,k)\in\bar{\phi}_{s,b,c}} \int x_{i,j,k}(s, b, c)\, d\mu^{i,j,k}(s) + \textit{similar sums}, \quad \mu^{i,j,k} \in V.$$

The jump set $\mathscr{J}_s$ of F relative to $\mathscr{B}^*$ may be defined as the countable set of points other than $s = \tilde{\alpha}$ in I_s which are points of discontinuity of

$$\begin{aligned} &|\mu^{i,j,k}|(s, \tilde{\beta}, \tilde{\gamma}), && (i, j, k) \in \bar{\phi}_{s,t,u}\text{; or} \\ &|\mu^{i,j,k}|(s, \tilde{\beta}), && (i, j, k) \in \bar{\phi}_{s,t,c}\text{; or} \\ &|\mu^{i,j,k}|(s, \tilde{\gamma}), && (i, j, k) \in \bar{\phi}_{s,b,u}\text{; or} \\ &|\mu^{i,j,k}|(s), && (i, j, k) \in \bar{\phi}_{s,b,c}; \end{aligned}$$

where the bars indicate total variations. The sets $\mathscr{J}_t$, $\mathscr{J}_u$ are defined similarly.

The sets $\mathscr{J}_s$, $\mathscr{J}_t$, $\mathscr{J}_u$ as just defined are larger than need be.

If $F \in B^*$, the Lebesgue extension of F, defined by the right member of equation (37), is an element of $\mathscr{B}^*$. Conversely if $F \in \mathscr{B}^*$, then the restriction of F to B is an element of B^* and the relations (36) may be replaced by

$$\lambda^{i,j,k}(\tilde{s}) = F[(t - b)^{(j)}(u - c)^{(k)} T^i_s \theta(\tilde{s}, s)],$$

$$\alpha < \tilde{s} \notin \mathscr{J}_s, \quad (i, j, k) \in \bar{\omega}_{s,b,c};$$

similarly for $\bar{\omega}_{a,t,c}$ and $\bar{\omega}_{a,b,u}$;

(41) $$\lambda^{i,j,k}(\tilde{t}, \tilde{u}) = F[(s-a)^{(i)}T_{\tilde{t}}^{j}\theta(\tilde{t}, t)T_{\tilde{u}}^{k}\theta(\tilde{u}, u)],$$
$$\beta < \tilde{t} \notin \mathscr{J}_t \text{ and } \gamma < \tilde{u} \notin \mathscr{J}_u,\ (i, j, k) \in \bar{\omega}_{a,t,u};$$

similarly for $\bar{\omega}_{s,b,u}$ and $\bar{\omega}_{s,t,c}$;

$$\lambda^{p,q,r}(\tilde{s}, \tilde{t}, \tilde{u}) = F[T_{\tilde{s}}^{p}\theta(\tilde{s}, s)T_{\tilde{t}}^{q}\theta(\tilde{t}, t)T_{\tilde{u}}^{r}\theta(\tilde{u}, u)],$$
$$\alpha < \tilde{s} \notin \mathscr{J}_s,\ \beta < \tilde{t} \notin \mathscr{J}_t, \text{ and } \gamma < \tilde{u} \notin \mathscr{J}_u.$$

This is the analogue of Theorem 6 : 23.

§ 42. **The spaces $Z(a, b, c)$ and $Z(a, b, c)^*$.** All of § 6 : 31, generalizes in a direct fashion. We define $Z(a, b, c)$ as the space of functions $x(s, t, u)$ continuous on I which vanish when $s = a$ or $t = b$ or $u = c$:

$$Z(a, b, c) = \{x \in B_{0,0,0} : x(a, t, u) = x(s, b, u) = x(s, t, c) = 0 \text{ for all } (s, t, u) \in I\}.$$

The norm is

$$\|x\|_{Z(a,b,c)} = \|x\|_{B_{0,0,0}} = \sup |x(s, t, u)|, \qquad x \in Z(a, b, c).$$

43. Mass theorem. *Suppose that $F \in Z(a, b, c)^*$. Put*

(44) $$\lambda(\tilde{s}, \tilde{t}, \tilde{u}) = \begin{cases} \lim\limits_{\nu,\nu',\nu''} F[\psi^{\nu}(a, \tilde{s}, s)\psi^{\nu'}(b, \tilde{t}, t)\psi^{\nu''}(c, \tilde{u}, u)], & \tilde{s} > \alpha, \tilde{t} > \beta, \tilde{u} > \gamma; \\ 0 & \textit{otherwise.} \end{cases}$$

Then $\lambda \in V^{0,0}$, and

(45) $$Fx = \iiint x(s, t, u)\, d\lambda(s, t, u), \qquad x \in Z(a, b, c).$$

The function λ is the only element of $V^{0,0}$ for which this relation holds. Furthermore

(46) $$\|F\|_{Z(a,b,c)^*} = \iiint_{\substack{s\neq a, t\neq b,\\ u\neq c}} d|\lambda|(s, t, u).$$

The proof is like that of Theorem 6: 33.

§ 47. **The covered core ξ.** Consider a space B with pivot $x_{p,q,r}$. We have defined the complete core ω, the full core ϕ, the rule of ω and the rule of ϕ.

Let $x \in B$ and $(i, j, k) \in \bar{\phi}$. Then $x_{i,j,k}$ for certain arguments may be expanded in terms of ω. The expansion may be obtained from the Taylor formula (9) by differentiation and substitution. Consider an expansion of $x_{i,j,k}$. We say that its *variables are covered* if the following conditions all hold.

(1) If $x_{p,q,r}$ appears in the expansion, it appears only in the form $\cdots T_s \cdots T_t \cdots T_u x_{p,q,r}(s, t, u)$.

(48) (2) If $x_{i,j,k}$, $(i, j, k) \in \bar{\omega}_{a,t,u}$, appears, it appears only in the form $\cdots T_t \cdots T_u x_{i,j,k}(a, t, u)$. Likewise for $\omega_{s,b,u}$ and $\omega_{s,t,c}$.

(3) If $x_{i,j,k}$, $(i, j, k) \in \bar{\omega}_{s,b,c}$, appears, it appears only in the form $\cdots T_s x_{i,j,k}(s, b, c)$. Likewise for $\omega_{a,t,c}$ and $\omega_{a,b,u}$.

Thus whenever an element of $\omega - \omega_{a,b,c}$ appears, all its variables are present and Taylor operators are present for each variable.

We now consider which derivatives of x have expansions in which the variables are covered. Put

$$\bar{\xi}_{s,t,u} = \{(i, j, k) : (i, j, k) \in \bar{\phi}_{s,t,u}, \text{ and the variables in the expansion of } x_{i,j,k}(s, t, u) \text{ are covered for all } x \in B\},$$

$$\xi_{s,t,u} = \{x_{i,j,k}(s, t, u) : (i, j, k) \in \bar{\xi}_{s,t,u}\};$$

$$\bar{\xi}_{a,t,u} = \{(i, j, k) : (i, j, k) \in \bar{\phi}_{s,t,u} \cup \bar{\phi}_{a,t,u}, \text{ and } (i, j, k) \notin \bar{\xi}_{s,t,u}, \text{ and the variables in the expansion of } x_{i,j,k}(a, t, u) \text{ are covered for all } x \in B\},$$

(49) $$\xi_{a,t,u} = \{x_{i,j,k}(a, t, u) : (i, j, k) \in \bar{\xi}_{a,t,u}\};$$

similarly for $\xi_{s,b,u}$ and $\xi_{s,t,c}$;

$$\bar{\xi}_{s,b,c} = \{(i, j, k) : (i, j, k) \in \phi_{s,t,u} \cup \phi_{s,b,u} \cup \phi_{s,t,c} \cup \phi_{s,b,c}, \text{ and } (i, j, k) \notin \bar{\xi}_{s,t,u} \cup \bar{\xi}_{s,b,u} \cup \bar{\xi}_{s,t,c}, \text{ and the variables in the expansion of } x_{i,j,k}(s, b, c) \text{ are covered for all } x \in B\},$$

$$\xi_{s,b,c} = \{x_{i,j,k}(s, b, c) : (i, j, k) \in \bar{\xi}_{s,b,c}\};$$

similarly for $\xi_{a,t,c}$ and $\xi_{a,b,u}$.

The *covered core* is

$$\xi = \xi_{s,t,u} \cup \xi_{a,t,u} \cup \xi_{s,b,u} \cup \xi_{s,t,c} \cup \xi_{s,b,c} \cup \xi_{a,t,c} \cup \xi_{a,b,u}.$$

The indices in the covered core are the set $\bar{\xi}$ of triples given by the last relation with bars over all ξ's.

The covered cores of a number of spaces are given in Figures 1, 2, 3 and Tables 1, 2. To illustrate, consider B^{10}. By equation (13),

$$(0, 0, 0) \in \bar{\xi}_{s,t,u}.$$

By equation (14), $(1, 0, 0) \notin \bar{\xi}_{s,t,u}$ because of the term

$$T_t T_u x_{1,1,1}(s, t, u)$$

in which s is not covered. This term vanishes, however, if $t = b$ or if $u = c$. Thus

$$(1, 0, 0) \in \bar{\xi}_{s,b,u}, \qquad (1, 0, 0) \in \bar{\xi}_{s,t,c}.$$

Similarly, by (15),

$$(0, 1, 0) \notin \bar{\xi}_{a,t,u}, \qquad (0, 1, 0) \in \bar{\xi}_{s,t,c}.$$

In equation (16) the variable u is uncovered in the terms $T_sT_tx_{1,1,1}(s, t, u)$, $T_tx_{0,1,1}(a, t, u)$, and $T_s^2x_{2,0,1}(s, b, u)$. All three terms vanish if $s = a$ and $t = b$. Hence

$$(0, 0, 1) \in \bar{\xi}_{a,b,u}.$$

We need not consider (2, 0, 0), since $(2, 0, 0) \notin \bar{\omega}_{a,b,c}$. The reason is that any expansion of $x_{2,0,0}$ whether (17) or (18) or a relation derived therefrom by substitution, contains $x_{2,0,0}$ uncovered. A similar argument applies to any element of $\omega - \omega_{a,b,c}$. Thus $\bar{\xi} \subset \bar{\omega}_{a,b,c}$. Indeed

$$\bar{\xi} = \bar{\omega}_{a,b,c} \tag{50}$$

in all cases.

It remains to consider (1, 1, 0), (1, 0, 1), (2, 1, 0). By (21),

$$(1, 1, 0) \in \bar{\xi}_{s,t,c}.$$

By (22),

$$(1, 0, 1) \in \bar{\xi}_{a,b,u}.$$

By (24) in which $u = c$,

$$(2, 1, 0) \in \bar{\xi}_{s,b,c}.$$

Thus we have shown that in B^{10}

$$\begin{aligned}
\bar{\xi}_{s,t,u} &= \{(0, 0, 0)\},\\
\bar{\xi}_{a,t,u} &= 0,\\
\bar{\xi}_{s,b,u} &= \{(1, 0, 0)\},\\
\bar{\xi}_{s,t,c} &= \{(1, 0, 0), (0, 1, 0), (1, 1, 0)\},\\
\bar{\xi}_{s,b,c} &= \{(2, 1, 0)\},\\
\bar{\xi}_{a,t,c} &= 0,\\
\bar{\xi}_{a,b,u} &= \{(0, 0, 1), (1, 0, 1)\}.
\end{aligned} \tag{51}$$

The expansions for the elements of ξ are obtainable from (13)–(24) by substitution.

Consider the covered core ξ of a space B. We say that ξ is *well covered* if ξ is not empty and if each element of ξ may be obtained from $x(s, t, u)$ by a sequence of differentiations consistent with the rule of ϕ and substitutions $s = a$ or $t = b$ or $u = c$ such that each derivative in the sequence is in ξ or is obtainable from a derivative in ξ by substitution. The essential point is that any element of ξ is obtainable within ξ, if ξ is well covered. By the *rule of* ξ we mean the description of those orders of differentiation in $x_{i,j,k} \in \xi$ which for all $x \in B$ are permissible, consistent with the rule of ϕ, and which pass through only derivatives in ξ.

The rule of ξ for several spaces is indicated in Figures 1, 2, 3 and Tables 1,

2. Let us consider B^{10}, for example. It is immediate that all the derivatives referred to in (51) of order $\leqq 1$ are obtainable within ξ. Furthermore

$$x_{1,1,0}(s, t, c) = D_t x_{1,0,0} = D_s x_{0,1,0},$$
$$x_{1,0,0}(s, t, c) \in \xi_{s,t,c}, \qquad x_{0,1,0}(s, t, c) \in \xi_{s,t,c}.$$

Also,

$$x_{2,1,0}(s, b, c) = D_s x_{1,1,0}, \qquad x_{1,1,0} \in \xi_{s,t,c}.$$

Also,

$$x_{1,0,1}(a, b, u) = D_u x_{1,0,0}, \qquad x_{1,0,0} \in \xi_{s,b,u}.$$

On the other hand

$$x_{1,0,1}(a, b, u) = [D_s x_{0,0,1}(s, b, u)]_{s=a}$$

does not conform to the rule of ξ, because

$$(0, 0, 1) \notin \bar{\xi}_{s,t,u} \cup \bar{\xi}_{s,b,u}.$$

Thus the solid lines in our diagram of ξ for B^{10} indicate the entire rule of ξ for B^{10}.

§ 52. **The retracted core ρ and the space K.** Consider a space B with pivot $x_{p,q,r}$. Assume that B is such that

$$(53) \qquad \begin{aligned} pqr &\geqq 1, \\ i &\geqq 1 \text{ whenever } (i, j, k) \in \bar{\omega}_{s,b,c} \cup \bar{\omega}_{s,t,c} \cup \bar{\omega}_{s,b,u}, \\ j &\geqq 1 \text{ whenever } (i, j, k) \in \bar{\omega}_{a,t,c} \cup \bar{\omega}_{a,t,u} \cup \bar{\omega}_{s,t,c}, \\ k &\geqq 1 \text{ whenever } (i, j, k) \in \bar{\omega}_{a,b,u} \cup \bar{\omega}_{a,t,u} \cup \bar{\omega}_{s,b,u}. \end{aligned}$$

The retracted core ρ will be defined when and only when conditions (53) hold. Conditions (53) amount to the following: Whenever $x_{i,j,k}$ in ω contains s, $i \geqq 1$; and similarly for t, u.

Put

$$\rho_{a,b,c} = \omega_{a,b,c} = \{x_{i,j,k}(a, b, c) : (i, j, k) \in \bar{\omega}_{a,b,c}\}.$$
$$\rho_{s,b,c} = \{\delta_s x_{i-1,j,k}(s, b, c) : (i, j, k) \in \bar{\omega}_{s,b,c}\},$$

similarly for $\rho_{a,t,c}$ and $\rho_{a,b,u}$,

$$\rho_{a,t,u} = \{\delta_t \delta_u x_{i,j-1,k-1}(a, t, u) : (i, j, k) \in \bar{\omega}_{a,t,u}\},$$

similarly for $\rho_{s,b,u}$ and $\rho_{s,t,c}$,

$$\rho_{s,t,u} = \{\delta_s \delta_t \delta_u x_{p-1,q-1,r-1}(s, t, u)\};$$

and

$$\rho = \text{the union of the sets } \rho_{a,b,c}, \cdots, \rho_{s,t,u}.$$

We call ρ the *retracted core* of x in B.

Define $\bar{\rho}$, $\bar{\rho}_{a,b,c}, \cdots, \bar{\rho}_{s,t,u}$ as the indices in the undashed sets: for example,

$$\bar{\rho}_{s,b,c} = \{(i - 1, j, k) : (i, j, k) \in \bar{\omega}_{s,b,c}\}.$$

We say that ξ *contains* ρ if each element of ρ is obtainable from elements of ξ by subtraction and substitution. Thus, for example, in order that ξ contain ρ it is necessary that

$$(i-1, j, k) \in \bar{\xi}_{s,t,u} \cup \bar{\xi}_{s,t,c} \cup \bar{\xi}_{s,b,u} \cup \bar{\xi}_{s,b,c} \text{ whenever } (i, j, k) \in \bar{\omega}_{s,b,c}.$$

We *assume* for the remainder of the chapter *that the space B is such that*
(1) *ρ exists*, that is, (53) holds;
(2) *ξ contains ρ*; and
(3) *ξ is well covered.*

For this it is sufficient but not necessary that
(1′) $\bar{\omega} \supset \ulcorner p, q, r \urcorner$;
(2′) the analogous two dimensional conditions (6 : 40) apply to each cross-section B^y of B (cf. (5)); and
(3′) $pqr \geqq 1$.

By the *rule of* ρ we mean a particular specification which conforms to the rule of ξ of the orders of differentiation in the derivatives in ρ. If the rule of ρ may be chosen in different ways, it will in the end be immaterial which alternative was used.

The cores ω, ϕ, ξ, and ρ and their rules are indicated in Figures 1, 2, 3 and Tables 1, 2. The lines in each diagram indicate differentiations that are permissible according to the rule of the pertinent core. A differentiation according to the rule of ω surely conforms to the rule of ϕ; one according to the rule of ρ surely conforms to the rule of ξ. If ξ contains ρ, then $\bar{\xi} = \bar{\rho}$.

The *retract* K is defined as the space of functions $x(s, t, u)$ for which the elements of ρ interpreted according to the rule of ρ exist and are continuous in their variables, $(s, t, u) \in I$. Thus

$$B \subset K. \tag{54}$$

55. Expansion theorem. *If $x \in K$, then*

$$\begin{aligned} x(s, t, u) = &\sum_{\bar{\omega}_{a,b,c}} (s-a)^{(i)}(t-b)^{(j)}(u-c)^{(k)} x_{i,j,k}(a, b, c) \\ &+ \sum_{\bar{\omega}_{s,b,c}} (t-b)^{(j)}(u-c)^{(k)} T_s^{i-1}\delta_s x_{i-1,j,k}(s, b, c) + \textit{similar sums} \\ &+ \sum_{\bar{\omega}_{a,t,u}} (s-a)^{(i)} T_t^{j-1} T_u^{k-1} \delta_t \delta_u x_{i,j-1,k-1}(a, t, u) + \textit{similar sums} \\ &+ T_s^{p-1} T_t^{q-1} T_u^{r-1} \delta_s \delta_t \delta_u x_{p-1,q-1,r-1}(s, t, u), \qquad (s, t, u) \in I. \end{aligned} \tag{56}$$

Thus $x(s, t, u)$, $(s, t, u) \in I$, is determined by its retracted core ρ.

The proof is like the first proof of Theorem 6 : 41.

For the space K^{10} which is the retract of B^{10}, equation (56) is the following (cf. (13)):

$$
\begin{aligned}
x(s, t, u) = {} & \delta_s\delta_t\delta_u x(s, t, u) + T_sT_t\delta_s\delta_t x_{1,1,0}(s, t, c) + \delta_t\delta_u x(a, t, u) \\
& + T_s\delta_s\delta_u x_{1,0,0}(s, b, u) + (t - b)T_s^2\delta_s x_{2,1,0}(s, b, c) \\
& + T_s\delta_s x_{1,0,0}(s, b, c) + (s - a)T_t\delta_t x_{1,1,0}(a, t, c) \\
& + T_t\delta_t x_{0,1,0}(a, t, c) + (s - a)T_u\delta_u x_{1,0,1}(a, b, u) \\
& + T_u\delta_u x_{0,0,1}(a, b, u) + x(a, b, c) + (s - a)x_{1,0,0}(a, b, c) \\
& + (t - b)x_{0,1,0}(a, b, c) + (u - c)x_{0,0,1}(a, b, c) \\
& + (s - a)(t - b)x_{1,1,0}(a, b, c) + (s - a)(u - c)x_{1,0,1}(a, b, c) \\
& + (s - a)^{(2)}(t - b)x_{2,1,0}(a, b, c), \qquad (s, t, u) \in I,\ x \in K^{10}.
\end{aligned} \tag{57}
$$

The reader may wish to compare this equation with the diagram of ρ.

58. Corollary. *Consider a space K. Let*

$y^{i,j,k}$, $(i, j, k) \in \bar{\omega}_{a,b,c}$, be arbitrary constants;

$y^{i,j,k}(s)$, $(i, j, k) \in \bar{\omega}_{s,b,c}$, be arbitrary elements of $Z(a)$;

similarly for $\bar{\omega}_{a,t,c}$ and $\bar{\omega}_{a,b,u}$;

$y^{i,j,k}(t, u)$, $(i, j, k) \in \bar{\omega}_{a,t,u}$, be arbitrary elements of $Z(b, c)$;

similarly for $\bar{\omega}_{s,b,u}$ and $\bar{\omega}_{s,t,c}$;

$y^{p,q,r}(s, t, u)$ be an arbitrary element of $Z(a, b, c)$.

Put

$$
\begin{aligned}
x(s, t, u) = {} & \sum_{\bar{\omega}_{a,b,c}} (s - a)^{(i)}(t - b)^{(j)}(u - c)^{(k)}y^{i,j,k} \\
& + \sum_{\bar{\omega}_{s,b,c}} (t - b)^{(j)}(u - c)^{(k)}T_s^{i-1}y^{i,j,k}(s) + \text{similar sums} \\
& + \sum_{\bar{\omega}_{a,t,u}} (s - a)^{(i)}T_t^{j-1}T_u^{k-1}y^{i,j,k}(t, u) + \text{similar sums} \\
& + T_s^{p-1}T_t^{q-1}T_u^{r-1}y^{p,q,r}(s, t, u).
\end{aligned} \tag{59}
$$

Then $x \in K$, and the given elements $\{y^{i,j,k}\}$ constitute the retracted core ρ of x.

This corollary is just like 6 : 43.

60. Corollary. *Suppose that $x \in K$. Then the derivatives of x which are elements of ξ exist, are continuous, $(s, t, u) \in I$, and are given in terms of ρ by formulas obtained from the expansion formula* (56) *by differentiation in any way consistent with the rule of ξ.*

This corollary is just like 6: 45.

Corollary 60 implies that K depends on B alone and not on the particular rule of ρ that was used in the definition of K. Theorem 55 and Corollary 58 imply that ρ is a set of coordinates for x in K, just as ω is a set of coordinates for x in B.

§ 61. **The norm in** K. The space K consists of functions $x(s, t, u)$ for which the elements of ρ are continuous in their variables, if any, $(s, t, u) \in I$.

We have seen that if $x \in K$, then the elements of ξ are continuous and there is an expansion, obtained by differentiation of (56), of each element of ξ in terms of ρ.

The norms in K are defined as before:

$$\begin{aligned}\|x\|_K = \max [&|x_{i,j,k}(a, b, c)|, (i, j, k) \in \bar{\omega}_{a,b,c}; \sup |\delta_s x_{i-1,j,k}(s, b, c)|,\\ &(i, j, k) \in \bar{\omega}_{s,b,c}; \text{similar terms for } \bar{\omega}_{a,t,c} \text{ and } \bar{\omega}_{a,b,u};\\ &\sup |\delta_t \delta_u x_{i,j-1,k-1}(a, t, u)|, (i, j, k) \in \bar{\omega}_{a,t,u}; \text{similar terms}\\ &\text{for } \bar{\omega}_{s,b,u} \text{ and } \bar{\omega}_{s,t,c}; \sup |\delta_s\delta_t\delta_u x_{p-1,q-1,r-1}(s, t, u)|].\end{aligned}$$

The alternative norm is $|||x|||_K = \max_{(i,j,k)\in\xi} [\sup |x_{i,j,k}|]$, where the arguments of $x_{i,j,k}$ are $(s, b, c), \cdots, (s, t, u)$ according as (i, j, k) is in $\xi_{s,b,c}, \cdots, \xi_{s,t,u}$.

For any space K, *the norms* $\|x\|_K$ *and* $|||x|||_K$ *are equivalent*. By the norm in K we ordinarily mean $\|x\|_K$. The norm in the space K^* adjoint to K is based on $\|x\|_K$.

§ 62. **The space K^*.** Consider a space K and its adjoint space K^*.

63. MASS THEOREM. *Suppose that* $F \in K^*$. *Put*

$$c^{i,j,k} = F[(s-a)^{(i)}(t-b)^{(j)}(u-c)^{(k)}], \qquad (i, j, k) \in \bar{\omega}_{a,b,c}; \tag{64}$$

$$\lambda^{i,j,k}(\bar{s}) = \begin{cases} \lim_\nu F[(t-b)^{(j)}(u-c)^{(k)} T_s^{i-1}\psi^\nu(a, \bar{s}, s)], & \textit{if } \bar{s} > \alpha,\\ 0 & \textit{otherwise}, (i, j, k) \in \bar{\omega}_{s,b,c};\end{cases}$$

similarly for $\bar{\omega}_{a,t,c}$ *and* $\bar{\omega}_{a,b,u}$;

$$\lambda^{i,j,k}(\bar{t}, \bar{u}) = \begin{cases} \lim_{\nu,\nu'} F[(s-a)^{(i)} T_t^{j-1} T_u^{k-1}\psi^\nu(b, \bar{t}, t)\psi^{\nu'}(c, \bar{u}, u)] \\ \qquad\qquad \textit{if } \bar{t} > \beta \textit{ and } \bar{u} > \gamma,\\ 0 \qquad\qquad \textit{otherwise}, (i, j, k) \in \bar{\omega}_{a,t,u};\end{cases} \tag{65}$$

similarly for $\bar{\omega}_{s,b,u}$ *and* $\bar{\omega}_{s,t,c}$;

$$\lambda^{p,q,r}(\bar{s}, \bar{t}, \bar{u}) = \begin{cases} \lim_{\nu,\nu',\nu''} F[T_s^{p-1}T_t^{q-1}T_u^{r-1}\psi^\nu(a, \bar{s}, s)\psi^{\nu'}(b, \bar{t}, t)\psi^{\nu''}(c, \bar{u}, u)],\\ \qquad\qquad \textit{if } \bar{s} > \alpha, \bar{t} > \beta, \textit{and } \bar{u} > \gamma,\\ 0 \qquad\qquad \textit{otherwise}.\end{cases}$$

Then the functions $\lambda^{i,j,k}$, $(i, j, k) \in \bar{\omega} - \bar{\omega}_{a,b,c}$, *are well defined and are elements of* $V^{0,0}$. *Also*

$$\begin{aligned} Fx = &\sum_{\bar{\omega}_{a,b,c}} c^{i,j,k} x_{i,j,k}(a, b, c) - \sum_{\bar{\omega}_{s,b,c}} \int x_{i-1,j,k}(s, b, c)\, d\lambda^{i,j,k}(s)\\ &- \textit{similar sums} + \sum_{\bar{\omega}_{a,t,u}} \iint x_{i,j-1,k-1}(a, t, u)\, d\lambda^{i,j,k}(t, u)\\ &+ \textit{similar sums} - \iiint x_{p-1,q-1,r-1}(s, t, u)\, d\lambda^{p,q,r}(s, t, u), \qquad x \in K.\end{aligned} \tag{66}$$

The functions $\lambda^{i,j,k}$ are the only elements of $V^{0,0}$ and the constants $c^{i,j,k}$ are the only numbers for which the last relation holds. Furthermore

$$\begin{aligned} \|F\|_{K^*} = \sum_{\bar{\omega}_{a,b,c}} |c^{i,j,k}| &+ \sum_{\bar{\omega}_{s,b,c}} \int_{s \neq a} d|\lambda^{i,j,k}|(s) + \textit{similar sums} \\ \text{(67)} \qquad &+ \sum_{\bar{\omega}_{a,t,u}} \iint\limits_{\substack{t \neq b, \\ u \neq c}} d|\lambda^{i,j,k}|(t, u) + \textit{similar sums} \\ &+ \iiint\limits_{\substack{s \neq a,\, t \neq b, \\ u \neq c}} d|\lambda^{p,q,r}|(s, t, u). \end{aligned}$$

This theorem is just like 6: 48.

An alternative form of (66) is

$$\begin{aligned} Fx = \sum_{\bar{\omega}_{a,b,c}} c^{i,j,k} x_{i,j,k}(a, b, c) &- \sum_{\bar{\omega}_{s,b,c}} \int \delta_s x_{i-1,j,k}(s, b, c)\, d\lambda^{i,j,k}(s) \\ \text{(68)} \qquad &- \textit{similar sums} + \sum_{\bar{\omega}_{a,t,u}} \iint \delta_t \delta_u x_{i,j-1,k-1}(a, t, u)\, d\lambda^{i,j,k}(t, u) \\ &+ \textit{similar sums} - \iiint \delta_s \delta_t \delta_u x_{p-1,q-1,r-1}(s, t, u)\, d\lambda^{p,q,r}(s, t, u), \\ &\qquad\qquad x \in K. \end{aligned}$$

That (66) and (68) are equivalent follows from the fact that the masses $\lambda^{i,j,k}$ vanish everywhere on the boundaries.

§ 69. **The space $\mathscr{K}^*$.** The space $\mathscr{K}^*$ is defined as the space of functionals which are finite sums of Lebesgue-Stieltjes integrals relative to functions of bounded variation of the elements of the covered core ξ of the function operated on (cf. § 4: 80). Thus an element F of $\mathscr{K}^*$ is a functional of the form

$$\begin{aligned} Fx = \sum_{(i,j,k) \in \xi_{s,t,u}} &\iiint x_{i,j,k}(s, t, u)\, d\mu^{i,j,k}(s, t, u) \\ \text{(70)} \qquad + \sum_{(i,j,k) \in \xi_{a,t,u}} &\iint x_{i,j,k}(a, t, u)\, d\mu^{i,j,k}(t, u) + \textit{similar sums} \\ + \sum_{(i,j,k) \in \xi_{s,b,c}} &\int x_{i,j,k}(s, b, c)\, d\mu^{i,j,k}(s) + \textit{similar sums}, \qquad \mu^{i,j,k} \in V. \end{aligned}$$

The jump set $\mathscr{J}_s$ of F relative to $\mathscr{K}^*$ may be defined as the countable set of points interior to I_s which are points of discontinuity of

$$|\mu^{i,j,k}|(s, \tilde{\beta}, \tilde{\gamma}), \qquad (i, j, k) \in \bar{\xi}_{s,t,u}\,; \text{ or}$$
$$|\mu^{i,j,k}|(s, \tilde{\beta}), \qquad (i, j, k) \in \bar{\xi}_{s,t,c}\,; \text{ or}$$

$$|\mu^{i,j,k}|(s, \tilde{\gamma}), \qquad (i, j, k) \in \bar{\xi}_{s,b,u}; \text{ or}$$
$$|\mu^{i,j,k}|(s), \qquad (i, j, k) \in \bar{\xi}_{s,b,c};$$

together with the point $s = a$. The sets $\mathscr{J}_t$, $\mathscr{J}_u$ are defined similarly.

The sets $\mathscr{J}_s$, $\mathscr{J}_t$, $\mathscr{J}_u$ as just defined are larger than need be.

If $F \in K^*$, the Lebesgue extension of F, defined by the right-hand member of equation (66), is an element of $\mathscr{K}^*$. The next theorem includes the converse statement.

71. THEOREM. *If $F \in \mathscr{K}^*$, then the restriction of F to K is an element of K^*. The functions $\lambda^{i,j,k} \in V^{0,0}$ which enter in the standard form* (66) *for Fx satisfy the following relations:*

$$\lambda^{i,j,k}(\tilde{s}) = F[(t-b)^{(j)}(u-c)^{(k)}(s-\tilde{s})^{(i-1)}\psi(a, \tilde{s}, s)],$$
$$\alpha < \tilde{s} \notin \mathscr{J}_s,\ (i, j, k) \in \bar{\omega}_{s,b,c};$$

similarly for $\bar{\omega}_{a,t,c}$ and $\bar{\omega}_{a,b,u}$;

$$\lambda^{i,j,k}(\tilde{t}, \tilde{u}) = F[(s-a)^{(i)}(t-\tilde{t})^{(j-1)}\psi(b, \tilde{t}, t)(u-\tilde{u})^{(k-1)}\psi(c, \tilde{u}, u)], \tag{72}$$
$$\beta < \tilde{t} \notin \mathscr{J}_t \text{ and } \gamma < \tilde{u} \notin \mathscr{J}_u,\ (i, j, k) \in \bar{\omega}_{a,t,u};$$

similarly for $\bar{\omega}_{s,b,u}$ and $\bar{\omega}_{s,t,c}$;

$$\lambda^{p,q,r}(\tilde{s}, \tilde{t}, \tilde{u}) = F[(s-\tilde{s})^{(p-1)}\psi(a, \tilde{s}, s)(t-\tilde{t})^{(q-1)}\psi(b, \tilde{t}, t)(u-\tilde{u})^{(r-1)}$$
$$\times \psi(c, \tilde{u}, u)], \quad \alpha < \tilde{s} \notin \mathscr{J}_s,\ \beta < \tilde{t} \notin \mathscr{J}_t, \text{ and } \gamma < \tilde{u} \notin \mathscr{J}_u;$$

where $\mathscr{J}_s$, $\mathscr{J}_t$, $\mathscr{J}_u$ are the jump sets of F.

This theorem is just like 6: 55.

§ 73. **K^* as a subspace of B^*.** It is clear from the definition of K that

$$B \subset K.$$

Furthermore

$$|||x|||_B \geqq |||x|||_K, \qquad x \in B,$$

since the full core ϕ contains the covered core ξ. It follows that a functional bounded relative to the norm in K will be bounded relative to the norm in B. Hence

$$K^* \subset B^*.$$

We have defined the space B as the space of functions $x(s, t, u)$ such that the elements of ω exist and are continuous in their arguments, $(s, t, u) \in I$. We have shown that the Taylor formula (9) holds for each x in B. We now define the larger space $\boldsymbol{B}$ as the space of functions $x(s, t, u)$ for which the following conditions all hold.

(1) The derivative $x_{p,q,r}(s, t, u)$ exists almost everywhere in I and is Lebesgue integrable there.

(2) The elements of $\omega_{a,t,u}$ exist almost everywhere in $I_t \times I_u$ and are Lebesgue integrable there. Similarly for $\omega_{s,b,u}$ and $\omega_{s,t,c}$.

(3) The elements of $\omega_{s,b,c}$ exist almost everywhere in I_s and are Lebesgue integrable there. Similarly for $\omega_{a,t,c}$ and $\omega_{a,b,u}$.

(4) The elements of $\omega_{a,b,c}$ exist.

(5) The Taylor formula (9) holds for $x(s, t, u)$, $(s, t, u) \in I$.

The derivatives are to be understood according to the rule of ξ, extended as follows: an element of $\omega_{s,b,c}$ is a derivative with respect to s of an element of ξ, similarly for $\omega_{a,t,c}$ and $\omega_{a,b,u}$; an element of $\omega_{a,t,u}$ is a cross derivative D_tD_u or D_uD_t of an element of ξ, similarly for $\omega_{s,b,u}$ and $\omega_{s,t,c}$; and $x_{p,q,r}$ is a cross derivative in some order of $x_{p-1,q-1,r-1}$; where all elements of ξ are understood according to the rule of ξ.

Thus

$$B \subset \boldsymbol{B} \subset K,$$

because ξ is well covered. The generalization of Lemma 4: 83 is valid.

74. Kernel theorem. *Suppose that* $F \in K^*$. *Define* $c^{i,j,k}$ *by* (64) *and* $\lambda^{i,j,k} \in V^{0,0}$ *by* (65). *Then*

$$\begin{aligned} Fx = {} & \sum_{\bar{\omega}_{a,b,c}} c^{i,j,k} x_{i,j,k}(a, b, c) + \sum_{\bar{\omega}_{s,b,c}} \int x_{i,j,k}(s, b, c)\lambda^{i,j,k}(s)\, ds \\ & + \textit{similar sums} + \sum_{\bar{\omega}_{a,t,u}} \iint x_{i,j,k}(a, t, u)\lambda^{i,j,k}(t, u)\, dt\, du \qquad (75) \\ & + \textit{similar sums} + \iiint x_{p,q,r}(s, t, u)\lambda^{p,q,r}(s, t, u)\, ds\, dt\, du \end{aligned}$$

for all x *in* $\boldsymbol{B}$.

The proof is like that of Theorem 6: 58. We transform the integrals in (66) by parts and use the fact that each $\lambda^{i,j,k}$ vanishes on the appropriate boundary.

If $F \in \mathscr{K}^*$, then (75) holds and the functions $\lambda^{i,j,k}$ may be determined from (72), by Theorem 71.

§ 76. **An illustration.** Consider the remainder

$$\begin{aligned} Rx = {} & \int_{-1}^{1}\int_{-1}^{1}\int_{-1}^{1} x(s, t, u)\, ds\, dt\, du \\ & - \frac{4}{3}[x(1, 0, 0) + x(-1, 0, 0) + x(0, 1, 0) + x(0, -1, 0) \qquad (77) \\ & \qquad + x(0, 0, 1) + x(0, 0, -1)] \end{aligned}$$

in the approximation of the triple integral of x over the interval

$$I = \{-1 \leqq s, t, u \leqq 1\}$$

by the indicated combination of axial values.

We shall apply Theorem 74 to R, taking $F = R$. Since Rx is a Stieltjes integral on x,

$$R \in K^* \quad \text{iff} \quad x(s, t, u) \in \xi.$$

We thus have a wide choice of spaces B.

Let us take $B = B^{12}$ (cf. Figure 3), with

$$(a, b, c) = (0, 0, 0).$$

Then $R \in K^{12*}$. The functional R and the space B^{12} are symmetric in s, in t, and in u. By putting

$$x(s, t, u) = 1, s, t, u, s^2, st, \cdots, stu$$

successively, we see that $Rx = 0$ whenever x is a polynomial in s, t, u of degree 3.

In B^{12}, $\bar{\omega}_{a,b,c}$ consists of 10 elements (i, j, k), for each of which

$$i + j + k \leqq 2.$$

Hence the constants $c^{i,j,k}$, $(i, j, k) \in \bar{\omega}_{a,b,c}$, defined by (64) all vanish.

We shall compute the kernels $\lambda^{i,j,k}$, $(i, j, k) \in \bar{\omega} - \bar{\omega}_{a,b,c}$. Because of the symmetry, these kernels have the following property (cf. § 4 : 94). If i is even and $\lambda^{i,j,k}$ contains s, then $\lambda^{i,j,k}$ is even in s; if i is odd and $\lambda^{i,j,k}$ contains s, then $\lambda^{i,j,k}$ is odd in s. Similarly for t and u.

The set $\bar{\omega} - \bar{\omega}_{a,b,c}$ is the union of the following sets:

$$\begin{aligned}
\bar{\omega}_{s,b,c} &= \{(3, 0, 0)\},\\
\bar{\omega}_{a,t,c} &= \{(0, 3, 0), (1, 2, 0)\},\\
\bar{\omega}_{a,b,u} &= \{(0, 0, 3), (1, 0, 2), (0, 1, 2)\},\\
\bar{\omega}_{a,t,u} &= \{(0, 2, 1)\},\\
\bar{\omega}_{s,b,u} &= \{(2, 0, 1)\},\\
\bar{\omega}_{s,t,c} &= \{(2, 1, 0)\},\\
\bar{\omega}_{s,t,u} &= \{(1, 1, 1)\}.
\end{aligned}$$

For the functional R, the set $\mathscr{I}_s$ consists of three points $s = -1, 0$, and 1. Likewise for $\mathscr{I}_t$, $\mathscr{I}_u$. These sets are of no importance in the use of (75). Furthermore, any values of $\lambda^{i,j,k}$ that are omitted in the following calculation are not needed for (75). We will not explicitly note inclusions or exclusions of special values of $\tilde{s}$, $\tilde{t}$, $\tilde{u}$.

Consider $\lambda^{3,0,0}(s)$ first. By (72),

$$\lambda^{3,0,0}(\tilde{s}) = R[(s - \tilde{s})^{(2)}\psi(0, \tilde{s}, s)] = R\left[\frac{(s - \tilde{s})^2}{2}\,\psi(0, \tilde{s}, s)\right].$$

Suppose that $\tilde{s} > 0$. Then

$$\psi(0, \tilde{s}, s) = \begin{cases} 1 & \text{if } \tilde{s} < s, \\ 0 & \text{otherwise,} \end{cases}$$

by (11 : 6). Hence

$$\int_{-1}^{1}\int_{-1}^{1}\int_{-1}^{1}\frac{(s-\tilde{s})^2}{2}\,\psi(0,\tilde{s},s)\,ds\,dt\,du = 4\int_{\tilde{s}}^{1}\frac{(s-\tilde{s})^2}{2}\,ds = \frac{2(1-\tilde{s})^3}{3},$$

$$\lambda^{3,0,0}(\tilde{s}) = \frac{2(1-\tilde{s})^3}{3} - \frac{4}{3}\left[\frac{(1-\tilde{s})^2}{2}\right]$$

$$= -\frac{2\tilde{s}(1-\tilde{s})^2}{3}, \qquad \tilde{s} > 0,$$

since $\psi(0, \tilde{s}, s)$ vanishes for $s = -1$ and for $s = 0$.

Suppose that $\tilde{s} < 0$. Then

$$\psi(0,\tilde{s},s) = \begin{cases} -1 & \text{if } s \leqq \tilde{s}, \\ 0 & \text{otherwise,} \end{cases}$$

by (11 : 6). Hence

$$\int_{-1}^{1}\int_{-1}^{1}\int_{-1}^{1}\frac{(s-\tilde{s})^2}{2}\,\psi(0,\tilde{s},s)\,ds\,dt\,du = 4\int_{-1}^{\tilde{s}} -\frac{(s-\tilde{s})^2}{2}\,ds$$

$$= \frac{2(-1-\tilde{s})^3}{3} = -\frac{2}{3}(1+\tilde{s})^3,$$

$$\lambda^{3,0,0}(\tilde{s}) = -\frac{2}{3}(1+\tilde{s})^3 - \frac{4}{3}\left[-\frac{(-1-\tilde{s})^2}{2}\right]$$

$$= -\frac{2\tilde{s}(1+\tilde{s})^2}{3}, \qquad \tilde{s} < 0.$$

Thus

$$\lambda^{3,0,0}(s) = \lambda(s),$$

where

(78) $$\lambda(s) = -\frac{2s(1-|s|)^2}{3}.$$

Note that $\lambda(s)$ is odd in s.

Next consider $\lambda^{0,3,0}(t)$. By (72), interchanging s and t,

$$\lambda^{0,3,0}(t) = \lambda(t).$$

Likewise

$$\lambda^{0,0,3}(u) = \lambda(u).$$

Next consider $\lambda^{1,2,0}(t)$. By (72),

$$\lambda^{1,2,0}(\tilde{t}) = R[s(t-\tilde{t})\psi(0,\tilde{t},t)].$$

Suppose that $\tilde{t} > 0$. Then

$$\int_{-1}^{1}\int_{-1}^{1}\int_{-1}^{1} s(t-\tilde{t})\psi(0,\tilde{t},t)\,ds\,dt\,du = 0,$$

$$\lambda^{1,2,0}(\tilde{t}) = 0.$$

The same relations hold if $\tilde{t} < 0$. Thus

$$\lambda^{1,2,0}(t) = 0;$$

and $\lambda^{1,2,0}$ is even in t.

Likewise

$$\lambda^{0,1,2}(u) = 0,$$
$$\lambda^{1,0,2}(u) = 0.$$

Next consider $\lambda^{0,2,1}(t, u)$. By (72),

$$\lambda^{0,2,1}(\tilde{t}, \tilde{u}) = R[(t - \tilde{t})\psi(0, \tilde{t}, t)\psi(0, \tilde{u}, u)].$$

Hence

$$\lambda^{0,2,1}(\tilde{t}, \tilde{u}) = 2\int_{\tilde{u}}^{1} du \int_{\tilde{t}}^{1} (t - \tilde{t})\, dt = (1 - \tilde{u})(1 - \tilde{t})^2 \qquad \text{if } \tilde{t} > 0, \tilde{u} > 0;$$

$$\lambda^{0,2,1}(\tilde{t}, \tilde{u}) = -2\int_{-1}^{\tilde{u}} du \int_{\tilde{t}}^{1} (t - \tilde{t})\, dt = -(1 + \tilde{u})(1 - \tilde{t})^2 \quad \text{if } \tilde{t} > 0, \tilde{u} < 0;$$

$$\lambda^{0,2,1}(\tilde{t}, \tilde{u}) = 2\int_{\tilde{u}}^{1} du \int_{-1}^{\tilde{t}} -(t - \tilde{t})\, dt = (1 - \tilde{u})(1 + \tilde{t})^2 \qquad \text{if } \tilde{t} < 0, \tilde{u} > 0;$$

$$\lambda^{0,2,1}(\tilde{t}, \tilde{u}) = 2\int_{-1}^{\tilde{u}} du \int_{-1}^{\tilde{t}} (t - \tilde{t})\, dt = -(1 + \tilde{u})(1 + \tilde{t})^2 \quad \text{if } \tilde{t} < 0, \tilde{u} < 0.$$

Thus

$$\lambda^{0,2,1}(t, u) = \kappa(t, u),$$

where

(79) $$\kappa(t, u) = (1 - |t|)^2(1 - |u|) \text{ signum } u.$$

Note that $\kappa(t, u)$ is even in t and odd in u.

Likewise

$$\lambda^{2,0,1}(s, u) = \kappa(s, u),$$
$$\lambda^{2,1,0}(s, t) = \kappa(s, t).$$

Next consider $\lambda^{1,1,1}(s, t, u)$. By (72),

$$\lambda^{1,1,1}(\tilde{s}, \tilde{t}, \tilde{u}) = R[\psi(0, \tilde{s}, s)\psi(0, \tilde{t}, t)\psi(0, \tilde{u}, u)].$$

Hence

$$\lambda^{1,1,1}(\tilde{s}, \tilde{t}, \tilde{u}) = \int_{\tilde{s}}^{1} ds \int_{\tilde{t}}^{1} dt \int_{\tilde{u}}^{1} du = (1 - \tilde{s})(1 - \tilde{t})(1 - \tilde{u})$$
$$\text{if } \tilde{s} > 0, \tilde{t} > 0, \tilde{u} > 0,$$

with the usual modifications in the other cases. Thus

$$\lambda^{1,1,1}(s, t, u) = \eta(s, t, u),$$

where

$$(80) \qquad \eta(s, t, u) = (1 - |s|)(1 - |t|)(1 - |u|) \text{ signum } (stu),$$

a function which is odd in each variable.

We have calculated all the kernels. The relation (75) now becomes the remainder formula:

$$(81) \qquad \begin{aligned} Rx = & \iiint x_{1,1,1}(s, t, u)\eta(s, t, u)\, ds\, dt\, du \\ & + \iint x_{0,2,1}(0, t, u)\kappa(t, u)\, dt\, du + \iint x_{2,0,1}(s, 0, u)\, \kappa(s, u)\, ds\, du \\ & + \iint x_{2,1,0}(s, t, 0)\kappa(s, t)\, ds\, dt + \int x_{3,0,0}(s, 0, 0)\lambda(s)\, ds \\ & + \int x_{0,3,0}(0, t, 0)\lambda(t)\, dt + \int x_{0,0,3}(0, 0, u)\lambda(u)\, du, \qquad x \in \boldsymbol{B}^{12}, \end{aligned}$$

where all variables of integration are taken from -1 to 1, and η, κ, λ are given by (80), (79), (78). The derivatives that appear in (81) are elements of ω and therefore are independent; each may be an arbitrary integrable function of its variables. The equality (81) for the remainder (77) may be transformed in many ways, but it cannot be simplified since each term is independent of the other terms and contributes to Rx.

B^{10} and K^{10}

$p = q = r = 1$

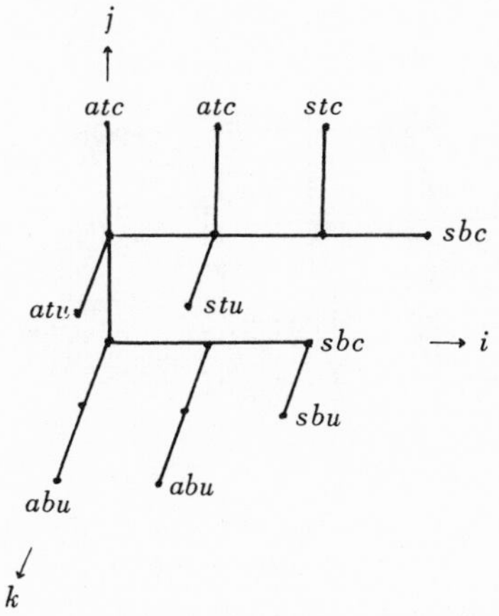

ω

Arguments *abc* at unmarked vertices.

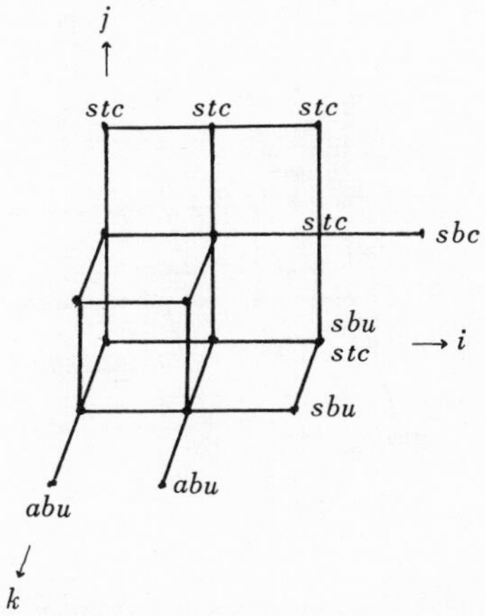

ϕ

Arguments *stu* at unmarked vertices.

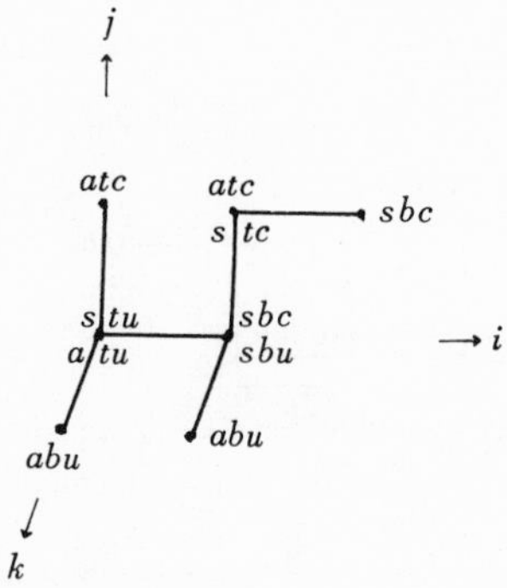

ρ

Arguments *abc* everywhere

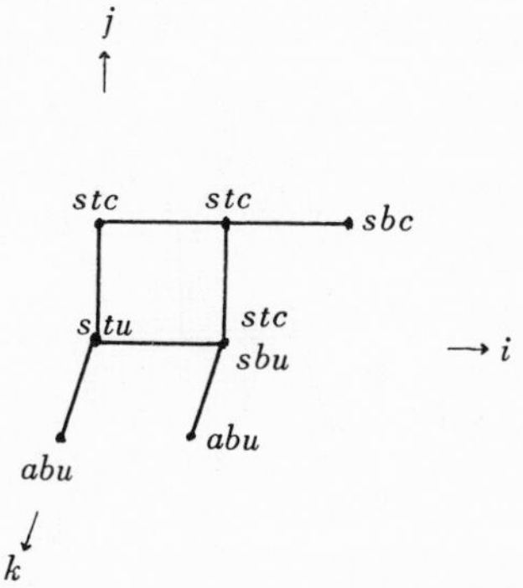

ξ

FIGURE 1. Cores and rules of cores.

B^{11} and K^{11}

$p = 2, \quad q = 1, \quad r = 1$

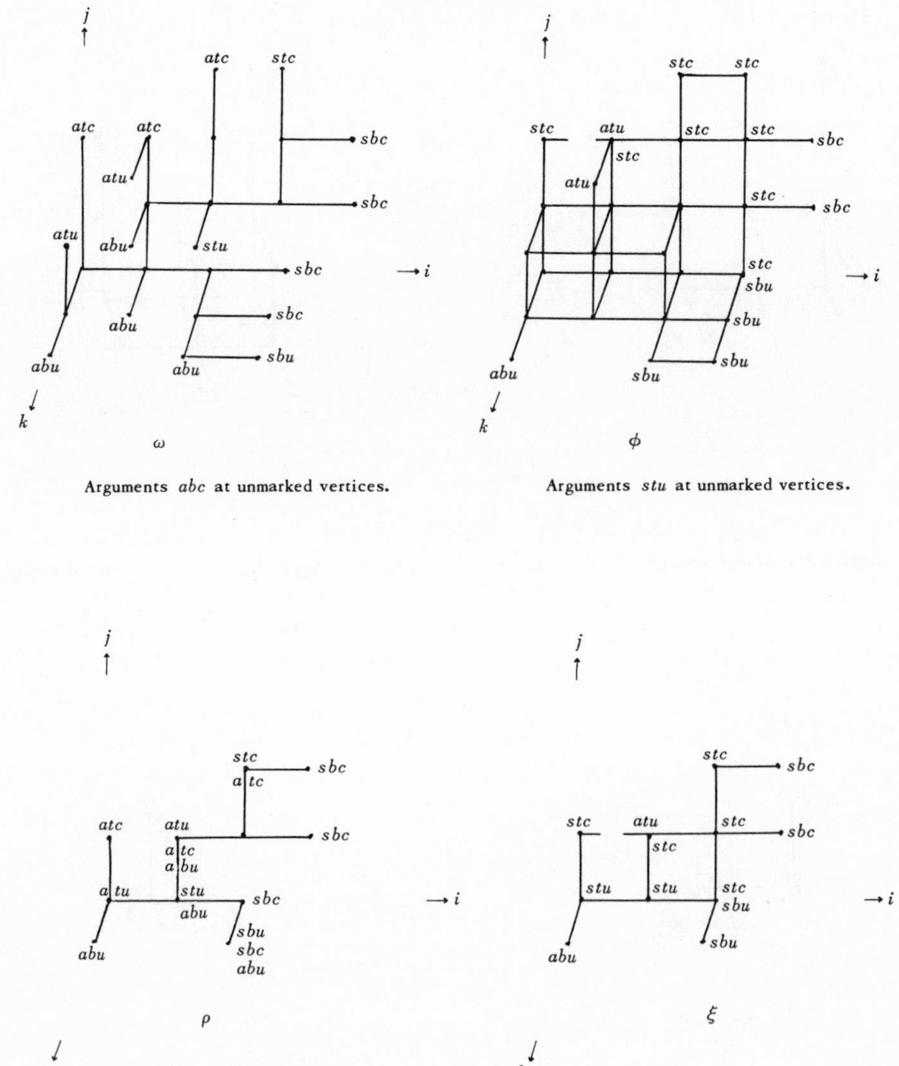

Arguments *abc* everywhere.

FIGURE 2. Cores and rules of cores.

B^{12} and K^{12}

$p = q = r = 1$

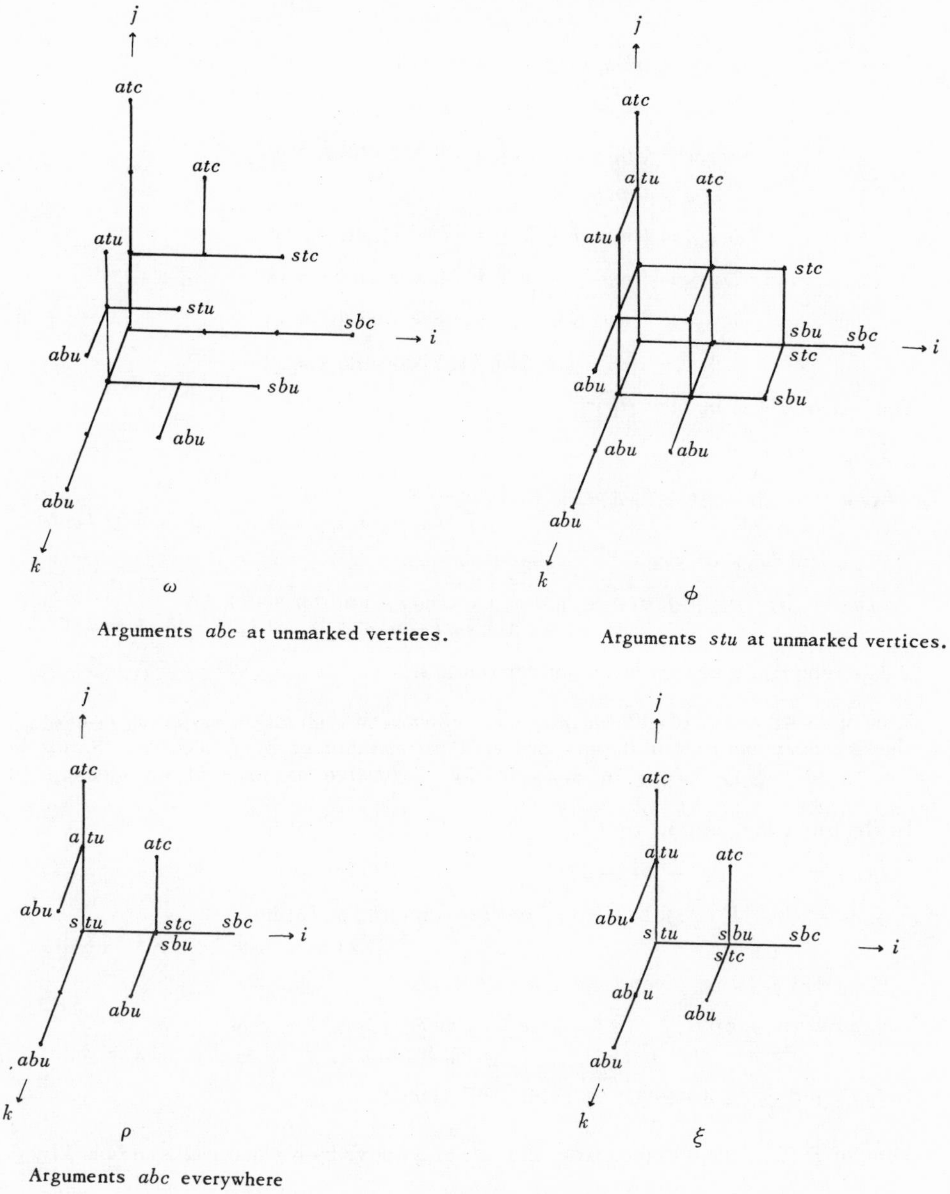

FIGURE 3. Cores and rules of cores.

TABLE 1

CORES AND RULES OF CORES IN $B_{p,q,r}$ AND, IF $pqr \geqq 1$, $K_{p,q,r}$

The pivot is $x_{p,q,r} = D_s^p D_t^q D_u^r x$.

$$n = p + q + r.$$

$$\bar{\omega}_{a,b,c} = \{(i, j, k) : i + j + k < n\}.$$

$$\bar{\omega}_{a,b,u} = \{(n - j - k, j, k) : k > r\}.$$

$$\bar{\omega}_{a,t,u} = \{(n - j - k, j, k) : k = r \text{ and } j > q\}.$$

$$\bar{\omega}_{s,t,u} = \{(p, q, r)\}.$$

$$\bar{\omega}_{s,b,u} = \{(n - j - k, j, k) : k = r \text{ and } j < q\}.$$

$$\bar{\omega}_{a,t,c} = \{(n - j - k, j, k) : k < r \text{ and } j > q\}.$$

$$\bar{\omega}_{s,t,c} = \{(n - j - k, j, k) : k < r \text{ and } j = q\}.$$

$$\bar{\omega}_{s,b,c} = \{(n - j - k, j, k) : k < r \text{ and } j < q\}.$$

The space B^{12} is in fact $B_{1,1,1}$.

$\bar{\phi}_{s,t,u} = \ulcorner p, q, r \urcorner$.

$\bar{\phi}_{a,t,u} = \{(i, j, k) : (i, j, k) \notin \bar{\phi}_{s,t,u}$, and for some (i_0, j_0, k_0) in $\bar{\omega}_{a,t,u}$, $i = i_0, j \leqq j_0, k \leqq k_0\}$.

$\bar{\phi}_{s,b,u}$ and $\bar{\phi}_{s,t,c}$ are given by similar relations.

$\bar{\phi}_{s,b,c} = \{(i, j, k) : (i, j, k) \notin \bar{\phi}_{s,t,u} \cup \bar{\phi}_{s,b,u} \cup \bar{\phi}_{s,t,c}$, and for some (i_0, j_0, k_0) in $\bar{\omega}_{s,b,c}$, $i \leqq i_0, j = j_0, k = k_0\}$.

$\bar{\phi}_{a,t,c}$ and $\bar{\phi}_{a,b,u}$ are given by similar relations.

Rule of ϕ: All orders of differentiation are allowed in elements of $\phi_{s,t,u}$. $x_{i,j,k}$ in $\phi_{a,t,u}$ is the derivative as to t, u in any order of an element of $\phi_{s,t,u} \cup \phi_{a,t,u}$. Similarly for $\phi_{s,b,u}$ and $\phi_{s,t,c}$. $x_{i,j,k}$ in $\phi_{s,b,c}$ is the derivative as to s of an element of $\phi_{s,t,u} \cup \phi_{s,b,u} \cup \phi_{s,t,c} \cup \phi_{s,b,c}$.

In the following, assume that $pqr \geqq 1$.

$\bar{\xi}_{s,t,u} = \ulcorner p - 1, q - 1, r - 1 \urcorner$.

$\bar{\xi}_{a,t,u} = \{(i, j, k) : (i, j, k) \notin \bar{\xi}_{s,t,u}$, and for some (i_0, j_0, k_0) in $\bar{\omega}_{a,t,u}$, $i = i_0, j < j_0, k < k_0\}$.

$\bar{\xi}_{s,b,u}$ and $\bar{\xi}_{s,t,c}$ are given by similar relations.

$\bar{\xi}_{s,b,c} = \{(i, j, k) : (i, j, k) \notin \bar{\xi}_{s,t,u} \cup \bar{\xi}_{s,b,u} \cup \bar{\xi}_{s,t,c}$, and for some (i_0, j_0, k_0) in $\bar{\omega}_{s,b,c}$, $i < i_0, j = j_0, k = k_0\}$.

$\bar{\xi}_{a,t,c}$ and $\bar{\xi}_{a,b,u}$ are given by similar relations.

Rule of ξ: The rule obtained from the rule of ϕ above by replacing all symbols ϕ by ξ.

Table 2

Cores and rules of cores in $B_{\ulcorner p,q,r \urcorner}$ and, if $pqr \geqq 1$, $K_{\ulcorner p,q,r \urcorner}$

The pivot is $x_{p,q,r} = D_s^p D_t^q D_u^r x$.

The complete core ω is the set of derivatives $x_{i,j,k}(\sigma, \tau, \lambda)$, $i \leqq p$, $j \leqq q$, and $k \leqq r$. where

$$\sigma = \begin{cases} s & \text{if } i = p, \\ a & \text{if } i < p; \end{cases} \qquad \tau = \begin{cases} t & \text{if } j = q, \\ b & \text{if } j < q; \end{cases} \qquad \lambda = \begin{cases} u & \text{if } k = r, \\ c & \text{if } k < r. \end{cases}$$

$$\bar{\phi} = \bar{\phi}_{s,t,u} = \ulcorner p, q, r \urcorner.$$

The rule of ϕ permits all orders of differentiation.

$$\bar{\xi} = \bar{\xi}_{s,t,u} = \ulcorner p - 1, q - 1, r - 1 \urcorner, \quad \text{if } pqr \geqq 1.$$

The rule of ξ permits all orders of differentiation.

$B_{\ulcorner 3,2,1 \urcorner}$ and $K_{\ulcorner 3,2,1 \urcorner}$

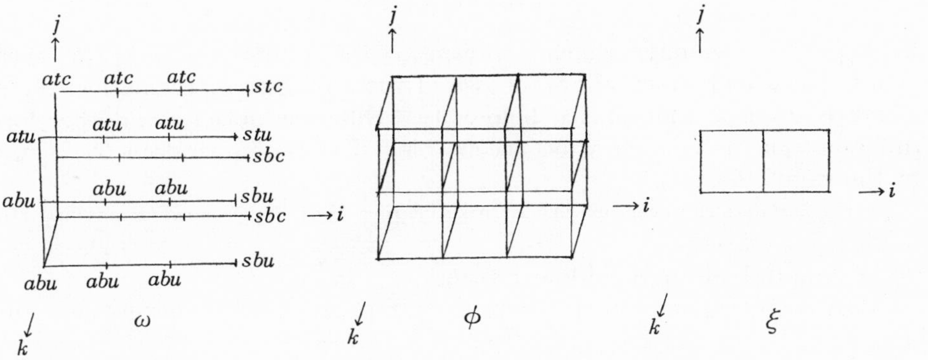

Arguments abc at unmarked vertices. | Arguments stu everywhere. | Arguments stu everywhere.

CHAPTER 8

Factors of Operators

§ 1. **Introduction.** Consider a preproblem in which (X) and (Y) are spaces vaguely defined and (G) is an operator vaguely defined on (X) to (Y), and in which we seek an operator (A) to approximate (G). Alternatively we may be given a vague (A). In either case we study the remainder (R), where

$$(R) = (G) - (A).$$

Our procedure is to formulate a problem in which X, Y, G, A and

$$R = G - A$$

have precise meanings which conform to the vague meanings of their counterparts and which allow the use of the strongest mathematical tools. There is often a wide choice before us. Different norms† and therefore different spaces X, Y may be acceptable. Different operators G, A may fit the vague (G), (A).

Mathematical expertness can often arrange that X, Y, and R satisfy the following conditions.

(1) X and Y are normed linear spaces.

(2) R is a continuous operator on X to Y (relative to the norms in X and Y).

(3) $R0 = 0$.

If R were linear, the last condition would surely hold. We have not assumed however that R is linear.

We seek to analyze R and to appraise $Rx, x \in X$, in useful ways. If $\|Rx\|_Y$ is small, the approximation of Gx by Ax is perhaps successful.

Now conditions (2) and (3) imply that Rx will be small whenever x in X is sufficiently small. We should like to have Rx small even in cases in which x is not small, if possible. Clearly any appraisal of Rx must be in terms of something related to x.

We may be able to find a continuous operator U on X to a normed linear space $\tilde{X}$ such that

$$Rx = 0 \qquad \text{whenever} \qquad Ux = 0,\ x \in X.$$

If so, we might expect that Rx would be small whenever Ux is small, and

† Besides the norms studied in earlier chapters, there are norms based on integrals. Cf. § 9: 1.

we might perhaps expect that Rx would be expressible in terms of Ux for all x in X.

Both expectations are fulfilled, if the spaces X, Y, and $U(X)$ are complete and if the operators R and U are linear (Theorem 20).

The linearity is the crux of the analysis. If the preproblem is linear, we may often be able to formulate the problem so that Theorem 20 applies. Applications are given after § 25.

§ 2. **Banach spaces.** Consider a normed linear space X. By a *Cauchy sequence* in X we mean a sequence $\{x^\nu\}$, $\nu = 1, 2, \cdots$, of elements x^ν of X with the following property: For each $\eta > 0$, there is a ν_0 such that

$$\|x^\nu - x^{\nu'}\|_X < \eta \quad \text{whenever} \quad \nu, \nu' > \nu_0.$$

If a Cauchy sequence has a limit, that limit is unique. We say that the space X is *complete* if every Cauchy sequence in X has a limit in X.

A complete normed linear space is called a *Banach space.*

The spaces C_n, Z, B, K of the preceding chapters *are complete.* This is easily proved, as follows. Consider $C_0 = C_0(I)$ first. If $\{x^\nu\}$ is a Cauchy sequence in C_0, the quantities $x^\nu(s)$, $s \in I$, converge uniformly on I, by the definition of the norm in C_0. Their limit therefore exists and is a continuous function. Hence there is an element of C_0 which is the limit of $\{x^\nu\}$, that is, C_0 is complete.

Similarly $B_{0,0}$, $Z(a)$, $Z(a, b)$ are complete.

Now consider $C_n = C_n(I)$, $n > 0$. Take a in I. If $\{x^\nu\}$ is a Cauchy sequence in C_n, then

$$\{x^\nu(a)\}, \quad \{x_1^\nu(a)\}, \cdots, \quad \{x_{n-1}^\nu(a)\}$$

are Cauchy sequences of reals and $\{x_n^\nu(s)\}$ is a Cauchy sequence in C_0, by the definition of the norm in C_n. Let c^i be the limit as $\nu \to \infty$ of $\{x_i^\nu(a)\}$, $i < n$, and let $y(s)$ be the continuous function which is the limit of $\{x_n^\nu(s)\}$ in C_0. By Taylor's formula (3 : 80), the function

$$z(s) = c^0 + c^1(s - a) + c^2(s - a)^{(2)} + \cdots + c^{n-1}(s - a)^{(n-1)} + T_s^n y(s)$$

is an element of C_n. As z is the limit of $\{x^\nu\}$ in C_n, it follows that C_n is complete.

Similarly B and K are complete. The proofs use Theorem 4 : 55 and Corollary 4 : 61, and Theorem 6 : 41 and Corollary 6 : 43.

Any finite dimensional normed linear space is complete. This is an aspect of Tychonoff's Theorem (cf. § 3 : 2).

Suppose that X is a normed linear space, not necessarily complete. It is often permissible and advantageous to replace X by its completion $\hat{X}$. The completion may be constructed by the Cantor process similar to a standard construction of the real numbers from the rationals [Hausdorff 1, p. 106], as follows.

Two Cauchy sequences $\{x^\nu\}$ and $\{\tilde{x}^\nu\}$ in X are said to be *equivalent* if

$$\lim_\nu (x^\nu - \tilde{x}^\nu) = 0.$$

The *completion* $\hat{X}$ of X consists of elements $\hat{x}$ each of which is a set of equivalent Cauchy sequences in X. If $\{x^\nu\} \in \hat{x} \in \hat{X}$, then $\hat{x}$ is the set of all Cauchy sequences in X equivalent to $\{x^\nu\}$. The norm $\|\hat{x}\|_{\hat{X}}$ is

$$\lim_\nu \|x^\nu\|_X,$$

where $\{x^\nu\} \in \hat{x}$. Addition and scalar multiplication in $\hat{X}$ are defined in the natural way:

$$\{x^\nu + y^\nu\} \in \hat{x} + \hat{y}, \qquad \{cx^\nu\} \in c\hat{x},$$

where

$$\{x^\nu\} \in \hat{x} \in \hat{X}, \qquad \{y^\nu\} \in \hat{y} \in \hat{X}, \qquad c \in \mathsf{N}.$$

It follows from the definition of a Cauchy sequence that the above definitions of norm, scalar multiplication, and addition are unambiguous, and that *$\hat{X}$ is a Banach space.* The condition that

$$\|\hat{x}\|_{\hat{X}} = 0, \quad \hat{x} \in \hat{X} \quad \text{implies} \quad \hat{x} = 0$$

is satisfied because of the use of equivalence sets of Cauchy sequences.

We may and shall think of X as a dense subset of its completion $\hat{X}$. The precise situation is as follows. Establish a map of X into $\hat{X}$ by letting x in X correspond to the element $\hat{x}$ in $\hat{X}$ which contains the Cauchy sequence $\{x, x, \cdots\}$. Let X^1 be the image of X under this map. Then the map of X onto X^1 is one-to-one, linear, and preserves norm; furthermore, X^1 is dense in $\hat{X}$. We consider X^1 to be the same as X. Each element x^1 of X^1 is in fact an equivalence set of Cauchy sequences in X; and if $x^1 \in X^1$, there exists an $x \in X$ such that $\{x, x, \cdots\} \in x^1$.

The construction of the completion $\hat{X}$ of X is deep, interesting, and well known.

If X is a space of functions, the elements of the completion $\hat{X}$ need not be functions. For example, if X is the space of continuous functions x on a compact line segment I, with norm

$$\|x\| = \int_I |x(s)|\, ds,$$

then X is not complete. Each element $\hat{x}$ of the completion $\hat{X}$ may be considered an equivalence set of integrable functions any two of which are equal almost everywhere on I [Zaanen 1, p. 73].

An advantage in the use of equivalence sets is that several spaces that we consider are separable as well as complete (cf. Chapters 9, 10).

3. Lemma. *Suppose that F is a linear continuous operator on a normed linear space X to a normed linear space Y. There is a unique extension $\hat{F}$*

of F which is a linear continuous operator on $\hat{X}$ to $\hat{Y}$ and which coincides with F on X, where $\hat{X}$, $\hat{Y}$ are the completions of X, Y, respectively. Furthermore the norm of $\hat{F}$ is precisely that of F.

PROOF. (Cf. [Zaanen 1, p. 134].) If $\hat{F}$ exists, it must have the following property:

$$\text{(4)} \qquad \text{If } \{x^\nu\} \in \hat{x} \in \hat{X}, \quad \text{then} \quad \{Fx^\nu\} \in \hat{F}\hat{x} \in \hat{Y},$$

because $\hat{F}$ is to be an extension of F and continuous. Now (4) does define an operator on $\hat{X}$ to $\hat{Y}$. Thus $\{Fx^\nu\}$ is a Cauchy sequence in Y, since

$$\|Fx^\nu - Fx^{\nu'}\|_Y \leqq \|F\| \, \|x^\nu - x^{\nu'}\|_X.$$

Furthermore if $\{\tilde{x}^\nu\}$ is a Cauchy sequence in X equivalent to $\{x^\nu\}$, then $\{F\tilde{x}^\nu\}$ is equivalent to $\{Fx^\nu\}$ in Y. If $x \in X$, then

$$\{Fx, Fx, \cdots\} \in \hat{F}\{x, x, \cdots\}.$$

Hence $\hat{F}$ is an extension of F.

Clearly $\hat{F}$ is linear on $\hat{X}$ to $\hat{Y}$. Finally, $\hat{F}$ is bounded, with bound $\|F\|$, since

$$\|\hat{F}\hat{x}\|_{\hat{Y}} = \lim_\nu \|Fx^\nu\|_Y \leqq \|F\| \lim_\nu \|x^\nu\|_X = \|F\| \, \|\hat{x}\|_{\hat{X}},$$

where $\{x^\nu\} \in \hat{x} \in \hat{X}$.

This completes our discussion of the proof.

§ 5. **Baire's theorem on category.** We shall state and prove Baire's theorem for Banach spaces (complete normed linear spaces). The discussion applies to any complete metric space, and is based on [Banach 1, p. 14]. The original theorem [Baire 1, p. 65] is essentially Theorem 8 below.

Consider a Banach space X. By a *sphere* in X we mean a set

$$\text{(6)} \qquad S = S(x^0, r) = \{x \in X : \|x - x^0\| < r\},$$

where $x^0 \in X$ and $r > 0$. We call x^0 the center and r the radius. Thus a sphere is open and has a positive radius. By a *closed sphere* we mean the closure of a sphere S; that is, a set

$$\hat{S} = \{x \in X : \|x - x^0\| \leqq r\}, \qquad x^0 \in X, \quad r > 0.$$

7. LEMMA. *For each monotone descending sequence of closed spheres whose radii approach zero, there exists a point common to all the closed spheres.*

This elementary lemma, sufficient for our purposes, is an instance of the theorem that a descending sequence of compact, closed, nonempty sets has a nonempty intersection [Hausdorff 1, p. 129].

PROOF. Let the sequence be $\{\hat{S}_\nu\}$, where S_ν is the closed sphere with center x^ν and radius r^ν. We are given that

$$\hat{S}_{\nu+1} \subset \hat{S}_\nu, \qquad r^\nu \to 0.$$

For any integers ν and ν' such that $\nu' > \nu$,

$$x^{\nu'} \in \hat{S}_{\nu'} \subset \hat{S}_{\nu};$$

hence

$$\|x^{\nu'} - x^{\nu}\| \leqq r^{\nu}.$$

It follows that $\{x^{\nu}\}$ is a Cauchy sequence. Since X is complete, $\{x^{\nu}\}$ converges to, say, x^0 in X.

Now x^0 is contained in all the closed spheres $\hat{S}_{\nu}$. Thus, for each ν,

$$\|x^0 - x^{\nu}\| \leqq \|x^0 - x^{\nu'}\| + \|x^{\nu'} - x^{\nu}\| \quad \text{for all } \nu';$$

hence

$$\|x^0 - x^{\nu}\| \leqq \|x^0 - x^{\nu'}\| + r^{\nu} \quad \text{for all } \nu' > \nu,$$

and

$$\|x^0 - x^{\nu}\| \leqq r^{\nu},$$

since we may let $\nu' \to \infty$. This completes the proof.

Consider a set $\Psi \subset X$. We say that Ψ is *nowhere dense* if the closure of Ψ contains no sphere. We say that Ψ is *meager* if Ψ is the union of countably many nowhere dense sets. We say that Ψ is *nonmeager* if Ψ is not meager. Meager and nonmeager sets are also called sets of the first and second category, respectively. Nowhere dense sets are also called rare.

8. THEOREM. *A Banach space is nonmeager.*

PROOF. We shall show that if a Banach space X is the union of countably many sets A_{ν}, $\nu = 1, 2, \cdots$, then the closure $\hat{A}_{\nu}$ of at least one of the sets A_{ν} must contain a sphere.

Assume the contrary. Then for each $\nu = 1, 2, \cdots$, $\hat{A}_{\nu}$ contains no sphere.

The complement $\hat{A}_1'$ of $\hat{A}_1$ is nonempty and open, else $\hat{A}_1$ would contain a sphere. Let S_1 be a sphere of radius $r^1 < 1$ such that the closure $\hat{S}_1$ is contained in $\hat{A}_1'$. Then

$$\hat{S}_1 \cap \hat{A}_1 = 0, \qquad r^1 < 1. \tag{9}$$

The open set $\hat{A}_2' \cap S_1$ also is nonempty, else $\hat{A}_2$ would contain the sphere S_1. Let S_2 be a sphere of radius $r^2 < 1/2$ such that the closure $\hat{S}_2$ is contained in $\hat{A}_2' \cap S_1$. Then

$$\hat{S}_2 \cap \hat{A}_2 = 0, \qquad \hat{S}_2 \subset \hat{S}_1, \qquad r^2 < \frac{1}{2}.$$

Continue in this fashion. Having constructed spheres $S_1, \cdots, S_k$, consider the open set $\hat{A}_{k+1}' \cap S_k$ which is surely nonempty, else $\hat{A}_{k+1}$ would contain the sphere S_k. Let S_{k+1} be a sphere of radius $r^{k+1} < 1/(k+1)$ such that the closure $\hat{S}_{k+1}$ is contained in $\hat{A}_{k+1}' \cap S_k$. Then

$$\hat{S}_{k+1} \cap \hat{A}_{k+1} = 0, \quad \hat{S}_{k+1} \subset \hat{S}_k, \quad r^{k+1} < \frac{1}{k+1}; \qquad k = 1, 2, \cdots. \tag{10}$$

By Lemma 7, there is a point x^0 in X common to all the spheres $\hat{S}_1, \hat{S}_2, \cdots$. By (9) and (10), x^0 is not an element of any one of the sets $\hat{A}_1, \hat{A}_2, \cdots$. This contradicts the hypothesis

$$X = A_1 \cup A_2 \cup \cdots;$$

and the proof is complete.

§ 11. The inverse of a linear continuous map. If a one-to-one map is continuous, its inverse is not necessarily continuous. For example the unit circumference in the plane is the one-to-one continuous image of a half open line segment, but not vice versa. It is of interest to consider what hypothesis on a one-to-one map will insure the continuity of the inverse. An elementary fact (which we do not use) is that compactness of domain is sufficient: The inverse of a one-to-one continuous map of a compact topological space into a topological space is surely continuous. As a normed linear space of more than one point is not compact, we need other criteria.

In 1929 Banach showed that linearity of the map and completeness of the image are sufficient. The precise statement is Theorem 14 below. Our treatment is based on [Banach 1, p. 41; Schauder 1].

In considering an operator F, we denote by $F(\Psi)$ the set

$$\{y : y = Fx \text{ and } x \in \Psi\}.$$

We call $F(\Psi)$ the *image* of Ψ. If X is the domain on which F is defined, we call $F(X)$ the *range* of F.

12. Lemma. *Suppose that the range $F(X)$ of a linear continuous operator F on a Banach space X into a Banach space Y is nonmeager. Then the image of each open sphere in X centered at the origin contains an open sphere in Y centered at the origin.*

Proof. Our usage of the term "sphere" requires that the radius be strictly positive and that the sphere be an open set. We divide the proof into three parts which deal respectively with the closure of the image, the derived set of the image, and the image itself.

Part 1. Let S_r denote the sphere in X with center at the origin and radius r. For any positive radii r and r',

$$F(S_{r'}) = \frac{r'}{r} F(S_r) = r' F(S_1),$$

since the operator F is linear. Thus the images $F(S_r)$ are identical, except for a positive scalar factor.

Now

$$X = \bigcup_{\nu=1, 2, \ldots} S_\nu,$$

since each x in X is within a finite distance $\|x\|$ of the origin in X. Hence

$$F(X) = F(\bigcup_\nu S_\nu) = \bigcup_\nu F(S_\nu).$$

Thus the range $F(X)$ is the union of countably many sets $F(S_\nu)$, $\nu = 1, 2, \cdots$. By hypothesis $F(X)$ is nonmeager. It follows that one of the sets $F(S_\nu)$ is not nowhere dense. For some integer ν_0, the closure $\hat{F}(S_{\nu_0})$ of $F(S_{\nu_0})$ contains a sphere. By similarity, then, for any $r > 0$, $\hat{F}(S_r)$ contains a sphere.

Part 2. We show next that the derived set of $F(S_r)$, that is, the set of limit points† of $F(S_r)$, contains a sphere centered at the origin in Y, if $r > 0$.

Consider $\hat{F}(S_1)$. By Part 1, there is a sphere T contained in $\hat{F}(S_1)$. Some point $\tilde{y}$ of T is the image $F\tilde{x}$ of a point $\tilde{x}$ in S_1. (Otherwise $F(S_1) \cap T = 0$ and $F(S_1) \subset T'$, where T', the complement of T, is closed. Then $\hat{F}(S_1) \subset T'$, which contradicts the fact that $T \subset \hat{F}(S_1)$.)

Let $\tilde{T}$ be a sphere with center $\tilde{y}$ contained in T. Consider the translations $S_1 - \tilde{x}$ and $F(S_1) - \tilde{y}$. Since F is linear,

$$F(S_1 - \tilde{x}) = F(S_1) - \tilde{y};$$

and, by closure,

$$\hat{F}(S_1 - \tilde{x}) = \hat{F}(S_1) - \tilde{y}.$$

Since $\hat{F}(S_1)$ contains $\tilde{T}$, $\hat{F}(S_1 - \tilde{x})$ contains $\tilde{T} - \tilde{y}$. But $\tilde{T} - \tilde{y}$ is a sphere U with center at the origin in Y. Now $\hat{F}(S_1 - \tilde{x})$ contains U. Let m be so large that S_m contains $S_1 - \tilde{x}$. Then $\hat{F}(S_m)$ contains U. By similarity, $\hat{F}(S_1)$ contains a sphere V with center at the origin in Y, and, for all $r > 0$, $\hat{F}(S_r)$ contains the sphere rV.

Furthermore, for each $r > 0$, each point of the open sphere rV is a limit point of $F(S_r)$. Otherwise a point z of rV would be an isolated point of $F(S_r)$ and the neighborhood of z could not be in the closure $\hat{F}(S_r)$, a contradiction of the fact that the neighborhood of z is in rV.

Part 3. We now complete the proof of the Lemma by showing that for each $\eta > 0$, there exists $\zeta > 0$ such that $F(S_\eta)$ includes the sphere T_ζ in Y with center at the origin and radius ζ. Thus put

$$\eta_i = \eta/2^i, \qquad i = 1, 2, \cdots.$$

We know that for each i there exists $\zeta_i > 0$ such that the derived set of $F(S_{\eta_i})$ contains T_{ζ_i}. Choose ζ_i so that, in addition, $\zeta_i \to 0$ as $i \to \infty$.

Now define sequences $\{x_\nu\}$ and $\{y_\nu\}$ by induction as follows.

Consider any element y of T_{ζ_1}. Since y is a limit point of $F(S_{\eta_1})$, there exist x_1 in X and y_1 in Y such that

$$y_1 = F(x_1), \qquad \|x_1\| < \eta_1, \quad \|y - y_1\| < \zeta_2.$$

Since $y - y_1 \in T_{\zeta_2}$, it follows that $y - y_1$ is a limit point of $F(S_{\eta_2})$.

† Points in any neighborhood of which there are infinitely many points of $F(S_r)$.

Hence x_2 in X and y_2 in Y exist such that

$$y_2 = F(x_2), \qquad \|x_2\| < \eta_2, \quad \|y - y_1 - y_2\| < \zeta_3.$$

Since $y - y_1 - y_2 \in T_{\zeta_3}$, it follows that $y - y_1 - y_2$ is a limit point of $F(S_{\eta_3})$. Hence x_3 in X and y_3 in Y exist such that

$$y_3 = F(x_3), \qquad \|x_3\| < \eta_3, \quad \|y - y_1 - y_2 - y_3\| < \zeta_4.$$

We continue in this fashion. Having defined $x_1, \cdots, x_k$; $y_1, \cdots, y_k$, we take x_{k+1} in X and y_{k+1} in Y such that

$$y_{k+1} = F(x_{k+1}), \qquad \|x_{k+1}\| < \eta_{k+1}, \quad \|y - y_1 - \cdots - y_{k+1}\| < \zeta_{k+2}.$$

Then

$$y = \sum_{\nu=1}^{\infty} y_\nu$$

and

$$\sum_{\nu=1}^{\infty} \|x_\nu\| < \sum \eta_\nu = \sum \eta/2^\nu = \eta.$$

Hence $\sum_{\nu=1}^{\infty} x_\nu$ is convergent in X; put

$$x = \sum_\nu x_\nu.$$

Then

$$\|x\| < \eta$$

and

$$Fx = F\sum_\nu x_\nu = \sum_\nu Fx_\nu = y.$$

The operations of this paragraph with infinite sums are readily justified [Banach 1, p. 37].

Thus each y in T_{ζ_1} is the image of an element x of S_η; that is, $F(S_\eta)$ includes T_{ζ_1}. This completes the proof of Part 3 since we may take $\zeta = \zeta_1$.

13. Theorem. *The range $F(X)$ of a linear continuous operator F on a Banach space X into a Banach space Y is either all of Y or else meager.*

Proof. If $F(X)$ is nonmeager, then $F(S_1)$ contains a sphere by Lemma 12, where S_r is the sphere in X with center at the origin and radius r. Hence $F(S_r)$ for sufficiently large r contains any point in Y. Hence $F(X) = Y$.

14. Theorem (Banach). *Suppose that F is a one-to-one, linear, continuous operator on a Banach space X onto all of a Banach space Y. Then the inverse of F is one-to-one, linear, and continuous on Y onto all of X.*

Proof. Since F is one-to-one, linear, and $F(X) = Y$, it follows that the inverse F^{-1} is one-to-one, linear, and $F^{-1}(Y) = X$.

It remains to show that F^{-1} is continuous. For this it is sufficient that F^{-1} be bounded. For this it is in turn sufficient that F^{-1} be bounded on the unit sphere T_1 in Y. By similarity and Lemma 12, there is a sphere S_r in X such that $F(S_r) \supset T_1$. Then $F^{-1}(T_1) \subset S_r$. That is, F^{-1} is bounded on T_1 with bound $r < \infty$. This proves the theorem.

15. REMARK. The results of this section are easily proved by means of dimension if either X or Y is finite dimensional. It is only when both X and Y are infinite dimensional that the above analysis is needed. Consider Theorem 13 for example. If Y is n-dimensional, $n < \infty$, then $F(X)$ being a linear manifold in Y is either n-dimensional or of dimension $< n$. In the former case, $F(X) = Y$; in the latter, $F(X)$ is nowhere dense in Y. If Y is infinite dimensional and X is m-dimensional, $m < \infty$, then $F(X)$ is of dimension $\leqq m$ and $F(X)$ is necessarily nowhere dense in Y.

§ 16. **The factor space X/X_0.** Suppose that X is a Banach space and that X_0 is a closed linear subspace of X. The *factor space*

$$M = X/X_0 = X \ (\text{mod } X_0)$$

is defined as follows. Each element m of M is a set (equivalence class) of elements of X, with

$$x_1 \in m, \quad x_2 \in m \quad \text{iff} \quad x_2 - x_1 \in X_0, \quad x_1 \in X, \quad x_2 \in X.$$

The *sum* $m_1 + m_2$ of m_1 and m_2, both in M, is the element of M which contains $x_1 + x_2$, where $x_1 \in m_1$ and $x_2 \in m_2$; the *scalar product* cm_1, $c \in \mathsf{N}$, is the element of M which contains cx_1. The *norm* of m in M is

$$(17) \qquad \|m\|_M = \inf_{x_0 \in X_0} \|x + x_0\|_X, \qquad x \in m$$

[Banach 1, p. 232; Zaanen 1, p. 99].

18. THEOREM. *The factor space X/X_0 of a Banach space X relative to a closed linear subspace X_0 is itself a Banach space.*

PROOF. *Part* 1. We show that the definitions are unambiguous. If

$$x_1, x_1' \in m_1 \in M; \qquad x_2, x_2' \in m_2 \in M;$$

then (i) $x_1 + x_2$ and $x_1' + x_2'$ are in the same element of M, since their difference is surely in X_0;

(ii) cx_1 and cx_1' are in the same element of M since their difference is in X_0, whenever $c \in \mathsf{N}$;

(iii) $\|m_1\|_M$ is the same whether x in (17) is taken as x_1 or x_1'.

Part 2. M is a linear space, and 0 in M is the element of M that contains 0 in X. If $m_1, m_2 \in M$ and $c \in \mathsf{N}$, then $m_1 + m_2 \in M$ and $cm_1 \in M$.

Part 3. M is a normed space, that is, the definition (17) satisfies the conditions (0)–(4) of § 3 : 2. Thus

$$\|0\|_M = \inf_{x_0 \in X_0} \|0 + x_0\|_X = \|0\|_X = 0.$$

Conversely suppose that

$$\|m\|_M = 0, \qquad m \in M.$$

We shall show that $m = 0$. Take x in m and a sequence $\{\eta_\nu\}$, $\nu = 1, 2, \cdots$, of positive numbers convergent to 0. By (17) there exists a sequence $\{x^\nu\}$ of elements of X_0 such that

$$\eta_\nu > \|x + x^\nu\|_X \to 0.$$

Hence $\{x^\nu\}$ converges to $-x$, and, since X_0 is closed, $-x \in X_0$. Hence $x \in X_0$ and $x - x = 0 \in m$. Hence $m = 0$.

That

$$\|cm\| = |c| \, \|m\|, \qquad m \in M, \quad c \in \mathsf{N},$$

is immediate.

Finally, we establish the triangle inequality:

$$\|m_1 + m_2\| \leqq \|m_1\| + \|m_2\|, \qquad m_1, m_2 \in M.$$

Given $\eta > 0$, take x_1, x_2 such that

$$\|x_1\| - \eta < \|m_1\| \leqq \|x_1\|, \qquad x_1 \in m_1;$$
$$\|x_2\| - \eta < \|m_2\| \leqq \|x_2\|, \qquad x_2 \in m_2.$$

Then

$$\|m_1 + m_2\|_M = \inf_{x_0 \in X_0} \|x_1 + x_2 + x_0\|_X \leqq \|x_1 + x_2\|_X \leqq \|x_1\|_X + \|x_2\|_X$$
$$< \|m_1\|_M + \|m_2\|_M + 2\eta.$$

Since η was arbitrary,

$$\|m_1 + m_2\| \leqq \|m_1\| + \|m_2\|.$$

Part 4. M is a complete space. Consider the map

$$f: X \to M$$

which carries x in X into m in M, where $x \in m \in M$. The map f is clearly linear and continuous, since the relation

$$\|m\|_M \leqq \|x\|_X$$

implies that f is bounded with bound $\leqq 1$. We shall use the map f to show that M is complete.

Suppose that $\{m_\nu\}$, $\nu = 1, 2, \cdots$, is a Cauchy sequence in M. Put $m_0 = 0 \in M$. We extract a subsequence $\{m_{\nu_i}\}$, $i = 1, 2, \cdots$, such that

$$\sum_i (m_{\nu_i} - m_{\nu_{i-1}})$$

is absolutely convergent, as follows. Put

$$\nu_0 = 0, \qquad m_{\nu_0} = m_0 = 0.$$

Take ν_1 so that

$$\|m_{\nu_1+p} - m_{\nu_1}\|_M < \frac{1}{2}, \qquad \nu_1 > \nu_0, \quad \text{all } p.$$

Take ν_2 so that

$$\|m_{\nu_2+p} - m_{\nu_2}\|_M < \frac{1}{4}, \qquad \nu_2 > \nu_1, \quad \text{all } p.$$

Continuing in this fashion, we obtain a subsequence $\{m_{\nu_i}\}$ such that

$$\|m_{\nu_{i+1}} - m_{\nu_i}\|_M < \frac{1}{2^i}, \qquad i = 1, 2, \cdots.$$

For brevity we now drop the extra subscript and write m_i instead of m_{ν_i}. Put

$$\Delta m_i = m_i - m_{i-1}, \qquad i = 1, 2, \cdots.$$

There are elements Δx_i, $i = 1, 2, \cdots$, and $x_0 = 0$, all in X, such that

$$\Delta m_i = f(\Delta x_i), \qquad \|\Delta m_i\|_M \leqq \|\Delta x_i\|_X < \|\Delta m_i\|_M + \frac{1}{2^i}, \quad i = 1, 2, \cdots.$$

Therefore

$$\sum_i \|\Delta x_i\|_X < \sum_i \left[\|\Delta m_i\|_M + \frac{1}{2^i}\right] < 2.$$

Put

$$x_i = \Delta x_1 + \Delta x_2 + \cdots + \Delta x_i.$$

Then $\{x_i\}$ is a Cauchy sequence in X, by the absolute convergence of the series $\sum_i \Delta x_i$, since

$$x_{i+p} - x_i = \Delta x_{i+1} + \Delta x_{i+2} + \cdots + \Delta x_p, \quad p > i.$$

Put

$$x = \lim_i x_i,$$

and

$$m = f(x) \in M.$$

Since f is linear and continuous,

$$m = \lim_i m_i.$$

Thus the subsequence $\{m_i\}$ has the limit m in M. Hence also the original sequence $\{m_\nu\}$ has the limit m in M. Thus M is complete. The theorem is proved.

§ 19. **The quotient theorem.** The present section is of fundamental importance in the theory of approximation, as we shall see.

20. THEOREM. *Suppose that X, $\tilde{X}$, Y are Banach spaces, that U is a linear continuous operator on X onto all of $\tilde{X}$, and that R is a linear continuous operator on X to Y. If*

$$Rx = 0 \quad \textit{whenever} \quad Ux = 0, \quad x \in X, \tag{21}$$

then there exists a linear continuous operator Q on $\tilde{X}$ to Y such that

$$Rx = QUx, \qquad x \in X. \tag{22}$$

An essential feature of the conclusion is that the operator Q whose existence is affirmed is continuous. We may think of Q as the quotient R/U. The theorem is due to Sard [1]. Earlier results in the literature were more restricted. For example, several authors proved the theorem in the case in which U is a linear differential operator

$$D_s^n + a_1 D_s^{n-1} + \cdots + a_n, \qquad a_1, \cdots, a_n \in C_0,$$

on C_n. Cf. § 32.

It is immediate that conversely (22) implies (21) if Q is a linear operator, for then $Q0 = 0$.

The fact that

$$U(X) = \tilde{X}$$

implies that Q, if existent, is unique: If $\tilde{x} \in \tilde{X}$, then the value $Q\tilde{x}$ is the unique value Rx, where $\tilde{x} = Ux$.

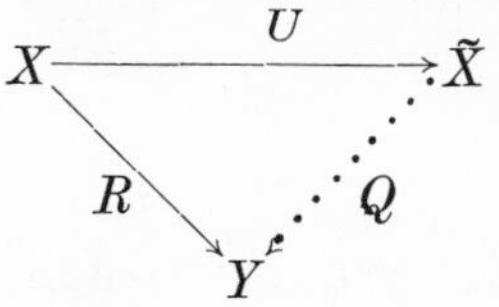

PROOF OF THEOREM. Let X_0 be the subspace of X on which U vanishes:

$$X_0 = \{x \in X : Ux = 0\}.$$

The continuity of U implies that X_0 is closed; the linearity of U implies that X_0 is linear. We may therefore consider the factor space

$$M = X \ (\text{mod } X_0) = X/X_0.$$

We now define operators $\tilde{U}$ and $\tilde{R}$ on M as follows:

$$\tilde{U}m = Ux, \qquad \tilde{R}m = Rx,$$

where

$$x \in m \in M.$$

Observe first that $\tilde{U}$ and $\tilde{R}$ are well defined. Thus if $x' \in m$, then

$$x - x' \in X_0, \qquad U(x - x') = 0, \qquad Ux = Ux'.$$

Hence also $Rx = Rx'$, since $U(x - x') = 0$ implies that $R(x - x') = 0$. Now $\tilde{U}$ and $\tilde{R}$ are clearly additive. Furthermore $\tilde{U}$ and $\tilde{R}$ are bounded operators. Thus for any m in M and any $\eta > 0$, take x so that

$$x \in m, \qquad \|x\|_X - \eta < \|m\|_M \leqq \|x\|_X.$$

Then

$$\|\tilde{U}m\|_{\tilde{X}} = \|Ux\|_{\tilde{X}} \leqq \|U\| \, \|x\|_X \leqq \|U\|[\|m\|_M + \eta].$$

Since η is arbitrary,

$$\|\tilde{U}m\|_{\tilde{X}} \leqq \|U\| \, \|m\|_M.$$

Likewise $\tilde{R}$ is bounded. Hence $\tilde{U}$ and $\tilde{R}$ are linear continuous operators on M to $\tilde{X}$ and Y, respectively.

Furthermore $\tilde{U}$ carries M onto all of $\tilde{X}$, since

$$\tilde{U}(M) = U(X) = \tilde{X}.$$

Finally $\tilde{U}$ is one-to-one: If

$$\tilde{U}m = 0, \qquad m \in M,$$

then

$$Ux = 0, \quad \text{for all } x \text{ in } m;$$

hence m contains elements of X_0, by the definition of X_0, and therefore $m = 0$. Hence $\tilde{U}$ is one-to-one.

It follows that we may apply Theorem 14 to $\tilde{U}$. The inverse $\tilde{U}^{-1}$ of $\tilde{U}$ is a linear continuous operator on $\tilde{X}$ to M.

If $x \in m \in M$, then

$$Ux = \tilde{U}m,$$
$$\tilde{U}^{-1}Ux = \tilde{U}^{-1}\tilde{U}m = m,$$
$$\tilde{R}\tilde{U}^{-1}Ux = \tilde{R}m = Rx.$$

Hence

$$Rx = QUx, \qquad x \in X,$$

where

$$Q = \tilde{R}\tilde{U}^{-1}.$$

Thus Q is linear and continuous, since $\tilde{R}$ and $\tilde{U}^{-1}$ both are; and the theorem is proved.

23. Remark. The condition that $U(X)$ be complete is essential to the quotient theorem. Suppose that the normed linear space $U(X)$ is not assumed to be complete but that all the other hypotheses of the quotient theorem hold. Then much of the proof remains valid. There exists a unique linear operator Q on $U(X)$ to Y such that

$$Rx = QUx, \qquad x \in X;$$

and the operator Q is closed (its graph in $U(X) \times Y$ is a closed set), but Q is not necessarily continuous [Zaanen 1, p. 163].

An example is the following:

$$I = \{\alpha \leqq s \leqq \tilde{\alpha}\},$$
$$X = Y = C_0 = C_0(I),$$
$$Rx = x, \qquad x \in X,$$

$$Ux = \int_\alpha^t x(s)\, ds, \qquad x \in X, \tag{24}$$

and $\tilde{X} = U(X)$ is the space of all functions of the form (24) considered as a subspace of X. Thus the norm $\|\tilde{x}\|$ of an element $\tilde{x}$ in $\tilde{X}$ is to be precisely its norm in C_0. Here X and Y are Banach spaces; $\tilde{X}$ is a normed linear space; R and U are linear continuous operators; and $U(X) = \tilde{X}$. Also

$$Rx = 0 \quad \text{whenever} \quad Ux = 0, \quad x \in X.$$

Thus the hypothesis of Theorem 20, except for the completeness of $\tilde{X}$, is in force.

The unique operator Q is $d/dt = D_t$:

$$Rx = QUx = \frac{d}{dt} \int_{\alpha}^{t} x(s)\, ds, \qquad x \in X.$$

The operator Q is linear on $\tilde{X}$ to Y and closed; but Q is not continuous, since two continuously differentiable functions in C_0 which are close relative to the norm in C_0 may nonetheless have derivatives which are very different.

We may alter the example by considering $\tilde{X}$ as a subspace of $C_1 = C_1(I)$. The norm of $\tilde{x}$ in $\tilde{X}$ is then equivalent to

$$|||\tilde{x}|||_{C_1} = \max\,[\sup|\tilde{x}(s)|, \sup|\tilde{x}_1(s)|].$$

Then $\tilde{X}$ is a complete space and the theorem applies. The operator Q is then continuous, since differentiation is indeed continuous relative to the norm in C_1.

§ 25. **Import of the quotient theorem.** The conclusion of Theorem 20 allows us to express Rx in terms of Ux by an exact formula

$$Rx = QUx, \qquad x \in X. \tag{26}$$

Furthermore the form of the operator Q on $\tilde{X}$ to Y is often known and accessible, since the form of Q is determined by the nature of the spaces $\tilde{X}$ and Y. We will illuminate this remark by examples in later sections.

The relation (26) implies that

$$\|Rx\| \leq \|Q\|\,\|Ux\|, \qquad x \in X; \tag{27}$$

and this appraisal is sharp. In particular, Rx will be small when Ux is small.

Consider the hypothesis of Theorem 20. Suppose that R is given as linear and continuous on the Banach space X to the Banach space Y. We may then search for an operator U such that

(28)
- (i) The image $\tilde{X} = U(X)$ is a Banach space (complete, normed, and linear).
- (ii) U is linear and continuous on X to $\tilde{X} = U(X)$.
- (iii) $Rx = 0$ whenever $Ux = 0$, $x \in X$.

If we find such an operator U, we may apply Theorem 20.

In the reverse direction, suppose that U is given and satisfies (i) and (ii). We may then search for a procedure of approximation in which the remainder R will satisfy (iii) and will be linear and continuous on X to Y.

§ 29. **An instance in which $U = D_s^n$.** Take

$$\begin{aligned} I &= \{\alpha \leqq s \leqq \tilde{\alpha}\}, \\ X &= C_n(I) = C_n, \\ U &= \left(\frac{d}{ds}\right)^n = D_s^n, \\ \tilde{X} &= U(X) = C_0(I) = C_0, \\ Y &= \mathsf{R} = \text{the real numbers.} \end{aligned}$$

Since R and Q will be operators to Y, they will be functionals. Suppose that Rx is the remainder in an approximate integration or another sort of approximation, and is such that

$$R \in C_n^*,$$

that is, R is a linear continuous functional on C_n. Suppose that $Rx = 0$ whenever $x(s)$ is a polynomial of degree $n - 1$. This last condition, so frequent in the literature, is precisely the following:

$$Rx = 0 \quad \text{whenever} \quad Ux = 0,$$

since $Ux = x_n(s)$, and a necessary and sufficient condition that $x(s)$ be a polynomial of degree $n - 1$ is that $Ux = 0$.

By Theorem 20, Q exists on $\tilde{X}$ to Y such that

$$Rx = QUx = Qx_n, \qquad x \in C_n.$$

Now Q, being linear and continuous on $\tilde{X}$ to Y, is an element of C_0^* and so may be expressed as a Stieltjes integral by Theorem 3 : 34. Thus, for suitable λ in V^0,

$$Rx = \int_I x_n(s)\, d\lambda(s), \qquad x \in C_n.$$

This is in accordance with the conclusion of Theorem 3 : 39. The coefficients c^i, $i < n$, all vanish by (3 : 40), since $R = F$ vanishes for degree $n - 1$.

§ 30. **A related instance.** We may modify the previous illustration so as to obtain all of Theorem 3 : 39 from the quotient theorem. Take

$$\begin{aligned} I &= \{\alpha \leqq s \leqq \tilde{\alpha}\}, \qquad a \in I, \\ X &= C_n(I) = C_n, \\ \tilde{X} &= \text{the direct product of } n \text{ real lines } \mathsf{R} \text{ and } C_0(I) = C_0. \end{aligned}$$

Thus $\tilde{x} \in \tilde{X}$ means that

$$\tilde{x} = \{\tilde{x}^i, i < n; \tilde{x}^n(s)\},$$

where

$$\tilde{x}^i \in \mathsf{R}, \quad i < n, \quad \text{and} \quad \tilde{x}^n(s) \in C_0.$$

The norm of $\tilde{x}$ in $\tilde{X}$ is

$$\|\tilde{x}\|_{\tilde{X}} = \max\,[|\tilde{x}^i|,\ i < n;\ \|\tilde{x}^n\|_{C_0}].$$

Suppose that U is the operator on X to $\tilde{X}$ such that

$$Ux = \{x_i(a),\ i < n;\ x_n(s)\}, \qquad x \in C_n.$$

Take

$$Y = \mathsf{R},$$
$$R \in C_n^*.$$

Then U is linear and continuous on C_n to $\tilde{X}$ and, by Taylor's formula (3 : 80),

$$U(C_n) = \tilde{X}.$$

Also by Taylor's formula,

$$Ux = 0, \quad x \in C_n \quad \text{implies that } x = 0.$$

Hence

$$Rx = R0 = 0 \quad \text{whenever} \quad Ux = 0, \quad x \in C_n.$$

It follows that the quotient theorem applies: there is a linear continuous functional Q on $\tilde{X}$ such that

$$Rx = QUx, \qquad x \in C_n.$$

Now the general form of a linear continuous functional on a direct product is the sum of linear continuous functionals on the factors (an immediate consequence of linearity and the definition of the norm on the direct product). Hence Rx is the sum of terms

$$c^i x_i(a), \qquad i < n; \qquad \int_I x_n(s)\, d\lambda(s),$$

where $c^i \in \mathsf{R}$ and $\lambda \in V^0$. This gives (3 : 42) with $R = F$. Further study of Q would establish (3 : 40, 41).

§ 31. **Related instances involving functions of several variables.** In a similar fashion, we may deduce Theorem 6 : 14 from the quotient theorem as follows. We take

$I = I_s \times I_t,$

$X = B =$ a space with pivot $x_{p,q}(s, t), \qquad (s, t \in I),$

$\tilde{X} =$ the direct product of $B_{0,0}(I)$ and q spaces $C_0(I_s)$ and p spaces $C_0(I_t)$ and k spaces R, where k is the number of elements in $\omega_{a,b}$;

$$Ux = \{x_{i,j}(a, b),\ (i, j) \in \bar{\omega}_{a,b};\ x_{i,j}(s, b),\ (i, j) \in \bar{\omega}_{s,b};$$
$$x_{i,j}(a, t),\ (i, j) \in \bar{\omega}_{a,t};\ x_{p,q}(s, t)\}, \qquad x \in X,$$

$Y = \mathsf{R},$

$F \in B^*.$

The quotient theorem now leads to Theorem 6: 14, because of Theorem 4: 55.

§ 32. **U a linear homogeneous differential operator.** We next consider an instance similar to that of § 29 in which however D_s^n is replaced by a linear homogeneous differential expression

$$U = D_s^n + a^1(s)\, D_s^{n-1} + \cdots + a^n(s),$$

where

$$a^1, \cdots, a^n \in C_0(I), \quad I = \{\alpha \leqq s \leqq \tilde{\alpha}\}.$$

Take

$$X = C_n(I) = C_n, \qquad \tilde{X} = C_0(I) = C_0, \qquad Y = \mathsf{R}.$$

Then

$$U(X) = C_0(I).$$

Thus $Ux \in C_0$ if $x \in C_n$. Conversely given y in C_0, the equation $Ux = y$ has solutions x in C_n.

Now suppose that $R \in C_n^*$ and that

$$Rx = 0 \quad \text{whenever} \quad Ux = 0, \quad x \in C_n.$$

The quotient theorem implies that

$$Rx = QUx = Q[x_n + a^1x_{n-1} + \cdots + a^n], \qquad x \in C_n,$$

where subscripts indicate derivatives and Q is a linear continuous functional on C_0. Theorem 3: 34 applies to Q and may be used to obtain an explicit integral formula for Q [Radon 2; Rémès 1, 2].

§ 33. **An instance related to approximation by least squares in terms of solutions of a linear homogeneous differential equation.** Consider a *linear homogeneous differential operator*

$$U = D_s^n + a^1(s)D_s^{n-1} + \cdots + a^n(s); \tag{34}$$

where

$$a^1, \cdots, a^n \in C_0(I), \qquad I = \{\alpha \leqq s \leqq \tilde{\alpha}\}.$$

Let

$$\phi^1(s), \quad \phi^2(s), \cdots, \phi^n(s), \quad s \in I, \tag{35}$$

be n *independent solutions of the differential equation* $Ux = 0$, that is, the equation

$$x_n + a^1x_{n-1} + \cdots + a^nx = 0. \tag{36}$$

Suppose that we wish to approximate an arbitrary function $x(s) \in C_n = C_n(I)$

by a linear combination $y(s)$ of the functions (35). A useful and reasonable procedure is to *choose* y *so that the integral*

$$J = \int_I |x(s) - y(s)|^2 \, dm(s)$$

is minimal, where $m(s)$ is a *given nondecreasing function* on I. The rôle of $m(s)$ is that $dm(s)$ measures the importance of the approximation at s: the greater $dm(s)$, the more is y required to approximate x at s. Thus $dm(s)$ may equal the ordinary differential ds, or $dm(s)$ may be of the form $p(s)\,ds$ where $p(s)$ is nonnegative, Lebesgue measurable, and bounded. Alternatively $m(s)$ may include positive jumps. We assume that

$$m(I) = \int_I dm(s) > 0;$$

otherwise J would vanish identically.

We have taken x as an element of C_n because we will later deal with the nth derivative of x. It would be sufficient in Theorem 40 below to specify merely that x be measurable and that $|x|^2$ be integrable.

The linear combinations of the functions (35) constitute a linear subspace $\mathscr{M} \subset C_n$. In our approximation of x by y we specify that y be an element of $\mathscr{M}$. Whether y be expressed in terms of the functions (35) or in terms of an equivalent set is unessential. It is advantageous to replace the functions (35) by an equivalent set

$$\xi^1(s), \quad \xi^2(s), \cdots, \xi^n(s), \quad s \in I, \tag{37}$$

of the following sort:

$$\xi^i \in \mathscr{M}, \qquad i = 1, \cdots, n; \tag{38}$$

$$(\xi^i, \xi^j) = \delta^{i,j} = \begin{cases} 0 & \text{if } i \neq j, \\ 1 & \text{if } i = j, \end{cases} \qquad i, j = 1, \cdots, n;$$

where

$$(u, v) = \int_I u(s)\bar{v}(s)\, dm(s) \tag{39}$$

and $\bar{v}$ stands for the complex conjugate of v. In the real case the sign of conjugation may be omitted.

Functions (37) may be constructed from the functions (35) by the usual Schmidt process (§ 9: 60) in various ways. In the language of the next chapter, the functions (37) span $\mathscr{M}$ and are orthonormal relative to the inner product (39).

We have assumed that the functions (35) are independent in C_n. If the measure m is very simple, it may nonetheless occur that the functions (35) are dependent relative to the inner product (39), in which case the Schmidt process would produce fewer than n elements in its orthonormal set. We *assume* specifically *that the set* (38) *does have n elements.* This amounts to a modest restriction on m. In practice the execution of the Schmidt process of orthogonalization on the functions (35) will of itself reveal whether the orthonormal set that spans $\mathscr{M}$ has n elements or fewer. If fewer, the program of approximating x in terms of the functions (35) would doubtless be changed. One would either use fewer functions (35) or a different m.

40. THEOREM. *There is a unique operator A on C_0 to $\mathscr{M}$ such that*

$$y = Ax,$$

is the element of $\mathscr{M}$ which minimizes the integral

$$J = \int_I |x(s) - y(s)|^2 \, dm(s)$$

for each x in C_0. Furthermore A is linear and continuous; and

$$y(t) = \int_I x(s)a(s, t) \, dm(s), \qquad x \in C_0, \quad t \in I, \tag{41}$$

where

$$a(s, t) = \sum_{i=1}^{n} \bar{\xi}^i(s)\xi^i(t). \tag{42}$$

PROOF. Theorem 9 : 34 of the next chapter implies the present theorem. A direct proof is as follows.

Consider a given element x of C_0. Put

$$\begin{aligned} c^i &= \int x(s)\bar{\xi}^i(s) \, dm(s), \qquad i = 1, \cdots, n; \\ z(t) &= \sum_i c^i \xi^i(t), \\ y(t) &= \sum_i b^i \xi^i(t), \qquad t \in I, \quad b_i \in \mathsf{C}. \end{aligned}$$

Here and elsewhere in the present section integrals are taken over I unless otherwise indicated. Consider $b^1, \cdots, b^n$ as variables. Then y varies over $\mathscr{M}$. We shall show that J takes on a minimum when $y = z$ and only then. Thus

$$\begin{aligned} J &= \int |x - y|^2 \, dm = \int |x - z + z - y|^2 \, dm \\ &= \int |x - z|^2 \, dm + \int (x - z)(\bar{z} - \bar{y}) \, dm + \int (\bar{x} - \bar{z})(z - y) \, dm + \int |z - y|^2 \, dm \\ &= \int |x - z|^2 \, dm + \int |z - y|^2 \, dm, \end{aligned}$$

since

$$\int (x - z)(\bar{z} - \bar{y})\, dm = \sum_j (\bar{c}^j - \bar{b}^j) \int (x - z)\bar{\xi}^j\, dm$$
$$= \sum_j (\bar{c}^j - \bar{b}^j) \left[c^j - \sum_i c^i\, \delta^{i,j} \right] = \sum_j (\bar{c}^j - \bar{b}^j) \cdot 0 = 0$$

and

$$\int (\bar{x} - \bar{z})(z - y)\, dm = 0.$$

Hence J is minimal iff

$$\int |z - y|^2\, dm = 0;$$

that is,

$$\int \left| \sum_i (c^i - b^i)\xi^i \right|^2 dm = \sum_i |c^i - b^i|^2 = 0$$

or

$$c^i = b^i, \qquad i = 1, \cdots, n.$$

But this last condition is precisely (41), because of (42). Thus (41) is established.

The linearity of the operator A follows from (41).

Since the functions ξ^i, $i = 1, \cdots, n$, are elements of C_n, (41) implies also that A is bounded in the strong sense that

$$|||y|||_{C_n} \leqq N \|x\|_{C_0}, \qquad x \in C_0,$$

where

$$N = \sup_{\substack{t \in I, \\ j=0, \cdots, n}} \int_I |D_t^j a(s, t)|\, dm(s).$$

Hence A considered as an operator on C_0 to C_n is continuous.

This completes the proof.

The functions $\xi^1, \cdots, \xi^n$ are, by construction, orthonormal relative to the inner product (39) and are solutions of the differential equation

$$Ux = x_n + a^1 x_{n-1} + a^2 x_{n-2} + \cdots + a^n x = 0.$$

Furthermore $\xi^1, \cdots, \xi^n$ are independent solutions. For if

$$\sum_i c^i \xi^i(s) = 0, \qquad s \in I_s, \quad c^i \in \mathsf{C},$$

then

$$\int |\sum_i c^i \xi^i|^2\, dm = 0 = \sum_i |c^i|^2$$

and

$$c^i = 0, \qquad i = 1, \cdots, n.$$

Let us now study the least square approximation Ax of x. Put

$$Rx = x - Ax, \qquad x \in C_n \subset C_0.$$

Then the operator R is linear and continuous on C_n to C_n. Now the operator U is linear and continuous on C_n to C_0. Furthermore

$$Ux = 0, \quad x \in C_n \quad \text{implies that } Rx = 0.$$

For $Ux = 0$, $x \in C_n$, implies that $x \in \mathcal{M}$. Then the approximation $y = x$ of x certainly minimizes J. Hence $Ax = x$ and $Rx = 0$.

Put

$$\tilde{X} = U(C_n).$$

Then $\tilde{X} \subset C_0$, and, conversely, $C_0 \subset \tilde{X}$, since the equation

$$Ux = \tilde{x}, \qquad \tilde{x} \in C_0,$$

may always be solved for x in C_n. Thus $\tilde{X} = C_0$ and $\tilde{X}$ is a complete space.

The hypothesis of the quotient theorem is therefore satisfied, with

$$Y = X = C_n, \qquad \tilde{X} = C_0.$$

Hence there exists a linear continuous operator Q on C_0 to C_n such that

$$(43) \qquad Rx = QUx, \qquad x \in X.$$

The error committed in the approximation of x by least squares is entirely determined by Ux, and is determined in the simple fashion indicated by (43).

We shall express Q as an integral.

In considering elements $x, \tilde{x}, y$ of $X, \tilde{X}, Y$, we will designate their independent variables as $s, \tilde{s}, t$, respectively:

$$(44) \qquad x(s) \in X, \quad \tilde{x}(\tilde{s}) \in \tilde{X}, \quad y(t) \in Y; \qquad s, \tilde{s}, t \in I.$$

Since $\xi^1, \cdots, \xi^n$ are linearly independent solutions of the equation $Ux = 0$, we know that, for each $\tilde{x} \in \tilde{X}$, the solution x of the equation $Ux = \tilde{x}$ which vanishes together with its first $n - 1$ derivatives at $s = \alpha$ is

$$(45) \qquad x(s) = \int_\alpha^s \tilde{x}(\tilde{s}) g(\tilde{s}, s)\, d\tilde{s}, \qquad \tilde{x} \in C_0, \quad s \in I,$$

where

$$(46) \quad g(\tilde{s}, s) = \begin{vmatrix} \xi^1(\tilde{s}) & \xi^2(\tilde{s}) & \cdots & \xi^n(\tilde{s}) \\ \xi^1_1(\tilde{s}) & \xi^2_1(\tilde{s}) & \cdots & \xi^n_1(\tilde{s}) \\ \vdots & & & \\ \xi^1_{n-2}(\tilde{s}) & \xi^2_{n-2}(\tilde{s}) & \cdots & \xi^n_{n-2}(\tilde{s}) \\ \xi^1(s) & \xi^2(s) & \cdots & \xi^n(s) \end{vmatrix} \div \begin{vmatrix} \xi^1(\tilde{s}) & \cdots & \xi^n(\tilde{s}) \\ \xi^1_1(\tilde{s}) & \cdots & \xi^n_1(\tilde{s}) \\ \vdots & & \\ \xi^1_{n-1}(\tilde{s}) & \cdots & \xi^n_{n-1}(\tilde{s}) \end{vmatrix}$$

and subscripts indicate derivatives [Goursat 1]. Alternative descriptions of g may be given. For example, $g(\tilde{s}, s)$, for each fixed $\tilde{s}$, is the solution of $Ux = 0$ which vanishes together with its first $n - 2$ derivatives at $s = \tilde{s}$ and whose $(n - 1)$th derivative equals 1 at $s = \tilde{s}$.

47. THEOREM. *In the approximation of $x(t)$, $t \in I$, by a solution of the differential equation*

$$x_n + a^1 x_{n-1} + \cdots + a^n x = 0, \qquad a^1, \cdots, a^n \in C_0(I),$$

according to the criterion of least squares relative to the measure $m(s)$ on I, the remainder is

$$(48) \quad Rx = \int_I [x_n(\tilde{s}) + a^1(\tilde{s})x_{n-1}(\tilde{s}) + \cdots + a^n(\tilde{s})x(\tilde{s})]\lambda(\tilde{s}, t)\, d\tilde{s}, \quad t \in I; \qquad x \in C_n(I);$$

where the kernel λ is

$$(49) \qquad \lambda(\tilde{s}, t) = \begin{cases} -\displaystyle\int_{\tilde{s}}^{\tilde{\alpha}} g(\tilde{s}, s)a(s, t)\, dm(s) & \text{if } \alpha \leqq t \leqq \tilde{s}, \\ g(\tilde{s}, t) - \displaystyle\int_{\tilde{s}}^{\tilde{\alpha}} g(\tilde{s}, s)a(s, t)\, dm(s) & \text{if } \tilde{s} < t \leqq \tilde{\alpha}; \end{cases}$$

$a(s, t)$ is given by (42), *and $I = \{\alpha \leqq s \leqq \tilde{\alpha}\}$.*

Observe that (48) is an integral form of (43). The remainder Rx is given exactly for all $t \in I$.

PROOF. We know that (43) holds with Q a linear continuous operator on C_0 to C_n. For each fixed t in I, Q is therefore a linear continuous functional on C_0, to which we may apply Theorem 3: 34. Hence, by (3: 35, 36),

$$(50) \qquad Q\tilde{x} = \int_I \tilde{x}(\tilde{s})\, d_{\tilde{s}}\gamma(\tilde{s}, t), \qquad \tilde{x} \in C_0,$$

where

$$(51) \qquad \gamma(s', t) = \begin{cases} \lim\limits_{\nu} Q\, \theta^\nu(s', \tilde{s}) & \text{if } s' > \alpha, \\ 0 & \text{otherwise.} \end{cases}$$

Put

$$(52) \qquad z^\nu(s', s) = \int_\alpha^s \theta^\nu(s', u)g(u, s)\, du,$$

an instance of (45). Then for each fixed s', $z^\nu(s', s)$ is a solution of the equation

$$Uz^\nu(s', s) = \theta^\nu(s', \tilde{s}).$$

By (43) and (41),

$$(53) \qquad \begin{aligned} Q\theta^\nu(s', \tilde{s}) &= QUz^\nu(s', s) = Rz^\nu(s', s) \\ &= z^\nu(s', t) - \int_I z^\nu(s', s)a(s, t)\, dm(s). \end{aligned}$$

Now, by (52) and (11 : 3),

$$(54)\quad z(s', s) \underset{\text{def}}{=} \lim_{\nu} z^{\nu}(s', s) = \int_{\alpha}^{s} \theta(s', u) g(u, s)\, du = \begin{cases} \displaystyle\int_{\alpha}^{s} g(u, s)\, du \text{ if } s < s', \\ \displaystyle\int_{\alpha}^{s'} g(u, s)\, du \text{ if } s' < s. \end{cases}$$

Hence, by (51) and (53), for $s' > \alpha$,

$$(55)\qquad \gamma(s', t) = z(s', t) - \int_I z(s', s) a(s, t)\, dm(s).$$

Furthermore (55) is valid for $s' = \alpha$ also, since it then reduces to

$$\gamma(\alpha, t) = z(\alpha, t) - \int_I z(\alpha, s) a(s, t)\, dm(s),$$

which vanishes because

$$z(\alpha, s) = \int_{\alpha}^{s} \theta(\alpha, u) g(u, s)\, du = \int_{\alpha}^{s} 0\, du = 0, \qquad \alpha \leqq s,$$

by (11 : 3).

By (55) and (54), $\gamma(s', t)$ is absolutely continuous in s' for each fixed t; and

$$\frac{\partial z(s', s)}{\partial s'} = \begin{cases} 0 & \text{if } s < s', \\ g(s', s) & \text{if } s' < s; \end{cases}$$

and

$$d_{s'} \gamma(s', t) = ds' \left[\frac{\partial z(s', t)}{\partial s'} - \int_I \frac{\partial z(s', s)}{\partial s'} a(s, t)\, dm(s) \right]$$
$$= \lambda(s', t)\, ds',$$

where

$$\lambda(s', t) = \begin{cases} \displaystyle -\int_{s'}^{\tilde{\alpha}} g(s', s) a(s, t)\, dm(s) & \text{if } \alpha \leqq t < s', \\ \displaystyle g(s', t) - \int_{s'}^{\tilde{\alpha}} g(s', s) a(s, t)\, dm(s) & \text{if } s' < t \leqq \tilde{\alpha}. \end{cases}$$

As the values of $\lambda(s', t)$ when $t = s'$ are immaterial, this establishes (48) and (49) and completes the proof.

§ 56. **A particular trigonometric approximation.** We now cite an instance of the approximation considered in the preceding section. Let

$$I = \{-\pi \leqq s \leqq \pi\}, \qquad dm(s) = ds, \qquad n = 3.$$

For any x in $C_3 = C_3(I)$, we approximate $x(s)$ by that linear combination $y(s)$ of

$$\text{(57)} \qquad 1, \quad \cos s, \quad \sin s$$

which minimizes

$$J = \int_{-\pi}^{\pi} |x - y|^2 \, ds.$$

As the functions (57) are three independent solutions of the homogeneous linear differential equation

$$x_3(s) + x_1(s) = 0$$

of order 3, we will express the error in the approximation of x by y as an integral of

$$x_3(s) + x_1(s), \qquad x \in C_3.$$

Thus

$$U = D_s(D_s^2 + 1).$$

We replace the functions (57) by the set

$$\xi^1(s) = \frac{1}{(2\pi)^{1/2}}, \qquad \xi^2(s) = \frac{\cos s}{\pi^{1/2}}, \qquad \xi^3(s) = \frac{\sin s}{\pi^{1/2}},$$

orthonormal on I relative to ds. By (41), (42),

$$y(t) = \int_{-\pi}^{\pi} x(s) a(s, t) \, ds, \qquad t \in I, \quad x \in C_3,$$

where

$$a(s, t) = \frac{1}{2\pi} + \frac{\cos s \cos t}{\pi} + \frac{\sin s \sin t}{\pi} = \frac{1}{\pi}\left(\frac{1}{2} + \cos (s - t)\right).$$

The remainder in the approximation of x by y is

$$Rx = x(t) - y(t) = x - Ax = \int_{-\pi}^{\pi} [x_3(s) + x_1(s)] \lambda(s, t) \, ds, \quad t \in I, \ x \in C_3,$$

where

$$\text{(58)} \quad \lambda(s', t) = \begin{cases} -\dfrac{1}{\pi} \displaystyle\int_{s'}^{\pi} [1 - \cos (s - s')][.5 + \cos (s - t)] \, ds \\ \qquad\qquad \text{if } -\pi \leqq t \leqq s', \\ 1 - \cos (t - s') - \dfrac{1}{\pi} \displaystyle\int_{s'}^{\pi} [1 - \cos (s - s')][.5 + \cos (s - t)] \, ds \\ \qquad\qquad \text{if } s' < t \leqq \pi, \end{cases}$$

since

$$g(\tilde{s}, s) = 1 - \cos (s - \tilde{s})$$

by (49) and (46) or its alternative. Clearly for each fixed $\tilde{s}$, $g(\tilde{s}, s)$ as written is the solution of $Ux = 0$ such that

$$g(\tilde{s}, \tilde{s}) = 0, \qquad g_{0,1}(\tilde{s}, \tilde{s}) = 0, \qquad g_{0,2}(\tilde{s}, \tilde{s}) = 1.$$

The relation (58) may be transformed by, for example, introducing the variable of integration $u = s - s'$. Thus,

$$\begin{aligned}\lambda(s, t) = {} & [1 - \cos(t - s)]\theta(t, s) \\ & - \frac{1}{2\pi}[(\pi - s)\{1 - \cos(s - t)\} - \sin s + 2\sin t \\ & \qquad + 2\cos s \sin t - \sin s \cos t],\end{aligned}$$

where the step function $\theta(t, s)$ is given by (11 : 3).

§ 59. **A case in which U involves difference operators.** We have seen that U may be an operator of the form

$$D_s^n + a^1(s)D_s^{n-1} + \cdots + a^n(s); \qquad a^1, \cdots, a^n \in C_0.$$

In a similar fashion, U may be a linear homogeneous difference operator

$$U = \Delta^n + a^1(s)\Delta^{n-1} + \cdots + a^n(s); \qquad a^1, \cdots, a^n \in C_0;$$

where

$$\Delta x(s) = x(s + 1) - x(s).$$

A simple example is the following: X is the space $C_0[0, 3]$ of functions continuous on $\{0 \leqq s \leqq 3\}$;

$$Ux = \Delta x = x(s + 1) - x(s), \qquad 0 \leqq s \leqq 2;$$

$\tilde{X}$ is the space $C_0[0, 2]$ of functions continuous on $\{0 \leqq s \leqq 2\}$; and

$$Rx \underset{\text{def}}{=} \int_0^3 x(s)\, ds - 3\int_1^2 x(s)\, ds.$$

Then $Ux = 0$ means that x is periodic, of period 1; and

$$Ux = 0, \qquad x \in C_0[0, 3],$$

implies that $Rx = 0$. For each $\tilde{x}$ in $C_0[0, 2]$, there is an x in $C_0[0, 3]$ such that

$$\Delta x(s) = \tilde{x}(s), \qquad s \in [0, 2].$$

By the quotient theorem an operator Q exists such that

$$Rx = Q\Delta x, \qquad x \in X.$$

The operator Q can be found here by elementary transformations of the equation defining Rx. Thus,

$$\begin{aligned} Rx &= \int_0^1 x(s)\,ds - 2\int_1^2 x(s)\,ds + \int_2^3 x(s)\,ds \\ &= \int_0^1 x(s)\,ds - \int_0^1 x(s+1)\,ds - \int_1^2 x(s)\,ds + \int_1^2 x(s+1)\,ds \\ &= -\int_0^1 \Delta x(s)\,ds + \int_1^2 \Delta x(s)\,ds. \end{aligned}$$

Hence

$$Rx = \int_0^2 \Delta x(s)\lambda(s)\,ds, \qquad x \in C_0[0, 3],$$

where

$$\lambda(s) = \begin{cases} -1 & \text{if } 0 < s < 1, \\ +1 & \text{if } 1 < s < 2. \end{cases}$$

§ 60. **Functions of several variables.** We have indicated in § 31 how Theorem 6: 14 (which gives the representation of elements of B^*) may be deduced from the quotient theorem.

There may be a multiplicity of formal complications. We cite a simple example.

Consider the approximation of

$$\iint_I x(s, t)\,ds\,dt, \qquad I = \{-1 \leqq s, t \leqq 1\},$$

by

$$2\int_{-1}^1 x(s, 0)\,ds + 2\int_{-1}^1 x(0, t)\,dt - 4x(0, 0).$$

Consider functions x with continuous cross derivative $x_{1,1}(s, t)$ on I. Here

$$Rx = \int_{-1}^1\int_{-1}^1 x(s, t)\,ds\,dt - 2\int_{-1}^1 x(s, 0)\,ds - 2\int_{-1}^1 x(0, t)\,dt + 4x(0, 0).$$

Put

$$Ux = D_sD_tx = x_{1,1}(s, t).$$

Then $Ux = 0$ implies that

$$x(s, t) = f(s) + g(t)$$

for suitable functions f, g; hence that

$$\begin{aligned} Rx = {} & 2\int_{-1}^1 f(s)\,ds + 2\int_{-1}^1 g(t)\,dt - 2\int_{-1}^1 f(s)\,ds - 4g(0) \\ & - 2\int_{-1}^1 g(t)\,dt - 4f(0) + 4f(0) + 4g(0) \\ = {} & 0. \end{aligned}$$

Hence, by the quotient theorem,

$$Rx = QUx = Qx_{1,1},$$

where Q is a linear continuous functional on $B_{0,0}$.

Indeed

$$\begin{aligned} Rx &= \int_{-1}^{1}\int_{-1}^{1} [x(s,t) - x(s,0) - x(0,t) + x(0,0)]\, ds\, dt \\ &= \int_{-1}^{1}\int_{-1}^{1} ds\, dt \int_{0}^{t}\int_{0}^{s} x_{1,1}(\sigma,\tau)\, d\sigma\, d\tau \\ &= \int_{-1}^{1}\int_{-1}^{1} ds\, dt \int_{-1}^{1}\int_{-1}^{1} d\sigma\, d\tau\, x_{1,1}(\sigma,\tau)\psi(0,\sigma,s)\psi(0,\tau,t) \end{aligned}$$

by (1: 14). Hence

$$Rx = \int_{-1}^{1}\int_{-1}^{1} x_{1,1}(\sigma,\tau)\lambda(\sigma,\tau)\, d\sigma\, d\tau,$$

where

$$\lambda(\sigma,\tau) = \int_{-1}^{1}\int_{-1}^{1} \psi(0,\sigma,s)\psi(0,\tau,t)\, ds\, dt = (\text{signum}\ \sigma - \sigma)(\text{signum}\ \tau - \tau),$$

since, by (11: 18),

$$\int_{0}^{1} \psi(0,\sigma,s)\, ds = (1 - \sigma)\psi(0,\sigma,1),$$

$$\int_{0}^{-1} \psi(0,\sigma,s)\, ds = (-1 - \sigma)\psi(0,\sigma,-1),$$

$$\begin{aligned} \int_{-1}^{1} \psi(0,\sigma,s)\, ds &= \psi(0,\sigma,1) + \psi(0,\sigma,-1) - \sigma[\psi(0,\sigma,1) - \psi(0,\sigma,-1)] \\ &= \begin{cases} 1 + 0 - \sigma[1 - 0] & \text{if } 0 < \sigma < 1, \\ 0 - 1 - \sigma[0 + 1] & \text{if } -1 < \sigma < 0 \end{cases} \\ &= \text{signum}\ \sigma - \sigma. \end{aligned}$$

This elementary example could alternatively be analyzed in terms of a space B with pivot $x_{1,1}$.

§ 61. **Application to the use and design of machines.** Suppose that a machine produces an output $A(x + \delta x)$ which is intended to approximate Gx, where δx is the error in the input $x + \delta x$, G is a given fixed operator, and A is the operator which describes the working of the machine. The total error is

$$e = A(x + \delta x) - Gx = A(x + \delta x) - G(x + \delta x) + G(x + \delta x) - Gx.$$

In some circumstances we will know that δx is so small that $G(x + \delta x) - Gx$ is adequately small. The effectiveness of the approximation will then be assured if

$$R(x + \delta x) \underset{\text{def}}{=} A(x + \delta x) - G(x + \delta x)$$

is adequately small. The operator R here defined may be such that for suitable U the quotient theorem will apply. Then

$$R(x + \delta x) = QU(x + \delta x),$$

$$\|R(x + \delta x)\| \leqq \|Q\| \|U(x + \delta x)\|.$$

Thus we may control the total error e by controlling δx and $U(x + \delta x)$. It may be easier to do this than to control e directly.†

Part of our machine may produce $A(x + \delta x)$, the desired approximation of Gx. Another part of our machine may produce $\|U(x + \delta x)\|$. If the latter quantity is sufficiently small and if δx is sufficiently small, the total error will be adequately small.

The reader may think of pertinent instances. Simple examples are that U might be D_s or $D_s^3 + D_s$, where x is a function of elapsed time s.

---

† The next chapter will study e as an entity.

CHAPTER 9

Efficient and Strongly Efficient Approximation

§ 1. **Norms based on integrals.** Consider an arbitrary space S and a nonnegative measure μ on S. Let X be a space of numerical functions on S. It is often advantageous, as we shall see, to define a norm in X by means of an integral relative to μ. For example, $\|x\|$ may be

$$\int_S |x(s)|\, d\mu(s), \qquad x \in X, \tag{2}$$

or

$$\left[\int_S |x(s)|^p\, d\mu(s)\right]^{1/p}, \tag{3}$$

or

$$[w|x(a)|^p + \int_S |x_1(s)|^p\, d\mu(s)]^{1/p}, \tag{4}$$

where $p \geqq 1$ and, in (4), S is a subset of the real line, $a \in S$, $w > 0$, and $x_1(s) = D_s x$.

In the spaces B, K, Z of our earlier chapters, the norms involved suprema. The norms (2), (3), (4) involve averages, since $d\mu$ is nonnegative. Both suprema and averages are useful to the approximator.

In the present and next chapter we consider spaces with norms based on integrals. We concentrate on cases in which $p = 2$. The spaces X are then Hilbert spaces, to be defined below, in which powerful tools such as orthogonal projections are available. Orthogonal projections do not exist when $p \neq 2$, except when the measure μ is especially simple.

For the mathematician who approximates, the essential feature of norms defined by integrals is that the norm is an average. What kind of average is often of secondary importance. If one interpretation ($p = 2$) of the term average makes the theory go more easily and deeply than another interpretation ($p \neq 2$), the first will usually be preferred.

The artful mathematician does things which are pertinent and reasonable, and which, in addition, allow the use and advantage of tools of the greatest power.

Although we take $p = 2$ and deal exclusively with Hilbert spaces, there is still a wide choice of courses of action. This is because there are many possible ways to set up the Hilbert spaces. The approximator must decide which measure μ to use and which derivatives, if any, of x are to enter in the definition of $\|x\|$.

The rôle of μ in a norm

$$\left[\int_S |x(s)|^2 \, d\mu(s)\right]^{1/2} \tag{5}$$

is as follows: $d\mu(s)$ measures the importance of the integrand near s. Different measures μ lead to different approximations. There is an immense choice of possible measures μ. For each choice of μ, the space X will be a Hilbert space. The dimension of X will depend on S and μ.

Any two Hilbert spaces of the same dimension are isomorphic. It does not follow, however, that any two Hilbert spaces of the same dimension have the same meaning in approximation. For, the isomorphism between the spaces may disturb qualities that we are interested in. Thus an element f^1 in X^1 may correspond to an element f^2 in X^2, when X^1 and X^2 are isomorphic Hilbert spaces with norms of the form (5), despite the fact that f^1 and f^2 are different sorts of functions. The difference between f^1 and f^2 may be described as follows: f^1 will be small where $d\mu^1$ is large at the expense of being large where $d\mu^1$ is small; f^2 will be in the similar relation to $d\mu^2$; where μ^1 and μ^2 are the measures that enter in the respective norms.

The spaces of this chapter have such varied qualities for the approximator that it is quite adequate to consider only these spaces. That all our spaces are Hilbert spaces does not mean that all are the same from the point of view of approximation. It does mean that methods are accessible which are, as methods, the same in all cases. There is simplicity of method and multiplicity of application.

The problem of efficient approximation is described in §§ 174–176; also in §§ 13–19 of the Introduction. Our principal results thereon are Theorems 232 and 253. Illustrations are in § 267 ff. In § 311 ff. we consider the relation between Pythagorean theory and that of Wiener-Kolmogorov.

§ 6. **Inner product spaces. Hilbert spaces.** For preciseness we shall take the scalars N to be the complex numbers C. There is an analagous theory in which $\mathsf{N} = \mathsf{R}$.

By an *inner product space* we mean a complex linear space X together with an *inner product* (x, y), $x \in X$, $y \in X$, with the following properties:

(i) For each $x \in X$ and $y \in X$, there is defined a complex number (x, y), called the inner product of x into y.

(ii) For $x, y, z \in X$ and $c \in \mathsf{C}$,

$$(x + y, z) = (x, z) + (y, z), \tag{7}$$

$$(cx, z) = c(x, z), \tag{8}$$

$$(y, x) = \text{complex conjugate of } (x, y) = \overline{(x, y)}. \tag{9}$$

(iii) For $x \in X$, $x \neq 0$,

$$(x, x) > 0.$$

Suppose henceforth that X is an inner product space, except where otherwise noted.

Condition (9) implies that (x, x) is real, for all $x \in X$. Condition (7) implies that

$$(0, x) = (0, x) + (0, x) = 0, \qquad x \in X,$$

and

$$(0, 0) = 0.$$

It follows from (iii) that

$$(10) \qquad (x, x) \geqq 0, \qquad x \in X,$$

with equality iff $x = 0$. Furthermore

$$(11) \qquad (x, y + z) = (x, y) + (x, z),$$

$$(12) \qquad (x, cz) = \bar{c}(x, z), \qquad x, y, z \in X, \quad c \in \mathbf{C};$$

by (7), (8), (9). For example,

$$(x, cz) = \overline{(cz, x)} = \overline{c(z, x)} = \bar{c}(x, z).$$

As there are a number of excellent developments of the theory of inner product spaces and Hilbert spaces in books in English, we shall usually omit proofs that are in such books, in which cases however we shall give exact references.

13. Lemma. *For $x, y \in X$,*

$$|(x, y)|^2 \leqq (x, x)(y, y),$$

with equality iff x and y are linearly dependent.

Proof. [Riesz-Nagy 1, p. 196.]

For $x \in X$, we define $\|x\|$ as the positive square root of (x, x). We shall see shortly that $\|x\|$ is a norm on X. For this reason, $\|x\|$ is called the norm induced by the inner product. Until it is established that $\|x\|$ is a norm, the temporary name double bar x may be used. Lemma 13 implies Schwarz's inequality

$$(14) \qquad |(x, y)| \leqq \|x\| \, \|y\|, \qquad x, y \in X;$$

equality holds here iff x and y are linearly dependent.

15. Lemma (Minkowski's inequality). *For $x, y \in X$,*

$$\|x + y\| \leqq \|x\| + \|y\|,$$

with equality iff $x = 0$ or $y = 0$ or $y = px$, $p > 0$.

Proof. [von Neumann 2, II, p. 6; Zaanen 1, p. 109.]

16. Corollary. *An inner product space X with*

$$(17) \qquad \|x\| = (x, x)^{1/2}, \qquad x \in X,$$

is a normed linear space.

Proof. Immediate, since

$$\|cx\| = (cx, cx)^{1/2} = [c\bar{c}(x, x)]^{1/2} = |c| \, \|x\|; \qquad x \in X, \quad c \in \mathsf{C};$$

and $\|x\| = 0$ implies $x = 0$.

It follows that cx, $x + y$, $\|x\|$, (x, y) are continuous in c, x, y, for $c \in \mathsf{C}$, $x, y \in X$. As regards cx, $x + y$, $\|x\|$, this has been established in § 3 : 2. That (x, y) is continuous follows from the relations

$$(18) \quad \begin{aligned} &(x^1, y^1) - (x, y) = (x^1 - x, y^1 - y) + (x^1 - x, y) + (x, y^1 - y), \\ &|(x^1, y^1) - (x, y)| \leqq \|x^1 - x\| \, \|y^1 - y\| + \|x^1 - x\| \, \|y\| + \|x\| \, \|y^1 - y\|, \\ &\qquad\qquad\qquad\qquad x, y, x^1, y^1 \in X. \end{aligned}$$

Cf. [Zaanen 1, p. 110].

By a *Hilbert space* we mean an inner product space which is complete† (§ 8 : 2). We do not for the present require that the space be separable (§ 27). Many Hilbert spaces that enter in approximation are in fact separable and our later theory will add the hypothesis of separability where used. Euclidean space of n dimensions is the real part of a separable Hilbert space.

If X is an inner product space, the completion $\hat{X}$ of X may always be constructed. The construction is like that of § 8 : 2. Thus $\hat{X}$ is the space of equivalence sets of Cauchy sequences in X and the inner product is defined on $\hat{X}$ by extension of the inner product on X. Cf. [Naimark 1, p. 85].

If X is a Hilbert space, any closed linear subspace of X is itself a Hilbert space.

§ 19. **Orthogonality.** Elements x, y of an inner product space X are said to be *orthogonal*

$$x \perp y$$

if $(x, y) = 0$. Sets $A, B \subset X$ are orthogonal

$$A \perp B,$$

if $a \perp b$ whenever $a \in A$, $b \in B$.

20. Lemma. *Suppose that A is an arbitrary subset of an inner product space X. Then the set*

$$B = \{x \in X : x \perp A\}$$

† Our usage of the term linear space requires that the space be nonempty. Hence linear subspaces, inner product spaces, and Hilbert spaces are nonempty.

of elements orthogonal to A is a linear space closed in X. It is denoted $A^{\perp}$ or $X \dot{-} A$.

What is meant here is that B consists of all elements $x \in X$ such that

$$(x, y) = 0 \quad \text{for all} \quad y \in A.$$

Thus

$$B = A^{\perp} \perp A.$$

That B is closed in X means that whenever a sequence of points of B has a limit point in X, that limit point is an element of B. If X is a Hilbert space, then B will be closed and itself a Hilbert space. The set B includes 0 and therefore is never empty.

PROOF OF LEMMA 20. [Naimark 1, p. 86.]

21. THEOREM OF DECOMPOSITION. *Suppose that M is a closed linear subspace of a Hilbert space X. Then each element x of X may be written as the sum of an element in M and an element in $M^{\perp}$:*

$$x = x^1 + x^2, \qquad x^1 \in M, \quad x^2 \in M^{\perp}; \tag{22}$$

and this may be done in only one way.

PROOF. [Riesz-Nagy 1, pp. 70–72; Naimark 1, p. 88.]

23. COROLLARY. *If M is a closed linear subspace of a Hilbert space, then*

$$M^{\perp\perp} = M.$$

PROOF. Immediate. [Naimark 1, p. 88.]

We say that M and $M^{\perp}$ are orthogonal complements in X and that X is the direct sum (§ 69) of M and $M^{\perp}$, if M is a closed linear subspace of a Hilbert space X.

According to the theorem of decomposition the element x^1 in (22) is determined unambiguously by x. We define the *orthogonal projection onto M* (briefly, the projection on M) as the operator

$$\text{Proj}_M$$

defined by the relations (22) and

$$\text{Proj}_M\, x = x^1, \qquad x \in X. \tag{24}$$

An immediate consequence of Theorem 21 is that

$$\text{Proj}_{M^{\perp}} = \text{Identity} - \text{Proj}_M. \tag{25}$$

26. THEOREM. *Suppose that M is a closed linear subspace of a Hilbert space X. The operator* Proj$_M$ *of projection on M is linear and continuous on X onto M. Furthermore*

$$(\text{Proj}_M)^2 = \text{Proj}_M,$$
$$(\text{Proj}_M\, x, y) = (x, \text{Proj}_M\, y), \qquad x, y \in X;$$
$$\text{Proj}_M\, x = x \quad \textit{iff} \quad x \in M.$$

PROOF. [Riesz-Nagy 1, p. 264.]

§ 27. L^2-spaces and other function spaces that are Hilbert spaces. Consider an arbitrary nonempty space S and a measure μ on† S. We shall define the *L^2-space* relative to S and μ, a space which we designate as $H(S, \mu)$ or H. The strict definition of H is as follows. We first define the *prespace* $\mathscr{H}$ as the set of complex functions x which are measurable μ on S and which are such that

$$\int_S |x(s)|^2 \, d\mu(s) < \infty.$$

We say that two functions in $\mathscr{H}$ are *equivalent* if their values are equal almost everywhere μ on S. We define H as the set of equivalence sets of elements of $\mathscr{H}$. That is, $\xi \in H$ means that ξ is a set of elements of $\mathscr{H}$ any two of which are equal almost everywhere μ and that, furthermore, if $x \in \xi$, $y \in \mathscr{H}$, and $y(s)$ and $x(s)$ are equal almost everywhere μ, then $y \in \xi$.

Suppose that

$$\xi, \eta \in H.$$

Sum, scalar product, and inner product in H are defined in the natural way as follows. Choose $x \in \xi$ and $y \in \eta$. Then $\xi + \eta$ is the element of H such that $x + y \in \xi + \eta$; $c\xi$ is the element of H such that $cx \in c\xi$, $c \in \mathbf{C}$; and

$$(\xi, \eta) = (\xi, \eta)_H = \int_S x(s)\bar{y}(s) \, d\mu(s).$$

These definitions must be shown to be independent of the choice of elements $x \in \xi$ and $y \in \eta$. This fact and others are asserted in the following theorem.

28. THEOREM. *The L^2-space $H = H(S, \mu)$ is well defined and is a Hilbert space.*

PROOF. [Riesz-Nagy 1, pp. 57–59; Munroe 1, p. 243; Bourbaki 1, p. 133.]

A few remarks about the proof may be of interest. That H is an inner product space is quite immediate. The condition that (ξ, ξ) vanish iff $\xi = 0$ is satisfied because of the use of equivalence sets. Thus, the relation

$$\int_S |x(s)|^2 \, d\mu(s) = 0 \tag{29}$$

implies that $x(s) = 0$ almost everywhere μ and therefore that $x \in 0 \in H$. The element 0 in H is the equivalence set of functions on S each vanishing almost everywhere. The completeness of H is the Riesz-Fischer Theorem.

---

† Thus, μ is a nonnegative possibly infinite function on a Borel field of subsets of S, called the measurable sets. We assume that S is itself measurable and that μ is complete (any subset of a set of measure zero is measurable). The reader may wish to assume also that μ is sigma-finite (S is the union of countably many sets of finite measure).

As is customary, we describe H as the *space of complex functions on* S, measurable and *absolute square integrable* μ. Strictly speaking, the description is inexact: Each function is defined on S less a set of μ measure zero, and H is rather a space of equivalence sets of such functions. In the theory of approximation we are interested in functions and so we indicate an element ξ of H by citing a particular function x which is itself an element of ξ. We must then keep in mind that x may be replaced by any function which is equal to x almost everywhere μ. Doubtless there are situations in which this procedure is good and others in which an alternative would be better. The usage is analogous to writing a rational number as 4/6 rather than as a set of equivalent fractions.

30. Lemma. *Suppose that* $\{x^i\}$, $i = 1, 2, \cdots$, *is a sequence of elements of* $H = H(S, \mu)$ *which converges to* x *in* H. *Then for a suitably chosen subsequence* $\{x^{i_j}\}$, $i_1 < i_2 < i_3 < \cdots$, *the sequence of complex numbers*

$$\{x^{i_j}(s)\}, \qquad j = 1, 2, \cdots, \tag{31}$$

converges to $x(s)$, *for almost all* $s \in S$.

Here and elsewhere phrases like "almost all," "almost everywhere," "except on a null set," refer to the measure indicated by the context. Thus the sequence (31) converges for each $s \in S^1 \subset S$, where $\mu(S - S^1) = 0$.

Proof. This lemma is usually proved in the course of proving Theorem 28. Cf. the references cited above.

Lemma 30 extends to infinite series because a series has only countably many partial sums. Thus if

$$u = \sum_{i=1,2,\cdots} u^i, \qquad u, u^i \in H = H(S, \mu),$$

then for a properly chosen sequence of partial sums

$$u(s) = \sum_{i=1,2,\cdots} u^i(s), \quad \text{almost all } s.$$

For, by Lemma 30, there is a sequence of partial sums

$$\sum_{i \leqq n_j} u^i, \qquad n_1 < n_2 < \cdots,$$

such that

$$\Big(\sum_{i \leqq n_j} u^i\Big)(s) \rightarrow u(s) \text{ as } j \rightarrow \infty, \quad \text{almost all } s.$$

Furthermore

$$\Big(\sum_{i \leqq n_j} u^i\Big)(s) = \sum_{i \leqq n_j} u^i(s), \quad \text{almost all } s, j = 1, 2, \cdots,$$

since only finite sums are involved. Now all the points in S at which the last equality fails are countably many null sets and therefore a null set. Hence

$$\sum_{i \leqq n_j} u^i(s) \to u(s) \text{ as } j \to \infty, \quad \text{almost all } s.$$

A normed linear space X is *separable* if X contains a countable set

$$\{x^i\}, \quad x^i \in X, \quad i = 1, 2, \cdots,$$

which is dense in X, that is, has the following property: For any $x \in X$ and any $\zeta > 0$, i_0 exists such that

$$\|x - x^{i_0}\|_X < \zeta.$$

Although nonseparable Hilbert spaces are of interest, the function spaces which we consider in the theory of approximation are usually separable. This is because of the following facts.

The space $H(S, \mu)$ is separable if the measure μ is separable [Halmos 1, p. 177; Zaanen 1, p. 75].

The space $H(S, \mu)$ is separable if S is a Euclidean space and if μ is Lebesgue measure or a Lebesgue-Stieltjes measure [Riesz-Nagy 1, pp. 64, 65; von Neumann 2, I, pp. 104, 160, 170 and II, p. 42].

Examples of nonseparable Hilbert spaces are given in [Naimark 1, p. 95; Riesz-Nagy 1, p. 252].

We now mention a few separable Hilbert spaces.

The space H^1 is defined as the space of complex functions Lebesgue measurable on $I = \{\alpha \leqq s \leqq \tilde{\alpha}\}$, $\alpha < \tilde{\alpha}$, and absolute square integrable on I, with

$$(x, y) = \int_\alpha^{\tilde{\alpha}} x(s)\bar{y}(s)\, ds, \qquad x, y \in H^1.$$

The space H^2 is similar to H^1 except that the measure s on I is replaced by an atomic measure μ of the following type. Take $a_1, \cdots, a_k$ such that

$$\alpha \leqq a_1 < a_2 < \cdots < a_k \leqq \tilde{\alpha}.$$

Take

$$d\mu(s) = \begin{cases} w^j > 0 & \text{if } s = a_j,\ j = 1, \cdots, k; \\ 0 & \text{otherwise.} \end{cases} \tag{32}$$

Then $H^2 = H(I, \mu)$. Thus

$$(x, y) = \int_\alpha^{\tilde{\alpha}} x(s)\bar{y}(s)\, d\mu(s) = \sum_{j=1}^{k} x(a_j)\bar{y}(a_j)w^j, \qquad x, y \in H^2.$$

Since two functions $x(s)$ which are equal almost everywhere μ correspond to the same element of H^2, a function in H^2 is determined by its values

$$x(a_1), \cdots, x(a_k),$$

each of which must be defined unambiguously, by (32). If a table of these values is given, that table is a complete description of the function $x \in H^2$, since the table describes x almost everywhere μ. We may think of the weight w^j as measuring the importance of the value $x(a_j)$.

The space H^3 is not itself an L^2-space but rather a space of functions whose nth derivatives are in an L^2-space. To define H^3, let

$$w^0 > 0, \cdots, \quad w^n > 0; \qquad n \geqq 1; \qquad a \in I = \{\alpha \leqq s \leqq \tilde{\alpha}\};$$

be given. Let H^3 be the space of complex functions x on I with nth derivative x_n in the space H^1 and with absolutely continuous $(n-1)$th derivative, the inner product in H^3 being

$$(x, y) = w^0 x(a)\bar{y}(a) + w^1 x_1(a)\bar{y}_1(a) + \cdots + w^{n-1} x_{n-1}(a)\bar{y}_{n-1}(a)$$
$$+ w^n \int_\alpha^{\tilde{\alpha}} x_n(s)\bar{y}_n(s)\, ds; \qquad x, y \in H^3.$$

In the space H^3, the possible replacement of x_n by a function which equals x_n almost everywhere presents no complication whatever. For, by Taylor's formula, such replacement leads to the original x. We may take x_n to be the derivative $D_s^n x$ in the strict sense: $x_n(s)$ is defined iff the derivative exists.

That the space H^3 is separable may be seen from Taylor's formula. Thus we may construct a countable set $\{x^\nu\}$, $\nu = 1, 2, \cdots$, dense in H^3 as follows. Let $\{r^i\}$, $i = 1, 2, \cdots$, be the rationals. Since H^1 is separable, there exists a countable set $\{\xi^i\}$ of elements of H^1, dense in H^1. Arrange all $(n + 1)$-tuples

$$[r^{i_0}, r^{i_1}, \cdots, r^{i_{n-1}}, \xi^i], \qquad i, i_0, \cdots, i_{n-1} = 1, 2, \cdots,$$

into one sequence, say,

$$\{[r_0^\nu, r_1^\nu, \cdots, r_{n-1}^\nu, \xi^{i_\nu}]\}, \qquad \nu = 1, 2, \cdots.$$

Put

$$x^\nu(s) = r_0^\nu + (s - a)r_1^\nu + \cdots + (s - a)^{(n-1)} r_{n-1}^\nu + \int_a^s (s - \tilde{s})^{(n-1)} \xi^{i_\nu}(\tilde{s})\, d\tilde{s},$$
$$\nu = 1, 2, \cdots;$$

then the countable set $\{x^\nu\}$ is dense in H^3, by Taylor's formula.

Similarly one may consider functions of several variables. Suppose for example that a space B of functions on $I = I_s \times I_t$ with pivot $x_{p,q}$ is given (§ 4: 49). Suppose that

$$w^{i,j}, \qquad (i, j) \in \bar{\omega},$$

are given positive constants. Let H^4 be the space of complex functions x

whose real and imaginary parts are elements of $\boldsymbol{B}$ (§ 4 : 80) and which are such that

$$x_{i,j}(s, b) \in H(I_s, s), \qquad (i, j) \in \bar{\omega}_{s,b};$$
$$x_{i,j}(a, t) \in H(I_t, t), \qquad (i, j) \in \bar{\omega}_{a,t};$$
$$x_{p,q}(s, t) \in H(I, st);$$

with inner product

$$(x, y) = \sum_{(i,j)\in\bar{\omega}_{a,b}} w^{i,j} x_{i,j}(a, b)\, \bar{y}_{i,j}(a, b) + \sum_{(i,j)\in\bar{\omega}_{a,t}} w^{i,j} \int_{I_t} x_{i,j}(a, t)\bar{y}_{i,j}(a, t)\, dt$$
$$+ \text{ dual term } + w^{p,q} \iint_I x_{p,q}(s, t)\bar{y}_{p,q}(s, t)\, ds\, dt, \qquad x, y \in H^4.$$

Then H^4 is a separable Hilbert space.

§ 33. **The Pythagorean theorem and approximation.** Suppose that N is a closed linear subspace of a Hilbert space Y. Suppose that for each $y \in Y$, we wish to approximate y by an element b of N. Let us agree to choose b so as to minimize

$$\|b - y\|_Y^2,$$

subject to the condition

$$b \in N.$$

34. THEOREM. *For each fixed $y \in Y$, there is a unique b which minimizes*

$$\|b - y\|_Y,$$

subject to the condition

$$b \in N.$$

The minimizing b is

$$b = Py,$$

where P is the projection on N. The error in the approximation of y by b is

$$e = b - y = -Qy,$$

where Q is the projection on $N^\perp$.

PROOF. By (25), $P + Q$ is the identity. Consider a fixed $y \in Y$. If we approximate y by an arbitrary element b, the error in the approximation is

$$e = b - y = (b - Py) + (Py - y) = (b - Py) - Qy.$$

Now

$$Py \in N, \qquad -Qy \in N^\perp.$$

If we specify that $b \in N$, then

$$b - Py \in N,$$
$$b - Py \perp -Qy,$$
$$(e, e) = \|e\|^2 = \|b - Py\|^2 + \|Qy\|^2,$$

since the cross term $(b - Py, Qy)$ and its conjugate vanish.

Now Qy is independent of b. Hence $\|e\|^2$ is minimal iff

$$b = Py;$$

in which case

$$e = -Qy.$$

This completes the proof.

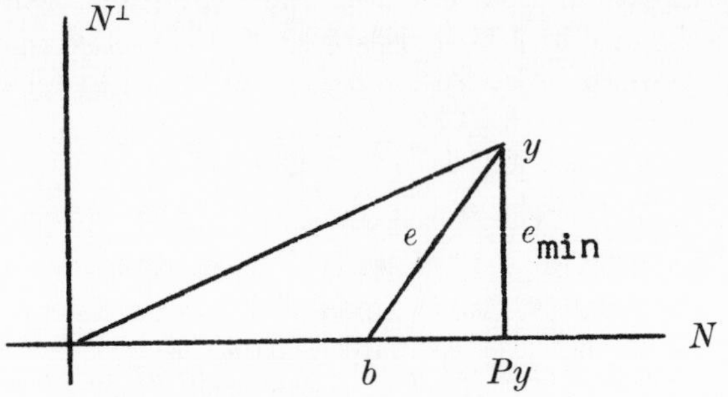

Y

35. Corollary. *Suppose that X is an arbitrary space, Y a Hilbert space, N a closed linear subspace of Y, and G an operator on X to Y. Then the operator A which, for each fixed $x \in X$, minimizes*

$$\|Ax - Gx\|_Y$$

subject to the condition

$$Ax \in N,$$

is

$$A = PG,$$

where P is the projection on N. The error in the approximation is

$$e = Ax - Gx = -QGx,$$

where Q is the projection on $N^{\perp}$.

Proof. This is merely a restatement of Theorem 34, with $y = Gx$.

Approximations related to the one described in Corollary 35 often occur. An essential feature of the approximation is the condition

$$Ax \in N, \qquad x \in X.$$

This condition is imposed from outside. In particular cases, N might be the span (see next section) of functions that are known or stored or conveniently computable. Alternatively N might be the space of solutions of a pertinent linear homogeneous equation.

Theorem 34, which is an immediate consequence of properties of orthogonality, illuminates the theory of approximations based on criteria of least squares. The theorem is well known. It is difficult to cite its first appearance in the literature. The idea is present in [E. Schmidt 1, 2; Nikodym 1; Weyl 1; Kolmogorov 3].

Later in the chapter we study generalizations of Theorem 34, in which the character of the set of inputs is part of what is given.

Because of Theorem 34 we will often want to calculate

$$\mathrm{Proj}_N\, y$$

as an approximation of $y \in Y$, where N is a closed linear subspace of a Hilbert space Y. A technique for the calculation will be given in §§ 55, 60.

If N is of high dimension, the calculation may be difficult or even impracticable. It is then natural to consider a closed linear subspace N_1 of N and to calculate

$$\mathrm{Proj}_{N_1}\, y$$

as a substitute for $\mathrm{Proj}_N\, y$. The following lemma asserts in part that the larger N_1 is, the better the approximation will be.

36. LEMMA. *Suppose that*

(37) $$N \supset N_1 \supset N_2$$

are closed linear subspaces of a Hilbert space Y. Then

(38) $$\|\mathrm{Proj}_N\, y\| \geqq \|\mathrm{Proj}_{N_1}\, y\| \geqq \|\mathrm{Proj}_{N_2}\, y\|$$

and

(39) $$\|y - \mathrm{Proj}_N\, y\| \leqq \|y - \mathrm{Proj}_{N_1}\, y\| \leqq \|y - \mathrm{Proj}_{N_2}\, y\|$$

for all $y \in Y$.

PROOF. Consider a fixed $y \in Y$. By Theorem 34, $\|y - b\|$ is minimal, $b \in N$, when

$$b = \mathrm{Proj}_N\, y.$$

Thus the three numbers in (39) are the minima of $\|y - b\|$ when b varies over N, N_1, N_2, respectively. Hence (37) implies (39).

We now deduce (38) from (39). By the definition of orthogonal complement,

$$N^{\perp} \subset N_1^{\perp} \subset N_2^{\perp}.$$

Hence, by (39) applied to these spaces,

$$\|y - \text{Proj}_{N^{\perp}}\, y\| \geqq \|y - \text{Proj}_{N_1^{\perp}}\, y\| \geqq \|y - \text{Proj}_{N_2^{\perp}}\, y\|.$$

This relation is precisely (38), by (25). The proof is complete.

§ 40. **Bases. Fourier coefficients.** We continue the study of Hilbert spaces, with a view to obtaining tools to describe projections and other operators.

Let X be a Banach space and $\mathscr{E}$ an arbitrary subset of X. By the *span of* $\mathscr{E}$

$$\text{span}\, \mathscr{E}$$

we mean the set of all finite linear combinations (with complex coefficients) of elements of $\mathscr{E}$. We denote the *closed span* of $\mathscr{E}$, that is, the closure of span $\mathscr{E}$, by

$$\text{Span}\, \mathscr{E}.$$

Elements of X are said to be *free* (*linearly independent*) if no finite linear combination of them vanishes unless all the coefficients of combination are zero. We say that $\mathscr{E}$ is of *dimension* $n < \infty$, if $\mathscr{E}$ contains n free elements and if $\mathscr{E}$ does not contain $n + 1$ free elements. Then $\mathscr{E}$ is of dimension $n < \infty$ iff span $\mathscr{E}$ is of dimension n.

If span $\mathscr{E}$ is finite dimensional, then span $\mathscr{E}$ is closed [Dunford-Schwarz 1, p. 244] and

$$\text{Span}\, \mathscr{E} = \text{span}\, \mathscr{E}.$$

Suppose that $\mathscr{E} = \{f\}$, that is, $\mathscr{E}$ consists of the single element f. Then

$$\text{span}\, \mathscr{E} = \text{Span}\, \mathscr{E}$$

consists of all elements

$$cf, \qquad c \in \mathbf{C},$$

and Span $\mathscr{E}$ is one or zero-dimensional according as $f \neq 0$ or $f = 0$.

Now suppose that X is a Hilbert space. Consider $f \in X$. By the *projection on* f we mean the projection on Span $\{f\}$. If

$$f \in X \quad \text{and} \quad \|f\| = 1,$$

we describe the number

$$(x, f)$$

as the *Fourier coefficient* of x relative to f, $x \in X$.

41. LEMMA. *Suppose that f is an element of the Hilbert space X. The projection of x on f is*

$$\text{Proj}_f\, x = \begin{cases} \dfrac{(x, f)}{\|f\|^2} f & \text{if } f \neq 0, \\ 0 & \text{if } f = 0, \end{cases} \qquad x \in X. \tag{42}$$

PROOF. Assume first that

$$\|f\| = 1.$$

Put

$$x^1 = (x, f)f, \tag{43}$$
$$x^2 = x - x^1, \qquad x \in X.$$

Then

$$x^1 \in \text{span}\,\{f\}.$$

It follows from the decomposition theorem that

$$x^1 = \text{Proj}_f\, x,$$

iff x^2 is orthogonal to span $\{f\}$; that is, iff

$$(x^2, f) = 0.$$

But

$$\begin{aligned}(x^2, f) &= (x - x^1, f) = (x, f) - (x^1, f) = (x, f) - ((x, f)f, f) \\ &= (x, f) - (x, f)(f, f) = (x, f) - (x, f) = 0,\end{aligned}$$

since $\|f\|^2 = 1$. Thus (42) is established if $\|f\| = 1$.

Suppose now that f is any nonzero element of X. Then $f/\|f\|$ is of length 1. By (43),

$$\text{Proj}_f\, x = \text{Proj}_{f/\|f\|}\, x = \left(x, \frac{f}{\|f\|}\right)\frac{f}{\|f\|} = \frac{(x, f)}{\|f\|^2} f, \qquad x \in X.$$

Finally, if $f = 0$,

$$\text{Proj}_f\, x = 0, \qquad x \in X,$$

by the decomposition theorem, since

$$x = 0 + x.$$

Thus (42) is established in all cases, and the proof is complete.

A nonempty set $\mathscr{E}$ of nonzero elements of X is an *orthogonal system* if any two distinct elements of $\mathscr{E}$ are orthogonal. If, in addition, each element of $\mathscr{E}$ is of length unity, then $\mathscr{E}$ is an *orthonormal system*. A set $\mathscr{B}$ of elements of X is a *basis* for X if $\mathscr{B}$ is an orthonormal system and if span $\mathscr{B}$ is dense in X, or, what is the same,

$$\text{Span}\, \mathscr{B} = X.$$

If $\{x^1, \cdots, x^n\}$ is an orthogonal finite system, then

$$\|x^1 + \cdots + x^n\|^2 = \|x^1\|^2 + \cdots + \|x^n\|^2;$$

as follows from the fact that

$$\|x + y\|^2 = (x + y, x + y) = \|x\|^2 + \|y\|^2 + (x, y) + (y, x)$$
$$= \|x\|^2 + \|y\|^2$$

if $(x, y) = 0$.

If $\{x^i\}$, $i = 1, 2, \cdots$, is a countably infinite orthogonal system, then the series

$$x^1 + x^2 + \cdots$$

converges in X iff the arithmetical series

$$\|x^1\|^2 + \|x^2\|^2 + \cdots$$

converges [Naimark 1, p. 91].

44. THEOREM. *Suppose that $\mathscr{E}$ is an orthonormal system in a Hilbert space X and that x is an arbitrary element of X. Then all except countably many Fourier coefficients*

$$(x, u), \qquad u \in \mathscr{E},$$

of x relative to elements of $\mathscr{E}$ vanish. Furthermore

$$\sum_{u \in \mathscr{E}} |(x, u)|^2 \leq \|x\|^2. \tag{45}$$

Since the sum in (45) consists of a countable number of positive terms, those terms may be added in any order.

A proof of Theorem 44 is given in [Zaanen 1, p. 114].

The relation (45) is known as Bessel's inequality.

An orthonormal system $\mathscr{E}$ in a Hilbert space X is said to be *complete* if 0 is the only element of X orthogonal to all the elements of $\mathscr{E}$.

46. THEOREM. *Suppose that $\mathscr{E}$ is an orthonormal system in a Hilbert space X. Then the following conditions are equivalent (that is, each condition implies all the others):*

(i) *$\mathscr{E}$ is complete.*

(ii) *For each $x \in X$,*

$$x = \sum_{u \in \mathscr{E}} (x, u)u$$

for some order of summation.

(ii′) *For each $x \in X$,*

$$x = \sum_{u \in \mathscr{E}} (x, u)u \tag{47}$$

for all orders of summation.

(iii) *For any* $x, y \in X$,

$$(x, y) = \sum_{u \in \mathscr{E}} (x, u)(u, y)$$

for some order of summation.

(iii′) *For any* $x, y \in X$,

$$(x, y) = \sum_{u \in \mathscr{E}} (x, u)(u, y) \tag{48}$$

for all orders of summation.

(iv) *For each* $x \in X$,

$$\|x\|^2 = \sum_{u \in \mathscr{E}} |(x, u)|^2. \tag{49}$$

(v) span $\mathscr{E}$ *is dense in* X.

(vi) $\mathscr{E}$ *is a basis for* X.

Proof. [Zaanen 1, p. 114; Naimark 1, pp. 92–94.] Observe that the formulas involving determinants on p. 93 of the latter reference are not needed or used.

Suppose that $\mathscr{B}$ is a basis for X. We may describe the Fourier coefficients

$$(x, u), \qquad u \in \mathscr{B},$$

of x relative to the elements of $\mathscr{B}$ as the *coordinates* of x, $x \in X$. By (47) with $\mathscr{B} = \mathscr{E}$, the coordinates of x determine x; by (48), the coordinates of x and y determine (x, y), $x, y \in X$.

The coordinates of a finite linear combination of elements of X are precisely the linear combination of the coordinates, because

$$(ax + by, u) = a(x, u) + b(y, u); \qquad x, y, u \in X, \quad a, b, \in \mathbf{C}.$$

As regards infinite series

$$\sum_{i=1}^{\infty} x^i, \qquad x^i \in X, \tag{50}$$

the following remark is useful in dealing with coordinates. If the series (50) converges in X, then

$$\left(\sum_i x^i, \xi\right) = \sum_i (x^i, \xi), \qquad \xi \in X. \tag{51}$$

Thus any coordinate of a convergent series equals the series of coordinates. To establish (51), let

$$y = \sum_i x^i.$$

Then

$$\left\| y - \sum_{i<n} x^i \right\| \to 0 \quad \text{as } n \to \infty;$$

and for each $\xi \in X$,

$$(y, \xi) - \sum_{i<n} (x^i, \xi) = \left(y - \sum_{i<n} x^i, \xi \right) \to 0,$$

since the inner product is continuous in its arguments. Thus (51) holds.

Suppose that $\mathscr{B}$ is a basis for X. If the series

$$\sum_{u \in \mathscr{B}} a_u u \tag{52}$$

is such that

$$\sum_{u \in \mathscr{B}} |a_u|^2 < \infty, \tag{53}$$

where $a_u \in \mathbf{C}$, $u \in \mathscr{B}$, then the series (52) defines an element $x \in X$ for which

$$(x, u) = a_u, \qquad u \in \mathscr{B}.$$

This is a consequence of (47) and (45). Note that (53) implies that $a_u = 0$ except for countably many u in $\mathscr{B}$.

54. Theorem. *Any Hilbert space X of more than one point contains a basis. Any two bases in X have the same number of elements, that is, the same cardinality. The space X is separable iff X has a countable basis.*

Proof. [Naimark 1, pp. 92–94; Riesz-Nagy 1, p. 197.]

By the *dimension* of a Hilbert space X, we mean the cardinality of a basis in X. This definition agrees with our earlier definition of finite dimensionality.

§ 55. **Projections.** Consider a Hilbert space X.

56. Theorem. *Suppose that $M \subset X$ is a closed linear subspace of more than one point. Then the projection* Proj_M *on M may be expressed as*

$$\mathrm{Proj}_M\, x = \sum_{u \in \mathscr{B}} (x, u)u, \qquad x \in X, \tag{57}$$

where $\mathscr{B}$ is any basis for M.

Proof. Since M is a Hilbert space of more than one point, M has a basis $\mathscr{B}$. By the decomposition theorem

$$x = y + z, \qquad y \in M, z \in M^\perp;$$

and

$$y = \mathrm{Proj}_M\, x.$$

Now

$$y = \sum_{u \in \mathscr{B}} (y, u)u,$$

since $\mathscr{B}$ is a basis in M and $y \in M$. But

$$(y, u) = (x - z, u) = (x, u) - (z, u) = (x, u),$$

since $u \in \mathscr{B} \subset M$, $z \in M^{\perp}$.

It follows that

$$\mathrm{Proj}_M\, x = y = \sum_{u \in \mathscr{B}} (x, u)u,$$

as was to be shown. The terms herein which do not vanish may be summed in any order, by Theorem 46.

In the following corollary, $\mathscr{I}$ is an arbitrary set of indices.

58. COROLLARY. *If* $\{f^i\}$, $i \in \mathscr{I}$, *is an orthogonal system of elements of* X, *then*

$$\mathrm{Proj}_M\, x = \sum_{i \in \mathscr{I}} \frac{(x, f^i)f^i}{\|f^i\|^2}, \qquad x \in X, \tag{59}$$

where

$$M = \mathrm{Span}\,\{f^i : i \in \mathscr{I}\}.$$

PROOF. An orthogonal system is a nonempty set of nonzero elements any pair of which are orthogonal. The corollary is immediate, since

$$\mathscr{B} = \left\{\frac{f^i}{\|f^i\|} : i \in \mathscr{I}\right\}$$

is a basis for M.

§ 60. **Orthogonalization.** Suppose that $\mathscr{F}$ is a countable nonempty set of elements of a Hilbert space X and that we are interested in

$$M = \mathrm{Span}\,\mathscr{F}.$$

We may replace any element of $\mathscr{F}$ by a nonzero multiple of itself without changing span $\mathscr{F}$ or M. More generally, we may replace any subset $\mathscr{E}$ of $\mathscr{F}$ by a set which has the same span as $\mathscr{E}$.

We shall construct, in an elementary and natural fashion, a basis $\mathscr{B}$ for M whenever $M \neq \{0\}$. Each element of $\mathscr{B}$ will be in span $\mathscr{F}$ and not merely in Span $\mathscr{F}$. The construction does not require any initial knowledge of linear independence or dependence of elements of $\mathscr{F}$. Indeed *the construction itself reveals the dimension of* M and any facts about $\mathscr{F}$ that are needed.

The construction is as follows.

Suppose that

$$\mathscr{F} = \{f^j\}, \qquad f^j \in X, \quad j \in J,$$

where J is the set of positive integers $\leqq m$ and $1 \leqq m \leqq \infty$.

Consider the elements

$$f^j, \qquad j \in J.$$

If these all vanish, then

$$M = \{0\}$$

and there is no need for a basis in M. In the contrary case, let j_1 be the smallest positive integer for which f^{j_1} does not vanish. Put

$$g^1 = f^{j_1} \neq 0,$$
$$M^1 = \text{span}\,\{g^1\} = \text{Span}\,\{g^1\}.$$

Then

$$M^1 = \text{span}\,\{f^1, f^2, \cdots, f^{j_1}\}.$$

If $j_1 = m$, then $M = M^1$ and a basis for M is

(61) $$\mathscr{B} = \left\{\frac{g^1}{\|g^1\|}\right\}.$$

In any case

$$\text{Proj}_{M^1}x = \frac{(x, g^1)}{\|g^1\|^2}\, g^1, \qquad x \in X.$$

If $j_1 < m$, consider the elements

(62) $$f^j - \text{Proj}_{M^1} f^j, \qquad j_1 < j \in J.$$

If these all vanish, then all elements of $\mathscr{F}$ are multiples of g^1 and $M = M^1$, the basis for M is (61). In the contrary case, let j_2 be the smallest integer $>j_1$ for which $f^{j_2} - \text{Proj}_{M^1} f^{j_2}$ does not vanish. Put

$$g^2 = f^{j_2} - \text{Proj}_{M^1} f^{j_2} = f^{j_2} - \frac{(f^{j_2}, g^1)}{\|g^1\|^2}\, g^1 \neq 0,$$
$$M^2 = \text{span}\,\{g^1, g^2\} = \text{Span}\,\{g^1, g^2\}.$$

Then

$$M^2 = \text{span}\,\{f^1, f^2, \cdots, f^{j_2}\},$$

and

$$g^1, g^2 \text{ are orthogonal,}$$

since $g^2 \in M^{1\perp}$. If $j_2 = m$, then $M = M^2$, and a basis for M is

(63) $$\mathscr{B} = \left\{\frac{g^1}{\|g^1\|}, \frac{g^2}{\|g^2\|}\right\}.$$

In any case

$$\operatorname{Proj}_{M^2} x = \frac{(x, g^1)}{\|g^1\|^2} g^1 + \frac{(x, g^2)}{\|g^2\|^2} g^2, \qquad x \in X.$$

If $j_2 < m$, consider the elements

(64) $$f^j - \operatorname{Proj}_{M^2} f^j, \qquad j_2 < j \in J.$$

If these all vanish, then all elements of $\mathscr{F}$ are in M^2 and $M = M^2$, the basis for M is (63). In the contrary case, let j_3 be the smallest integer $> j_2$ for which $f^{j_3} - \operatorname{Proj}_{M^2} f^{j_3}$ does not vanish. Put

$$g^3 = f^{j_3} - \operatorname{Proj}_{M^2} f^{j_3} = f^{j_3} - \frac{(f^{j_3}, g^1)}{\|g^1\|^2} g^1 - \frac{(f^{j_3}, g^2)}{\|g^2\|^2} g^2 \neq 0,$$

$$M^3 = \operatorname{span}\{g^1, g^2, g^3\} = \operatorname{Span}\{g^1, g^2, g^3\}.$$

Then

$$M^3 = \operatorname{span}\{f^1, f^2, \cdots, f^{j_3}\},$$

and

$$g^1, g^2, g^3 \text{ are an orthogonal system,}$$

since $g^3 \in M^{2\perp}$. If $j_3 = m$, then $M = M^3$, and a basis for M is

$$\mathscr{B} = \left\{\frac{g^1}{\|g^1\|}, \frac{g^2}{\|g^2\|}, \frac{g^3}{\|g^3\|}\right\}.$$

If $j_3 < m$, we continue in the way indicated. If the construction terminates after a finite number k of steps, then

$$M = M^k = \operatorname{span}\{g^1, \cdots, g^k\}$$

and the basis for M is

$$\mathscr{B} = \left\{\frac{g^1}{\|g^1\|}, \cdots, \frac{g^k}{\|g^k\|}\right\}.$$

If the construction does not terminate, it defines a countably infinite orthogonal system

$$g^1, g^2, \cdots$$

in M. Then

$$\operatorname{span} \mathscr{F} \subset \operatorname{span}\{g^1, g^2, \cdots\} \subset \operatorname{span} \mathscr{F}$$

since each finite linear combination of $f^1, f^2, \cdots$ is surely a finite linear combination of $g^1, g^2, \cdots$ and vice versa. Hence,

$$\operatorname{span} \mathscr{F} = \operatorname{span}\{g^1, g^2, \cdots\},$$

$$M = \operatorname{Span} \mathscr{F} = \operatorname{Span}\{g^1, g^2, \cdots\},$$

and a basis for M is

$$\mathscr{B} = \left\{\frac{g^1}{\|g^1\|}, \frac{g^2}{\|g^2\|}, \cdots\right\},$$

by Theorem 46. This completes the construction.

The projection on M may be written, by (59),

$$\text{Proj}_M\, x = \sum_i \frac{(x, g^i)}{\|g^i\|^2}\, g^i, \qquad x \in X. \tag{65}$$

No square roots enter here. The elements g^i are linear combinations of the given elements of $\mathscr{F}$ with coefficients of combination that are rational in the quantities

$$(f^j, f^{j'}), \qquad j, j' \in J.$$

In particular, $\|f^j\|$ enters only as $\|f^j\|^2$, $j \in J$.

The above construction is known as the Gram-Schmidt process of orthogonalization of $\mathscr{F}$. The construction, or at least its beginning, can be programmed for a computing machine. At any point of the construction we may replace g^i, $i = 1, 2, \cdots$, by a nonzero multiple of g^i, as convenient, without changing the basis $\mathscr{B}$.

As an illustration of the Gram-Schmidt orthogonalization, we now calculate a basis for the span of the rows of the matrix

$$\begin{pmatrix} 1 & 3 & 2 & 4 \\ -1 & 2 & -1 & 0 \\ 1 & 8 & 3 & 8 \end{pmatrix}. \tag{66}$$

We consider each row to be a vector in Euclidean 4-space, relative to a fixed coordinate system.

Here

$$\mathscr{F} = \{f^1, f^2, f^3\},$$

where

$$\begin{aligned} f^1 &= (1, 3, 2, 4), \\ f^2 &= (-1, 2, -1, 0), \\ f^3 &= (1, 8, 3, 8). \end{aligned}$$

Since $\mathscr{F}$ has 3 elements, the dimension of

$$M = \text{span}\, \mathscr{F} = \text{Span}\, \mathscr{F}$$

is at most 3.

Put

$$\begin{aligned} g^1 = f^1 &= (1, 3, 2, 4), \\ M^1 &= \text{span}\, \{(1, 3, 2, 4)\}. \end{aligned}$$

Next

$$g^2 = f^2 - \frac{(f^2, g^1)}{\|g^1\|^2}\, g^1$$

unless this element is zero. But

$$\|g^1\|^2 = 1 + 9 + 4 + 16 = 30,$$

$$(f^2, g^1) = -1 + 6 - 2 + 0 = 3,$$

$$g^2 = f^2 - \frac{(f^2, g^1)}{\|g^1\|^2} g^1 = (-1, 2, -1, 0) - \frac{1}{10}(1, 3, 2, 4)$$

$$= (-1.1, 1.7, -1.2, -.4).$$

Hence

$$\|g^2\|^2 = 1.21 + 2.89 + 1.44 + .16 = 5.70,$$

and, as a check,

$$(g^2, g^1) = -1.1 + 5.1 - 2.4 - 1.6 = 0.$$

Put

$$M^2 = \text{span}\,\{g^1, g^2\}.$$

Next

$$g^3 = f^3 - \frac{(f^3, g^1)}{\|g^1\|^2} g^1 - \frac{(f^3, g^2)}{\|g^2\|^2} g^2,$$

unless this element is zero. But

$$(f^3, g^1) = 1 + 24 + 6 + 32 = 63,$$

$$(f^3, g^2) = -1.1 + 13.6 - 3.6 - 3.2 = 5.7,$$

$$g^3 = (1, 8, 3, 8) - \frac{63}{30}(1, 3, 2, 4) - \frac{5.7}{5.70}(-1.1, 1.7, -1.2, -.4) = 0.$$

Our tentative g^3 will not be used.

As $\mathscr{F}$ is exhausted, the process has terminated. Thus

$$M = M^2 = \text{span}\,\{g^1, g^2\};$$

and the orthonormal basis for M is

$$\mathscr{B} = \left\{\frac{g^1}{\sqrt{30}}, \frac{g^2}{\sqrt{5.70}}\right\}.$$

The rank of the matrix (66) has incidentally been shown to be 2.

§ 67. **An illustration of Corollary 35. Elementary harmonic analysis of a derivative.** Suppose that

$$I_s = \{-\pi \leqq s \leqq \pi\}$$

and that X is the space of functions which are absolutely continuous on I_s and are such that the derivative

$$x_1 = \frac{dx}{ds} = D_s x$$

is an element of $H(I_s, s)$, that is, x_1 is Lebesgue measurable and absolute square integrable on I_s. We do not need a norm in X for the present example.

Suppose that Y is the L^2-space $H(I_t, t)$, $I_t = \{-\pi < t < \pi\}$, and that G is the operator $D_s|_{s=t}$ on X to Y. Thus

$$Gx = x_1(t), \quad t \in I_t; \quad x \in X.$$

Suppose that N is the space in Y spanned by

$$1, \quad \cos t, \quad \sin t.$$

According to Corollary 35, the approximation Ax which minimizes

$$\|Ax - Gx\|_Y$$

subject to the condition

$$Ax \in N,$$

for each fixed $x \in X$, is

$$Ax = \mathrm{Proj}_N\, x_1, \qquad x \in X.$$

Since

$$N = \mathrm{span}\,\{1, \cos t, \sin t\}$$

and since the vectors 1, $\cos t$, $\sin t$ are already orthogonal in Y, the explicit form of Ax is

$$Ax = \alpha + \beta \cos t + \gamma \sin t,$$

where

$$\alpha = \frac{(x_1, 1)_Y}{\|1\|_Y^2} = \frac{\int_{-\pi}^{\pi} x_1(t)\, dt}{\int_{-\pi}^{\pi} 1^2\, dt} = \frac{1}{2\pi}\int_{-\pi}^{\pi} x_1(t)\, dt,$$

$$\beta = \frac{(x_1, \cos t)_Y}{\|\cos t\|_Y^2} = \frac{\int_{-\pi}^{\pi} x_1(t) \cos t\, dt}{\int_{-\pi}^{\pi} \cos^2 t\, dt} = \frac{1}{\pi}\int_{-\pi}^{\pi} x_1(t) \cos t\, dt,$$

$$\gamma = \frac{1}{\pi}\int_{-\pi}^{\pi} x_1(t) \sin t\, dt.$$

In the present example, we approximate Gx by Ax. The space X is at the edge of the problem and is not really involved. In later problems we will approximate Gx by $A(x + \delta x)$, where δx is the error in the datum $x + \delta x$. There X will enter more deeply.

The error in the above approximation is

$$e = Ax - x_1 = \alpha + \beta \cos t + \gamma \sin t - x_1(t).$$

Since

$$e \in N^{\perp},$$

we may express e as a series in $\cos nt$, $\sin nt$, $n = 2, 3, 4, \cdots$; and

$$\|e\|_Y^2 = \int_{-\pi}^{\pi} |e(t)|^2 \, dt$$

will equal the sum of the absolute squares of the Fourier coefficients of x_1 relative to the normalization of $\cos nt$, $\sin nt$, $n = 2, 3, 4, \cdots$. The series for e is a series in the space Y: its partial sums approach e relative to the norm in Y.

As regards pointwise convergence, it follows from known theorems in Fourier series that, if $x_1(t)$ is of bounded variation on I_t, then the series for $e(t)$ will converge for all t and will equal $e(t)$ at each point of continuity of $x_1(t)$, $t \in I_t$.

A general comment may be appropriate here. Whether a particular type of convergence is acceptable is partly or entirely a matter of choice and decision by the approximator. It is the opinion of many mathematicians, including myself, that convergence relative to the norm in an L^2-space is particularly appropriate in the theory of approximation, because L^2-convergence involves an overall, average measure of the remainder.

Convergence of a series for $e(t)$, $t \in I_t$, relative to a norm

$$\sup_{t \in I_t} |e(t)|$$

implies uniform pointwise convergence on I_t. Such convergence might very well be satisfactory, where attainable without loss of other qualities. But the imposition of a condition of uniform convergence may be unduly restrictive.

Approximation based on minimizing

$$\sup_{t \in I_t} |e(t)|$$

(called minimax or Chebychev approximation) leads to nonlinear approximations even when the operator that we approximate is linear. This induces numerical complications. Approximation based on a Hilbert norm leads to a linear approximation, if the approximated operator is itself linear.

Returning to the illustration, we may note that an advantage of having taken Y as a Hilbert space is that we were able to carry out the minimization easily and effectively by means of a projection (cf. [Buck 1]).

§ 68. **Another illustration.** Here X and Y will be similar to the spaces of the preceding section; N will be somewhat different. The operator G will be as before.

Suppose that

$$I_s = \{-1 \leqq s \leqq 1\}, \qquad I_t = \{-1 < t < 1\},$$

and that X is the space of functions x which are absolutely continuous on I_s and are such that the derivative

$$x_1 = \frac{dx}{ds} = D_s x$$

is an element of $H(I_s, s)$. We do not need a norm in X for the present example.

Suppose that Y is the L^2-space $H(I_t, t)$ and that

$$Gx = x_1(t), \quad t \in I_t; \quad x \in X.$$

Suppose that

$$N = \text{span}\,\{1, t, t^2\} \subset Y.$$

The approximation Ax of Gx which minimizes

$$\|Ax - Gx\|_Y,$$

subject to the condition

$$Ax \in N,$$

for each $x \in X$, is

$$Ax = \text{Proj}_N\, Gx = \text{Proj}_N\, x_1.$$

To obtain a detailed formula, we orthogonalize

$$\mathscr{F} = \{1, t, t^2\}$$

and construct the basis $\mathscr{B}$ for N, as follows.

$$g^1(t) = 1, \qquad \|g^1\|^2 = \int_{-1}^{1} 1\, dt = 2, \qquad N^1 = \text{span}\,\{g^1\}.$$

$$g^2(t) = t - \text{Proj}_{N^1}\, t = t - \frac{(t, 1)1}{2} = t - \frac{1}{2}\int_{-1}^{1} t\, dt = t,$$

$$\|g^2\|^2 = \int_{-1}^{1} t^2\, dt = \frac{2}{3}, \qquad N^2 = \text{span}\,\{g^1, g^2\}.$$

$$g^3(t) = t^2 - \text{Proj}_{N^2}\, t^2 = t^2 - \frac{(t^2, 1)1}{2} - \frac{(t^2, t)t}{2/3}$$

$$= t^2 - \frac{1}{2}\int_{-1}^{1} t^2\, dt - \frac{3t}{2}\int_{-1}^{1} \bar{t}^3\, d\bar{t},$$

$$g^3(t) = t^2 - \frac{1}{3}, \qquad \|g^3\|^2 = \int_{-1}^{1}\left(t^2 - \frac{1}{3}\right)^2 dt = \frac{8}{45}.$$

One may check that $\{g^1, g^2, g^3\}$ are indeed an orthogonal set. Furthermore,

$$N = \text{span}\,\mathscr{F} = \text{span}\,\{g^1, g^2, g^3\},$$

$$\mathscr{B} = \left\{\frac{g^1}{\sqrt{2}}, \frac{g^2}{\sqrt{2/3}}, \frac{g^3}{\sqrt{8/45}}\right\}.$$

Thus

$$Ax = \text{Proj}_N\, x_1 = \alpha + \beta t + \gamma\left(t^2 - \frac{1}{3}\right),$$

where

$$\alpha = \frac{(x_1, g^1)}{\|g^1\|^2} = \frac{1}{2}\int_{-1}^{1} x_1(t)\,dt,$$

$$\beta = \frac{(x_1, g^2)}{\|g^2\|^2} = \frac{3}{2}\int_{-1}^{1} x_1(t)t\,dt,$$

$$\gamma = \frac{(x_1, g^3)}{\|g^3\|^2} = \frac{45}{8}\int_{-1}^{1} x_1(t)\left(t^2 - \frac{1}{3}\right)dt;$$

and

$$e = Ax - x_1.$$

We may write e as a series in span $N^{\perp}$, convergence being relative to the norm in Y.

§ 69. **The direct sum of two Hilbert spaces.** To formulate and solve an important problem in approximation we will need the idea of the direct product of two Hilbert spaces. We shall define and study direct products in the next sections. Before doing so, we mention the simpler concept of the direct sum.

Consider two Hilbert spaces X, Y. We may construct a Hilbert space Z of ordered pairs $[x, y]$ of elements $x \in X$, $y \in Y$, just as we construct the x, y-plane out of two number axes. The space Z, called the *direct sum*† of X and Y, is defined as the set of all ordered pairs $[x, y]$, $x \in X$, $y \in Y$, with scalar product, addition, and inner product as follows:

$$c[x, y] = [cx, cy], \qquad c \in \mathbf{C}, \quad [x,y] \in Z;$$

$$[x^1, y^1] + [x^2, y^2] = [x^1 + x^2, y^1 + y^2], \qquad [x^1, y^1], [x^2, y^2] \in Z;$$

$$([x^1, y^1], [x^2, y^2])_Z = (x^1, x^2)_X + (y^1, y^2)_Y.$$

† The term direct product as used earlier, for example in § 8: 30, is similar to the term direct sum as used here.

Then Z is a Hilbert space [Naimark 1, p. 97]. The norm in Z satisfies the Pythagorean relation

$$\|[x, y]\|_Z^2 = \|x\|_X^2 + \|y\|_Y^2, \qquad [x, y] \in Z,$$

as follows immediately from the definition of the inner product in Z.

§ 70. **The direct product of two Hilbert spaces.** Just as the direct sum is based on the idea of adding components, so the direct product is related to the idea of multiplying components.

Direct products are treated in [Murray-von Neumann 1, Chapter 2; von Neumann 3; Schatten 1; Dixmier 1, pp. 22–26]. For our applications we need the direct product of two separable Hilbert spaces, so we develop only that case. We need also a number of natural lemmas, some of which are not given explicitly in the references, which we will establish in detail. Theorem 75 provides a good introduction to the direct product.

Consider two *separable* Hilbert spaces X and Ψ, each of positive dimension. We shall define the direct product $X\Psi$ of X and Ψ.

Let $\{\xi^j\}$, $j \in J$, be a basis for X and $\{\psi^\nu\}$, $\nu \in N$, a basis for Ψ. The index sets J and N are nonempty and countable, since the spaces are separable. Let Π^0 designate the space of all finite formal linear combinations

$$c^1\xi^{j_1}\psi^{\nu_1} + c^2\xi^{j_2}\psi^{\nu_2} + \cdots + c^k\xi^{j_k}\psi^{\nu_k};$$
$$c^h \in \mathsf{C}, \quad j_h \in J, \quad \nu_h \in N; \qquad h = 1, \cdots, k;$$

with the natural definitions of addition and scalar multiplication in Π^0. Then Π^0 is a linear space.

Define an inner product in Π^0 by the relations

(71) $$(\xi^j\psi^\nu, \xi^{j'}\psi^{\nu'})_{\Pi^0} = (\xi^j, \xi^{j'})_X(\psi^\nu, \psi^{\nu'})_\Psi = \delta^{j,j'}\,\delta^{\nu,\nu'};$$
$$j, j' \in J; \qquad \nu, \nu' \in N;$$

and their distributive extensions. This is indeed an unambiguous and valid definition of an inner product on Π^0. Part of the proof involves showing that the condition

$$\left\|\sum_{h=1}^{k} c^h\xi^{j_h}\psi^{\nu_h}\right\|_{\Pi^0} = 0, \qquad j_h \in J, \quad \nu_h \in N, \quad c^h \in \mathsf{C},$$

where the pairs $(j_1, \nu_1), (j_2, \nu_2), \cdots, (j_k, \nu_k)$ are different, implies that

$$c^h = 0, \qquad h = 1, \cdots, k.$$

Now this is indeed the case, since

$$\left\|\sum_{h=1}^{k} c^h\xi^{j_h}\psi^{\nu_h}\right\|_{\Pi^0}^2 = \left(\sum_h c^h\xi^{j_h}\psi^{\nu_h}, \sum_{h'} c^{h'}\xi^{j_{h'}}\psi^{\nu_{h'}}\right)_{\Pi^0}$$
$$= \sum_{h,h'} c^h\bar{c}^{h'}(\xi^{j_h}\psi^{\nu_h}, \xi^{j_{h'}}\psi^{\nu_{h'}})_{\Pi^0}$$
$$= \sum_{h,h'} c^h\bar{c}^{h'}\,\delta^{j_h,j_{h'}}\,\delta^{\nu_h,\nu_{h'}} = \sum_{h=1}^{k} |c^h|^2.$$

Since Π^0 is an inner product space, we may construct its completion Π (§ 6). That completion is called the *direct product* of X and Ψ, and is denoted

$$\Pi = X\Psi.$$

72. LEMMA. *The set*

$$\{\xi^j\psi^\nu\}, \qquad j \in J, \quad \nu \in N,$$

is a basis for Π.

PROOF. By construction, the set consists of orthonormal elements. Furthermore

$$\operatorname{span}\{\xi^j\psi^\nu : j \in J,\ \nu \in N\} = \Pi^0$$

and Π^0 is dense in Π. This completes the proof, by Theorem 46.

73. LEMMA. *The direct product $X\Psi$ depends on X and Ψ alone and is independent of the bases for X and for Ψ that were used in the definition.*

PROOF. Suppose that X is defined as above in terms of bases $\{\xi^j : j \in J\}$ and $\{\psi^\nu : \nu \in N\}$:

$$\Pi^0 = \operatorname{span}\{\xi^j\psi^\nu : j \in J,\ \nu \in N\},$$

$$\Pi = X\Psi = \text{completion of } \Pi^0.$$

Suppose also that $\{\xi'^j : j \in J\}$ is another basis for X and $\{\psi'^\nu : \nu \in N\}$ another basis for Ψ. Put

$$\tilde{\Pi}^0 = \operatorname{span}\{\xi'^j\psi'^\nu : j \in J,\ \nu \in N\}.$$

It will be sufficient to show that $\tilde{\Pi}^0$ is dense in Π, with preservation of inner product, because the argument may be repeated with bases interchanged.

Consider the preservation of inner product. It will be sufficient to show that

$$q \underset{\text{def}}{=} (\xi'^j\psi'^\nu,\ \xi'^{j'}\psi'^{\nu'})_\Pi = \delta^{j,j'}\,\delta^{\nu,\nu'}; \qquad j, j' \in J, \quad \nu, \nu' \in N.$$

Now, by Theorem 46,

$$\xi'^j = \sum_{k \in J} \xi^j_k \xi^k, \quad \text{where} \quad \xi^j_k = (\xi'^j, \xi^k)_X \in \mathsf{C},$$

$$\psi'^\nu = \sum_{\lambda \in N} \psi^\nu_\lambda \psi^\lambda, \quad \text{where} \quad \psi^\nu_\lambda = (\psi'^\nu, \psi^\lambda)_\Psi \in \mathsf{C},$$

with similar relations for $\xi'^{j'}$, $\psi'^{\nu'}$. Since Π is the completion of Π^0 and since the inner product in Π is continuous in its arguments, q is the limit of what is obtained when partial sums are used instead of the full sums in the above expressions for ξ'^j, ψ'^ν, $\xi'^{j'}$, $\psi'^{\nu'}$. Hence

$$q = \lim \left(\sum_{k,\lambda} \xi_k^j \xi^k \psi_\lambda^\nu \psi^\lambda, \sum_{k',\lambda'} \xi_{k'}^{j'} \xi^{k'} \psi_{\lambda'}^{\nu'} \psi^{\lambda'} \right)_{\Pi^0},$$

where the sums are finite. Hence

$$\begin{aligned} q &= \lim \sum_{\substack{k,k',\\ \lambda,\lambda'}} \xi_k^j \psi_\lambda^\nu \bar{\xi}_{k'}^{j'} \bar{\psi}_{\lambda'}^{\nu'} (\xi^k, \xi^{k'})_X (\psi^\lambda, \psi^{\lambda'})_\Psi \\ &= \lim \sum_{k,\lambda} \xi_k^j \bar{\xi}_k^{j'} \psi_\lambda^\nu \bar{\psi}_\lambda^{\nu'} = \lim \sum_k \xi_k^j \bar{\xi}_k^{j'} \sum_\lambda \psi_\lambda^\nu \bar{\psi}_\lambda^{\nu'} \\ &= \sum_{k \in J} \xi_k^j \bar{\xi}_k^{j'} \sum_{\lambda \in N} \psi_\lambda^\nu \bar{\psi}_\lambda^{\nu'} = (\xi^j, \xi^{j'})_X (\psi^\nu, \psi^{\nu'})_\Psi = \delta^{j,j'} \delta^{\nu,\nu'}, \end{aligned}$$

by Theorem 46.

It remains to show that $\tilde{\Pi}^0$ is dense in Π. Consider an element π of Π. We may find elements

$$\sum_{h=1}^{k} c^h \xi^{j_h} \psi^{\nu_h}, \qquad k < \infty, \tag{74}$$

as close to π as we please. And we may find elements of $\tilde{\Pi}^0$ as close to the element (74) as we please. This completes the proof.

75. THEOREM. *Consider two separable L^2-spaces $H(T, m)$ and $H(\Omega, p)$, where m is a nonnegative measure on a space T and p is a nonnegative measure on a space Ω. The L^2-space*

$$H(T \times \Omega, mp) \tag{76}$$

is precisely the direct product

$$H(T, m)H(\Omega, p). \tag{77}$$

PROOF. The space (76) is the space of functions $y(t, \omega)$, $t \in T$, $\omega \in \Omega$, measurable and absolute square integrable mp, with

$$(y, y') = \int_\Omega \int_T y(t, \omega)\bar{y}'(t, \omega)\, dm(t)\, dp(\omega), \qquad y, y' \in H(T \times \Omega, mp).$$

Let $\{\xi^j, j \in J\}$ be a basis for $H(T, m)$ and $\{\psi^\nu : \nu \in N\}$ be a basis for $H(\Omega, p)$. Then

$$\xi^j \psi^\nu \in H \underset{\text{def}}{=} H(T \times \Omega, mp), \qquad j \in J, \quad \nu \in N,$$

and

$$(\xi^j \psi^\nu, \xi^{j'} \psi^{\nu'})_H = \delta^{j,j'} \delta^{\nu,\nu'}, \qquad j, j' \in J, \quad \nu, \nu' \in N,$$

by Fubini's Theorem. Hence

$$\{\xi^j \psi^\nu : j \in J, \nu \in N\} \tag{78}$$

is an orthonormal system in H. Now this orthonormal system is complete. For, suppose that

$$z(t, \omega), \quad t \in T, \quad \omega \in \Omega,$$

is such that

$$z \in H$$

and

$$(z, \xi^j \psi^\nu)_H = 0 = \int_T \bar{\xi}^j \, dm \int_\Omega z \bar{\psi}^\nu \, dp, \qquad j \in J, \quad \nu \in N.$$

In these integrals, z is a function of (t, ω), ξ^j a function of t, ψ^ν a function of ω; $t \in T$, $\omega \in \Omega$.

For each ν, the inner integral

$$q \underset{\text{def}}{=} \int_\Omega z \bar{\psi}^\nu \, dp$$

is measurable m (part of the Theorem of Fubini); and

$$\int_T |q|^2 \, dm = \int_T dm \left| \int_\Omega z \bar{\psi}^\nu \, dp \right|^2 \leqq \int_T dm \left[\int_\Omega |z|^2 \, dp \int_\Omega |\psi^\nu|^2 \, dp \right]$$

$$= \int_T dm \int_\Omega |z|^2 \, dp = \|z\|_H^2 < \infty,$$

since

$$\int_\Omega |\psi^\nu|^2 \, dp = \|\psi^\nu\|^2_{H(\Omega, p)} = 1.$$

Hence

$$q = \int_\Omega z \bar{\psi}^\nu \, dp \in H(T, m).$$

Furthermore the Fourier coefficients of q relative to $\{\xi^j : j \in J\}$ are all zero. Hence

$$q = 0 \in H(T, m);$$

and the function q is zero for almost all $t \in T$.

For almost all $t \in T$, then, all the functions

$$\int_\Omega z \bar{\psi}^\nu \, dp, \qquad \nu \in N,$$

vanish, since N is countable. Thus for each fixed $t \in T$, with null exceptions, the Fourier coefficients of $z(t, \omega)$ in $H(\Omega, p)$ all vanish; and therefore

$$z(t, \omega) = 0 \in H(\Omega, p) \quad \text{for almost all } t \in T.$$

Now the function z is measurable mp. It follows, by the Theorem of Fubini, that

$$z(t, \omega) = 0$$

for almost all (t, ω) in $T \times \Omega$. Hence

$$z = 0 \in H(T \times \Omega, mp).$$

Hence the orthonormal system (78) is complete in H.

On the other hand, the direct product (77) is precisely the closure of the span of (78). Hence the spaces (76) and (77) are the same, as was to be shown.

Thus the direct product of two L^2-spaces is an L^2-space.

§ 79. **Direct products and function spaces.** In preparation for the formulation and study of the problem of efficient approximation, we now consider three separable Hilbert spaces X, Y, and Ψ, described below, and the direct products $X\Psi$ and $Y\Psi$. We exclude the uninteresting cases in which X, Y, or Ψ consists only of the element 0.

Let X be a *separable Hilbert space*, with *basis* $\{\xi^j : j \in J\}$. In our applications, X may or may not be an L^2-space.

Let Y be a *separable L^2-space*

$$Y = H(T, m)$$

of functions on a space T measurable and absolute square integrable relative to a measure m. Let $\{\eta^k : k \in K\}$ be a *basis* for Y.

Let Ψ be a *separable L^2-space*

$$\Psi = H(\Omega, p)$$

of functions on a space Ω measurable and absolute square integrable relative to a measure p. Let $\{\psi^\nu : \nu \in N\}$ be a *basis* for Ψ. In later applications we will specify that p is a probability, i.e., that

$$p(\Omega) = 1,$$

and we will denote the integral operator $\int_\Omega \cdots dp$ by the symbol E for expected value. For the present, we do not specify that p be a probability.

For the rest of the chapter, X, Y, and Ψ are to be the spaces just described, unless the contrary is stated.

In the following lemmas, the space X may be replaced by Y, because Y satisfies our hypothesis about X; but Y may not always be replaced by X.

80. Lemma. *If $u \in X\Psi$, then*

$$u = \sum_{j,\nu} u^{j,\nu} \xi^j \psi^\nu = \sum_j u^j \xi^j, \tag{81}$$

where

$$u^{j,\nu} = (u, \xi^j \psi^\nu)_{X\Psi}, \tag{82}$$

$$u^j = \sum_\nu u^{j,\nu} \psi^\nu \in \Psi, \qquad j \in J, \ \nu \in N. \tag{83}$$

Furthermore

(84) $$\|u\|^2_{X\Psi} = \sum_{j,\nu} |u^{j,\nu}|^2 = \sum_j \|u^j\|^2_{\Psi}.$$

The summations here are to be understood in the pertinent space. Thus both sums in (81) are in $X\Psi$, and convergence is relative to the norm in $X\Psi$. The sum in (83) is in Ψ, with convergence relative to the norm in Ψ. As regards notation, letters with two superscripts, like $u^{j,\nu}$, will be numbers. Other letters also may be numbers.

PROOF. The first equations in (81) and (84) are consequences, by Theorem 46, of the fact that $\{\xi^j\psi^\nu\}$ is a basis in $X\Psi$. The element u^j defined by (83) is indeed in Ψ, since

$$\sum_\nu |u^{j,\nu}|^2 \leqq \sum_{j,\nu} |u^{j,\nu}|^2 = \|u\|^2_{X\Psi} < \infty.$$

Since $u^j \in \Psi$, the product $u^j\xi^j$, defined as

(85) $$u^j\xi^j = \sum_\nu u^{j,\nu}\psi^\nu\xi^j, \qquad j \in J,$$

is in $X\Psi$, by the definition of the direct product $X\Psi$. Furthermore

$$\|u^j\xi^j\|^2_{X\Psi} = \sum_\nu |u^{j,\nu}|^2 = \|u^j\|^2_{\Psi}, \qquad j \in J;$$

and this implies (84).

It remains to establish the second equation of (81); that is, that the partial sums of

(86) $$\sum_j u^j\xi^j$$

approach u in $X\Psi$. This is immediate, by the use of coordinates (Theorem 46) relative to the basis $\{\xi^j\psi^\nu\}$. Thus, the coordinates of u are $\{u^{j,\nu}\}$. The coordinates of the partial sums of (86), by (85), are $\{u^{j,\nu}\}$ with its elements replaced by 0 for sufficiently large j. Hence the coordinates of u minus a partial sum of (86) are $\{u^{j,\nu}\}$ with its elements replaced by 0 except for sufficiently large j. Since $\sum_{j,\nu} |u^{j,\nu}|^2 < \infty$, the sum restricted to $j > j_0$ must approach zero as $j_0 \to \infty$. This completes the proof.

Consider $u \in X\Psi$ and the elements $u^j, j \in J$, of Ψ defined by (83). Since $u^j \in \Psi$, there is a function $u^j(\omega)$, p-measurable and absolute square integrable on Ω, such that $u^j(\omega)$ is an element of the equivalence set u^j. We may write, somewhat inexactly,

$$u^j = u^j(\omega) \in H(\Omega,p) = \Psi.$$

For almost all ω, $u^j(\omega)$ is a number. Put

(87) $$u_\omega = \sum_j u^j(\omega)\,\xi^j, \quad \text{almost all } \omega.$$

The summation here is in X.

88. Lemma. *If* $u \in X\Psi$, *then*

$$u_\omega \in X \textit{ for almost all } \omega, \tag{89}$$

and

$$\|u_\omega\|_X^2 = \sum_j |u^j(\omega)|^2, \quad \textit{almost all } \omega. \tag{90}$$

If $u, u' \in X\Psi$, *then*

$$(u, u')_X \underset{\text{def}}{=} (u_\omega, u'_\omega)_X, \quad \textit{almost all } \omega, \tag{91}$$

is integrable p *on* Ω *and*

$$(u, u')_{X\Psi} = \int_\Omega (u, u')_X \, dp. \tag{92}$$

In particular

$$\|u\|_{X\Psi}^2 = \int_\Omega \|u_\omega\|_X^2 \, dp = \int_\Omega \|u\|_X^2 \, dp. \tag{93}$$

Finally

$$u = 0 \in X\Psi$$

iff

$$u_\omega = 0 \in X, \quad \textit{almost all } \omega.$$

Proof. To establish (89) and (90), it is sufficient to show that the series in (90) converges. Now

$$\int_\Omega \sum_j |u^j(\omega)|^2 \, dp = \sum_j \int_\Omega |u^j(\omega)|^2 \, dp = \sum_j \|u^j\|_\Psi^2 = \|u\|_{X\Psi}^2 < \infty,$$

by (84) and Fubini's Theorem. It follows that the integrand

$$\sum_j |u^j(\omega)|^2$$

does indeed converge, for almost all ω.

Now consider $(u, u')_X$, defined by (91). By (87) and Theorem 46,

$$(u, u')_X = (u_\omega, u'_\omega)_X = \sum_j u^j(\omega)\bar{u}'^j(\omega), \quad \text{almost all } \omega.$$

Hence $(u, u')_X$ is p-measurable. Furthermore

$$\int_\Omega (u, u')_X \, dp = \sum_j \int_\Omega u^j(\omega)\bar{u}'^j(\omega) \, dp = \sum_j \sum_\nu u^{j,\nu}\bar{u}'^{j,\nu} = (u, u')_{X\Psi}, \tag{94}$$

by (83) and the use of coordinates in Ψ. The inversion of the operators $\sum_j$ and $\int_\Omega$ is permissible by Fubini's Theorem, since

$$\left[\sum_j \int_\Omega |u^j(\omega)\bar{u}'^j(\omega)|\, dp\right]^2 \leqq \left[\sum_j \int_\Omega |u^j(\omega)|^2\, dp\right]\cdot\left[\sum_j \int_\Omega |u'^j(\omega)|^2\, dp\right]$$

$$= \left[\sum_j \sum_\nu |u^{j,\nu}|^2\right]\cdot\left[\sum_j \sum_\nu |u'^{j,\nu}|^2\right]$$

$$= \|u\|^2_{X\Psi}\|u'\|^2_{X\Psi} < \infty.$$

Hence $(u, u')_X$ is integrable on Ω, and (92) is established. Now (92) implies (93).

Finally, suppose that

$$u = 0 \in X\Psi.$$

Then

$$u^{j,\nu} = 0, \qquad u^j = 0 \in \Psi, \qquad j \in J, \quad \nu \in N;$$

by (83);

$$u^j(\omega) = 0, \qquad \|u_\omega\|_X = 0, \qquad \text{almost all } \omega;$$

by (90); and

$$u_\omega = 0 \in X, \quad \text{almost all } \omega.$$

Conversely, suppose that the last relation holds. Then

$$u^j(\omega) = 0, \qquad j \in J, \qquad \text{almost all } \omega,$$

by (90); and

$$u^j = 0 \in \Psi.$$

Then

$$u^{j,\nu} = 0 \qquad j \in J, \quad \nu \in N,$$

by (83), and

$$u = 0 \in X\Psi.$$

This completes the proof.

Consider an element $u \in X\Psi$. We have defined a number of objects related to u as follows.

(95) $$u^{j,\nu} = (u, \xi^j\psi^\nu)_{X\Psi}, \qquad j \in J, \quad \nu \in N.$$

Thus $\{u^{j,\nu}\}$ are coordinates of u, and

(96) $$u = \sum_{j,\nu} u^{j,\nu}\xi^j\psi^\nu.$$

(97) $$u^j = \sum_\nu u^{j,\nu}\psi^\nu \in \Psi = H(\Omega, p).$$

(98) $$u^j = u^j(\omega), \quad \text{almost all } \omega \text{ in } \Omega.$$

Equality in the last relation is really a manner of speaking; the function $u^j(\omega)$ on almost all of Ω to $\mathbf{C}$ is in fact an element of the equivalence set u^j.

$$u_\omega = \sum_j u^j(\omega)\xi^j \in X, \quad \text{almost all } \omega. \tag{99}$$

These definitions use the bases $\{\xi^j\}$ and $\{\psi^\nu\}$.

The following lemmas are not necessary for our study of $X\Psi$, but they illuminate the interpretation of the problem of efficient approximation to be introduced in § 174. That problem involves u_ω, $u \in X\Psi$, and it is related to the spaces X, Ψ and the element u but not at all to the bases in X, Ψ.

100. Lemma. *The element u^j is independent of the basis $\{\psi^\nu\}$ in Ψ.*

Clearly u^j does depend on the basis $\{\xi^j\}$ in X.

Proof. Suppose that $\{\tilde\psi^\nu\}$ is a basis in Ψ, and that

$$\tilde u^{j,\nu} = (u, \xi^j\tilde\psi^\nu)_{X\Psi}, \qquad j \in J, \quad \nu \in N;$$

and

$$\tilde u^j = \sum_\nu \tilde u^{j,\nu}\tilde\psi^\nu \in \Psi. \tag{101}$$

We shall show that

$$\tilde u^j = u^j$$

by using coordinates in Ψ relative to $\{\psi^\nu\}$.

Thus the μth coordinate, $\mu \in N$, of $\tilde u^j$ is the μth coordinate of the convergent series (101) in Ψ, which equals the series of coordinates

$$\sum_\nu \tilde u^{j,\nu}(\tilde\psi^\nu, \psi^\mu)_\Psi = \sum_\nu (u, \xi^j\tilde\psi^\nu)_{X\Psi}(\tilde\psi^\nu, \psi^\mu)_\Psi,$$

by (51). On the other hand the μth coordinate of u^j is

$$u^{j,\mu} = (u, \xi^j\psi^\mu)_{X\Psi} = (u, \xi^j \sum_\nu (\psi^\mu, \tilde\psi^\nu)_\Psi\tilde\psi^\nu)_{X\Psi}$$

$$= \sum_\nu (\tilde\psi^\nu, \psi^\mu)_\Psi(u, \xi^j\tilde\psi^\nu)_{X\Psi},$$

since the inner product is continuous in its arguments.

Hence the μth coordinates of u^j and $\tilde u^j$ are equal, for all $\mu \in N$. This completes the proof.

102. Lemma. *For each ω with null exceptions the element $u_\omega \in X$ is independent of the bases $\{\xi^j\}$ in X and $\{\psi^\nu\}$ in Ψ.*

If X is an L^2-space, this assertion follows from Lemma 108.

Proof. Suppose that $\{\tilde\xi^j\}$ is a basis in X and $\{\tilde\psi^\nu\}$ a basis in Ψ. We shall show that a change to these bases from $\{\xi^j\}$ and $\{\psi^\nu\}$ does not change u_ω, for almost all ω. The change can be made in two steps: first to $\{\tilde\xi^j\}$, $\{\psi^\nu\}$ and second, thereafter, to $\{\tilde{\xi}^j\}$, $\{\tilde{\psi}^\nu\}$. In the second step the elements u^j do not change, by Lemma 100; and therefore u_ω does not change, by (99), for almost all ω. It is sufficient therefore to consider only the first step, which we now do.

Put

$$\begin{aligned} \tilde{u}^{j,\nu} &= (u, \xi^j\psi^\nu)_{X\Psi}, \qquad j \in J, \quad \nu \in N; \\ \tilde{u}^j &= \sum_\nu \tilde{u}^{j,\nu}\psi^\nu \in \Psi; \\ \tilde{u}^j &= \tilde{u}^j(\omega), \quad \text{almost all } \omega; \\ \tilde{u}_\omega &= \sum_j \tilde{u}^j(\omega)\xi^j \in X. \end{aligned}$$

We shall show that

$$\tilde{u}_\omega = u_\omega, \quad \text{almost all } \omega,$$

by using coordinates relative to $\{\xi^j\}$.

The ith coordinate, $i \in J$, of u_ω is

$$u^i(\omega) \in \mathsf{C}, \quad \text{almost all } \omega; \tag{103}$$

and of $\tilde{u}_\omega$ is

$$\begin{aligned} (\tilde{u}_\omega, \xi^i)_X &= \left(\sum_j \tilde{u}^j(\omega)\xi^j, \xi^i\right)_X \\ &= \sum_j \tilde{u}^j(\omega)(\xi^j, \xi^i)_X \in \mathsf{C}, \quad \text{almost all } \omega, \end{aligned} \tag{104}$$

by (51).

Consider (103), (104) as functions on almost all of Ω to C. We know that

$$u^i(\omega) \in \Psi, \qquad i \in J. \tag{105}$$

Also

$$\tilde{u}^j(\omega)(\xi^j, \xi^i)_X \in \Psi, \qquad j \in J,$$

and

$$\sum_j \tilde{u}^j(\omega)(\xi^j, \xi^i)_X \in \Psi, \tag{106}$$

since

$$\begin{aligned} \left\|\sum_j \tilde{u}^j(\omega)(\xi^j, \xi^i)_X\right\|_\Psi^2 &\leqq \left[\sum_j \|\tilde{u}^j(\omega)\|_\Psi |(\xi^j, \xi^i)_X|\right]^2 \\ &\leqq \sum_j \|\tilde{u}^j(\omega)\|_\Psi^2 \sum_j |(\xi^j, \xi^i)_X|^2 \\ &= \|\xi^i\|_X^2 \sum_j \|\tilde{u}^j(\omega)\|_\Psi^2 = \|u\|_{X\Psi}^2 < \infty, \end{aligned}$$

by Minkowski's inequality, Schwarz's inequality, and (96), (97).

We now show that the elements (105), (106) of Ψ' are equal, by using coordinates relative to $\{\psi^\nu\}$. Thus the νth coordinate, $\nu \in N$, of $u^i(\omega)$ is

$$u^{i,\nu} = (u, \xi^i\psi^\nu)_{X\Psi} = \left(u, \sum_j (\xi^i, \tilde{\xi}^j)_X \xi^j \psi^\nu\right)_{X\Psi}$$

$$= \sum_j (\tilde{\xi}^j, \xi^i)_X (u, \tilde{\xi}^j\psi^\nu)_{X\Psi} = \sum_j (\tilde{\xi}^j, \xi^i)_X \tilde{u}^{j,\nu}, \qquad i \in J,$$

by coordinates in $X\Psi'$. On the other hand the νth coordinate of (106) is

$$\left(\sum_j \tilde{u}^j(\omega)(\tilde{\xi}^j, \xi^i)_X, \psi^\nu\right)_\Psi = \sum_j (\tilde{\xi}^j, \xi^i)_X (\tilde{u}^j(\omega), \psi^\nu)_\Psi = \sum_j (\tilde{\xi}^j, \xi^i)_X \tilde{u}^{j,\nu},$$

by (97). This completes the proof.

In our considerations, X has been an arbitrary separable Hilbert space. Now it may be that X is a space of functions $x(s)$, $s \in S$, on a space S or perhaps a space of equivalence sets of such functions. Indeed this will usually be the case in applications. Then the elements $\xi^j, j \in J$, in the basis for X will be functions on S and u_ω, defined by (87), will be a function on S, for each fixed $\omega \in \Omega$ with null exceptions. Then also u, being in $X\Psi'$, will be a function $u(s, \omega)$, $s \in S$, $\omega \in \Omega$, or an equivalence set of such functions. For each fixed ω with null exceptions, $u(s, \omega)$ will determine a function on S. By considering the relation between the norm $\|x\|_X$ of $x \in X$ and the values of the function x, one may show that in an appropriate sense

$$u(s, \omega) = u_\omega \in X \tag{107}$$

for each fixed ω with null exceptions, for each space X that we use. The relation (107) is relevant to the philosophical interpretation of the problem of efficient approximation, to be described later. The relation (107) is not needed for the abstract problem or for its solution.

If the space X is an L^2-space, say

$$X = Y = H(T, m),$$

the relation (107) is established in the following lemma. If X is a space in which the norm of x involves derivatives or partial derivatives of x, an analogous argument uses Taylor formulas.

108. LEMMA. *If $u(t, \omega)$, $t \in T$, $\omega \in \Omega$, is an element of $Y\Psi'$, then*

$$u_\omega = u(t, \omega) \in Y$$

for each fixed ω with null exceptions.

PROOF. By (95)–(99), with the basis $\{\xi^j\}$ in X replaced by the basis $\{\eta^k\}$ in Y,

(109) $$u = \sum_{k,\nu} u^{k,\nu}\eta^k\psi^\nu, \quad u^{k,\nu} = (u, \eta^k\psi^\nu)_{Y\Psi}, \quad k \in K, \nu \in N;$$

(110) $$u^k = \sum_\nu u^{k,\nu}\psi^\nu \in \Psi,$$

(111) $$u^k = u^k(\omega), \quad \text{almost all } \omega;$$

and

(112) $$u_\omega = \sum_k u^k(\omega)\eta^k \in Y, \quad \text{almost all } \omega.$$

By Theorem 75,

$$Y\Psi = H(T \times \Omega, mp).$$

Hence

$$u(t, \omega), \qquad t \in T, \quad \omega \in \Omega,$$

is absolute square integrable mp. For each fixed ω with null exceptions,

$$u(t, \omega) \in H(T, m) = Y,$$

by Fubini's Theorem. In Y,

(113) $$u(t, \omega) = \sum_k (u(t, \omega), \eta^k)_Y\eta^k, \quad \text{almost all } \omega,$$

by Theorem 46. But

$$(u(t, \omega), \eta^k)_Y = \int_T u(t, \omega)\bar{\eta}^k(t)\, dm(t),$$

a function of ω which is measurable p. Furthermore

$$\begin{aligned}\|(u(t, \omega), \eta^k)_Y\|_\Psi^2 &= \int_\Omega dp(\omega)\left|\int_T u(t, \omega)\bar{\eta}^k(t)\, dm(t)\right|^2 \\ &\leqq \int_\Omega dp(\omega)\left[\int_T |u(t, \omega)|^2\, dm(t)\right]\left[\int_T |\eta^k(t)|^2\, dm(t)\right] \\ &= \|u\|_{Y\Psi}^2 < \infty,\end{aligned}$$

since η^k is a unit vector in Y. Hence

$$(u(t, \omega), \eta^k)_Y \in \Psi;$$

and, expanding in Ψ,

$$(u(t, \omega), \eta^k)_Y = \sum_\nu a^{k,\nu}\psi^\nu,$$

where

$$a^{k,\nu} = ((u(t, \omega), \eta^k)_Y, \psi^\nu)_\Psi = \int_\Omega \bar{\psi}^\nu(\omega)\, dp(\omega) \int_T u(t, \omega)\bar{\eta}^k(t)\, dm(t) = u^{k,\nu},$$

$$k \in K, \quad \nu \in N.$$

Hence, by (113), (110), (111), (112),

$$u(t, \omega) = u_\omega, \quad \text{almost all } \omega.$$

The proof is complete.

114. Corollary. *If $u(t, \omega)$, $t \in T$, $\omega \in \Omega$, is an element of $Y\Psi$, then*

$$u_t = u(t, \omega) \in \Psi \tag{115}$$

for each fixed t with null exceptions, where

$$u = \sum_{k,\nu} u^{k,\nu}\eta^k\psi^\nu, \qquad u^{k,\nu} = (u, \eta^k\psi^\nu)_{Y\Psi}, \qquad k \in K, \quad \nu \in N; \tag{116}$$

$$u^\nu = \sum_k u^{k,\nu}\eta^k \in Y; \tag{117}$$

$$u^\nu = u^\nu(t), \quad \textit{almost all } t; \tag{118}$$

and

$$u_t = \sum_\nu u^\nu(t)\psi^\nu \in \Psi, \quad \textit{almost all } t. \tag{119}$$

Proof. This is Lemma 108 with Y and Ψ interchanged.

In our notation u^ν in (117) and u^k in (110) are different objects distinguished by the fact that $\nu \in N$ and $k \in K$. Likewise u_ω and u_t are different, because $\omega \in \Omega$ and $t \in T$.

120. Theorem. *If the sequence $\{u^i\}$ converges to u in $X\Psi$ as $i \to \infty$, then for a suitable subsequence $\{u^{i_h}\}$, $i_1 < i_2 < \cdots$, $\{u^{i_h}_\omega\}$ converges to u_ω in X for almost all ω as $h \to \infty$.*

Proof. By Lemma 88,

$$\|u^i - u\|^2_{X\Psi} = \int_\Omega \|u^i_\omega - u_\omega\|^2_X \, dp(\omega) \to 0; \tag{121}$$

and

$$\|u^i_\omega - u_\omega\|_X, \qquad i = 1, 2, \cdots,$$

is a measurable function on Ω absolute square integrable, that is, an element of $\Psi = H(\Omega, p)$. Thus, by (121),

$$\|[\|u^i_\omega - u_\omega\|_X]\|^2_\Psi \to 0$$

and

$$\|u^i_\omega - u_\omega\|_X \to 0 \text{ in } \Psi \text{ as } i \to \infty.$$

Lemma 30 therefore applies to the sequence

$$\{\|u^i_\omega - u_\omega\|_X\}.$$

There exist $i_1 < i_2 < \cdots$ such that, for each ω with null exceptions,

$$\|u_\omega^{i_h} - u_\omega\|_X \to 0 \text{ in } \mathbf{C} \text{ as } h \to \infty.$$

This implies the conclusion of the theorem and completes the proof.

122. COROLLARY. *If the sequence $\{u^i\}$ converges to u in $Y\Psi$, then for a suitable subsequence $\{u^{i_h}\}$, $i_1 < i_2 < \cdots$, $\{u_\omega^{i_h}\}$ converges to u_ω in Y for almost all ω and $\{u_t^{i_h}\}$ converges to u_t in Ψ for almost all t, as $h \to \infty$.*

PROOF. Apply Theorem 120 twice, first with $(Y, \Psi) = (X, \Psi)$ and then with Y and Ψ interchanged.

123. LEMMA. *Suppose that the sequences $\{u^i\}$ and $\{v^i\}$ converge to u and v respectively in $Y\Psi$. Then*

(124)
$$\int_\Omega dp \int_T dm|u\bar{v} - u^i\bar{v}^i| \to 0$$

and

(125)
$$\int_T dm\left|\int_\Omega dp(u\bar{v} - u^i\bar{v}^i)\right| \to 0, \quad \textit{as } i \to \infty.$$

PROOF. Note first that

$$\int_\Omega dp \int_T dm|(u - u^i)\bar{v}^i| \leqq \|v^i\|_{Y\Psi}\|u - u^i\|_{Y\Psi} \to 0,$$

and

$$\int_\Omega dp \int_T dm\, |u(\bar{v} - \bar{v}^i)| \leqq \|u\|_{Y\Psi}\|v - v^i\|_{Y\Psi} \to 0.$$

Hence

$$\int_\Omega dp \int_T dm|u\bar{v} - u^i\bar{v}^i| = \int_\Omega dp \int_T dm|u(\bar{v} - \bar{v}^i) + (u - u^i)\bar{v}^i|$$
$$\leqq \int_\Omega dp \int_T dm|u(\bar{v} - \bar{v}^i)|$$
$$+ \int_\Omega dp \int_T dm|(u - u^i)\bar{v}^i| \to 0.$$

This establishes (124). Now (124) implies (125) since the integral in (125) is dominated by the integral in (124).

The proof is complete.

Suppose that

$$x \in X, \qquad \phi \in \Psi.$$

We define the elements ϕx and $x\phi$ in $X\Psi$ as follows. Let the coordinates of x be $\{x^j\}$ and those of ϕ be $\{\phi^\nu\}$:

$$x = \sum_j x^j \xi^j, \qquad x^j = (x, \xi^j)_X, \qquad \phi = \sum_\nu \phi^\nu \psi^\nu, \qquad \phi^\nu = (\phi, \psi^\nu)_\Psi.$$

Then $\phi x = x\phi$ is defined as the element in $X\Psi$ whose coordinates are $\{x^j \phi^\nu\}$:

$$\phi x = x\phi = \sum_{j,\nu} x^j \phi^\nu \xi^j \psi^\nu. \tag{126}$$

127. Lemma. *Suppose that* $x \in X$ *and* $\phi(\omega) \in \Psi = H(\Omega, p)$. *Then* ϕx *is indeed an element of* $X\Psi$, *and, for each fixed* ω *with null exceptions,*

$$\phi(\omega)x = (\phi x)_\omega \in X. \tag{128}$$

Furthermore

$$(\phi x, \phi' x')_{X\Psi} = (\phi, \phi')_\Psi (x, x')_X; \qquad \phi, \phi' \in \Psi; \qquad x, x' \in X; \tag{129}$$

and

$$\|\phi x\|^2_{X\Psi} = \|\phi\|^2_\Psi \|x\|^2_X. \tag{130}$$

Proof. Here ϕx is defined by (126); that $\phi x \in X\Psi$ is immediate since

$$\sum_{j,\nu} |x^j \phi|^2 = \sum_j |x^j|^2 \sum_\nu |\phi^\nu|^2 = \|x\|^2_X \|\phi\|^2_\Psi < \infty.$$

This establishes (130) also. The relation (129) follows Theorem 46:

$$(\phi x, \phi' x')_{X\Psi} = \sum_{j,\nu} x^j \phi^\nu \bar{x}'^j \bar{\phi}'^\nu = \sum_\nu \phi^\nu \bar{\phi}'^\nu \sum_j x^j \bar{x}'^j$$
$$= (\phi, \phi')_\Psi (x, x')_X.$$

To establish (128), note that the element $(\phi x)_\omega$ is defined by (99) and (97). Hence

$$(\phi x)_\omega = \sum_j \xi^j \Big(\sum_\nu x^j \phi^\nu \psi^\nu \Big)(\omega) = \sum_j \xi^j x^j \phi(\omega) = \phi(\omega) x, \quad \text{almost all } \omega,$$

because

$$\phi = \sum_\nu \phi^\nu \psi^\nu.$$

This completes the proof.

131. Lemma. *Suppose that* Y_1 *and* Ψ_1 *are closed linear subspaces of* Y *and* Ψ, *respectively. Then*

$$\text{Proj}_{Y_1\Psi_1} u = \text{Proj}_{Y_1} \text{Proj}_{\Psi_1} u = \text{Proj}_{\Psi_1} \text{Proj}_{Y_1} u, \qquad u \in Y\Psi.$$

PROOF. The lemma is immediate if either Y_1 or Ψ_1 is of dimension zero. In the contrary case, suppose that the bases $\{\eta^k : k \in K\}$ and $\{\psi^\nu : \nu \in N\}$ for Y and Ψ have been taken in such a way that $\{\eta^k : k \in K_1\}$ and $\{\psi^\nu : \nu \in N_1\}$ are bases for Y_1 and Ψ_1, respectively, where $K_1 \subset K$ and $N_1 \subset N$.

Then

$$\begin{aligned}
\text{Proj}_{Y_1\Psi_1} u &= \sum_{\substack{k \in K_1,\\ \nu \in N_1}} (u, \eta^k\psi^\nu)_{Y\Psi}\eta^k\psi^\nu \\
&= \sum_{K_1,N_1} \eta^k\psi^\nu \int_\Omega (u, \eta^k)_Y \bar{\psi}^\nu \, dp \\
&= \sum_{N_1} \psi^\nu \int_\Omega \sum_{K_1} (u, \eta^k)_Y \eta^k \bar{\psi}^\nu \, dp \\
&= \sum_{N_1} \psi^\nu \int_\Omega (\text{Proj}_{Y_1} u)\bar{\psi}^\nu \, dp \\
&= \text{Proj}_{\Psi_1} \text{Proj}_{Y_1} u, \qquad u \in Y\Psi,
\end{aligned}$$

by (92), (51), and Theorems 56, 46.

A similar argument with Y and Ψ interchanged completes the proof.

§ 132. **Matrices.** Consider separable Hilbert spaces X and Y with bases $\{\xi^j\}$, $j \in J$, and $\{\eta^k\}$, $k \in K$, respectively. Suppose that

$$x \in X, \qquad y \in Y;$$

and that F is a linear continuous operator on X to Y. It is sometimes useful to represent x, y, F by matrices relative to the bases $\{\xi^j\}$, $\{\eta^k\}$ in the following way.

As regards x and y, we have already seen that

(133) $$x = \sum_j x^j\xi^j, \qquad x^j = (x, \xi^j)_X, \quad j \in J;$$

(134) $$y = \sum_k y^k\eta^k, \qquad y^k = (y, \eta^k)_Y, \quad k \in K.$$

We may consider $\{x^j\}$, $\{y^k\}$ to be column matrices and write

(135) $$x = \{x^j\}, \qquad y = \{y^k\}$$

as abbreviations for (133), (134).

We form the two way matrix

(136) $$\{f^{k,j}\}, \qquad k \in K, \quad j \in J;$$

where k is the row index, j the column index, and

(137) $$f^{k,j} = (F\xi^j, \eta^k)_Y.$$

We then write

(138) $$F = \{f^{k,j}\},$$

since

(139) $$y = Fx$$

iff

(140) $$y^k = \sum_j f^{k,j}x^j, \quad k \in K$$

[Naimark 1, p. 112; Zaanen 1, p. 206.] The relation (140) is precisely the matrix relation

(141) $$\{y^k\} = \{f^{k,j}\}\{x^j\};$$

and (141) is another form of (139).

In considering matrices it will sometimes be convenient to indicate explicitly whether an index is a row or column index. We will do this by writing the row index as a suffix to the left brace and the column index as a prefix to the right brace. Thus (138), (135), and (141) may be written

(142) $$F = \{_k f^{k,j}{}_j\} = \{f^{k,j}\},$$

(143) $$x = \{_j x^j\} = \{x^j\}, \qquad y = \{_k y^k\} = \{y^k\},$$

(144) $$\{_k y^k\} = \{_k f^{k,j}{}_j\}\{_j x^j\}.$$

§ 145. **Probability spaces.** Heretofore Ψ has been an arbitrary separable L^2-space

$$\Psi = H(\Omega, p)$$

of functions measurable p and absolute square integrable on a space Ω. In most of our applications, the measure p will in fact be a probability, that is,

(146) $$p(\Omega) = 1.$$

When p is a probability, we denote integration on Ω relative to p by the symbol E, since such integration gives the *expected value* of the integrand:

(147) $$Ez = \int_\Omega z \, dp.$$

In considering the space Ψ henceforth, we *assume*, unless the contrary is stated explicitly, *that p is a probability*. Then

(148) $$(z, z')_\Psi = \int_\Omega z\bar{z}' \, dp = Ez\bar{z}', \qquad z, z' \in \Psi.$$

The function z which is identically 1 on Ω is an element of Ψ of norm 1, since

$$E1^2 = \int_\Omega dp = p(\Omega) = 1.$$

It follows that a basis $\{\psi^\nu\}$, $\nu \in N$, exists in Ψ in which

$$\psi^1(\omega) = 1, \qquad \omega \in \Omega. \tag{149}$$

Whenever we consider a basis $\{\psi^\nu\}$ in Ψ, we shall *assume* (149), unless the contrary is explicitly stated. Then

$$\begin{aligned} E\psi^\nu\bar{\psi}^{\nu'} &= (\psi^\nu, \psi^{\nu'})_\Psi = \delta^{\nu,\nu'}; \\ E\psi^\nu = E\psi^\nu\bar{\psi}^1 &= \delta^{\nu,1}; \qquad \nu, \nu' \in N. \end{aligned} \tag{150}$$

Consider $u \in X\Psi$. We define Eu as

$$Eu = \sum_j \xi^j Eu^j, \tag{151}$$

where u^j is given by (83).

152. Lemma. *If $u \in X\Psi$, then*

$$Eu \in X$$

and

$$\|Eu\|_X^2 \leqq E\|u\|_X^2 = \|u\|_{X\Psi}^2. \tag{153}$$

Proof. By (151),

$$Eu \in X$$

if

$$\sum_j |Eu^j|^2 < \infty.$$

By Schwarz's inequality and the fact that p is a probability,

$$|Eu^j|^2 \leqq E|u^j|^2E1^2 = E|u^j|^2 = \|u^j\|_\Psi^2 = \sum_\nu |u^{j,\nu}|^2, \qquad j \in J;$$

$$\sum_j |Eu^j|^2 \leqq \sum_{j,\nu} |u^{j,\nu}|^2 = \|u\|_{X\Psi}^2 < \infty.$$

This establishes (153) also, by (151) and (93), since

$$\|Eu\|_X^2 = \sum_j |Eu^j|^2.$$

The proof is complete.

154. Lemma. *If the sequence $\{u^i\}$ converges to u in $X\Psi$ as $i \to \infty$, then the sequence $\{Eu^i\}$ converges to Eu in X as $i \to \infty$.*

PROOF. By hypothesis and (93),

$$\|u^i - u\|_{X\Psi}^2 = E\|u^i - u\|_X^2 \to 0.$$

Hence

$$\|Eu^i - Eu\|_X^2 \to 0$$

by Lemma 152. This completes the proof.

§ 155. **The extension of operators to direct products.** We continue to consider the separable Hilbert spaces X, Y, Ψ. Both Y and Ψ are L^2-spaces and Ψ is based on a probability.

156. THEOREM. *Suppose that F is a linear continuous operator on X to Y. There exists a unique linear continuous operator F' on $X\Psi$ to $Y\Psi$ such that*

(157) $$F'(\phi x) = \phi F x \quad \textit{whenever} \quad \phi \in \Psi, \quad x \in X.$$

In particular ϕ may be unity. The Banach norm of F' equals that of F. If $u \in X\Psi$, then

(158) $$FEu = EF'u;$$

also

(159) $$F(u_\omega) = (F'u)_\omega, \quad \textit{almost all } \omega.$$

This theorem is quite natural. Parts of the proof, as will be seen, are somewhat delicate. In the notation of Dixmier,

$$F' = F \times I,$$

where I is the identity on Ψ.

PROOF OF THE THEOREM. *Part* 1. We define F' and show that

$$\|F'\| \leqq \|F\|.$$

To this end, let

(160) $$F = \{_k\, f^{k,j}\, _j\}, \qquad f^{k,j} = (F\xi^j, \eta^k)_Y, \quad j \in J, \quad k \in K,$$

be the matrix of the operator F on X to Y, relative to the bases $\{\xi^j\}$, $\{\eta^k\}$.

We have seen that

(161) $$\{\xi^j\psi^\nu\}, \quad \{\eta^k\psi^{\nu'}\}, \qquad j \in J, \quad \nu \in N, \quad k \in K, \quad \nu' \in N,$$

are bases on $X\Psi$, $Y\Psi$, respectively. Define F' as the operator on $X\Psi$ to $Y\Psi$ whose matrix, relative to these bases, is

(162) $$F' = \{_{k,\nu'}\, f^{k,j}\delta^{\nu',\nu}\, _{j,\nu}\}.$$

Here and elsewhere the indices vary over the sets indicated in (161). Consider the coordinate forms of $u \in X\Psi$ and $v \in Y\Psi$:

$$u = \{_{j,\nu}\, u^{j,\nu}\}, \qquad u^{j,\nu} = (u, \xi^j\psi^\nu)_{X\Psi};$$
$$v = \{_{k,\nu'}\, v^{k,\nu'}\}, \qquad v^{k,\nu'} = (v, \eta^k\psi^{\nu'})_{Y\Psi}.$$

These matrices for u and v are column matrices. Then the definition of the operator F' on $X\Psi$ to $Y\Psi$ by the matrix (162) amounts to the assertion that

$$v = F'u$$

iff

$$\{_{k,\nu'}\; v^{k,\nu'}\} = \{_{k,\nu'}\; f^{k,j}\,\delta^{\nu',\nu}\;_{j,\nu}\}\{_{j,\nu}\; u^{j,\nu}\}$$
$$= \Big\{_{k,\nu'}\; \sum_{j,\nu} f^{k,j}\,\delta^{\nu',\nu}u^{j,\nu}\Big\},$$

that is,

$$\{_{k,\nu'}\; v^{k,\nu'}\} = \Big\{_{k,\nu'}\; \sum_{j} f^{k,j}u^{j,\nu'}\Big\}.$$

The last relation, however, may also be written

$$\{_k\; v^{k,\nu'}\;_{\nu'}\} = \Big\{_k\; \sum_j f^{k,j}u^{j,\nu'}\;_{\nu'}\Big\}, \tag{163}$$

since both forms state exactly the same set of relationships among the elements $v^{k,\nu'}, f^{k,j}, u^{j,\nu'}$; $k \in K$, $j \in J$, $\nu' \in N$. Furthermore, the last relation may be written

$$\{_k\; v^{k,\nu}\;_\nu\} = \{_k\; f^{k,j}\;_j\}\{_j\; u^{j,\nu}\;_\nu\}, \tag{164}$$

a form which is similar to (144).

Let us write the coordinates of u, v as the two way matrices

$$u = \{_j\; u^{j,\nu}\;_\nu\}, \qquad v = \{_k\; v^{k,\nu}\;_\nu\}.$$

Then F' is the operator defined by (164), where $\{_k\; f^{k,j}\;_j\}$ is precisely the matrix (160) of the operator F on X to Y.

Now the operator F' is well defined, linear, and bounded, with bound $\leqq \|F\|$. Since the linearity is immediate, it is sufficient to show that $F'u$ is well defined, $u \in X\Psi$, with

$$\|F'u\|^2_{Y\Psi} \leqq \|F\|^2\|u\|^2_{X\Psi}.$$

But

$$\|u\|^2_{X\Psi} = \sum_{j,\nu} |u^{j,\nu}|^2 < \infty;$$

hence, by (163) and (160),

$$\|F'u\|^2_{Y\Psi} = \sum_{k,\nu} |v^{k,\nu}|^2 = \sum_\nu \sum_k \Big|\sum_j f^{k,j}u^{j,\nu}\Big|^2$$
$$\leqq \sum_\nu \|F\|^2 \sum_j |u^{j,\nu}|^2 = \|F\|^2\|u\|^2_{X\Psi},$$

by the definition of $\|F\|$, since $\{u^{j,\nu}\}$, ν fixed, are coordinates of an element in X.

Part 2. We establish (157). Suppose that

$$x = \{_j\, x^j\} \in X, \qquad \phi = \{_\nu\, \phi^\nu\} \in \Psi.$$

Then by (126)

$$\phi x = \{_j\, x^j \phi^\nu\,_\nu\} \in X\Psi, \tag{165}$$

and, by (163),

$$F'(\phi x) = \Big\{_k \sum_j f^{k,j} x^j \phi^\nu \Big\}_\nu = \Big\{_k \phi^\nu \sum_j f^{k,j} x^j \Big\}_\nu = \phi F x.$$

Part 3. We show that $\|F'\| = \|F\|$. Put

$$\phi = 1 = \psi^1$$

in Part 2. Then

$$F'(1x) = 1Fx = Fx, \qquad x \in X,$$

by Lemmas 127 and 108. Furthermore, by Lemma 88,

$$\|1x\|^2_{X\Psi} = E\|1x\|^2_X = \|x\|^2_X,$$

$$\|F'(1x)\|^2_{Y\Psi} = \|1Fx\|^2_{Y\Psi} = E\|Fx\|^2_Y = \|Fx\|^2_Y.$$

It follows that

$$\|F'\| \geqq \|F\|.$$

Thus, for each $\rho > 0$, there exists an $x_0 \in X$ such that

$$\|Fx_0\|_Y > [\|F\| - \rho]\|x_0\|_X,$$

by the definition of the norm of F. Hence

$$\|F'(1x_0)\|_{Y\Psi} > [\|F\| - \rho]\|(1x_0)\|_{X\Psi}.$$

Hence

$$\|F'\| \geqq \|F\|.$$

By Part 1, it follows that

$$\|F'\| = \|F\|.$$

Part 4. The operator F' satisfying (157) is unique among linear continuous operators on $X\Psi$ to $Y\Psi$. For, F' is entirely determined by its matrix relative to the bases

$$\{\xi^j\psi^\nu\}, \quad \{\eta^k\psi^{\nu'}\}, \qquad j \in J, \quad k \in K, \quad \nu, \nu' \in N.$$

Now the elements of the matrix of F' are

$$(F'\xi^j\psi^\nu, \eta^k\psi^{\nu'})_{Y\Psi} = (\psi^\nu F\xi^j, \eta^k\psi^{\nu'})_{Y\Psi}$$

by (157). These numbers depend only on F and the bases. Thus the matrix of F' is determined.

Part 5. If $u \in X\Psi$, then $FEu = EF'u$. Thus suppose that

$$u = \{u^{j,\nu}\} = \sum_{j,\nu} u^{j,\nu}\xi^j\psi^\nu \in X\Psi.$$

Then by (151),

$$Eu = \sum_j u^{j,1}\xi^j = \{u^{j,1}\} \in X,$$

since

$$E\sum_\nu u^{j,\nu}\psi^\nu = \left(\sum_\nu u^{j,\nu}\psi^\nu, \psi^1\right)_\Psi = u^{j,1},$$

by (150). Hence

$$FEu = \{f^{k,j}\}\{u^{j,1}\} = \left\{\sum_j f^{k,j}u^{j,1}\right\} = \sum_k \eta^k \sum_j f^{k,j}u^{j,1} \in Y.$$

On the other hand, by (164),

$$F'u = \{f^{k,j}\}\{u^{j,\nu}\} = \left\{\sum_j f^{k,j}u^{j,\nu}\right\}$$

$$= \sum_{k,\nu} \eta^k\psi^\nu \sum_j f^{k,j}u^{j,\nu} \in Y\Psi.$$

Hence, by a repetition of the argument in the preceding paragraph, $EF'u$ is the multiplier of ψ^1, that is,

$$EF'u = \sum_k \eta^k \sum_j f^{k,j}u^{j,1} = FEu.$$

Part 6. We establish (159). Suppose that

$$u = \{u^{j,\nu}\} = \sum_{j,\nu} u^{j,\nu}\xi^j\psi^\nu \in X\Psi.$$

Then

$$u_\omega = \{u^j(\omega)\} = \sum_j u^j(\omega)\xi^j \in X, \qquad \text{almost all } \omega,$$

where

(166) $$u^j = \sum_\nu u^{j,\nu}\psi^\nu \in \Psi, \qquad j \in J,$$

by (99), (97). Hence

$$F(u_\omega) = \{f^{k,j}\}\{u^j(\omega)\} = \{\sum_j f^{k,j}u^j(\omega)\}$$

$$= \sum_k \eta^k \sum_j f^{k,j}u^j(\omega) \in Y, \quad \text{almost all } \omega.$$

Note that $u^j(\omega)$ is not defined as the sum of the numerical series $\sum_\nu u^{j,\nu}\psi^\nu(\omega)$, although a sequence of properly chosen partial sums of the latter series does converge to $u^j(\omega)$ almost everywhere. The series (166) converges in $\Psi^\cdot$, that is, relative to the norm in $\Psi^\cdot$.

Now

$$v \underset{\text{def}}{=} F'u = \left\{\sum_j f^{k,j}u^{j,\nu}\right\} = \sum_k \eta^k v^k \in Y\Psi^\cdot,$$

where

$$v^k = \sum_\nu \psi^\nu \sum_j f^{k,j}u^{j,\nu}, \tag{167}$$

by Lemma 80. Hence by (99)

$$v_\omega = (F'u)_\omega = \sum_k \eta^k v^k(\omega) = \{v^k(\omega)\} \in Y, \quad \text{almost all } \omega.$$

Thus to show that

$$v_\omega = F(u_\omega), \quad \text{almost all } \omega, \tag{168}$$

it is sufficient, comparing coordinates, to show that

$$v^k(\omega) = \sum_j f^{k,j}u^j(\omega) \qquad k \in K, \quad \text{almost all } \omega; \tag{169}$$

a numerical relation.

Consider a fixed but arbitrary $k \in K$.

Assume first that all but a finite number of coordinates $u^{j,\nu}$ of u are zero. Then (169) and (166) are finite sums. By the definition of addition and scalar multiplication in the L^2-space $\Psi^\cdot = H(\Omega, p)$, a finite linear combination of elements of $\Psi^\cdot$ corresponds to the same linear combination of numerical functions representing the elements, for almost all $\omega \in \Omega$. Hence to establish (169) it is sufficient to show that

$$v^k = \sum_j f^{k,j}u^j; \tag{170}$$

a relation in $\Psi^\cdot$. But (170) is indeed valid, because of (167), (166). If (170) were an infinite series, it would not however of itself imply (169).

We have shown that (168) holds in the special case in which all but a finite number of $u^{j,\nu}$, $j \in J$, $\nu \in N$, vanish. We deduce the general case from this preliminary result as follows. Given $u \in X\Psi^\cdot$, take a sequence

$$\{u^n\}$$

such that

$u^n \in X\Psi^\cdot, \qquad n = 1, 2, \cdots,$

u^n has only a finite number of nonzero coordinates,

$u^n \to u$ in $X\Psi^\cdot$ as $n \to \infty$.

Then

$$F(u^n_\omega) = (F'u^n)_\omega, \quad \text{almost all } \omega, n = 1, 2, \cdots, \tag{171}$$

by (168), special case. Take a subsequence

$$\{u^{n_i}\}, \qquad n_1 < n_2 < \cdots,$$

of $\{u^n\}$ such that

$$u^{n_i}_\omega \to u_\omega, \quad \text{almost all } \omega, \text{ as } i \to \infty,$$

as is possible by Theorem 120. Then, since F and F' are continuous,

$$\begin{aligned} F(u^{n_i}_\omega) &\to F(u_\omega), \quad \text{almost all } \omega, \\ F'u^{n_i} &\to F'u, \qquad \text{as } i \to \infty. \end{aligned} \tag{172}$$

The latter relation implies, again by Theorem 120, that for a properly chosen subsequence

$$\{u^{n_{i_j}}\}, \qquad i_1 < i_2 < \cdots,$$

$$(F'u^{n_{i_j}})_\omega \to (F'u)_\omega, \quad \text{almost all } \omega, \text{ as } j \to \infty. \tag{173}$$

But

$$(F'u^{n_{i_j}})_\omega = F(u^{n_{i_j}}_\omega), \quad \text{almost all } \omega, j = 1, 2, \cdots,$$

by (171). Hence, by (172), (173),

$$F(u_\omega) = (F'u)_\omega, \quad \text{almost all } \omega,$$

as was to be shown.

This completes the proof of the theorem.

§ 174. **The general problem of approximation.** In this chapter we have so far introduced the tools (Hilbert spaces, projections, direct products of Hilbert spaces) which we shall use in formulating and solving a problem that lies at the very center of the theory of approximation. The problem is that of efficient approximation.

A theory consists of the formulation as well as the solution of problems. Often a successful formulation leads to a useful solution while an awkward formulation leads to problems which are too hard to solve and in which nonetheless the difficulties do not belong to nature. A scientist is willing and eager to cope with difficulties, if the difficulties are essential to the preproblem that commands his attention. He seeks however to remove difficulties which are removable.

It is my opinion that the problem of efficient approximation, as will be formulated, retains the essence of what is appropriate to very much approximation and also uses technical hypotheses which are philosophically acceptable and mathematically rewarding.

Suppose that an *input* $x + \delta x$ will be operated upon by a process of approximation A to produce an *actual output* $A(x + \delta x)$ which is intended to approximate the *desired output* y. The *error* in the approximation is

$$e = A(x + \delta x) - y.$$

For brevity we write

$$z = x + \delta x,$$
$$e = Az - y.$$

Suppose that the input z is a function on a space S, and the desired output y a function on a space T. In particular T may be a single point, in which case y is a number.

We consider the problem of the *choice of* A, that is, the design of the process of approximation. We envisage a *multiplicity of inputs* z and *desired outputs* y. This is reasonable, because mathematicians often do in fact use a process A repeatedly. Furthermore, in cases in which a mathematician will use A only once, he very often in designing A has to consider a multiplicity of inputs and outputs because he knows at the time of design only that the input and output will be individuals of a certain set.

Let us consider the input z. Similar remarks will apply to the desired output y. To provide for a multiplicity of inputs z, we can, as heretofore in the book, say that z is an arbitrary element of a set X of functions. Some elements of X, however, may never be actual inputs. Furthermore, among those elements of X that may be inputs, some may occur more often than others or some may be more important than others.

An effective and powerful way to procede is to use the theory of probability as follows. Specify a space Ω and a probability p on Ω, defined for all p-measurable subsets of Ω (cf. § 145). Consider that

$$z(s, \omega), \qquad s \in S, \quad \omega \in \Omega,$$

is a function of s and ω. For each fixed $\omega \in \Omega$ with null exceptions, $z(s, \omega)$ is an element of X and a possible input. The contemplated *trial* which will determine the input will be the specification of one element $\omega \in \Omega$. Furthermore, the probability p is such as to describe the anticipated importance of inputs in the following sense: If Ω_1 is any measurable subset of Ω, then $p(\Omega_1)$ is the probability that the input will be $z(s, \omega)$ for an $\omega \in \Omega_1$. Thus $p(\Omega_1)$ is the anticipated relative frequency of occurrence of inputs $z(s, \omega)$ with $\omega \in \Omega_1$.

The function $z(s, \omega)$ on $S \times \Omega$ and the probability p describe the inputs. Similarly, another function $y(t, \omega)$ on $T \times \Omega$ and the same probability p can describe the desired outputs. For each fixed $\omega \in \Omega$ with null exceptions, the input is $z(s, \omega)$, the actual output is Az, and Az is intended to approximate $y(t, \omega)$. For example, an operator G on X to Y may be given and $y = G'z$, where G' is the extension of G to an operator on $X\Psi$ to $Y\Psi$ of Theorem 156. Then A will be intended to approximate G.

More generally, p may be a nonnegative measure, not necessarily a probability, on Ω, such that $p(\Omega_1)$ measures the anticipated importance of inputs $z(s, \omega)$ and desired outputs $y(t, \omega)$, ω fixed and in Ω_1. If $p(\Omega) = \infty$, some of our theory may not apply.

The space Ω and the probability p may be simple or not, depending on the reality that is being studied and the extent to which simplifying assumptions have been made. Instances are given below in §§ 267 ff.

Our object is to design the process A. We make this object precise in the following way. We suppose that we are given a set $\mathscr{A}$ of operators on X to Y, where X is a space of functions on S and Y a space of functions on T. We seek to choose an operator $A \in \mathscr{A}$ in such a way as to make the approximation of y by Az good, in some sense. Thus $\mathscr{A}$ consists of those operators which for some reason or other are suitable. Our analysis is directed towards choosing an element A of $\mathscr{A}$ and thereafter towards analyzing the error

$$e = Az - y.$$

We use norms in X and Y to measure the overall size of elements therein, and the expected value operator

$$E \cdots = \int_\Omega \cdots dp$$

to take into account the multiplicity of inputs and desired outputs. Indeed our problem is characterized by E rather than Ω, p, for the following reason. We introduce Ω, p to describe the multiplicity of inputs and desired outputs; but different pairs Ω, p may be used equivalently. On the other hand, E has the following unique meaning in any application of the theory, because of the strong law of large numbers: Eq is the unique object which, with probability 1, is the limit of

$$\frac{q_1 + \cdots + q_n}{n}$$

as $n \to \infty$, where $q_1, q_2, \cdots$ are values of q realized in independent trials [Doob 1, p. 142]. Thus if we take probability 1 to mean virtual certainty in any application, then Eq is determined by q.

§ 175. **The precise problem.** *Suppose that S, T, Ω are nonempty spaces and that m is a nonnegative measure on T and p is a probability on Ω. Suppose that*

$$Y = H(T, m),$$
$$\Psi = H(\Omega, p)$$

and that *X is a Hilbert space of functions on S* or of equivalence sets of functions on S. Thus Y and Ψ are L^2-spaces and X may be an L^2-space. *Suppose that X, Y, Ψ are separable* (cf. § 27) and contain elements other than 0.

The above assumptions are perfectly acceptable to an approximator because they allow such a variety of choice of S, T, Ω, X, m, and p.

A reader wishing to simplify the problem may take X to be an L^2-space. Then $X\Psi$ and $Y\Psi$ are L^2-spaces, by Theorem 75; and many of the results of § 79 are more easily established than in the general case.

Suppose that $\mathscr{A}$ is a linear set of linear continuous operators on X to Y. Each operator $A \in \mathscr{A}$ will be considered as a potential process of approximation, as will be indicated below.

The assumption here that $\mathscr{A}$ is a linear set is essentially unrestrictive. For, starting with a set $\mathscr{A}$ which was not linear, we could replace $\mathscr{A}$ by span $\mathscr{A}$. We do not require that $\mathscr{A}$ be closed in any sense. The assumption that each element of $\mathscr{A}$ is a continuous operator on X to Y is natural and not too restrictive, since continuity depends on the norms in X and Y and since we have such a wide choice of norms. The assumption that each operator $A \in \mathscr{A}$ is linear is indeed restrictive. It has wide scope, however, since integration, differentiation, substitution, and summation are linear operators.

For each $A \in \mathscr{A}$, there exists a unique operator A' on $X\Psi$ to $Y\Psi$ such that

$$A'(\phi x) = \phi A x, \qquad x \in X, \quad \phi \in \Psi,$$

by Theorem 156. Since A' is the natural extension of A and since

$$A'(1x) = A'x = 1Ax = Ax, \qquad x \in X,$$

we shall henceforth drop the prime. The context, or explicit statement, will indicate whether A is an operator on X to Y or the related operator on $X\Psi$ to $Y\Psi$.

Suppose finally *that an element z of $X\Psi$ and an element y of $Y\Psi$ are given.*

The hypotheses made thus far are to apply for the rest of the chapter, unless the contrary is stated.

We shall approximate y by Az, $A \in \mathscr{A}$. We shall consider how to choose $A \in \mathscr{A}$, and we shall obtain expressions for the error

$$e = Az - y.$$

For each fixed $\omega \in \Omega$ with null exceptions, z_ω is an element of X and

$$(Az)_\omega = A(z_\omega), \quad y_\omega, \text{ and } e_\omega$$

are elements of Y, by Lemma 88 and Theorem 156. Then z_ω is the input, $A(z_\omega)$ the output, y_ω the desired output, and e_ω the error in the approximation of y_ω by $A(z_\omega)$. The probability p which enters in the definition of $\Psi = H(\Omega, p)$ describes the anticipated relative importance of the input z_ω and desired output y_ω.

A number of examples are given in §§ 267 ff.

Our analysis will depend on the data of the problem:

$$X, \quad Y = H(T, m), \quad \Psi = H(\Omega, p), \quad z, \quad y, \quad \mathscr{A}.$$

How these data might be obtained is an important question. The data in fact constitute a judgement by the approximator of what the precise problem before him is. Such a judgement will be based either on complete knowledge of the source of the problem or partial knowledge thereof or perhaps sheer hypothesis. If the data are hypothetical, so are the conclusions. In the fashion of inductive thinking, we would consider that suitable performance of the chosen A when actually used would indicate that the hypotheses had been reasonable.

The data z, y might be the result of a statistical analysis of past data in similar situations. Note that z and y are stochastic processes. If the true z and y are inaccessible to the approximator, direct approximations of z and y may be made, as follows (cf. § 304). We replace

$$\Omega, \quad p, \quad z, \quad y,$$

which are unknown, by a simpler set, based on observation. Thus, we may carry out n observations of inputs and desired outputs. Suppose that these are

$$z^1, y^1; \qquad z^2, y^2; \qquad \cdots; \qquad z^n, y^n;$$

where

$$z^i \in X, \quad y^i \in Y, \quad i = 1, \cdots, n;$$

are known and are assigned weights

$$w^1 > 0, \cdots, \quad w^n > 0$$

such that

$$w^1 + \cdots + w^n = 1.$$

These weights indicate our judgement of the relative importance of the observations. We now construct the finite space $\tilde{\Omega}$ of n points

$$\omega^1, \cdots, \omega^n,$$

of respective probabilities

$$\tilde{p}^1 = w^1, \cdots, \tilde{p}^n = w^n.$$

The related expected value is

$$\tilde{E}f = w^1 f^1 + \cdots + w^n f^n, \qquad f = (f^1, \cdots, f^n) \in \tilde{\Psi} = H(\tilde{\Omega}, \tilde{p}).$$

Our observation has given us the input

$$\tilde{z} = (z^1, \cdots, z^n) \in X\tilde{\Psi}$$

and desired output

$$\tilde{y} = (y^1, \cdots, y^n) \in Y\tilde{\Psi}$$

of a simpler problem with data

$$X, \quad Y, \quad \tilde{\Psi}, \quad \tilde{z}, \quad \tilde{y}, \quad \mathscr{A}$$

instead of

$$X, \quad Y, \quad \Psi, \quad z, \quad y, \quad \mathscr{A}.$$

The simpler problem, which is indeed classical, is a direct and natural statistical estimate of the underlying, unknown problem. This is because of two facts:

(i) $E\tilde{E}\tilde{f} = Ef$, where $f \in X\Psi$ or $f \in Y\Psi$, and $\tilde{f}$ is the set of n observations of f.

(ii) The probability is unity that $\lim_{n\to\infty} \tilde{E}\tilde{f} = Ef$, providing that the weights w^i, $i = 1, \cdots, n$, satisfy a suitable condition, one which is surely satisfied if $w^i = 1/n$. Now our entire analysis, as will be seen, depends on expected values. An analysis of the simpler problem therefore will be a reasonable estimate of the inaccessible analysis of the underlying problem.

An example of the simpler problem is in § 304.

At the end of the chapter we consider Wiener-Kolmogorov theory, where it is assumed that S and T are the time axis; that z and y are stationary stochastic processes, and that $\mathscr{A}$ consists of operators acting on the past (§ 311). It is supposed that the correlation functions or their equivalent are known. The methods of the present chapter do not require any more or less data than those of Wiener-Kolmogorov theory. Each theory illuminates the other.

Large parts of the present chapter are classical. Much of the classical material, however, seems inaccessible without detours. Theorem 253 is important. Theorem 232 is important and somewhat difficult to prove.

§ 176. **Efficient and strongly efficient approximation.** Suppose that we are given the data

$$X, \quad Y = H(T, m), \qquad \Psi = H(\Omega, p), \quad z, \quad y, \quad \mathscr{A}$$

of the preceding section. We propose to approximate y by Az, $A \in \mathscr{A}$. Each operator $A \in \mathscr{A}$ is given as linear and continuous on X to Y; we extend A, by Theorem 156, to be linear and continuous on $X\Psi$ to $Y\Psi$.

In considering operators A^0 and A, put

$$e^0 = A^0 z - y, \qquad e = Az - y.$$

We say that $A^0 \in \mathscr{A}$ is *efficient* if

$$E\|e^0\|_Y^2 \leqq E\|e\|_Y^2 \tag{177}$$

for all $A \in \mathscr{A}$; and we say that $A^0 \in \mathscr{A}$ is *strongly efficient* if, for all $A \in \mathscr{A}$,

$$E|e_t^0|^2 \leqq E|e_t|^2, \quad \text{almost all } t. \tag{178}$$

The inequality in (178) holds for each $t \in T_1$, where T_1 is a set which depends on A,

$$T_1 \subset T \quad \text{and} \quad m(T - T_1) = 0.$$

Note that e is an element of the space $Y\Psi$ which is the L^2-space $H(T \times \Omega, mp)$. We may therefore think of $e(t, \omega)$ as a measurable function absolute square integrable mp on $T \times \Omega$. For each fixed ω with null exceptions, the error e is a function of t. Relation (178) asserts that for each t, with null exceptions, the expected error is minimal. It is natural to use a strongly efficient operator for our approximation, whenever a strongly efficient operator exists.

The relation (177) is weaker than (178), since by Lemma 108,

$$\|e\|_Y^2 = \int_T |e(t, \omega)|^2 \, dm(t) = \int_T |e_t|^2 \, dm(t). \tag{179}$$

(Cf. Lemma 183.) The norm $\|e\|_Y$ measures the over-all error in the approximation, weighted by the measure m, for each fixed ω with null exceptions. Thus an efficient operator is one which minimizes the expected over-all error. In cases in which a strongly efficient operator does not exist, it is natural to use an efficient operator if the latter exists.

To attain the minimum in either case may not be possible or if possible may require too much computation. We therefore introduce the concepts of near efficiency and near strong efficiency.

Let ρ be a positive number. We say that $A^0 \in A$ is *within* ρ *of efficiency if*

$$E\|e^0\|_Y^2 < E\|e\|_Y^2 + \rho^2 \tag{180}$$

for all $A \in \mathscr{A}$; and we say that $A^0 \in \mathscr{A}$ is *within* ρ *of strong efficiency* if a function ζ exists such that

$$\zeta \in Y = H(T, m),$$

$$\|\zeta\|_Y < \rho \tag{181}$$

and

$$E|e_t^0|^2 \leqq E|e_t|^2 + |\zeta_t|^2, \quad \text{almost all } t, \tag{182}$$

for all $A \in \mathscr{A}$. The null set in T on which the last inequality fails may depend on A.

Thus efficiency and strong efficiency involve expected values and thereby depend on the anticipated nature of the input z and the desired output y. The space Ω permits us to describe the multiplicity of inputs and desired outputs. The probability p discriminates between different inputs and desired outputs. The spaces X and Y permit the description of each input, desired output, and error. The norm in Y affords a measure of the over-all error. The norm in X affords a measure of inputs.

For some but not all of our results it would be sufficient to assume that X is a Banach space instead of a separable Hilbert space. The latter hypothesis enters through the use of Theorem 156 and in other ways.

183. Lemma. *Strong efficiency implies efficiency: If* A^0 *is strongly efficient, then* A^0 *is efficient. If* A^0 *is within* ρ *of strong efficiency, then* A^0 *is within* ρ *of efficiency.*

Proof. This is an immediate consequence of (179). We integrate both sides of (178) or (182) and obtain (177) or (180), since

$$\int_T |\zeta_t|^2\, dm(t) = \|\zeta\|_Y^2.$$

The proof is complete.

In this chapter we establish necessary and sufficient conditions that an operator A^0 be efficient, strongly efficient, within ρ of efficiency or within ρ of strong efficiency (Theorems 189 and 232). Our results include also the following facts. There is a unique element $\sigma \in Y\Psi$ such that

(i) $A^0 \in \mathscr{A}$ is efficient iff $A^0 z = \sigma$.

(ii) $A^0 \in \mathscr{A}$ is within ρ of efficiency ($\rho > 0$) iff

$$E\|A^0 z - \sigma\|_Y^2 < \rho^2.$$

Efficient operators need not exist, but operators within ρ of efficiency exist for each $\rho > 0$. The latter fact is immediate from the definition of near efficiency, since

$$\inf_{A \in \mathscr{A}} E\|e\|_Y^2$$

exists. If an efficient operator A^0 exists, then A^0 is not necessarily unique but the error

$$e^0 = A^0 z - y = \sigma - y$$

is unique. Thus any two efficient operators produce the same approximation σ of y.

It follows, by Lemma 183, that the search for strongly efficient operators or operators within ρ of strong efficiency may be carried out as follows. Search for an operator A^0 which is efficient or within ρ of efficiency. That very operator will be strongly efficient or within ρ of strong efficiency, if the latter exist.

We say that *efficiency is strong* if, for all $\rho > 0$, any operator within ρ of efficiency is automatically within ρ of strong efficiency and if any efficient operator is automatically strongly efficient. A necessary and sufficient condition that efficiency be strong is that an operator within ρ of strong efficiency exist for each $\rho > 0$.

To decide unequivocally whether efficiency is strong, one may calculate the functions σ_t and τ_t of Theorem 232 and observe whether

$$\sigma_t = \tau_t, \quad \text{almost all } t.$$

We say that an operator A on X to Y is of *finite rank* if the image AX of X under A is finite dimensional. One of our principal results is Theorem 253 that efficiency is strong if $\mathscr{A}$ includes all operators of finite rank. This important and useful fact implies in particular that efficiency is strong if $\mathscr{A}$ is sufficiently large.

§ 184. **Digression on unbiased approximation.** An operator A is said to be *unbiased* if

$$Ee = 0, \qquad e = Az - y.$$

One may wish in the search for an $A \in \mathscr{A}$ to consider only those elements of $\mathscr{A}$ which are unbiased. For example one may seek $A^0 \in \mathscr{A}$ such that $E\|e^0\|_Y^2$ is minimal among all unbiased elements of $\mathscr{A}$ rather than all elements of $\mathscr{A}$.

The exclusion of biased elements of $\mathscr{A}$, if desired, may be effected easily in the following way. Let C^0 be an arbitrary, fixed, unbiased element of $\mathscr{A}$. Let $\mathscr{B}$ be the subset of $\mathscr{A}$ consisting of all elements $B \in \mathscr{A}$ such that

$$EBz = BEz = 0$$

(Theorem 156). The set $\mathscr{B}$ is linear. The set of all unbiased elements of $\mathscr{A}$ is $C_0 + \mathscr{B}$, that is,

$$\{C_0 + B : B \in \mathscr{B}\}.$$

Suppose now that

$$A = C^0 + B.$$

Then

$$e = Az - y = (C^0 + B)z - y = Bz - (y - C^0z).$$

Thus, the error in the approximation of y by Az is precisely the error in the approximation of $y - C^0z$ by Bz. It follows that to add the restriction of being unbiased to our definitions related to efficiency, it is sufficient merely to replace $\mathscr{A}$ by $\mathscr{B}$ and y by $y - C^0z$ in $X, Y, \Psi, z, y, \mathscr{A}$.

§ 185. **Characterization of efficient operators.** The quantity

$$E\|e\|_Y^2$$

which enters in the definition of efficiency is the square norm $\|e\|_{Y\Psi}^2$ in $Y\Psi$. It follows, as we now show, that efficiency is related closely to projection in $Y\Psi$.

Put

$$L^\circ = \mathscr{A}z = \{Az : A \in \mathscr{A}\} \subset Y\Psi; \tag{186}$$

and

$$L = \text{closure of } L^\circ. \tag{187}$$

If $L = \{0\}$, the only approximation of y would be 0, an uninteresting case. *Assume that* $L \neq \{0\}$. Since $\mathscr{A}$ is a linear set of operators, L° and L are linear subspaces of $Y\Psi$. We may call L the *space of images*.

If L° is finite dimensional, then L° is surely closed and hence identical with L (§ 40).

Put

$$\sigma = \mathrm{Proj}_L\, y = \text{projection of } y \text{ on } L. \tag{188}$$

Then in all cases

$$\sigma \in L.$$

189. THEOREM. *An efficient operator exists iff*

$$\sigma \in L^\circ.$$

An operator $A \in \mathscr{A}$ *is efficient iff*

$$Az = \sigma. \tag{190}$$

An operator within ρ *of efficiency exists for each* $\rho > 0$. *An operator* $A \in \mathscr{A}$ *is within* ρ *of efficiency,* $\rho > 0$, *iff*

$$E\|Az - \sigma\|_Y^2 < \rho^2, \tag{191}$$

that is, iff Az *is within* ρ *of* σ *in* $Y\Psi$. *Furthermore*

$$\inf_{A \in \mathscr{A}} E\|e\|_Y^2 = E\|y\|_Y^2 - E\|\sigma\|_Y^2 = E\|f\|_Y^2, \tag{192}$$

where

$$e = Az - y,$$
$$f = \sigma - y. \tag{193}$$

An operator $A \in \mathscr{A}$ *is efficient iff*

$$e = f \tag{194}$$

or equivalently

$$e \perp L. \tag{195}$$

The normal equations in the classical treatment of many least square problems are equivalent to the condition

$$E(Az, A^0z - y)_Y = 0 \quad \text{for all } A \in \mathscr{A},$$

which is another form of (195).

PROOF. This theorem is an elaboration of Theorem 34 (the Theorem of Pythagoras), with the space Y replaced by $Y\Psi$. We are interested in L° rather than L; some of our statements are directed towards the possibility that $\sigma \notin L^\circ$.

By construction

$$\sigma \in L, \qquad f \in L^\perp. \tag{196}$$

Consider an arbitrary $A \in \mathscr{A}$, with

$$e = Az - y.$$

Then

(197) $$e - f = Az - \sigma \in L,$$

since $Az \in L^\circ \subset L$. Hence f and $e - f$ lie in orthogonal complements in $Y\Psi$, and

$$\|e\|^2_{Y\Psi} = \|f\|^2_{Y\Psi} + \|e - f\|^2_{Y\Psi},$$

(198) $$E\|e\|^2_Y = E\|f\|^2_Y + E\|e - f\|^2_Y,$$

since $e = f + (e - f)$.

Suppose that $\rho > 0$. There is an $A \in \mathscr{A}$ such that

(199) $$E\|e - f\|^2_Y = E\|Az - \sigma\|^2_Y < \rho^2,$$

since σ is a limit point of L°. Hence (198) implies that

$$\inf_{A \in \mathscr{A}} E\|e\|^2_Y = E\|f\|^2_Y;$$

and that $A \in \mathscr{A}$ is within ρ of efficiency iff (199) = (191) holds. Also $A \in \mathscr{A}$ is efficient iff

$$E\|e - f\|^2_Y = E\|Az - \sigma\|^2_Y = 0.$$

This establishes (190).

If $\sigma \in L^\circ$, then $\sigma = Az$ for some $A \in \mathscr{A}$ and that A is efficient. Conversely if an efficient operator exists, then $\sigma \in L^\circ$, by (190).

By (198), the infimum of $E\|e\|^2_Y$, $A \in \mathscr{A}$, is

$$E\|f\|^2_Y = E\|y\|^2_Y - E\|\sigma\|^2_Y,$$

by (193), (196).

An element $A \in \mathscr{A}$ is efficient iff (190) or equivalently (194) holds. If $A \in \mathscr{A}$ is efficient, then (195) holds by (194), (196). Conversely if $A \in \mathscr{A}$ is such that

$$e = Az - y \in L^\perp,$$

then

$$e - f = Az - \sigma \in L^\perp$$

by (196); and also

$$e - f \in L$$

by (197). Hence $e - f = 0$ by Theorem 21. This completes the proof.

200. Remark. We describe σ as the *efficient approximation* of y, because

$\sigma = Az$ whenever A is an efficient operator and σ is within ρ of Az whenever A is within ρ of efficiency, $\rho \geqq 0$. Likewise we describe

$$f = \sigma - y$$

as the *error in efficient approximation*, because

$$f = e = Az - y$$

whenever A is an efficient operator, and f is within ρ of $Az - y$ in $Y\Psi$ whenever A is within ρ of efficiency. We use these appellations whether an efficient operator exists or not.

Efficient operators, if existent, need not be unique. However *any two efficient operators*, A^1 and A^2, *are entirely equivalent for our approximation because both yield identical approximations*

$$A^1z = A^2z = \sigma$$

and identical errors

$$e^1 = A^1z - y = e^2 = A^2z - y = f.$$

The elements σ and f are uniquely determined by L° and y.

If A^3 and A^4 are any operators each within ρ of efficiency, the approximations A^3z and A^4z will be within 2ρ of one another

$$E\|A^3z - A^4z\|_Y^2 < 4\rho^2$$

in $Y\Psi$; and the errors $e^3 = A^3z - y$ and $e^4 = A^4z - y$ will be within 2ρ of one another

$$E\|e^3 - e^4\|_Y^2 < 4\rho^2.$$

This is an immediate consequence of Minkowski's inequality (Lemma 15) in $Y\Psi$ and the fact that

$$\|u\|_{Y\Psi}^2 = E\|u\|_Y^2, \qquad u \in Y\Psi.$$

Thus

$$E\|A^3z - y\|_Y^2 < \rho^2, \qquad E\|A^4z - y\|_Y^2 < \rho^2$$

imply that

$$\|A^3z - y\|_{Y\Psi} < \rho, \qquad \|A^4z - y\|_{Y\Psi} < \rho,$$
$$\|A^3z - A^4z\|_{Y\Psi} < 2\rho.$$

We may say then that if ρ is small any two operators within ρ of efficiency lead to sensibly the same approximations and errors of approximation, as measured by their expected over-all difference.

Applications of Theorem 189 are given in §§ 267 ff. which the reader may consult now, if he wishes.

201. Remark. Since L and $L^\perp$ are Hilbert spaces, we may write Fourier

series for σ and f. Let $\{\lambda^j, j \in J\}$ be a basis for L and $\{\mu^k, k \in K\}$ be a basis for $L^\perp$. We may think of λ^j, μ^k, σ, f as functions in the L^2-space $Y\Psi = H(T \times \Omega, mp)$. In the sense of convergence in the mean square relative to mp, by Theorem 56,

$$\sigma(t, \omega) = \sum_{j \in J} \sigma^j \lambda^j(t, \omega),$$

$$f(t, \omega) = \sum_{k \in K} f^k \mu^k(t, \omega), \qquad t \in T, \quad \omega \in \Omega,$$

where

$$\sigma^j = (\sigma, \lambda^j)_{Y\Psi} = (y, \lambda^j)_{Y\Psi} = E(y, \lambda^j)_Y,$$

$$f^k = (f, \mu^k)_{Y\Psi} = -(y, \mu^k)_{Y\Psi} = -E(y, \mu^k)_Y,$$

since $y = \sigma - f$, $\sigma \in L, f \in L^\perp$.

§ 202. **Calculation of operators near efficiency.** It may be impracticable to determine a basis for L and to calculate σ exactly, but it is always possible to carry out the following finite calculation of nearly efficient operators.

By the process of orthogonalization of § 60, construct a finite orthonormal system

$$\Lambda' = \{\lambda^j : j \in J'\}$$

in L°. If Λ' is not a basis for L, we may later enlarge Λ'. Let $A^j \in \mathscr{A}$ be the operator such that

$$\lambda^j = A^j z \qquad j \in J';$$

that A^j exists follows from the definition of L°.

Using Theorem 56, put

$$L' = \text{span } \Lambda' = \text{Span } \Lambda',$$

$$\sigma' = \text{Proj}_{L'} \, y = \sum_{j \in J'} (y, \lambda^j)_{Y\Psi} \lambda^j = \sum_{j \in J'} \lambda^j E(y, \lambda^j)_Y, \tag{203}$$

$$A' = \sum_{j \in J'} A^j E(y, \lambda^j)_Y,$$

and

$$e' = A'z - y = \sigma' - y.$$

Then

$$A' \in \mathscr{A};$$

and

$$\sigma' \in L', \qquad e' \in L'^\perp,$$

by (203). Hence

$$E\|y\|_Y^2 = E\|\sigma'\|_Y^2 + E\|e'\|_Y^2,$$

and, by Theorem 46 applied to the space L',

$$E\|e'\|_Y^2 = E\|y\|_Y^2 - \sum_{j \in J'} |E(y, \lambda^j)_Y|^2. \tag{204}$$

Both A' and $E\|e'\|_Y^2$ have now been calculated in a finite number of steps. If $E\|e'\|_Y^2$ is adequately small, then A' is an adequate operator in the approximation of y by $A'z$. If not, consider the orthonormal system Λ'. If Λ' is complete in L, then Λ' is a basis for L and A' is an efficient operator. No improvement can be effected.

If Λ' is not complete in L, we may enlarge Λ' to a new orthonormal system Λ'', by adding a finite number of elements

$$\lambda^j = A^j z, \qquad A^j \in \mathscr{A}, \quad j \in J'' - J'.$$

We may then calculate the operator

$$A'' = A' + \sum_{j \in J'' - J'} A^j E(y, \lambda^j)_Y \in \mathscr{A}$$

and the measure of error

$$E\|e''\|_Y^2 = E\|e'\|_Y^2 - \sum_{j \in J'' - J'} |E(y, \lambda^j)_Y|^2, \tag{205}$$

where

$$e'' = A''z - y.$$

This calculation uses the earlier results, none of which is lost.

Continuing in this fashion, we may arrive at a basis for L. If so, we have calculated an efficient operator. If not, we may continue as long as we will. At each step we improve the approximation or at any rate do not weaken it, because of the subtraction in (205).

§ 206. **Conditions that $L^\circ = L$.** If the space L° is closed, then $L^\circ = L$ and the hypothesis $\sigma \in L^\circ$ of Theorem 189 will surely be satisfied, for all $y \in Y\Psi$.

Since L° is linear, L° will surely be closed if L° is of finite dimension (§ 40).

If L° is of infinite dimension, L° need not be closed. In the present section we establish a necessary and sufficient condition that L° be closed. The section is a digression from our main development and may be omitted.

In practice an approximation within ρ of efficiency, for sufficiently small ρ, is usually as satisfactory as one which is truly efficient. It follows that the condition $\sigma \in L^\circ$ and a fortiori the closure of L° are often not of direct consequence.

In the present section and only here we introduce the following hypothesis about z, an hypothesis which may be described as requiring the essential denseness of sections z_ω. We know that $z_\omega \in X$ for all $\omega \in \Omega_1$, where Ω_1 is almost all of Ω, by Lemma 88. Put

$$Z = \text{Span}\,\{z_\omega : \omega \in \Omega_1\}. \tag{207}$$

Thus Z is a closed linear space $\subset X$. *Our hypothesis is that*

$$\text{span}\,\{z_\omega : \omega \in \Omega_2\}$$

is dense in Z whenever Ω_2 is almost all of Ω_1.

Denote by $\mathscr{U}$ the Banach space of linear continuous operators on Z to Y and by $\|U\|$ the Banach norm of an operator $U \in \mathscr{U}$ (§ 3 : 8). The space $\mathscr{U}$ is a Banach space. That $\mathscr{U}$ is complete is easily proved as follows. Given a Cauchy sequence $\{T^i\}$ in $\mathscr{U}$, construct a subsequence $\{T^{i_j}\}$ such that

$$\|T^{i_{j+1}} - T^{i_j}\| < \frac{1}{2^j}, \qquad i_1 < i_2 < \cdots.$$

Then

$$T^{i_1} + \sum_j (T^{i_{j+1}} - T^{i_j})$$

defines an element of $\mathscr{U}$ which is the limit of $\{T^i\}$.

208. THEOREM. *Suppose that $\mathscr{A}$ is closed in $\mathscr{U}$. Then L° is closed in $Y\Psi$ iff a constant k exists such that*

$$\|Az\|_{Y\Psi} \geqq k\|A\|, \qquad k > 0, \tag{209}$$

for all $A \in \mathscr{A}$.

The hypothesis here that $\mathscr{A}$ be closed in $\mathscr{U}$ is not unduly restrictive. For if $\mathscr{A}$ were not closed, we could replace $\mathscr{A}$ by its closure in $\mathscr{U}$, at the beginning of our analysis.

The following proof is well known, except possibly for the use of the essential denseness of z [Riesz-Nagy 1, p. 264; Sard 10, p. 136].

PROOF. *Part* 1. *Necessity.* Suppose that $L^\circ = \mathscr{A}z$ is closed. Then the map

$$A \to Az, \qquad A \in \mathscr{A}, \tag{210}$$

is a linear map of the Banach space $\mathscr{A}$ onto all of the Banach space L°. The map is continuous, since

$$\|Az\|_{Y\Psi} \leqq \|A\|\;\|z\|_{X\Psi}$$

by Theorem 156. The map is one-to-one. For, suppose that

$$A^1 z = A^2 z, \qquad A^1, A^2 \in \mathscr{A}.$$

Then

$$(A^2 - A^1)z = 0 \in Y\Psi$$

and

$$(A^2 - A^1)z_\omega = 0 \in Y, \quad \text{almost all } \omega,$$

by Theorem 156. Hence

$$(A^2 - A^1)Z = 0,$$

since the sections z_ω are essentially dense. Hence, as elements of $\mathscr{U}$,

$$A^2 = A^1.$$

Since the map (210) is linear, continuous, and one-to-one, its inverse must be linear and continuous (Theorem 8: 14) and hence bounded. Hence a bound b exists, which we take as positive, such that

$$\|A\| \leqq b\|Az\|_Y, \qquad A \in \mathscr{A}.$$

This implies (209), with $k = 1/b$.

Part 2. *Sufficiency*. Suppose that $\{A^i z\}$, $i = 1, 2, \cdots$, $A^i \in \mathscr{A}$, is a Cauchy sequence in $Y\Psi$. Then

$$\|(A^i - A^j)z\|_{Y\Psi} \to 0 \quad \text{as} \quad (i, j) \to (\infty, \infty);$$

and

$$\|A^i - A^j\| \to 0,$$

by (209). Since $\mathscr{A}$ is closed, A exists such that

$$\|A^i - A\| \to 0, \qquad A \in \mathscr{A}.$$

Hence

$$\|A^i z - Az\|_{Y\Psi} \to 0,$$

by Theorem 156. Thus the limit of $\{A^i z\}$ is Az, an element of L°. Hence L° is closed, and the theorem is proved.

§ 211. **The subspaces M_t.** Having considered the problem of minimizing $E\|e\|_Y^2$, we now turn to that of minimizing $E|e_t|^2$, for each fixed $t \in T$. Just as the first problem involved the linear manifold $L \subset Y\Psi$, the second will involve linear manifolds in Ψ.

For each fixed t, we should like to consider the linear set

$$\{(Az)_t : A \in \mathscr{A}\} \subset \Psi.$$

We cannot necessarily do this, because of the possible existence of exceptional values of t, values which may depend on A. We know that for each $A \in \mathscr{A}$, $(Az)_t$ is an element of Ψ for almost all t. The null set in T for which $(Az)_t$ is not in Ψ may however depend on A.

There is no deep problem here, for we choose a countable set of elements of $\mathscr{A}$ for our initial consideration, as follows.

Assume that $L^\circ \neq \{0\}$; that is, that L° *consists of more than the element* 0 *in* $Y\Psi$. Otherwise the problem of approximation has the uninteresting solution $A = 0$.

The spaces $X\Psi$ and $Y\Psi$ have countable bases, by Lemma 72, and are therefore separable, by Theorem 54. It follows that $L^\circ \subset Y\Psi$ is separable and that a countable set $\mathscr{S}$ of elements of L° is dense in L°. Then

$$L = \text{Span } \mathscr{S}.$$

Hence the orthogonalization process of § 60 may be used to construct a basis

$$\{\lambda^g\}, \qquad \lambda^g \in L^\circ, \quad g \in G, \tag{212}$$

for L, where G is either the set of all positive integers or the first n positive integers for some $n < \infty$. Since $\lambda^g \in L^\circ$, there is an operator A^g such that

$$\lambda^g = A^g z \in Y\Psi, \qquad A^g \in \mathscr{A}, \quad g \in G. \tag{213}$$

For each $g \in G$ and each $t \in T$ with null exceptions

$$\lambda_t^g \in \Psi,$$

by Corollary 114. Since G is countable, there is a set T_1 which is almost all of T, such that

$$\lambda_t^g \in \Psi, \qquad t \in T_1, \quad g \in G,$$

without exception. For each $t \in T_1$, put

$$\begin{aligned} M_t^\circ &= \text{span}\,\{\lambda_t^g : g \in G\} \subset \Psi, \\ M_t &= \text{closure of } M_t^\circ = \text{Span}\,\{\lambda_t^g : g \in G\} \subset \Psi. \end{aligned} \tag{214}$$

Thus M_t *is a linear subspace of* Ψ *for each* $t \in T$ *with null exceptions.* We may think of M_t as a *cross section* of L: It is something like what one would obtain from L by fixing t simultaneously in all the elements of L.

Our definition of the spaces M_t uses the basis (212). For almost all t, however, M_t does not depend on the choice of the basis. As we shall not use this fact, we omit its proof, which indeed may readily be supplied by the reader.

215. Lemma. *If*

$$u \in L,$$

then

$$u_t \in M_t \quad \textit{for almost all } t \in T.$$

Proof. Since u is a limit point of L°, a sequence $\{u^i\}$, $i = 1, 2, \cdots$, exists such that $u^i \to u$ and u^i, for each i, is a finite linear combination of elements of the basis (212). Hence, for each i and each $t \in T_1$,

$$u_t^i \in M_t^\circ.$$

By Corollary 122, a properly chosen subsequence $\{u^{i_h}\}$, $i_1 < i_2 < \cdots$, of $\{u^i\}$ is such that $u_t^{i_h} \to u_t$ in Ψ for almost all t as $h \to \infty$. Hence, for almost all t, u_t is in the closure of M_t°; that is,

$$u_t \in M_t.$$

This completes the proof.

§ 216. **Characterization of strongly efficient operators.** Just as efficiency is related to projection onto L, so strong efficiency is related to projections onto M_t, $t \in T_1$.

Put

$$\tau_t = \text{Proj}_{M_t}\, y_t, \quad \text{almost all } t; \tag{217}$$

$$\sigma = \text{Proj}_L\, y. \tag{218}$$

Thus for almost all t, $y_t \in \Psi$ and $M_t \subset \Psi$ and τ_t is the projection of y_t in Ψ onto M_t. Since

$$\sigma \in L \subset Y\Psi,$$

it follows that

(219) $$\sigma_t \in M_t \subset \Psi, \quad \text{almost all } t,$$

by Lemma 215.

220. Lemma. *An operator $A \in \mathscr{A}$ is strongly efficient if*

(221) $$(Az)_t = \tau_t, \quad \textit{almost all } t.$$

An operator $A \in \mathscr{A}$ is within ρ of strong efficiency ($\rho > 0$) if a function ζ_t exists such that

$$\zeta \in Y, \qquad \|\zeta\|_Y < \rho,$$

and

(222) $$E|(Az)_t - \tau_t|^2 \leqq |\zeta_t|^2, \quad \textit{almost all } t.$$

Our next theorem will imply that the condition (221) is necessary for strong efficiency as well as sufficient (see Remark 251).

Proof. What is involved here is the same immediate consequence of orthogonality that entered in Theorems 34 and 189.

Put

(223) $$g_t = \tau_t - y_t;$$

then g_t is defined and an element of Ψ for almost all t. Also

(224) $$g_t \perp M_t, \quad \text{almost all } t,$$

by (217).

For an operator $A \in \mathscr{A}$, put

$$e = Az - y.$$

For almost all t,

(225) $$e_t = g_t + (e_t - g_t); \qquad e_t - g_t = (Az)_t - \tau_t \in M_t;$$

by Lemma 215 since $Az \in L$. Then g_t and $(e_t - g_t)$ are in orthogonal complements in Ψ, and

(226) $$E|e_t|^2 = E|g_t|^2 + E|e_t - g_t|^2, \quad \text{almost all } t,$$

(227) $$E|e_t|^2 \geqq E|g_t|^2, \quad \text{almost all } t.$$

Now suppose that $A^0 \in \mathscr{A}$ is such that

$$(A^0z)_t = \tau_t, \quad \text{almost all } t.$$

Put

$$e^0 = A^0z - y.$$

Then $e_t^0 = g_t$, almost all t, by (223). Hence, by (227),

$$E|e_t|^2 \geqq E|e_t^0|^2, \quad \text{almost all } t;$$

that is, A^0 is strongly efficient.

Finally suppose that $A^0 \in \mathscr{A}$ is such that

$$E|(A^0z)_t - \tau_t|^2 \leqq |\zeta_t|^2, \qquad \zeta \in Y, \quad \|\zeta\|_Y < \rho.$$

We shall show that A^0 is within ρ of strong efficiency. Thus

$$E|e_t^0|^2 = E|g_t|^2 + E|(A^0z)_t - \tau_t|^2, \quad \text{almost all } t,$$

by (226) and (225) with A replaced by A^0. Hence, by (227),

$$E|e_t|^2 + |\zeta_t|^2 \geqq E|g_t|^2 + |\zeta_t|^2 = E|e_t^0|^2 - E|(A^0z)_t - \tau_t|^2 + |\zeta_t|^2 \geqq E|e_t^0|^2.$$

Hence A^0 is within ρ of strong efficiency, by (181), (182).

This completes the proof.

228. LEMMA. *A necessary and sufficient condition that*

(229) $$\sigma_t = \tau_t, \quad \textit{almost all } t,$$

is that

(230) $$\sigma_t - y_t \perp M_t, \quad \textit{almost all } t.$$

PROOF. By Lemma 215,

$$\sigma_t - \tau_t \in M_t, \quad \text{almost all } t,$$

since $\sigma \in L$. Hence (229) is equivalent to the condition

(231) $$\sigma_t - \tau_t \perp M_t, \quad \text{almost all } t.$$

But

$$\tau_t - y_t \perp M_t, \quad \text{almost all } t,$$

by (217). Hence (231) is equivalent to the condition

$$\sigma_t - y_t \perp M_t, \quad \text{almost all } t,$$

as was to be shown.

232. THEOREM. *In order that an operator within ρ of strong efficiency exist for each $\rho > 0$, it is necessary and sufficient that*

(233) $$\tau_t = \sigma_t, \quad \textit{almost all } t,$$

where

$$\sigma = \operatorname{Proj}_L y,$$

$$\tau_t = \operatorname{Proj}_{M_t} y_t, \quad \textit{almost all } t.$$

If condition (233) holds, then any efficient operator is strongly efficient and any operator within ρ of efficiency is within ρ of strong efficiency, $\rho > 0$.

Because of this theorem it is natural and suggestive to use the following language: Efficiency is strong iff (233) holds. We may then rephrase Lemma 228: Efficiency is strong iff (230) holds.

PROOF [Sard 10, Theorem 4]. *Part* 1. *Sufficiency.* Suppose that (233) holds.

For each $\rho > 0$, an operator A^0 within ρ of efficiency surely exists. Let A^0 be such an operator. We shall show that A^0 is within ρ of strong efficiency.

By Theorem 189,

$$E\|A^0z - \sigma\|_Y^2 < \rho^2.$$

For almost all $t \in T$, define ζ_t as

$$\zeta_t = [E|(A^0z)_t - \sigma_t|^2]^{1/2} = [E|(A^0z)_t - \tau_t|^2]^{1/2}. \tag{234}$$

Then ζ_t is measurable m, by Lemma 108 and Fubini's Theorem; and

$$\zeta \in Y, \qquad \|\zeta\|_Y < \rho,$$

since

$$\|\zeta\|_Y^2 = \int_T |\zeta_t|^2\, dm(t) = \int_T dm(t) E|(A^0z)_t - \sigma_t|^2$$

$$= E\int_T dm(t)|(A^0z)_t - \sigma_t|^2 = E\|A^0z - \sigma\|_Y^2 < \rho^2 < \infty.$$

Furthermore (234) implies (222) (with equality) and $A = A^0$. Hence A^0 is within ρ of strong efficiency, by Lemma 220.

Similarly but more simply, if A^0 is efficient, then A^0 is surely strongly efficient.

Part 2. *Necessity.* Suppose that an operator within ρ of strong efficiency exists for each $\rho > 0$. We shall show that (233) holds.

To this end assume that (233) does not hold.

Then an operator $A^0 \in \mathscr{A}$ exists such that

$$q_t^0 \underset{\text{def}}{=} Ef_t\bar{\gamma}_t^0 \neq 0 \in Y, \tag{235}$$

where

$$f = \sigma - y, \qquad \gamma^0 = A^0z. \tag{236}$$

The relation (235) asserts that there is a measurable set $P \subset T$ of positive m-measure such that $q_t^0 \neq 0$ whenever $t \in P$, where A^0 is a properly chosen element of $\mathscr{A}$. For if not, f_t would be orthogonal in Ψ to $(Az)_t$ for almost all t, for all $A \in \mathscr{A}$, since q_t^0 is the inner product in Ψ of f_t into γ_t^0. Now M_t° is a span of elements $(Az)_t$ for almost all t, by (214). Hence f_t would be normal to M_t° and to M_t, for almost all t. Hence by Lemma 228, (229) =

(233) would hold, contrary to our assumption.

Choose a complex number c such that

$$\text{(237)} \qquad \text{Real } \bar{c}q_t^0 > 0, \qquad t \in P,$$

where P is a measurable subset of T of positive measure, suitably chosen. This is possible. For if not,

$$\text{(238)} \qquad \text{Real } \bar{c}q_t^0 \leqq 0, \text{ almost all } t, \text{ for all } c \in \mathsf{C}.$$

Then

$$\text{(239)} \qquad \text{Real } \bar{c}q_t^0 = 0, \text{ almost all } t, \text{ for all } c \in \mathsf{C}.$$

Otherwise Real $\bar{c}_1 q_t^0 < 0$ and Real $-\bar{c}_1 q_t^0 > 0$ somewhere, for some c_1, which is a contradiction of (238) with $c = -c_1$. But (239) implies that

$$q_t^0 = 0, \qquad \text{almost all } t,$$

a contradiction of (235).

Put

$$g = \sigma - c\gamma^0$$

$$h = g - y = f - c\gamma^0.$$

Then

$$\begin{aligned} E|h_t|^2 &= E|f_t|^2 - 2 \text{ Real } Ef_t\bar{c}\bar{\gamma}_t^0 + E|c\gamma_t^0|^2 \\ &= E|f_t|^2 - 2 \text{ Real } \bar{c}q_t^0 + |c|^2 E|\gamma_t^0|^2, \quad \text{almost all } t, \end{aligned}$$

and

$$\text{(240)} \qquad \int_P E|h_t|^2 = \int_P E|f_t|^2 - 2 \text{ Real } \bar{c} \int_P q_t^0 + |c|^2 \int_P E|\gamma_t^0|^2,$$

all integrations here and for the rest of this proof being relative to $dm(t)$. By (237),

$$\text{Real } \bar{c} \int_P q_t^0 > 0.$$

Now replace c by ac, where a is a positive number so small that the term in $\bar{c}$ in (240) dominates the term in $|c|^2$. Then (240) implies that

$$\text{(241)} \qquad \int_P E|h_t|^2 < \int_P E|f_t|^2.$$

Let $Q \subset T$ be the set on which

$$E|h_t|^2 < E|f_t|^2.$$

Then Q is measurable m, and (241) implies that

$$m(Q) > 0.$$

Put

$$\Delta = \int_Q (E|f_t|^2 - E|h_t|^2) > 0, \tag{242}$$

$$B^2 = \int_Q E|f_t|^2, \qquad B > 0. \tag{243}$$

Choose ρ so that

$$\rho > 0, \qquad \rho^2 < \frac{\Delta}{8}, \qquad \rho < \frac{\Delta}{8B}, \tag{244}$$

as is possible. Take A^1 within ρ of strong efficiency, as is possible by hypothesis. Then A^1 is within ρ of efficiency, by Lemma 183, and A^1z is within ρ of σ in $Y\Psi$, by Theorem 189. Take $A^2 \in \mathscr{A}$ so that A^2z is within ρ of g, as is possible since

$$g \in L = \text{Span}\,\{\mathscr{A}z\}.$$

Put

$$e^1 = A^1z - y, \qquad e^2 = A^2z - y.$$

Then

$$e^1 - f = A^1z - \sigma, \qquad e^2 - h = A^2z - g,$$

$$\int_Q E|e_t^1 - f_t|^2 = \int_Q E|(A^1z)_t - \sigma_t|^2 < \rho^2, \tag{245}$$

$$\int_Q E|e_t^2 - h_t|^2 = \int_Q E|(A^2z)_t - g_t|^2 < \rho^2, \tag{246}$$

since these inequalities would be true even with Q replaced by T.

For the rest of this proof, let

$$|||v|||^2 = \int_Q E|v|^2; \tag{247}$$

that is, $|||v|||^2$ is the square norm in the L^2-space $H(Q \times \Omega, mp)$. Denote the inner product in that space by

$$((v, w)) = \int_Q Ev\bar{w}.$$

We now establish the elementary fact that

$$\big|\, |||v|||^2 - |||w|||^2 \,\big| < \rho^2 + 2\rho \min\,[|||v|||, |||w|||] \tag{248}$$

whenever

$$|||v - w||| < \rho, \qquad v, w \in Y\Psi. \tag{249}$$

To this end, assume that

$$|||v||| \leqq |||w|||.$$

The contrary case may be treated by interchanging v and w. Now

$$\begin{aligned}
w &= (w - v) + v, \\
|||w|||^2 &= ((w, w)) = |||w - v|||^2 + |||v|||^2 + 2 \text{ Real } ((w - v, v)), \\
0 &\leqq |||w|||^2 - |||v|||^2 = |||w - v|||^2 + 2 \text{ Real } ((w - v, v)) \\
&\leqq |||w - v|||^2 + 2|||w - v|||\,|||v||| < \rho^2 + 2\rho|||v||| \\
&= \rho^2 + 2\rho \min [|||v|||, |||w|||],
\end{aligned}$$

by Schwarz's inequality. Thus (248) is established.

Since A^1 is within ρ of strong efficiency,

$$E|e_t^1|^2 \leqq E|e_t^2|^2 + |\zeta_t|^2, \quad \text{almost all } t,$$

where

(250) $$\zeta \in Y, \qquad \|\zeta\|_Y < \rho.$$

Hence, for almost all t,

$$E|f_t|^2 - E|h_t|^2 \leqq |\zeta_t^2| + [E|e_t^2|^2 - E|h_t|^2] - [E|e_t^1|^2 - E|f_t|^2].$$

Integrate over Q, and use (242), (250), (247), (248), (246), (245), (243), (244) and the fact that

$$B = |||f||| > |||h|||.$$

Then

$$\begin{aligned}
\Delta &< \rho^2 + \big|\, |||e^2|||^2 - |||h|||^2 \,\big| + \big|\, |||e^1|||^2 - |||f|||^2 \,\big| \\
&< \rho^2 + \rho^2 + 2\rho|||h||| + \rho^2 + 2\rho|||f||| < 3\rho^2 + 2\rho B + 2\rho B \\
&< \frac{3\Delta}{8} + \frac{4\Delta}{8} = \frac{7\Delta}{8}.
\end{aligned}$$

This contradicts the fact (242) that $\Delta > 0$, and the proof is complete.

251. REMARK. It follows from Theorem 232 that the condition (221) of Lemma 220 is necessary as well as sufficient for the strong efficiency of A. For, if A is strongly efficient, then A is within ρ of strong efficiency for each $\rho > 0$ and (233) holds, by Theorem 232. Also

$$Az = \sigma$$

by Theorem 189, since A is efficient by Lemma 183. Hence, by (233), (221) holds, as was to be shown.

Applications of Theorem 232 are given in §§ 267 ff. which the reader may consult now, if he wishes.

§ 252. **A sufficient condition for strong efficiency.** If the set $\mathscr{A}$, which is a datum of our problem, is sufficiently large, then efficiency is strong. This is a consequence of the next theorem.

We say that a linear continuous operator A on X to Y is *of finite rank* if the image

$$AX = \{Ax : x \in X\} \subset Y$$

of X under A is finite dimensional.

253. THEOREM. *If $\mathscr{A}$ contains all operators of finite rank, then efficiency is strong.*

Note that the hypothesis here bears solely on $\mathscr{A}$ and not on z or y. Efficiency will be strong for all data z and y.

The hypothesis on $\mathscr{A}$ implies that $\mathscr{A}$ is dense in the space of all completely continuous linear operators on X to Y relative to the Banach norm; $\mathscr{A}$ need not be dense in the space of all continuous linear operators, however [Riesz-Nagy 1, p. 219].

The present theorem is due to the author [10, Theorem 5].

PROOF. We shall show that

$$\tau_t = \sigma_t, \quad \text{almost all } t,$$

where

$$\tau_t = \text{Proj}_{M_t}\, y_t, \quad \text{almost all } t,$$

$$\sigma = \text{Proj}_L\, y.$$

By Lemma 228, it will be sufficient to show that

$$\sigma_t - y_t \perp M_t, \quad \text{almost all } t.$$

Now by the definition of σ,

$$\sigma - y \perp L.$$

For the present theorem it will therefore be sufficient to prove the following:

$$(254) \qquad w_t \perp M_t, \quad \text{almost all } t,$$

whenever

$$(255) \qquad w \perp L, \quad w \in Y\Psi.$$

Consider any element w satisfying conditions (255).

We shall use bases

$$\{\xi^j\}, \quad j \in J; \qquad \{\eta^k\}, \quad k \in K; \qquad \{\psi^\nu\}, \quad \nu \in N;$$

in X, Y, Ψ, respectively. Then

$$\{\xi^j\psi^\nu\}, \quad j \in J, \quad \nu \in N; \qquad \{\eta^k\psi^\nu\}, \quad k \in K, \quad \nu \in N,$$

are bases in $X\Psi$, $Y\Psi$, respectively, by Lemma 72. We describe elements and operators relative to these bases. Since Y and Ψ are L^2-spaces, we may think of the elements $\eta^k(t)$, $t \in T$, as functions of t, measurable and absolute square integrable relative to the measure m, $k \in K$; and similarly the elements $\psi^\nu(\omega)$, $\omega \in \Omega$, as functions of ω, measurable and absolute square integrable relative to the probability p, $\nu \in N$. Note that

(256) $$(\psi^\nu, \psi^{\nu'}) = E\psi^\nu(\omega)\bar{\psi}^{\nu'}(\omega) = \delta^{\nu,\nu'}, \qquad \nu, \nu' \in N.$$

In the following paragraphs, the index

j varies over J,

k, k' vary over K,

ν, ν' vary over N.

A linear continuous operator F on X to Y may be described by its matrix $\{f^{k,j}\}$, as in § 132. The quantities $f^{k,j}$ are given in equations (137). Then the extension of F to a linear continuous operator on $X\Psi$ to $Y\Psi$ has matrix $\{f^{k,j}\,\delta^{\nu',\nu}\}$, as given in (162). The relation

$$v = Fu \in Y\Psi, \qquad u \in X\Psi,$$

may be written as

$$\{v^{k,\nu}\} = \{f^{k,j}\}\{u^{j,\nu}\}$$

in terms of matrices, where $\{v^{k,\nu}\}$ are the coordinates of v and $\{u^{j,\nu}\}$ are the coordinates of u, by (164).

Let F^{k_0,j_0}, $k_0 \in K$, $j_0 \in J$, be the linear continuous operator on X to Y, whose matrix is

$$\{_k\, \delta^{k,k_0}\, \delta^{j,j_0}\, _j\}.$$

This matrix consists entirely of zeros except for a single 1 in the position $j = j_0$, $k = j_0$. Then F^{k_0,j_0} is of rank one and

$$F^{k_0,j_0} \in \mathscr{A},$$

since by hypothesis $\mathscr{A}$ includes all operators of finite rank.

Let the coordinates of w be $\{w^{k,\nu}\}$. By (255) and the fact that

$$L^\circ = \mathscr{A}z \subset L,$$

we know that

(257) $$(w, F^{k_0,j_0}z)_{Y\Psi} = E(w, F^{k_0,j_0}z)_Y = 0.$$

Now $F^{k_0,j_0}z$ has coordinates

$$\left\{_k \sum_j \delta^{k,k_0}\, \delta^{j,j_0} z^{j,\nu}\, _\nu\right\} = \{_k\, \delta^{k,k_0}\, z^{j_0,\nu}\, _\nu\}$$

where the coordinates of z are $\{z^{j,\nu}\}$. And

$$\sum_{k,\nu} w^{k,\nu}\, \delta^{k,k_0} \bar{z}^{j_0,\nu} = (w,\, F^{k_0,j_0} z)_{Y\Psi};$$

hence, by (257),

$$(258) \qquad \sum_{\nu} w^{k_0,\nu} \bar{z}^{j_0,\nu} = 0, \qquad k_0 \in K, \quad j_0 \in J.$$

Let $\{\lambda^g\}$, $g \in G$, be the basis for L used in § 211 for the construction of the spaces M_t. To establish (254), it will be sufficient by (214) to show that

$$(259) \qquad E w_t \bar{\lambda}_t^g = 0, \qquad g \in G, \quad \text{almost all } t.$$

This we shall do.

Consider λ^g, with g an arbitrary but fixed element of G. For brevity we will write λ instead of λ^g. An operator A exists such that

$$\lambda = Az, \qquad A \in \mathscr{A}, \qquad A = \{a^{k,j}\}.$$

Then the coordinates of λ are

$$(260) \qquad \{\lambda^{k,\nu}\} = \left\{ \sum_j a^{k,j} z^{j,\nu} \right\}.$$

The Fourier series for w and λ are

$$w = \sum_{k,\nu} w^{k,\nu} \eta^k \psi^\nu,$$

$$\lambda = \sum_{k',\nu'} \lambda^{k',\nu'} \eta^{k'} \psi^{\nu'}.$$

These series give the functions w and λ, in the sense of convergence in the mean square relative to mp. Thus

$$E \int_T dm \left| w - \sum_{\substack{k \leq \mathbf{k}, \\ \nu \leq \boldsymbol{\nu}}} w^{k,\nu} \eta^k \psi^\nu \right|^2 \to 0 \qquad \text{as } (\mathbf{k}, \boldsymbol{\nu}) \to (\infty, \infty);$$

$$E \int_T dm \left| \lambda - \sum_{\substack{k' \leq \mathbf{k}', \\ \nu' \leq \boldsymbol{\nu}'}} \lambda^{k',\nu'} \eta^{k'} \psi^{\nu'} \right|^2 \to 0 \text{ as } (\mathbf{k}', \boldsymbol{\nu}') \to (\infty, \infty).$$

Hence by Lemma 123,

$$E \int_T dm \left| w\bar{\lambda} - \sum_{\substack{k \leq \mathbf{k},\ k' \leq \mathbf{k}' \\ \nu \leq \boldsymbol{\nu},\ \nu' \leq \boldsymbol{\nu}'}} w^{k,\nu} \bar{\lambda}^{k',\nu'} \eta^k \bar{\eta}^{k'} \psi^\nu \bar{\psi}^{\nu'} \right| \to 0 \quad \text{as } \mathbf{k}, \mathbf{k}', \boldsymbol{\nu}, \boldsymbol{\nu}' \to \infty;$$

$$\int_T dm \left| E w\bar{\lambda} - \sum_{\substack{k \leq \mathbf{k},\ k' \leq \mathbf{k}', \\ \nu \leq \boldsymbol{\nu}}} w^{k,\nu} \bar{\lambda}^{k',\nu} \eta^k \bar{\eta}^{k'} \right| \to 0 \qquad \text{as } \mathbf{k}, \mathbf{k}', \boldsymbol{\nu} \to \infty;$$

by (256). Put

$$(261) \qquad \Sigma = \sum_{\substack{k \leq \mathbf{k},\ k' \leq \mathbf{k}', \\ \nu \leq \boldsymbol{\nu}}} w^{k,\nu} \bar{\lambda}^{k',\nu} \eta^k \bar{\eta}^{k'}.$$

We have thus shown that

$$(262) \qquad \int_T dm|Ew\bar{\lambda} - \sum| \to 0 \quad \text{as } \boldsymbol{k}, \boldsymbol{k}', \boldsymbol{\nu} \to \infty.$$

We now prove that if $\boldsymbol{k}, \boldsymbol{k}', \boldsymbol{\nu} \to \infty$ in a specified fashion, then

$$(263) \qquad \int_T dm|\sum| \to 0.$$

Thus, by (260),

$$\begin{aligned} \int_T dm|\sum| &= \int_T dm \Bigg| \sum_{\substack{k \leqq \boldsymbol{k},\, k' \leqq \boldsymbol{k}', \\ \nu \leqq \boldsymbol{\nu}}} w^{k,\nu} \eta^k \bar{\eta}^{k'} \sum_j \bar{a}^{k',j} \bar{z}^{j,\nu} \Bigg| \\ (264) \qquad &= \int_T dm \Bigg| \sum_{k \leqq \boldsymbol{k},\, k' \leqq \boldsymbol{k}'} \eta^k \bar{\eta}^{k'} \sum_{\nu \leqq \boldsymbol{\nu}} w^{k,\nu} \sum_j \bar{a}^{k',j} \bar{z}^{j,\nu} \Bigg| \\ &= \int_T dm \Bigg| \sum_{k \leqq \boldsymbol{k},\, k' \leqq \boldsymbol{k}'} \eta^k \bar{\eta}^{k'} \sum_j \bar{a}^{k',j} \sum_{\nu \leqq \boldsymbol{\nu}} w^{k,\nu} \bar{z}^{j,\nu} \Bigg|, \end{aligned}$$

since $\boldsymbol{\nu}$ is finite. Now by (258),

$$\sum_{\nu \leqq \boldsymbol{\nu}} w^{k,\nu} \bar{z}^{j,\nu} = - \sum_{\nu > \boldsymbol{\nu}} w^{k,\nu} \bar{z}^{j,\nu}.$$

Hence

$$\Bigg| \sum_{\nu \leqq \boldsymbol{\nu}} w^{k,\nu} \bar{z}^{j,\nu} \Bigg|^2 \leqq \sum_{\nu > \boldsymbol{\nu}} |w^{k,\nu}|^2 \sum_{\nu' > \boldsymbol{\nu}} |z^{j,\nu'}|^2,$$

and

$$\sum_j \Bigg| \sum_{\nu \leqq \boldsymbol{\nu}} w^{k,\nu} \bar{z}^{j,\nu} \Bigg|^2 \leqq \sum_{\nu > \boldsymbol{\nu}} |w^{k,\nu}|^2 \sum_{\substack{\nu' > \boldsymbol{\nu}, \\ j}} |z^{j,\nu'}|^2 < \infty.$$

Since A is bounded,

$$\sum_{k'} \Bigg| \sum_j \bar{a}^{k',j} \sum_{\nu \leqq \boldsymbol{\nu}} w^{k,\nu} \bar{z}^{j,\nu} \Bigg|^2 \leqq \|A\|^2 \sum_{\nu > \boldsymbol{\nu}} |w^{k,\nu}|^2 \sum_{\substack{\nu' > \boldsymbol{\nu}, \\ j}} |z^{j,\nu'}|^2.$$

Hence

$$(265) \qquad \sum_{\substack{k \leqq \boldsymbol{k}, \\ k' \leqq \boldsymbol{k}'}} |b^{k,k'}|^2 \leqq \|A\|^2 \sum_{\substack{\nu > \boldsymbol{\nu}, \\ k \leqq \boldsymbol{k}}} |w^{k,\nu}|^2 \sum_{\substack{\nu' > \boldsymbol{\nu}, \\ j}} |z^{j,\nu'}|^2 \to 0 \quad \text{as } \boldsymbol{\nu} \to \infty,$$

where

$$b^{k,k'} = \sum_j \bar{a}^{k',j} \sum_{\nu \leqq \boldsymbol{\nu}} w^{k,\nu} \bar{z}^{j,\nu}.$$

It follows from (264) that

$$\int_T dm|\Sigma| = \int_T dm \left| \sum_{\substack{k \leqq \boldsymbol{k}, \\ k' \leqq \boldsymbol{k}'}} \eta^k \bar{\eta}^{k'} b^{k,k'} \right| \leqq \sum_{\substack{k \leqq \boldsymbol{k}, \\ k' \leqq \boldsymbol{k}'}} |b^{k,k'}| \int_T dm |\eta^k \bar{\eta}^{k'}|;$$

(266)
$$\left[\int_T dm|\Sigma|\right]^2 \leqq \sum_{\substack{k \leqq \boldsymbol{k}, \\ k' \leqq \boldsymbol{k}'}} |b^{k,k'}|^2 \sum_{\substack{k \leqq \boldsymbol{k}, \\ k' \leqq \boldsymbol{k}'}} \left[\int_T dm|\eta^k \bar{\eta}^{k'}|\right]^2$$

$$\leqq \boldsymbol{k}\boldsymbol{k}' \sum_{\substack{k \leqq \boldsymbol{k}, \\ k' \leqq \boldsymbol{k}'}} |b^{k,k'}|^2,$$

since

$$\left[\int_T dm|\eta^k \bar{\eta}^{k'}|\right]^2 \leqq \int_T dm|\eta^k|^2 \int_T dm|\eta^{k'}|^2 = 1.$$

Fix $\boldsymbol{k}$ and $\boldsymbol{k}'$. Let $\boldsymbol{\nu} \to \infty$. By (265), (266),

$$\int_T dm\ |\Sigma| \to 0.$$

This is true for each $\boldsymbol{k}$, $\boldsymbol{k}'$. This establishes (263).

It follows from (262) that

$$\int_T dm|Ew\bar{\lambda}| \to 0,$$

when $\boldsymbol{k}, \boldsymbol{k}', \boldsymbol{\nu} \to \infty$ in specified fashion. The last integral is independent of $\boldsymbol{k}, \boldsymbol{k}', \boldsymbol{\nu}$, however. Hence

$$\int_T dm|Ew\bar{\lambda}| = 0$$

and

$$Ew\bar{\lambda} = 0, \quad \text{almost all } t.$$

This establishes (259), and completes the proof.

§ 267. **Applications.** We now consider a number of illustrations. These indicate applications of the theory. In future years, as our knowledge of the stochastic nature of actual inputs becomes more extensive, there are likely to be many applications outside the domain of mathematical invention.

Let us first review the problem.

S, T, and Ω are arbitrary nonempty spaces.

X is a separable Hilbert space whose elements are functions on S or perhaps equivalence sets of such functions.

m is a nonnegative measure on T.

Y is the separable L^2-space $H(T, m)$ of functions absolute square integrable m on T.

p is a probability on Ω.
Ψ is the separable L^2-space $H(\Omega, p)$.
$z = x + \delta x \in X\Psi$.
$y \in Y\Psi = H(T \times \Omega, mp)$.
Thus z is a function on $S \times \Omega$ and y is a function on $T \times \Omega$. Because of this interpretation we may describe z and y as stochastic processes.

$\mathscr{A}$ is a linear set of linear continuous operators on X to Y. Each operator $A \in \mathscr{A}$ engenders a unique linear continuous operator, also denoted A, on $X\Psi$ to $Y\Psi$.

We approximate y by Az, $A \in \mathscr{A}$. The error in the approximation is

$$e = Az - y.$$

For each $\omega \in \Omega$, with null exceptions, z_ω is an input, y_ω is the desired output, Az_ω is the actual output, and e_ω is the error in the approximation of y_ω by Az_ω.

In § 283, for example, z_ω consists of n tabulated values of a function contaminated by error; y_ω is the true function on the entire domain T and not merely at the n tabular points that in this example constitute S. Thus § 283 is pertinent to the use of tables.

§ 268. **A first calculation.** Suppose that

$$\{\xi^j\},\quad j \in J; \qquad \{\eta^k\},\quad k \in K; \qquad \{\psi^\nu\},\quad \nu \in N;$$

are bases in X, Y, and Ψ, respectively; and that $z \in X\Psi$ and $y \in Y\Psi$ are given relative to these bases:

$$z(s, \omega) = \sum_{j,\nu} z^{j,\nu} \xi^j \psi^\nu,$$

$$y(t, \omega) = \sum_{k,\nu} y^{k,\nu} \eta^k \psi^\nu,$$

where

$$z^{j,\nu} = (z, \xi^j \psi^\nu)_{X\Psi} = E(z, \xi^j)_X \bar{\psi}^\nu, \qquad \sum_{j,\nu} |z^{j,\nu}|^2 = \|z\|^2_{X\Psi} = E\|z\|^2_X < \infty,$$

$$y^{k,\nu} = (y, \eta^k \psi^\nu)_{Y\Psi} = E\left(\int_T y\bar{\eta}^k\, dm\right)\bar{\psi}^\nu, \qquad \sum_{k,\nu} |y^{k,\nu}|^2 = \|y\|^2_{Y\Psi} < \infty.$$

Suppose that $\mathscr{A}$ is the set of those linear continuous operators on X to Y whose matrices relative to $\{\xi^j\}$, $\{\eta^k\}$ are *diagonal*.

A diagonal matrix represents a bounded operator iff the elements of the diagonal are absolutely bounded. Thus $A \in \mathscr{A}$ iff

$$a^{k,j} = (A\xi^j, \eta^k)_Y = \delta^{k,j} a^k,$$

$$\sup |a^k| < \infty, \qquad k \in K, \quad j \in J.$$

Clearly $\mathscr{A}$ is a linear set.

This completes the initial statement of the data. Later we will specialize z and y.

In the solution, we use the elements

$$z^k = \sum_\nu z^{k,\nu}\psi^\nu,$$

$$y^k = \sum_\nu y^{k,\nu}\psi^\nu, \qquad k \in K,$$

of Ψ. These are well defined since

$$\sum_\nu |z^{k,\nu}|^2 \leqq \|z\|^2_{X\Psi} < \infty, \qquad k \in K,$$

$$\sum_\nu |y^{k,\nu}|^2 \leqq \|y\|^2_{Y\Psi} < \infty.$$

We first determine

$$L^\circ = \mathscr{A}z = \{Az : A \in \mathscr{A}\} = \text{span}\, \mathscr{A}z.$$

By (164) the coordinates of Az are

$$\{_k\, \delta^{k,j}a^k\,_j\}\{_j\, z^{j,\nu}\,_\nu\} = \{_k\, a^k z^{k,\nu}\,_\nu\}, \qquad k \in K, \quad \nu \in N.$$

If $k \in K$ and $k \notin J$, we take $z^{k,\nu} = 0$. Thus L° consists of all elements of $Y\Psi$ with coordinates

$$\{_k\, a^k z^{k,\nu}\,_\nu\}, \qquad k \in K, \quad \nu \in N, \tag{269}$$

where

$$\sup |a^k| < \infty.$$

In particular, L° includes the elements

$$\{\delta^{k,k_0}z^{k,\nu}\} = \sum_{k,\nu} \delta^{k,k_0}z^{k,\nu}\eta^k\psi^\nu = \sum_\nu z^{k_0,\nu}\eta^{k_0}\psi^\nu = \eta^{k_0}z^{k_0}, \qquad k_0 \in K. \tag{270}$$

Now the span of these elements is dense in L°. For we may approximate any element (269) by the element whose matrix is a sufficiently large leading matrix of (269) bordered by zeros elsewhere; and the latter is a finite linear combination of elements (270). Hence

$$L = \text{Span}\,\{\eta^k z^k : k \in K\}.$$

Furthermore the elements $\eta^k z^k$, $k \in K$, are pairwise orthogonal in $Y\Psi$, since

$$(\eta^k z^k, \eta^{k'} z^{k'})_{Y\Psi} = E z^k \bar{z}^{k'}(\eta^k, \eta^{k'})_Y = \delta^{k,k'} E z^k \bar{z}^{k'}, \qquad k, k' \in K. \tag{271}$$

It follows that we may calculate $\text{Proj}_L\, y$ forthwith, by Corollary 58. Thus let $\tilde{K}$ consist of those indices $k \in K$ for which $E|z^k|^2 = \|z^k\|^2_\Psi \neq 0$, that is,

$$\tilde{K} = \{k \in K : E|z^k|^2 \neq 0\}.$$

Then, by (271),

$$\sigma = \operatorname{Proj}_L y = \sum_{k \in \tilde{K}} \alpha^k \eta^k z^k = \sum_{\substack{k \in \tilde{K}, \\ \nu \in N}} \alpha^k z^{k,\nu} \eta^k \psi^\nu, \tag{272}$$

where

$$\alpha^k = \frac{(y, \eta^k z^k)_{Y\Psi}}{E|z^k|^2}, \qquad k \in \tilde{K}. \tag{273}$$

We may express α^k alternatively, by using coordinates. Thus

$$E|z^k|^2 = \|z^k\|_\Psi^2 = \sum_\nu |z^{k,\nu}|^2;$$

$$(y, \eta^{k_0} z^{k_0})_{Y\Psi} = \sum_{k,\nu} y^{k,\nu} \delta^{k,k_0} \bar{z}^{k_0,\nu} = \sum_\nu y^{k_0,\nu} \bar{z}^{k_0,\nu} = (y^{k_0}, z^{k_0})_\Psi, \qquad k_0 \in K.$$

Hence

$$\alpha^k = \frac{(y^k, z^k)_\Psi}{\|z^k\|_\Psi^2} = \frac{\sum_\nu y^{k,\nu} \bar{z}^{k,\nu}}{\sum_\nu |z^{k,\nu}|^2} = \frac{\|y^k\|_\Psi}{\|z^k\|_\Psi} \cos \theta^k, \qquad k \in \tilde{K}, \tag{274}$$

where θ^k is the angle between y^k and z^k in Ψ.

By Theorem 189 the operator $A \in \mathscr{A}$ with matrix $\{\delta^{k,j} a^k\}$ is efficient iff $Az = \sigma$, that is, iff

$$a^k = \alpha^k, \qquad k \in \tilde{K}. \tag{275}$$

The values of a^k, $k \in K - \tilde{K}$, are immaterial, since

$$z^k = 0, \qquad k \in K - \tilde{K}.$$

Furthermore efficient operators exist iff

$$\sup_{k \in \tilde{K}} |\alpha^k| < \infty.$$

Whether this condition holds or not, an operator within ρ of efficiency may be obtained by retaining a sufficiently large number of diagonal elements with $a^k = \alpha^k$ and letting other diagonal elements be zero, for each $\rho > 0$.

This completes the calculation of efficient operators in the present illustration, where $\mathscr{A}$ consists of diagonal operators.

Let us now investigate when efficiency will be strong. There is a set $T' \subset T$ such that the number η_t^k is defined for all $k \in K$ and all $t \in T'$ and such that $m(T - T') = 0$, by § 211. For each fixed $t \in T'$,

$$M_t^\circ = \operatorname{span} \{\eta_t^k z^k : k \in K\} \subset \Psi.$$

Since the span consists of all linear combinations, the values of η_t^k here are immaterial if different from zero and have the effect of excluding the corresponding vector $z^k \in \Psi$ when $\eta_t^k = 0$. The further calculation of M_t depends on the nature of the functions η^k, $k \in K$, which constitute the given basis in Y.

Assume, as will often be the case, that there is a set T'' which is almost all of T' and is such that

$$\eta_t^k \neq 0 \quad \text{whenever} \quad k \in \tilde{K}, \quad t \in T''.$$

Then

$$M_t^\circ = \text{span}\,\{z^k : k \in \tilde{K}\} \underset{\text{def}}{=} M^\circ, \qquad t \in T''.$$

Thus M_t° is independent of t, $t \in T''$.

By orthogonalizing (§ 60) the set $\{z^k : k \in \tilde{K}\}$ in Ψ, construct a basis $\{\phi^k : k \in K'\}$ for

$$M = \text{closure of } M^\circ = M_t, \qquad t \in T''.$$

Each element ϕ^k is a linear combination of elements z^k, $k \in \tilde{K}$. Then

$$\tau_t = \text{Proj}_{M_t}\, y_t = \sum_{k \in K'} (y_t, \phi^k)_\Psi\, \phi^k \in \Psi, \qquad t \in T''. \tag{276}$$

By Theorem 232, *efficiency is strong iff*

$$\tau_t = \sigma_t, \qquad \textit{almost all } t, \tag{277}$$

where σ_t is the element of Ψ obtained from the function σ of (272) by fixing t, for almost all t. By Corollary 122, we may choose partial sums in the series (272) so that

$$\sigma_t = \sum_{k \in \tilde{K}}{}' \alpha^k \eta_t^k z^k, \quad \text{almost all } t; \tag{278}$$

the ′ here indicates that suitable partial sums must be used.

To consider a particular instance, assume that the elements z^k, $k \in K$, are nonzero and pairwise orthogonal in Ψ and that, for almost all t, $z_t^k \neq 0$ for all $k \in K$. Then

$$K = \tilde{K} = K';$$

and we may take the basis $\{\phi^k\}$ above as $\{z^k/\|z^k\|_\Psi\}$. Then (276) becomes

$$\tau_t = \sum_k (y_t, z^k)_\Psi \frac{z^k}{E|z^k|^2}, \quad \text{almost all } t.$$

In this case (278) may be written without the restriction to special partial sums, by (119). Thus

$$\sigma_t = \sum_k \alpha^k \eta_t^k z^k, \quad \text{almost all } t.$$

It follows from (274) that efficiency is strong iff

$$(279) \qquad (y^k, z^k)_{\Psi} \, \eta_t^k = (y_t, z^k)_{\Psi}, \qquad k \in K, \quad \text{almost all } t.$$

Instances may be adduced in which (279) does not hold. Later we will give a simpler illustration in which efficiency is not strong.

It may be of interest to specialize X, Y, Ψ, z, y further. The spaces X, Y, Ψ might all be ordinary L^2-spaces on the unit interval:

$$\begin{aligned} Y &= H([0, 1], t), \\ X &= Y \text{ with } t \text{ replaced by } s, \\ \Psi &= Y \text{ with } t \text{ replaced by } \omega. \end{aligned}$$

The basis for Y might be $\{\eta^k\}$, where

$$\eta^k(t) = e^{2\pi i k t}, \qquad k \in K = \{\cdots, -2, -1, 0, 1, 2, \cdots\}, \quad i^2 = -1;$$

the basis for X, $\{\xi^j\}$, where

$$\xi^j(s) = \eta^j(s), \qquad j \in K;$$

the basis for Ψ, $\{\psi^\nu\}$, where

$$\psi^\nu(\omega) = \eta^\nu(\omega), \qquad \nu \in K.$$

The input $z \in X\Psi$ might have coordinates

$$z^{j,\nu} = \delta^{j,\nu} c^j, \qquad j, \nu \in K,$$

where

$$\sum_j |c^j|^2 < \infty, \qquad c^j \neq 0, \quad j \in K;$$

the desired output $y \in Y\Psi$ might have coordinates

$$y^{k,\nu} = \delta^{k,\nu} 2\pi i k c^k, \qquad k, \nu \in K.$$

Then

$$\begin{aligned} z(s, \omega) &= \sum_{j,\nu} z^{j,\nu} \xi^j \psi^\nu = \sum_j c^j e^{2\pi i j s} e^{2\pi i j \omega} = \sum_j c^j e^{2\pi i j (s+\omega)}, \\ y(t, \omega) &= \sum_{k,\nu} y^{k,\nu} \eta^k \psi^\nu = \sum_k 2\pi i k c^k e^{2\pi i k t} e^{2\pi i k \omega} \\ &= \sum_j 2\pi i j c^j e^{2\pi i j (t+\omega)}. \end{aligned}$$

Thus

$$y = \left[\frac{dz}{ds}\right]_{s=t}.$$

Our approximation is that of d/dt by an operator $A \in \mathscr{A}$.

Here

$$
\begin{aligned}
y^k(\omega) &= 2\pi i k c^k e^{2\pi i k \omega},\\
z^k(\omega) &= c^k e^{2\pi i k \omega},\\
(y^k, z^k)_\Psi &= 2\pi i k |c^k|^2,\\
(y^k, z^k)_\Psi \, \eta_t^k &= 2\pi i k |c^k|^2 e^{2\pi i k t}, \qquad k \in K.
\end{aligned}
$$

Also

$$
\begin{aligned}
y_t &= \sum_j 2\pi i j c^j e^{2\pi i j t} e^{2\pi i j \omega},\\
(y_t, z^k)_\Psi &= 2\pi i k c^k e^{2\pi i k t} \bar{c}^k = 2\pi i k |c^k|^2 e^{2\pi i k t}.
\end{aligned}
$$

Thus (279) holds and efficiency is now strong. This is not surprising since $\mathscr{A}$, z, and y have all been taken in diagonal form. Note furthermore that, by (274),

$$\alpha^k = \frac{2\pi i k |c^k|^2}{|c^k|^2} = 2\pi i k.$$

Hence

$$\sup_{k \in K} |\alpha^k| = \infty;$$

efficient operators do not exist in this case.

For each $\rho > 0$, operators A within ρ of strong efficiency exist. These are operators whose matrices consist entirely of zeros except that, for a properly chosen finite number of indices k, the kth element of the diagonal is equal to α^k.

§ 280. **An illustration: smoothing of one observation.** The desired output will be the function

$$y(t, \omega) = e^{2\pi i (t-\omega)}, \qquad -\frac{1}{2} \leq t, \omega \leq \frac{1}{2}, \qquad i^2 = -1.$$

This function is assumed to be contaminated by an error

$$b e^{2\pi i c (t-\omega)}$$

of different frequency; here b and c are constants and c is an integer $\neq 1$. The actual input $x + \delta x = z$ will be the observed value at $t = 0$ of the contaminated function:

$$z_\omega(0) = [e^{2\pi i (t-\omega)} + b e^{2\pi i c (t-\omega)}]_{t=0} = e^{-2\pi i \omega} + b e^{-2\pi i c \omega}. \tag{281}$$

The trial consists in fixing a value of ω and thereby the phase of the function y_ω and of the error. Our object is to approximate y_ω, given $z_\omega(0)$.

It is natural to admit approximations A of the form

$$Az = a(t)z_{\omega}(0),$$

where $a(t)$ is a function of t. We will choose A in such a way as to smooth out the error. If there were no contamination ($b = 0$), we would take

$$a(t) = e^{2\pi it}$$

and our approximation would be exact.

After these preliminaries, we now state the precise data of the present illustration.

Put

$$T = \left\{-\frac{1}{2} \leqq t \leqq \frac{1}{2}\right\},$$

$$Y = H(T, t) = \text{the } L^2\text{-space on } T \text{ based on ordinary measure;}$$

$$\eta^k(t) = e^{2\pi ikt}, \qquad k \in K = \{\cdots, -2, -1, 0, 1, 2, \cdots\}.$$

Thus $\{\eta^k : k \in K\}$ is a basis for Y.

Let Ω, Ψ, ψ^ν, be T, Y, η^ν, respectively, $\nu \in K$, with t replaced by ω.

Let X be any space of functions x on S, where S is a set of real numbers and $0 \in S$, such that

(i) X is a Hilbert space;

(ii) The value $x(0)$ of the function x at $s = 0$ is a linear continuous functional, $x \in X$.

For example, X may be the space of complex numbers, which is a Hilbert space of one complex dimension. This could be realized by taking $S = \{0\}$. Alternatively, X may be an L^2-space $H(S, \mu)$, where μ is a measure relative to which $s = 0$ is a point of positive measure:

$$\mu\{0\} > 0.$$

The dimension of X will depend on S and on μ. If X is the L^2-space $H(S, \mu)$, then μ may not be taken as Lebesgue measure, for $x(0)$ would not be unambiguously defined when $x \in X$. This is because $x(s)$ is defined almost everywhere μ when $x \in X$; if μ is Lebesgue measure, $x(0)$ may be any number or may be undefined when $x \in \tilde{x} \in X$. Alternatively, X may be the space of absolutely continuous functions on $\{-1/2 \leqq s \leqq 1/2\} = S$ whose first derivative is an element of the ordinary L^2-space $H(S, s)$ relative to Lebesgue measure. In this case X would be an instance of the spaces H^3 of § 27. And so on.

Let us consider the conditions that we have placed on X. Condition (i) is not restrictive in practice: one may usually choose X to be a Hilbert space and also to fit the intended application. Condition (ii) is natural since we will base our approximation on the value $x(0)$. For our procedure to be reasonable $x(0)$ must be well defined and continuous relative to the norm in X.

It is perhaps interesting to consider how $x(0)$ is indeed a linear continuous functional in the alternative choices of X that we have stated to be valid. We give the details for the second alternative: $X = H(S, \mu)$ and $\mu\{0\} > 0$. Suppose that $x \in X$. Then the values $x(s)$, $s \in S$, are determined almost everywhere μ on S. Since $\mu\{0\} > 0$, $x(0)$ must be unambiguously determined. Furthermore the functional $x(0)$ is bounded, with bound $[\mu\{0\}]^{-1/2}$, since

$$\frac{1}{\mu\{0\}} \|x\|_X^2 = \frac{1}{\mu\{0\}} \int_S |x(s)|^2 \, d\mu(s)$$
$$= \frac{1}{\mu\{0\}} \left[|x(0)|^2 \mu\{0\} + \int_{s \neq 0} |x(s)|^2 \, d\mu(s) \right]$$
$$\geqq |x(0)|^2; \qquad x \in X.$$

We have now described X, Y, and Ψ. We take

$$y(t, \omega) = e^{2\pi i(t-\omega)} \in Y\Psi,$$

and

$$z(s, \omega) = e^{2\pi i(s-\omega)} + be^{2\pi ic(s-\omega)} \in X\Psi,$$

where c is an integer different from 1 and $b \in \mathbf{C}$. Finally we take $\mathscr{A}$ as the set of all operators A of the form

$$Ax = a(t)x(0), \qquad x \in X,$$

where

$$a \in Y.$$

These operators are indeed linear on X to Y, and bounded since

$$\|Ax\|_Y = \|a\|_Y |x(0)| \leqq \|a\|_Y \|x\|_X B,$$

where B is the norm of the functional $x(0)$ on X. Thus $\mathscr{A}$ is a linear set of linear continuous operators on X to Y.

We have now set up an instance of the problem of the present chapter (§ 175). We proceed to obtain the efficient or nearly efficient operator A by the use of projections.

A basis for $L^\circ = \mathscr{A}z$ and for L is simply

$$\left\{ \frac{\eta^k z_\omega(0)}{\|z_\omega(0)\|_\Psi} \right\}, \qquad k \in K,$$

since any element in L° may indeed be written in terms of this set of orthonormal elements in $L^\circ \subset Y\Psi$. Also, by (281),

$$(y, \eta^k z_\omega(0))_{Y\Psi} = E\bar{z}_\omega(0)(y, \eta^k)_Y = E\bar{z}_\omega(0)(e^{2\pi i(t-\omega)}, \eta^k)_Y$$
$$= E\bar{z}_\omega(0)e^{-2\pi i\omega}(e^{2\pi it}, \eta^k)_Y = \delta^{k,1} E\bar{z}_\omega(0)e^{-2\pi i\omega}$$
$$= \delta^{k,1}, \qquad k \in K,$$

since $c - 1$ is an integer $\neq 0$. Hence

$$\sigma = \mathrm{Proj}_L\, y = \frac{\eta^1 z_\omega(0)}{E|z_\omega(0)|^2} = \frac{e^{2\pi i t} z_\omega(0)}{1 + |b|^2}.$$

Now $\sigma = Az = a(t)z_\omega(0)$ iff

$$a(t) = \frac{e^{2\pi i t}}{1 + |b|^2}, \quad \text{almost all } t.$$

Hence the operator A is efficient iff

$$Ax = a(t)x(0) = \frac{e^{2\pi i t}}{1 + |b|^2}\, x(0).$$

When applied to the input $z_\omega(0)$, the result is the efficient approximation

$$Az = \sigma = \frac{e^{2\pi i t} z_\omega(0)}{1 + |b|^2} = \frac{e^{2\pi i(t-\omega)} + b e^{2\pi i(t - c\omega)}}{1 + |b|^2}.$$

The elegant feature here is the divisor $1 + |b|^2$. This divisor compensates as well as possible for the fact that $z_\omega(0)$ contains the error $be^{-2\pi i c\omega}$ of amplitude b and frequency c different from that of the desired output y.

It is interesting to verify the Pythagorean relation:

$$E\|\sigma\|_Y^2 = E\|Az\|_Y^2 = \frac{1}{[1 + |b|^2]^2}[1 + |b|^2] = \frac{1}{1 + |b|^2},$$

$$e = Az - y = \frac{-|b|^2 e^{2\pi i(t-\omega)} + b e^{2\pi i(t - c\omega)}}{1 + |b|^2},$$

$$E\|e\|_Y^2 = \frac{|b|^4 + |b|^2}{[1 + |b|^2]^2} = \frac{|b|^2}{1 + |b|^2},$$

$$E\|y\|_Y^2 = 1 = E\|Az\|_Y^2 + E\|e\|_Y^2.$$

We now show that efficiency is strong. The basis

$$\{\eta^k\} = \{e^{2\pi i k t}\}, \qquad k \in K,$$

that we are using consists of functions defined as indicated everywhere. We may and do therefore consider all values of t without exception. For each t, by (214),

$$M_t^\circ = \mathrm{span}\,\{\eta^k(t)[e^{-2\pi i\omega} + b e^{-2\pi i c\omega}] : k \in K\} \subset \Psi.$$

Now for each t, $\eta^k(t) \neq 0$. Hence, for each t,

$$M_t^\circ \underset{\text{def}}{=} M^\circ = \mathrm{span}\,\{e^{-2\pi i\omega} + b e^{-2\pi i c\omega}\} = M_t \underset{\text{def}}{=} M.$$

Thus M_t is a one-dimensional space M, and is independent of t. Now

$$\tau_t = \text{Proj}_{M_t} y_t = \frac{(e^{2\pi i(t-\omega)}, e^{-2\pi i\omega} + be^{-2\pi ic\omega})_{\Psi}}{1 + |b|^2} [e^{-2\pi i\omega} + be^{-2\pi ic\omega}],$$

$$\tau_t = \frac{e^{2\pi it}}{1 + |b|^2} [e^{-2\pi i\omega} + be^{-2\pi ic\omega}].$$

Thus

$$\sigma_t = \tau_t;$$

and efficiency is strong.

§ 282. **Weak efficiency.** This section describes a simple example in which efficiency is not strong.

Suppose that

$$S = T = \Omega, \qquad m = p, \qquad X = Y = \Psi = H(\Omega, p),$$

and that Ψ is two-dimensional. Since

$$E1 = 1,$$

there is an orthonormal pair $\{\psi^1, \psi^2\}$ in Ψ, such that

$$\psi^1(\omega) = 1, \qquad \omega \in \Omega.$$

Let $\{\eta^1, \eta^2\}$ be the corresponding pair in Y; and $\{\xi^1, \xi^2\}$ be the corresponding pair in X. Thus

$$\eta^1(t) = \xi^1(t) = \psi^1(t) = 1, \qquad t \in T.$$
$$\eta^2(t) = \xi^2(t) = \psi^2(t).$$

The reader may, if he wishes, give an explicit description of a particular choice of Ω, p. For example, Ω might consist of two points only.

Suppose that

$$z = \xi^1\psi^1 \in X\Psi;$$
$$y = \eta^2\psi^1 + b\eta^1\psi^2 + c\eta^2\psi^2 \in Y\Psi;$$

where b, c are fixed numbers.

Suppose finally that $\mathscr{A}$ is the set of all numerical multiplications; that is, $\mathscr{A}$ consists of all operators A such that

$$Ax = ax, \qquad x \in X,$$

for some $a \in \mathbf{C}$. Since $Y = X$, A is an operator on X to Y.

This completes the data of the problem.

Now

$$L^\circ = \mathscr{A}z = \text{the span of } \eta^1\psi^1 \text{ in } Y\Psi = L;$$

$$M_t^\circ = \text{the span of } \eta^1(t)\psi^1 \text{ in } \Psi = \text{the span of 1 in } \Psi = M_t,$$

since $\eta^1(t) = 1 \neq 0$. Thus L is one-dimensional and is one of the coordinate axes in $Y\Psi$; and M_t is one-dimensional and is one of the coordinate axes in Ψ. Furthermore

$$M_t = M$$

is independent of t, $t \in T$. It follows that

$$\sigma = \mathrm{Proj}_L\, y = 0,$$

since y has no component along $\eta^1\psi^1$; and

$$\tau_t = \mathrm{Proj}_{M_t}\, y_t = \eta_t^2\psi^1 = \eta_t^2, \qquad t \in T,$$

since

$$(y_t, \psi^1)_\Psi = \eta_t^2.$$

Now τ_t cannot vanish for almost all $t \in T$; otherwise $\eta^2 = 0 \in Y$, a contradiction of the fact that η^2 is a unit vector in Y. Hence τ_t does not equal $\sigma_t = 0$, for almost all t. Hence efficiency is not strong.

The efficient operator is $A = 0$. For, by Theorem 189,

$$\begin{aligned} Ax &= ax, \qquad x \in X, \\ Az &= \sigma = 0 = a\eta^1\psi^1, \\ a &= 0. \end{aligned}$$

The error is

$$e = Az - y = -y;$$

and

$$E\|e\|_Y^2 = 1 + |b|^2 + |c|^2.$$

§ 283. **Smoothing and approximation of a function based on a table of contaminated values.** In the present section

$$S = T$$

and

$$X = H(S, \mu), \qquad Y = H(T, m),$$

where μ and m are measures on S. The measures μ and m indicate the relative importance of different parts of S for the input and for the output, respectively.

We say that the measure μ is *atomic*, with atoms at $s^1, \cdots, s^n$, if the following conditions hold:

(i) $s^1, \cdots, s^n$ are distinct elements of S.

(ii) There are positive constants $\mu^1, \cdots, \mu^n$ such that

$$\mu(R) = \sum_{s^j \in R} \mu^j$$

for any subset R of S. Then the n points $s^1, \cdots, s^n$ constitute almost all of S, relative to μ, since

$$\mu[S - \{s^1, \cdots, s^n\}] = 0.$$

Assume that the measure μ is atomic. Suppose that $u \in X$. Then u is an equivalence set of functions on S. We think of u as one function of that set. Put

$$u^j = u(s^j), \qquad j \in J = \{1, \cdots, n\}.$$

Then the n numbers u^j are well defined since each s^j has positive measure μ^j. (If functions u and v on S are equal almost everywhere μ, they must be equal for $s = s^j, j \in J$.) The numbers $u^j, j \in J$, are a table of values of u.

If $u, v \in X$, then

$$\begin{aligned} (u, v)_X &= \int_S u\bar{v}\, d\mu = u^1\bar{v}^1\mu^1 + u^2\bar{v}^2\mu^2 + \cdots + u^n\bar{v}^n\mu^n; \\ \|u\|_X^2 &= |u^1|^2\mu^1 + \cdots + |u^n|^2\mu^n. \end{aligned} \tag{284}$$

The last relation shows in what sense μ^j measures the importance of u at $s = s^j$. It shows also that values of u at s other than $s^1, \cdots, s^n$ are unimportant, as far as X is concerned.

Let ξ^j be the function on S which vanishes everywhere except at $s = s^j$ and which takes on the value

$$\xi^j(s^j) = (\mu^j)^{-1/2} \tag{285}$$

at $s = s^j$. Then $\{\xi^j, j \in J\}$ is a basis for X. The coordinates of u relative to this basis are

$$(u, \xi^j)_X = (\mu^j)^{1/2}u^j, \qquad j \in J,$$

where $u \in X$ and $u^j = u(s^j)$.

The case in which

$$\mu^1 = \cdots = \mu^n = 1$$

is particularly simple. The tabular entries u^j are then the coordinates of u. In any case, the tabular entries of u are the coordinates of u, except for constant factors.

Suppose that we wish to approximate a function on T, given a finite set of its values. We may take μ so that the given values constitute a description of an input. We then take m in some fashion appropriate to the purpose of our calculation. For example, m may be ordinary Lebesgue measure on an interval T. Then the desired output as well as the approximation thereof based on the input will be defined almost everywhere m on T. Or, m may itself be atomic but perhaps very different from μ. There is an immense variety of choices of m, since m may be any measure on T (subject merely to the general conditions of § 27).

If A is any linear operator on X to Y, A must be of the form

(286) $$Au = \sum_j a^j(t)u(s^j), \qquad u \in X,$$

where the functions $a^j, j \in J$, are elements of Y. Indeed

$$a^j = (\mu^j)^{1/2} A \xi^j, \qquad j \in J.$$

This is a consequence of the linearity of A, since

$$u = \sum_j (u, \xi^j)\xi^j = \sum_j (\mu^j)^{1/2} u^j \xi^j, \qquad u^j = u(s^j), \quad j \in J.$$

The relation (286) shows that A is continuous, since J is finite.†

Consider the problem of efficient approximation, with X, Y the spaces above, with $\mathscr{A}$ the set of all linear operators on X to Y, with

$$\Psi = H(\Omega, p)$$

but otherwise unspecified, and with given functions $x + \delta x = z \in X\Psi$ and $y \in Y\Psi$.

For each $\omega \in \Omega$ with null exceptions, the function $y_\omega \in Y$ is the desired output and $z_\omega \in X$ is the input, Az_ω the actual output, for some $A \in \mathscr{A}$. For any measurable set $\Omega_1 \subset \Omega$, $p(\Omega_1)$ is the probability that $\omega \in \Omega_1$.

Then

$$L^\circ = \mathscr{A}z = \left\{ \sum_{j \in J} a^j(t) z_\omega(s^j) : a^j \in Y \right\}.$$

It follows that

$$L^\circ = \text{span}\,\{a(t)z_\omega(s^j) : a \in Y, j \in J\}.$$

Suppose that $\{\eta^k : k \in K\}$ is a basis for Y. Then

(287) $$L^\circ \subset \text{Span}\,\{\eta^k z_\omega(s^j) : k \in K, j \in J\}.$$

By orthogonalizing the n elements $z_\omega(s^j) = z(s^j)$ of $\Psi, j \leqq n$, we may construct a basis

(288) $$\{\psi^\nu : \nu \leqq n'\}, \qquad n' \leqq n,$$

for their span. Then the elements (288) are orthonormal, and

(289) $$\text{span}\,\{\psi^\nu : \nu \leqq n'\} = \text{Span}\,\{\psi^\nu : \nu \leqq n'\} = \text{Span}\,\{z(s^j) : j \leqq n\}.$$

It follows from (287) that

(290) $$\{\eta^k \psi^\nu : k \in K, \nu \leqq n'\}$$

† Indeed a linear operator on any finite dimensional normed linear space to a normed linear space of any dimension is necessarily continuous. This is readily proved by Tychonoff's Theorem. Cf. [Dunford-Schwartz 1, p. 245].

is a basis for $L \subset Y\Psi$. For, the elements (290) are certainly orthonormal in $Y\Psi$. And any element in L may be written

$$\sum_{k,j} c^{k,j}\eta^k z(s^j) = \sum_k \eta^k \sum_j c^{k,j} z(s^j) = \sum_{k \in K} \eta^k \sum_{\nu \leqq n'} b^{k,\nu}\psi^\nu,$$

for appropriate $c^{k,j}, b^{k,\nu} \in \mathbf{C}$.

Hence

$$\sigma = \operatorname{Proj}_L y = \sum_{\substack{k \in K, \\ \nu \leqq n'}} (y, \eta^k\psi^\nu)_{Y\Psi}\eta^k\psi^\nu, \tag{291}$$

where

$$(y, \eta^k\psi^\nu)_{Y\Psi} = E(y, \eta^k)_Y\bar{\psi}^\nu.$$

A linear operator A is near efficiency according as

$$Az = \sum_j a^j(t)z(s^j) = \sum_j a^j z(s^j) \tag{292}$$

is near σ in terms of the norm in $Y\Psi$ (Theorem 189). Efficiency is strong, by Theorem 253.

The distance from Az to σ is readily computed, as follows. Augment the orthonormal set $\{\psi^\nu : \nu \leqq n'\}$ to a basis $\{\psi^\nu : \nu \in N\}$ of Ψ. The elements ψ^ν, $\nu \in N$, $\nu > n'$ need not in fact be calculated, as we shall see.

The coordinates of Az in $Y\Psi$ are

$$\begin{aligned}(Az, \eta^k\psi^\nu)_{Y\Psi} &= \left(\sum_j a^j z(s^j), \eta^k\psi^\nu\right)_{Y\Psi} \\ &= \sum_j (a^j, \eta^k)_Y E z(s^j)\bar{\psi}^\nu, \qquad k \in K, \quad \nu \in N.\end{aligned}$$

By (289), these coordinates surely vanish if $\nu > n'$. Hence, by (291),

$$\|Az - \sigma\|_{Y\Psi}^2 = \sum_{\substack{k \in K, \\ \nu \leqq n'}} \left| E\bar{\psi}^\nu \left(\sum_{j \leqq n} a^j z(s^j) - y, \eta^k\right)_Y \right|^2.$$

If this number is $< \rho^2$, then A is within ρ of strong efficiency. For any $\rho > 0$, an operator A within ρ of strong efficiency exists.

One may wonder what the advantages and disadvantages of the above approximation are. The disadvantages rest in the existence of the error $e = Az - y$, an entity which our theory has studied.

The advantages rest in the possibility that a smaller amount of storage be required of the computer. Suppose, to fix our ideas, that X, Y, Ψ are of n, p, q dimensions (all finite), respectively.

In order to produce the true values y_ω, given z_ω, one must know or store pq numbers (the coordinates of y in $Y\Psi$) and one must recognize ω when z_ω

is given. For the latter it would be sufficient to store nq numbers (the coordinates of z in $X\Psi$). Thus an exact determination of y_ω may require the storage of

$$(p + n)q$$

numbers.

For our approximation we must know or store pn numbers (the coordinates of the n functions a^j, $j \leqq n$, in Y) and we must execute n multiplications and $n - 1$ additions in using (292). If

$$\frac{(p + n)q}{pn}$$

is large, the approximate solution requires proportionately less storage. This is true in particular if

$$\frac{q}{n} = \frac{\dim \Psi}{\dim X}$$

is large.

§ 293. **The use of the nearest tabular entry.** Take

$$X, \quad Y, \quad \Psi, \quad y, \quad z$$

as at the beginning of the preceding section, with $S = T$ a subset of the real line and with

$$s^1 < s^2 < \cdots < s^n.$$

The space X is n-dimensional. The spaces Y, Ψ need not be finite dimensional. Choose constants $c^0, \cdots, c^n$ so that

$$c^0 < s^1 < c^1 < s^2 < \cdots < s^n < c^n.$$

For each ω with null exceptions, the datum z_ω will consist of n tabular values

$$z_\omega(s^1), \cdots, z_\omega(s^n).$$

The general form of a linear continuous operator on X to Y is given by (286) = (294). *Suppose that* $\mathscr{A}$ consists of those operators A for which

(294) $$Au = \sum_{j=1,\cdots,n} a^j(t)u(s^j), \qquad u \in X, \quad a^j \in Y,$$

and

(295) $$a^j(t) = 0 \text{ for all } t \text{ such that } t < c^{j-1} \text{ or } t > c^j, \qquad j = 1, \cdots, n.$$

Thus, for each t, Au involves only one tabular value $u(s^j)$ or, at the transition values $t = c^1, \cdots, c^{n-1}$, two tabular values. Except for the transition values, Au is simply an adjacent tabular value $u(s^{j_0})$ multiplied by the factor $a^{j_0}(t)$, a factor which depends on t. The use of an operator $A \in \mathscr{A}$ thus involves small storage (the functions $a^j(t), j = 1, \cdots, n$), the choice of one tabular entry (which in practice would often be $u(s^j)$ with s^j the atom closest to t), and a single multiplication. The approximation Au of y will be easily calculable for each t with null exceptions. The approximation however may be quite poor.

Using only one entry of a table is extreme. In the next section we consider an analogous procedure that uses two tabular entries. Our attack may be extended to the use of any finite number of tabular entries. The present section, in addition to introducing the next section, is of interest in its own right.

Note that the set $\mathscr{A}$ of operators (294) that satisfy (295) is indeed a linear set. We shall seek the efficient operator, relative to y, z, $\mathscr{A}$.

The sum (294) reduces to one term, or at the transition values, to two terms; which term or terms depends on the value of t.

For preciseness, let us suppose that $n = 1$, $s^1 = 0$, $X =$ the numbers $\mathbf{C}$ described as values of functions $x(s)$ at $s = s^1 = 0$, and

$$T = \{-1 \leqq t \leqq 1\}.$$

It will be clear in retrospect that no essential loss of generality has occurred.

Now

$$\mathscr{A} = \{A : Au = a(t)u(0),\ u \in X;\ a \in Y\}.$$

Any element a of Y determines an element A of $\mathscr{A}$. Then

$$L^0 = \mathscr{A}z = \{a(t)z(0) : a \in Y\} \subset Y\Psi.$$

If $E|z(0)|^2 = 0$, then

$$z(0) = 0;$$
$$L^\circ = \{0\};$$

and A $= 0$ is efficient. Assume that

$$E|z(0)|^2 \neq 0.$$

Suppose that $\{\eta^k : k \in K\}$ is a basis for Y. Then

$$\left\{\frac{\eta^k z(0)}{\sqrt{E|z(0)|^2}};\ k \in K\right\}$$

is a basis for L. Hence

$$\sigma = \text{Proj}_L\, y = \sum_k \frac{(y, \eta^k z(0))_{Y\Psi}}{E|z(0)|^2}\, \eta^k z(0),$$

(296) $$\sigma = \frac{z(0)}{E|z(0)|^2} \sum_k \eta^k E\bar{z}(0)(y, \eta^k)_Y = \frac{z(0)}{E|z(0)|^2} E\bar{z}(0)y.$$

The inversion of $\sum_k$ and E is valid by Lemma 154.

Thus an efficient operator exists; it is A, where

$$(297)\qquad Az = a(t)z(0) = \sigma,$$

$$a(t) = \frac{E\bar{z}(0)y(t)}{E|z(0)|^2}.$$

Furthermore, efficiency is strong by Theorem 253, since $\mathscr{A}$ here consists of all linear operators on the one-dimensional space X. Alternatively we may establish strong efficiency by using Theorem 232. Thus, for each t with null exceptions, η_t^k is a scalar; and

$$M_t^\circ = \text{span}\,\{\eta_t^k z(0) : k \in K\}.$$

Hence

$$(298)\qquad M_t^\circ = \text{span}\,\{z(0)\} = M^\circ = M, \quad \text{almost all } t;$$

unless t is such that $\eta_t^k = 0$ for all $k \in K$. Such values of t constitute a null set in T: otherwise $\{\eta^k\}$ would not be a basis in Y since its span could not approximate the function which equals unity on the common zeros or on a subset thereof of strictly positive, finite measure. We assume that m is such that sets of positive, finite measure exist.

Since M is one-dimensional,

$$\tau_t = \text{Proj}_{M_t}\, y_t = \frac{(y_t, z(0))_\Psi}{\|z(0)\|_\Psi^2}\, z(0) = z(0)\,\frac{E\bar{z}(0)y(t)}{E|z(0)|^2}.$$

Hence

$$\tau_t = \sigma_t, \quad \text{almost all } t,$$

by (296).

In the present example, the strongly efficient operator (297) may be obtained directly, without the use of projections. That efficiency is strong is quite natural, since there is no mixture of influence of different values of t in (294), because of (295). The variables t and ω separate.

§ 299. **Interpolation or approximation based on two tabular entries.** Take

$$X, \quad Y, \quad \Psi, \quad y, \quad z$$

as in the preceding sections, with $S = T$ a subset of the real line and with

$$s^1 < s^2 < \cdots < s^n.$$

Suppose that $\mathscr{A}$ consists of those operators

$$(300)\qquad Au = \sum_j a^j(t)u(s^j), \qquad u \in X,$$

in which, for each j,

$$(301)\qquad a^j(t) = 0 \quad \text{whenever} \quad t < s^{j-1} \quad \text{or} \quad t > s^{j+1},\ j = 1, \cdots, n,$$

where we take $s^0 = -\infty$, $s^{n+1} = \infty$.

Thus if

$$t \neq s^1, \cdots, s^n; \qquad s^1 < t < s^n,$$

the sum (300) involves two terms, those with s^j enclosing t; if

$$t = s^1, \cdots, \text{or } s^n,$$

the sum may involve three terms (which in the interpolatory case would reduce to one); if $t \notin [s^1, s^n]$, the sum reduces to one term.

Since $\mathscr{A}$ is a linear set of operators, we shall seek the efficient operator relative to y, z, $\mathscr{A}$.

The problem in fact separates into the study of the different intervals s^j, s^{j+1}. For preciseness (and without any essential loss of generality) suppose that

$$n = 2, \quad s^1 = 0, \quad s^2 = 1, \quad \text{and} \quad T = \{-\infty < t < \infty\}.$$

Then X is two-dimensional; and $\mathscr{A}$ consists of all linear operators A such that

$$Au = a(t)u(0) + b(t)u(1), \qquad u \in X, \tag{302}$$

where $a, b \in Y$, and

$$\begin{aligned} a(t) &= 0 \quad \text{if } t > 1, \\ b(t) &= 0 \quad \text{if } t < 0. \end{aligned} \tag{303}$$

Now

$$L^\circ = \mathscr{A}z = \{a(t)z(0) + b(t)z(1) : a, b \in Y \text{ and } a, b \text{ satisfy (303)}\} \subset Y\Psi.$$

Assume that $z(0)$, $z(1)$ are independent in Ψ. Otherwise one is dependent on the other and the problem is in fact that of the preceding section. Orthonormalize $z(0)$, $z(1)$ to, say, ζ^1, ζ^2.

To treat the condition (303), we break the problem into three parts, obtained by replacing T by T_1, T_2, T_3, respectively, where

$$\begin{aligned} T_1 &= \{t < 0\}, \\ T_2 &= \{0 \leqq t \leqq 1\}, \\ T_3 &= \{t > 1\}. \end{aligned}$$

Consider T as T_2. The restrictions (303) are vacuous for $t \in T_2$. We can readily determine $a(t)$, $b(t)$ for $t \in T_2$. Thus let $\{\eta^k : k \in K\}$ be a basis in $Y_2 = H(T_2, m)$. Then, using the orthonormal pair ζ^1, ζ^2 instead of $z(0)$, $z(1)$,

$$L^\circ = \{\alpha(t)\zeta^1 + \beta(t)\zeta^2 : \text{all } \alpha, \beta \in Y_2\}.$$

Hence

$$\{\eta^k\zeta^1, \eta^k\zeta^2 : k \in K\}$$

is a basis for L. Hence

$$\sigma = \mathrm{Proj}_L\, y = \sum_k (y, \eta^k\zeta^1)_{Y_2\Psi}\eta^k\zeta^1 + (y, \eta^k\zeta^2)_{Y_2\Psi}\eta^k\zeta^2$$

$$= \zeta^1\alpha(t) + \zeta^2\beta(t),$$

where

$$\alpha(t) = \sum_k \eta^k E\bar{\zeta}^1(y, \eta^k)_{Y_2} = E\bar{\zeta}^1 y(t),$$

$$\beta(t) = E\bar{\zeta}^2 y(t).$$

We may now find a, b so that

$$a(t)z(0) + b(t)z(1) = \alpha(t)\zeta^1 + \beta(t)\zeta^2, \qquad t \in T_2.$$

Thus an efficient operator exists and is strongly efficient, by Theorem 253 or 232.

Now consider T as T_1. Then, by (303), $b(t) = 0$. This case reduces to that of the preceding section, essentially. We find that

$$a(t) = \frac{E\bar{z}(0)y(t)}{E|z(0)|^2}, \qquad b(t) = 0, \quad t \in T_1.$$

Likewise, considering T as T_3,

$$a(t) = 0, \qquad b(t) = \frac{E\bar{z}(1)y(t)}{E|z(1)|^2}, \qquad t \in T_3.$$

Combining these results, we have determined a, b everywhere in T in such a way that (302) is strongly efficient.

The illustration of the present section may be extended to approximations based on the nearest q tabular entries, $q = 1, 2, \cdots, n$.

§ 304. **Estimation of the pertinent stochastic processes.** The solution of the problem of efficient approximation depends on the data y, z, $\mathscr{A}$ of the problem.

If we do not know y, z we may estimate both by the natural procedure of observing y, z in a number of instances, ascribing weights to the observations, and assuming that the weighted ensemble of past observations is our anticipation of a future observation. We have discussed this procedure in § 175. We illustrate it now, taking a simple case which may exhibit the salient points.

Suppose that we wish to approximate a function $y_\omega = x_\omega$ on $S = T$ in terms of a table of contaminated values $z_\omega = (x + \delta x)_\omega$. If the stochastic processes z and y are known, we proceed as we have in the preceding sections.

To fix our ideas, suppose that

$$\begin{aligned}
T &= \{0 \leqq t < \infty\}, \qquad dm(t) = dt, \qquad Y = H(T, m);\\
S &= T;\\
\mu &= \text{the atomic measure on } S \text{ with atoms of mass 1}\\
&\quad \text{at } s = 2\pi/3 \text{ and at } s = 4\pi/3 \text{ and nowhere else};\\
X &= H(S, \mu) = \text{a two-dimensional space};\\
\Omega &= \{0 \leqq \omega \leqq 2\pi\}, \quad dp(\omega) = (1/2\pi)\, d\omega, \quad \Psi = H(\Omega, p);\\
y(t, \omega) &= e^{-t/2\pi} \sin (t - \omega);\\
z(s, \omega) &= \text{the numerical value } y(s, \omega) \text{ rounded to the nearest tenth.}
\end{aligned}$$

For each $\omega \in \Omega$ with null exceptions, we are to approximate y_ω in terms of z_ω. It is only the values of z_ω at $s = 2\pi/3$ and $s = 4\pi/3$ that are available.

Take $\mathscr{A}$ as the set of all linear operators on X to Y. Efficiency will be strong, by Theorem 253.

This problem is typical of ones in which we are given from outside a table of contaminated values and wish to approximate the true function, using the table. Here the error δx is the rounding error at two values of t and almost all $\omega \in \Omega$. The image Az_ω is to approximate y_ω for all $t \in T$ on the basis of two values of z_ω.

We have completely defined y and z.

Now suppose that we were working with y and z as just defined but did not know what y and z and p were.

If in several instances we had observed particular elements $z_\omega \in X$ and $y_\omega \in Y$, we could use our observations as the basis of an estimate of $z \in X\Psi$ and $y \in Y\Psi$. For preciseness, suppose that we had observed the instances corresponding to the following values of ω:

$$\omega^1 = \frac{\pi}{2}, \qquad w^2 = \frac{3\pi}{4}, \qquad \omega^3 = \frac{-\pi}{6} + 2\pi.$$

These three points in Ω have been chosen arbitrarily by the author. We suppose that for each of these instances, z_ω and y_ω are known as elements of X and Y, respectively. Superscripts 1, 2, 3 refer to the three instances. Thus

$$y^1(t) = y(t, \omega^1) = y_{\omega^1} = e^{-t/2\pi} \sin\left(t - \frac{\pi}{2}\right),$$

$$z^1(s) = \begin{cases} .4 & \text{if } s = \dfrac{2\pi}{3}, \\[2ex] .3 & \text{if } s = \dfrac{4\pi}{3}. \end{cases}$$

The above values $z^1(s)$ are determined by the fact that z^1 is y^1 rounded to the nearest tenth and

$$y^1\left(\frac{2\pi}{3}\right) = e^{-1/3}\sin\left(\frac{2\pi}{3} - \frac{\pi}{2}\right) = .3583,$$
$$y^1\left(\frac{4\pi}{3}\right) = e^{-2/3}\sin\left(\frac{4\pi}{3} - \frac{\pi}{2}\right) = .2567.$$

The values of z^1 describe z^1 almost everywhere, because all positive measure on S resides in the atoms $s = 2\pi/3$ and $s = 4\pi/3$.

Similarly,

$$y^2(t) = y_{\omega^2} = e^{-t/2\pi}\sin\left(t - \frac{3\pi}{4}\right)$$

$$z^2(s) = \begin{cases} -.2 & \text{if } s = \dfrac{2\pi}{3}, \\ .5 & \text{if } s = \dfrac{4\pi}{3}. \end{cases}$$

$$y^3(t) = e^{-t/2\pi}\sin\left(t + \frac{\pi}{6}\right)$$

$$z^3(s) = \begin{cases} .4 & \text{if } s = \dfrac{2\pi}{3}, \\ -.5 & \text{if } s = \dfrac{4\pi}{3}. \end{cases}$$

Thus we know the following: In one instance the actual input was z^1 and the desired output was y^1, given above. In a second instance, these were z^2, y^2, above. In a third instance, these were z^3, y^3.

We assign weights or probabilities p^1, p^2, p^3,

$$p^1 + p^2 + p^3 = 1,$$

to these instances. Our procedure of estimation is to replace Ω, p, Ψ, which are unknown, by $\tilde{\Omega}$, $\tilde{p}$, $\tilde{\Psi}$, as follows. $\tilde{\Omega}$ consists of three points, of respective probabilities p^1, p^2, p^3. $\tilde{p}$ is the probability on $\tilde{\Omega}$ based on p^1, p^2, p^3. $\tilde{\Psi}$ is the space $H(\tilde{\Omega}, \tilde{p})$; that is, $\tilde{\Psi}$ is the space of triples, with the inner product

$$(\psi, \lambda)_{\tilde{\Psi}} = \psi^1\bar{\lambda}^1p^1 + \psi^2\bar{\lambda}^2p^2 + \psi^3\bar{\lambda}^3p^3, \qquad \psi = (\psi^1, \psi^2, \psi^3), \quad \lambda = (\lambda^1, \lambda^2, \lambda^3). \tag{305}$$

Our known data constitute descriptions of $\tilde{x} + \delta\tilde{x} = \tilde{z} \in X\tilde{\Psi}$ and $\tilde{y} \in Y\tilde{\Psi}$. Indeed,

$$\tilde{y}(t, \omega) = \begin{cases} e^{-t/2\pi}\sin\left(t - \dfrac{\pi}{2}\right) & \text{if } \omega = \omega^1, \\ e^{-t/2\pi}\sin\left(t - \dfrac{3\pi}{4}\right) & \text{if } \omega = \omega^2, \quad 0 \leqq t < \infty; \\ e^{-t/2\pi}\sin\left(t + \dfrac{\pi}{6}\right) & \text{if } \omega = \omega^3, \end{cases}$$

and $\tilde{z}(s, \omega)$ is given by the table.

	ω^1	ω^2	ω^3
s^1	.4	$-.2$	.4
s^2	.3	.5	$-.5$

$\tilde{z}(s, \omega)$

The input $\tilde{z}$ here is scanty. Hence the approximation $\tilde{A}\tilde{z}$ of $\tilde{y}$ will not be good. It will however be the best possible, subject to the condition $\tilde{A} \in \mathscr{A}$.

To fix our ideas, we take

$$p^1 = p^2 = p^3 = \frac{1}{3}.$$

We now calculate the efficient operator relative to $\tilde{z} \in X\tilde{\Psi}$, $\tilde{y} \in Y\tilde{\Psi}$, and $\mathscr{A}$ = the set of all linear operators on X to Y. To describe an element, say $\tilde{z}(s^1)$ of $\tilde{\Psi}$, we may give its coordinates relative to the natural orthonormal set in $\tilde{\Psi}$:

u^1 is the unit vector in $\tilde{\Psi}$ which is the function

$$u^1(\omega) = \begin{cases} \sqrt{3} & \text{if } \omega = \omega^1, \\ 0 & \text{if } \omega = \omega^2, \\ 0 & \text{if } \omega = \omega^3; \end{cases}$$

u^2 is the similar unit vector obtained by interchanging ω^2 and ω^1;

u^3 is the similar unit vector obtained by interchanging ω^3 and ω^1.

The coordinates of elements in $\tilde{\Psi}$ will then be $1/\sqrt{3}$ times their values at $\omega^1, \omega^2, \omega^3$. For example, the coordinates of $\tilde{z}(s^1)$ are

$$\left(\frac{.4}{\sqrt{3}}, \frac{-.2}{\sqrt{3}}, \frac{.4}{\sqrt{3}}\right) = \frac{1}{\sqrt{3}}(.4, -.2, .4),$$

since the components here are

$$(z(s^1), u^j)_{\tilde{\Psi}}, \qquad j = 1, 2, 3.$$

Alternatively, we may describe an element of $\tilde{\Psi}$ by giving its material values; for example,

$$\tilde{z}(s^1) = [.4, -.2, .4].$$

We shall use the material values.

The set $\mathscr{A}$ consists of all linear operators on X to Y; that is, all operators A such that

$$Ax = a^1(t)x(s^1) + a^2(t)x(s^2), \qquad x \in X,$$

where the functions a^1, a^2 are elements of Y, by (286). Hence

$$L^\circ = \mathscr{A}\tilde{z} = \{a^1(t)\tilde{z}(s^1) + a^2(t)\tilde{z}(s^2) : a^1, a^2 \in Y\} \subset Y\tilde{\Psi}. \tag{306}$$

Now $\tilde{z}(s^1)$, $\tilde{z}(s^2)$ are a pair of vectors in $\tilde{\Psi}$. Let us replace them by an equivalent orthogonal pair ϕ^1, ϕ^2; that is, a pair ϕ^1, ϕ^2 in $\tilde{\Psi}$ such that

$$(\phi^1, \phi^2)_{\tilde{\Psi}} = 0, \quad \text{span}\,\{\tilde{z}(s^1), \tilde{z}(s^2)\} = \text{span}\,\{\phi^1, \phi^2\}. \tag{307}$$

Many such pairs exist. We construct one (cf. § 60). Thus,

$$\tilde{z}(s^1) = [.4, -.2, .4]; \qquad \tilde{z}(s^2) = [.3, .5, -.5].$$

Put

$$\phi^1 = \tilde{z}(s^1) = [.4, -.2, .4]. \tag{308}$$

Then, by (305),

$$(\tilde{z}(s^2), \phi^1)_{\tilde{\Psi}} = \frac{1}{3}(.12 - .10 - .20) = -\frac{.18}{3},$$

$$\|\phi^1\|^2_{\tilde{\Psi}} = \frac{1}{3}(.16 + .04 + .16) = \frac{.36}{3}.$$

Put

$$\phi^2 = \tilde{z}(s^2) - \frac{(\tilde{z}(s^2), \phi^1)\phi^1}{\|\phi^1\|^2} = \tilde{z}(s^2) + \frac{1}{2}\phi^1, \tag{309}$$

$$\phi^2 = [.5, .4, -.3].$$

Then

$$\|\phi^2\|^2_{\tilde{\Psi}} = \frac{.50}{3}.$$

As a check of the construction, one may note that (307) is indeed satisfied.

We may write (306) as

$$L^\circ = \{a(t)\phi^1 + b(t)\phi^2 : a, b \in Y\} \subset Y\tilde{\Psi}.$$

Hence L° is closed, since Y is; and $L = L^\circ$. Also L is the direct product YM, where M is the two-dimensional space in $\tilde{\Psi}$ spanned by ϕ^1, ϕ^2.

Now

$$y = e^{-t/2\pi}\left[\sin\left(t - \frac{\pi}{2}\right), \sin\left(t - \frac{3\pi}{4}\right), \sin\left(t + \frac{\pi}{6}\right)\right] \in Y\tilde{\Psi}.$$

Hence, by Lemma 131,

$$\sigma = \text{Proj}_L\, y = \text{Proj}_{YM}\, y = \text{Proj}_Y\, \text{Proj}_M\, y = \text{Proj}_M\, y,$$

where Proj_Y, Proj_M refer to projections in Y, $\tilde{\Psi}$ respectively and accordingly $\mathrm{Proj}_Y =$ identity on Y. Hence

$$\sigma = \frac{(y, \phi^1)_{\tilde{\Psi}}\phi^1}{\|\phi^1\|^2} + \frac{(y, \phi^2)_{\tilde{\Psi}}\phi^2}{\|\phi^2\|^2},$$

$$\sigma = \frac{e^{-t/2\pi}}{.36}\left(.4 \sin\left(t - \frac{\pi}{2}\right) - .2 \sin\left(t - \frac{3\pi}{4}\right) + .4 \sin\left(t + \frac{\pi}{6}\right)\right)\phi^1$$

$$+ \frac{e^{-t/2\pi}}{.50}\left(.5 \sin\left(t - \frac{\pi}{2}\right) + .4 \sin\left(t - \frac{3\pi}{4}\right) - .3 \sin\left(t + \frac{\pi}{6}\right)\right)\phi^2.$$

Hence, by (308) and (309),

$$\sigma = \frac{e^{-t/2\pi}}{.36}\left(.580 \sin\left(t - \frac{\pi}{2}\right) - .056 \sin\left(t - \frac{3\pi}{4}\right) + .292 \sin\left(t + \frac{\pi}{6}\right)\right)\tilde{z}(s^1)$$

$$+ \frac{e^{-t/2\pi}}{.50}\left(.5 \sin\left(t - \frac{\pi}{2}\right) + .4 \sin\left(t - \frac{3\pi}{4}\right) - .3 \sin\left(t + \frac{\pi}{6}\right)\right)\tilde{z}(s^2).$$

Thus the efficient (and strongly efficient) operator is $\tilde{A}$, where

$$(310)\quad \tilde{A}u = a^1(t)u(s^1) + a^2(t)u(s^2), \qquad u \in X;$$

$$a^1(t) = \frac{e^{-t/2\pi}}{90}\left(145 \sin\left(t - \frac{\pi}{2}\right) - 14 \sin\left(t - \frac{3\pi}{4}\right) + 73 \sin\left(t + \frac{\pi}{6}\right)\right),$$

$$a^2(t) = e^{-t/2\pi}\left(\sin\left(t - \frac{\pi}{2}\right) + .8 \sin\left(t - \frac{3\pi}{4}\right) - .6 \sin\left(t + \frac{\pi}{6}\right)\right).$$

The operator $\tilde{A}$ in (310) is strongly efficient relative to the problem for $\tilde{z} \in X\tilde{\Psi}$, $\tilde{y} \in Y\tilde{\Psi}$, $\mathscr{A}$. It is a natural estimate of the strongly efficient operator relative to $z \in X\Psi$, $y \in Y\Psi$, $\mathscr{A}$. We cannot expect the estimate to be a good one, because it is based on merely three observations. Furthermore even the true strongly efficient operator cannot be expected to give a good approximation of y, since X is only two-dimensional and since the input error $z - y$ is substantial.

In this section we have carried out an experiment. We supposed that

$$y(t, \omega) = e^{-t/2\pi} \sin(t - \omega), \qquad 0 \leqq t < \infty, \quad 0 \leqq \omega \leqq 2\pi;$$

$$z(t, \omega) = \text{the numerical values of } y(t, \omega) \text{ at } t = \frac{2\pi}{3} \text{ and } t = \frac{4\pi}{3},$$

$$\text{rounded to the nearest tenth,}$$

with probability given by Lebesgue measure on Ω multiplied by $1/2\pi$. Then instead of using the full information just stated, we used y and z for only three values $\omega = \omega^1, \omega^2, \omega^3$. This led to $\tilde{A}$.

Note first that this type of problem seems important, because one will often not know $z \in X\Psi$ and $y \in Y\Psi$ fully and yet may be able to know something like $\tilde{z} \in X\tilde{\Psi}$, $\tilde{y} \in Y\tilde{\Psi}$.

In the present case we could in principle calculate the true efficient operator. The calculation would be complicated: it would involve using $z(t, \omega)$ for $t = 2\pi/3, 4\pi/3$ for almost all ω in $0 \leqq \omega \leqq 2\pi$. The end result of the calculation would be the efficient operator A, relative to $X\Psi$ and $Y\Psi$. If A were ever obtained, one could compare $\tilde{A}$, given explicitly above, with A.

Our theory indicates that among approximations

$$a^1(t) \times \left(\text{Rounded value of } y \text{ at } t = \frac{2\pi}{3}\right),$$

$$+a^2(t) \times \left(\text{Rounded value of } y \text{ at } t = \frac{4\pi}{3}\right)$$

of $y(t)$, the one in which a^1, a^2 are given by (310) is reasonable. This approximation involves two functions in Y and is simpler than the thing being approximated, since the latter is the stochastic process y and involves infinitely many functions in Y.

As a final calculation, which proves nothing, suppose that a future trial gives the value $\omega = 0$. Then

$$y_\omega = e^{-t/2\pi} \sin t;$$

$$z_\omega = \text{the numerical values of } y_\omega \text{ at } s = t = \frac{2\pi}{3}, \frac{4\pi}{3} \text{ rounded to the nearest tenth;}$$

that is,

$$z_\omega(s) = \text{the numbers} \left\{ \begin{matrix} e^{-1/3} \sin \dfrac{2\pi}{3} \\ e^{-2/3} \sin \dfrac{4\pi}{3} \end{matrix} \right\} \text{rounded to the nearest tenth}$$

$$= \begin{cases} .6 \text{ at } s = \dfrac{2\pi}{3}. \\ -.4 \text{ at } s = \dfrac{4\pi}{3}. \end{cases}$$

The approximation $\tilde{A}z_\omega$ of $y_\omega = e^{-t/2\pi} \sin t$ is

$$.6a^1(t) - .4a^2(t), \qquad 0 \leqq t < \infty,$$

where a^1, a^2 are given by (310). Thus the approximation of

$$e^{-t/2\pi} \sin t$$

is

$$\frac{e^{-t/2\pi}}{90}\left(51 \sin\left(t - \frac{\pi}{2}\right) - 37.2 \sin\left(t - \frac{3\pi}{4}\right) + 65.4 \sin\left(t + \frac{\pi}{6}\right)\right)$$

for all $t \geqq 0$. This is hardly a good approximation, but it is based on meager data (three observations of the desired output and pairs of rounding errors). Furthermore, the approximation $\tilde{A}$ may be of quality comparable to the true (and unknown) efficient approximation A, since the latter uses only two contaminated observations. The approximations A and $\tilde{A}$ are based on full and partial stochastic knowledge, respectively.

Similarly one could calculate $\tilde{A}z_\omega$ using (310), for any $\omega \in \Omega$, that is, for other results of the trial.

§ 311. **Stationary data.** Wiener and Kolmogorov independently have inaugurated an elegant theory of approximation in which $z = x + \delta x$ and $y = Gx$ are assumed to be stationary (see below). For brevity we refer to the theory as the Wiener theory. In the Wiener theory the spaces S and T are translatable into themselves. For preciseness we take T and S to be the infinite time axis

$$T = \{t : -\infty < t < \infty\} = S.$$

Alternatively, T and S could be the set of all integers or other sets.

In the Wiener theory the elements of $\mathscr{A}$ are assumed to be linear operations on the past that are invariant under translations. Then, as we shall see, efficiency is strong; the calculation of efficient approximations depends merely on the autocorrelation of z and the cross-correlation of y into z, or their equivalents, and the set $\mathscr{A}$.

A detailed treatment of the Wiener theory is given in [Doob 1, Chapter 12, §§ 4–6]. The rôle of the spectral representation (power spectrum) of a stationary stochastic process is set forth. It is essential in the Wiener theory that z be stationary. If z contains a nonstationary component, that component must be subtracted out [Wiener 1, p. 150].

Laning and Battin discuss the theory and work a number of examples [1, Chapters 7, 8]. Their calculations are based either on given correlations or on given spectra. In the case in which the data are correlations, the method of projections affords a direct solution of the problem.

In any event it is interesting to consider the Wiener theory in the setting of the theory of the present chapter. Each treatment has its own advantages. We have allowed a greater range of z, y, and $\mathscr{A}$. The Wiener theory uses the spectral representation, a powerful tool, which however is available only in the stationary case.

After these preliminaries, we describe the problem of the present section exactly.

Suppose that $S = T$ *is the set of real numbers,* considered as instants of time. *Suppose that* Ω, p *is a probability space,* as heretofore, and that

$$\Psi = H(\Omega, p)$$

is the L^2*-space of complex functions on* Ω, absolute square integrable p. *Suppose that*

$$z(s, \omega) \quad \textit{and} \quad y(t, \omega) \quad \textit{are complex functions}, \; s \in S, \quad t \in S, \quad \omega \in \Omega.$$

Suppose that $\mathscr{A}$ is a linear set of operators A, each of the form

$$Ax = \int_0^\infty x(t - s)\, d\alpha(s), \tag{312}$$

where α is a complex function of bounded variation on $0 \leqq s \leqq \infty$ (a totally finite complex measure on $0 \leqq s \leqq \infty$). The argument x in (312) is a complex function on S. We shall later place conditions on x to insure the existence of Ax.

Note that Ax is a function on T; and for each t, Ax depends only on the past $x(t - s)$, $s \geqq 0$, of x. The operator A is invariant under translation. If $x(s)$ is replaced by its translate $x(s + c)$, c a constant, then Ax is replaced by its translate, obtained by replacing t by $t + c$. If

$$x(s) = 1, \qquad s \in S,$$

then

$$Ax = \int_0^\infty d\alpha(s) = \alpha(\infty) - \alpha(0)$$

and Ax is finite. Thus our hypothesis on α implies that A admits 1 as argument. The hypothesis implies that the infinite past of x is of minor importance in Ax.

Corresponding to each $A \in \mathscr{A}$, there is a function α appearing in (312). Let $\mathscr{S}$ be the set of those functions α. Then $\mathscr{S}$ is a linear set, because $\mathscr{A}$ is linear. *Suppose that $\mathscr{S}$ is closed under conjugation*:

$$\bar{\alpha} \in \mathscr{S} \quad \textit{whenever} \quad \alpha \in \mathscr{S}.$$

Suppose that for each $t \in T$ and each $\alpha \in \mathscr{S}$,

$$\begin{aligned}&z(t - s, \omega) \textit{ is measurable and absolute square}\\ &\textit{integrable on } \{0 \leqq s \leqq \infty\} \times \Omega \textit{ relative to } |\alpha|\, p.\end{aligned} \tag{313}$$

Suppose that for each $t \in T$,

$$\begin{aligned} z_t &= z(t, \omega) \in \Psi, \\ y_t &= y(t, \omega) \in \Psi. \end{aligned} \tag{314}$$

If $\mathscr{S}$ is a large set, the assumption (313) and later assumptions may imply (314). In practice it is often a straightforward matter to determine that (314) applies or does not apply.

The *autocorrelation* a of z is defined as the function

$$a(s, s') = Ez_s\bar{z}_{s'} = (z_s, z_{s'})_\Psi; \tag{315}$$

and the *cross-correlation* b of y into z as

$$b(t, s) = Ey_t\bar{z}_s = (y_t, z_s)_\Psi; \qquad s, s', t \in T. \tag{316}$$

That the auto- and cross-correlations exist follows from conditions (314). In statistical usage it is sometimes required that

$$Ez_s = 0, \qquad Ey_t = 0; \qquad s, t \in T,$$

before the functions a and b are called correlations. We do not impose these conditions.

Suppose that the stochastic processes z and y are weakly stationary in the following sense. The autocorrelation a and the cross-correlation b are functions merely of the difference of their arguments:

$$\begin{aligned} a(s, s') &= a(s + h, s' + h) \underset{\text{def}}{=} a(s - s'), \\ b(t, s) &= b(t + h, s + h) \underset{\text{def}}{=} b(t - s), \qquad s, s', h, t \in T. \end{aligned} \tag{317}$$

Thus

$$a(s - s') = \bar{a}(s' - s), \qquad s, s' \in T.$$

We shall approximate y by Az, $A \in \mathscr{A}$. The error is

$$e = Az - y.$$

Observe that e, Az, and y depend on t and ω. We say that $A^0 \in \mathscr{A}$ is *efficient at $t \in T$* if

$$E|e_t|^2 = E|(Az)_t - y_t|^2$$

is minimal for $A \in \mathscr{A}$ when $A = A^0$. We say that A^0 is *within ρ of efficiency at t* if $E|e_t|^2$ is within ρ of its infimum for $A \in \mathscr{A}$ when $A = A^0$, where $\rho > 0$. We say that A^0 is *strongly efficient* if A^0 is efficient at each $t \in T$; and that A^0 is *within ρ of stationary efficiency* if A^0 is within ρ of efficiency at each $t \in T$. Thus being within ρ of stationary efficiency is not quite the same as being within ρ of strong efficiency (§ 176) but is quite similar.

For each $\rho > 0$, an operator within ρ of stationary efficiency surely exists, as we shall see. To find the operator, it is sufficient to consider the correlations a and b (rather than the input z and the desired output y) and the set $\mathscr{A}$. The operator that is within ρ of stationary efficiency for one pair z, y will also be within ρ of stationary efficiency for any other pair z, y which have the same auto- and cross-correlations.

§ 318. **The rôles of the correlations in Ψ.** Consider operators A, $A' \in \mathscr{A}$, where

$$\begin{aligned} Ax &= \int_0^\infty x(t - s)\, d\alpha(s), \\ A'x &= \int_0^\infty x(t - s)\, d\alpha'(s). \end{aligned} \tag{319}$$

The next lemma asserts that for each $t \in T$, Az and $A'z$ are elements of Ψ and that their relations to each other and to y are entirely determined by the correlations a, b and the measures α, α', and are independent of t.

320. LEMMA. *For each $t \in T$,*

(321) $$Az \in \Psi,$$

(322) $$(Az, A'z)_\Psi = \int_0^\infty \int_0^\infty a(s' - s)\, d\alpha(s)\, d\bar{\alpha}'(s'),$$

(323) $$E|Az|^2 = \int_0^\infty \int_0^\infty a(s' - s)\, d\alpha(s)\, d\bar{\alpha}(s') < \infty,$$

and

(324) $$(y, Az)_\Psi = \int_0^\infty b(s)\, d\bar{\alpha}(s).$$

PROOF. Consider a fixed $t \in T$. By (313), the integrand $z(t - s)$ in

(325) $$Az = \int_0^\infty z(t - s)\, d\alpha(s),$$

is absolute square integrable $|\alpha|\, p$ on $\{0 \leqq s \leqq \infty\} \times \Omega$.

Now

(326) $$(Az, A'z)_\Psi = EAz\overline{A'z} = E\int_0^\infty z(t - s)\, d\alpha(s) \int_0^\infty \bar{z}(t - s')\, d\bar{\alpha}'(s')$$

and the integrand is absolutely integrable $|\alpha|\, |\alpha'|\, p$ by Schwarz's inequality, since the fact that

$$\int_0^\infty d|\bar{\alpha}'|(s') = |\alpha'|(\infty) - |\alpha'|(0) < \infty$$

implies that $|z(t - s)|^2$ is integrable $|\alpha(s)|\, |\bar{\alpha}'(s')|\, p$. By Fubini's Theorem we may therefore rearrange the integrations in (326). Hence

$$(Az, A'z)_\Psi = \int_0^\infty \int_0^\infty d\alpha(s)\, d\bar{\alpha}'(s') Ez(t - s)\bar{z}(t - s')$$

$$= \int_0^\infty \int_0^\infty a(s' - s)\, d\alpha(s)\, d\bar{\alpha}'(s');$$

and

$$|(Az, A'z)_\Psi| < \infty.$$

This establishes (322), (323), and (321).

Similarly

$$(y, Az)_{\Psi} = Ey(t)\int_0^\infty \bar{z}(t-s)\,d\bar{\alpha}(s) = \int_0^\infty d\bar{\alpha}(s)Ey(t)\bar{z}(t-s)$$

$$= \int_0^\infty b(s)\,d\bar{\alpha}(s),$$

since

$$E\int_0^\infty |y(t)|^2\,d|\bar{\alpha}|(s) = [|\alpha|(\infty) - |\alpha|(0)]\,E|y(t)|^2 < \infty.$$

The proof is complete.

Thus even though Az, $A'z$, y depend on t, their inner products in Ψ are constants.

§ 327. **The spaces M_t.** Since $\mathscr{A}$ is a linear set,

$$\operatorname{span}\{(Az)_t : A \in \mathscr{A}\} = \{(Az)_t : A \in \mathscr{A}\}, \qquad t \in T.$$

For each $t \in T$, we define the space M_t *of images at t* as the closure in Ψ of

$$\{(Az)_t : A \in \mathscr{A}\}.$$

Consider a fixed $t \in T$, say $t = t_0$. By orthogonalization (§ 60), we may construct a countable set

$$\{A^j : j \in J\}, \qquad A^j \in \mathscr{A},$$

such that

$$\{(A^j z)_{t_0} : j \in J\}$$

is a basis for M_{t_0}. Now the construction of this basis depends only on the set $\mathscr{A}$ and the autocorrelation a of z. This is because the orthogonalization involves inner products in Ψ all of which may be calculated by (322).

For each A^j, $j \in J$, there is a function $\alpha^j \in \mathscr{S}$ such that

$$A^j x = \int_0^\infty x(t-s)\,d\alpha^j(s). \tag{328}$$

The calculation of the functions α^j, $j \in J$, depends on $\mathscr{S}$ and the autocorrelation of z only.

329. Lemma. *If the set*

$$\{(A^j z)_{t_0} : j \in J\}, \qquad A^j \in \mathscr{A},$$

is a basis for M_{t_0} for one $t_0 \in T$, then the set

$$\mathscr{Z}_t \underset{\text{def}}{=} \{(A^j z)_t : j \in J\} \tag{330}$$

is a basis for M_t for all $t \in T$.

Although M_t and $\mathscr{Z}_t$ vary with t, $\mathscr{Z}_t$ remains a basis for M_t at each instant.

PROOF. Since $\mathscr{Z}_{t_0}$ is a basis for M_{t_0},

$$((A^j z)_t, (A^k z)_t)_\Psi = ((A^j z)_{t_0}, (A^k z)_{t_0})_\Psi = \delta^{j,k}, \qquad j, k \in J_0,$$

by (322). Thus $\mathscr{Z}_t$ is an orthonormal system in M_t, $t \in T$. It remains to show that the system is complete.

Consider an element u_t of M_t for some fixed $t \in T$. By the definition of M_t, u_t is the limit in Ψ of a Cauchy sequence

$$\{u_t^\nu : \nu = 1, 2, \cdots\},$$

where

$$u_t^\nu = \int_0^\infty z(t - s)\, d\beta^\nu(s), \qquad \beta^\nu \in \mathscr{S}.$$

Use this relation to define u_t^ν for all $t \in T$. By (322), $\{u_t^\nu\}$ is a Cauchy sequence of elements of M_t for each $t \in T$. Define u_t as

$$\lim_\nu u_t^\nu, \qquad t \in T.$$

Now suppose that for some $t \in T$, u_t is orthogonal to all the elements of the orthonormal system $\mathscr{Z}_t$. We shall deduce that

$$u_t = 0, \qquad \text{all } t \in T.$$

Thus the fact that $u_t \perp \mathscr{Z}_t$ implies that $u_{t_0} \perp \mathscr{Z}_{t_0}$, by (322). Since $\mathscr{Z}_{t_0}$ is complete in M_{t_0}, by hypothesis, it follows that

$$u_{t_0} = 0.$$

Hence

$$u_{t_0}^\nu \to 0 \quad \text{as} \quad \nu \to \infty,$$

$$E|u_t^\nu|^2 = E|u_{t_0}^\nu|^2 \to 0,$$

$$u_t^\nu \to 0 = u_t, \qquad t \in T,$$

by (323). This completes the proof.

If M_t contains an element other than 0 for one $t \in T$, it must do the same for all t, by (323). Henceforth we exclude the uninteresting case

$$M_t = \{0\}, \quad \text{all } t \in T.$$

Let $\mathscr{Z}_t$ be the basis (330) for M_t, $t \in T$; and let the functions α^j, $j \in J$, of (328) correspond to the operators A^j that enter in $\mathscr{Z}_t$. Put

$$\tau_t = \text{Proj}_{M_t}\, y_t, \qquad t \in T. \tag{331}$$

332. LEMMA. *For each* $t \in T$,

$$\tau_t = \sum_{j \in J} c^j \int_0^\infty z(t - s)\, d\alpha^j(s) = \sum_{j \in J} c^j (A^j z)_t, \tag{333}$$

where

$$c^j = \int_0^\infty b(s)\, d\bar{\alpha}^j(s), \qquad j \in J. \tag{334}$$

Thus the projection τ_t of y_t on M_t is determined by the cross-correlation b and the basis $\mathscr{Z}_t$. The coordinates $c^j, j \in J$, of τ_t are independent of t; and

$$E|\tau_t|^2 = \sum_{j \in J} |c^j|^2. \tag{335}$$

PROOF. Since $\mathscr{Z}_t$ is a basis for M_t,

$$\tau_t = \text{Proj}_{M_t} y_t = \sum_{j \in J} (y_t, (A^j z)_t)_\Psi (A^j z)_t, \qquad t \in T,$$

by Theorem 56. Now this relation is precisely (333), by (324) and (325). This completes the proof.

336. THEOREM. *Consider an operator* $A \in \mathscr{A}$. *If* A *is efficient at one value* $t_0 \in T$, *then* A *is efficient at all* $t \in T$; *that is,* A *is strongly efficient. The operator* A *is efficient at* t_0 *iff*

$$(Az)_{t_0} = \tau_{t_0}, \tag{337}$$

in which case

$$E|e_t|^2 = E|y_t|^2 - E|\tau_t|^2 = E|y_t|^2 - \sum_{j \in J} |c^j|^2, \quad \text{all } t \in T, \tag{338}$$

where

$$e = Az - y. \tag{339}$$

If A *is within* ρ *of efficiency,* $\rho > 0$, *at one value* $t_0 \in T$, *then* A *is within* ρ *of efficiency at all* $t \in T$, *that is,* A *is within* ρ *of stationary efficiency. Finally,* A *is within* ρ *of stationary efficiency iff*

$$E|(Az)_t - \tau_t|^2 < \rho^2 \quad \text{for some } t \in T. \tag{340}$$

The elements τ_t and c^j are given in (333), (334).

PROOF. As regards $t = t_0$, this theorem is merely Theorem 34 with $N = M_{t_0}$, $Y = \Psi$, since

$$E|u|^2 = \|u\|_\Psi^2, \qquad u \in \Psi.$$

Cf. Lemma 220 also.

Furthermore the behaviour of A at one instant t_0 determines its behaviour at all $t \in T$, since the quantity

$$E|(Az)_t - \tau_t|^2 = \|(Az)_t - \tau_t\|^2_\Psi$$

is independent of t. To establish this assertion, note that since $(Az)_t \in M_t$, $(Az)_t$ may be expanded in terms of the basis $\mathscr{Z}_t$ of (330). Therefore

$$(Az)_t = \sum_{j \in J} d^j (A^j z)_t,$$

where

$$d^j = ((Az)_t, (A^j z)_t)_\Psi = \int_0^\infty \int_0^\infty a(s' - s)\, d\alpha(s)\, d\bar{\alpha}^j(s'), \qquad j \in J,$$

by (322). Thus the coordinates of τ_t and $(Az)_t$ are $\{c^j\}$ and $\{d^j\}$, respectively, by (333), and

$$\|(Az)_t - \tau_t\|^2_\Psi = \sum_j |d^j - c^j|^2, \qquad t \in T.$$

The last quantity is indeed independent of t, and the proof is complete.

341. COROLLARY. *For any $\rho > 0$ there is a finite set $J' \subset J$ such that the operator*

(342) $$A' = \sum_{j \in J'} c^j A^j$$

is within ρ of stationary efficiency, where

(343) $$c^j = \int_0^\infty b(s)\, d\bar{\alpha}^j(s).$$

Furthermore

(344) $$E|e'_t|^2 = E|y_t|^2 - \sum_{j \in J'} |c^j|^2,$$

where

$$e' = A'z - y.$$

Thus $E|e'_t|^2$ is independent of t iff $E|y_t|^2$ is. We have not needed or used the autocorrelation of y. If the autocorrelation of y is weakly stationary, that is, a function of the difference of its arguments, then $E|y_t|^2$ is constant.

PROOF. Choose $J' \subset J$ so that the partial sum of the series (333) corresponding to J' is within ρ of τ_t. Then A' defined by (342) is indeed within ρ of stationary efficiency.

Since $(A'z)_t$ is a projection of y, e'_t and $(A'z)_t$ lie in orthogonal complements of M_t, $t \in T$. This implies (344) and completes the proof.

345. REMARK. By a finite calculation, we may determine an operator near stationary efficiency as follows. Construct a finite orthogonal system

$$\mathscr{Z}'_t = \{(A^j z)_t : j \in J'\}, \qquad t \in T,$$

not necessarily a basis, in M_t. This finite construction is based on the set $\mathscr{A}$ and the autocorrelation of z. Then construct the operator A' in (342) and calculate $E|e'_t|^2$ by (344). If $E|e'_t|^2$ is adequately small, then the operator A' is adequate. If not, consider the possibility of enlarging $\mathscr{Z}'_t$. If $\mathscr{Z}'_t$ is complete in M_t, then enlargement is impossible. No improvement of A' can be effected. If $\mathscr{Z}'_t$ can be enlarged, say to $\mathscr{Z}''_t$, then an operator A'' may be calculated which will be better than or as good as A'. And so on. Cf. § 202.

§ 346. **The normal equation.** The following theorem gives a sufficient condition for efficiency.

347. THEOREM. *An operator $A \in \mathscr{A}$ is strongly efficient* (=*efficient*) *if*

$$b(t) - \int_0^\infty a(t - s)\, d\alpha(s) = 0, \quad \text{all } t \in T, \tag{348}$$

where

$$Ax = \int_0^\infty x(t - s)\, d\alpha(s), \qquad \alpha \in \mathscr{S};$$

a is the autocorrelation of z, and b is the cross-correlation of y into z. Furthermore A will also be strongly efficient relative to any linear set $\mathfrak{A}$ of operators of the form (312) *providing that*

$$A \in \mathfrak{A}.$$

If the correlations are known, the normal equation (348) is a condition on α. If $\alpha \in \mathscr{S}$ satisfies (348), then A is strongly efficient.

PROOF. By Theorem 335, $\tilde{A} \in \mathscr{A}$ is efficient iff

$$(\tilde{A}z)_t = \tau_t$$

for one $t \in T$ or equivalently for all $t \in T$. By the definition of M_t and the relation

$$\tau_t = \mathrm{Proj}_{M_t}\, y_t,$$

it follows that $\tilde{A}$ is efficient iff

$$(\tilde{A}z)_t - y_t \perp (Az)_t, \quad \text{all } A \in \mathscr{A};$$

that is,

$$E[(\tilde{A}z)_t - y_t]\overline{(Az)_t} = 0, \qquad A \in \mathscr{A},$$

or

$$E\left[\int_0^\infty z(t - \tilde{s})\, d\tilde{\alpha}(\tilde{s}) - y(t)\right]\int_0^\infty \bar{z}(t - s)\, d\bar{\alpha}(s) = 0, \qquad \alpha \in \mathscr{S},$$

or, by (317),

$$\int_0^\infty d\tilde{\alpha}(s)\left[\int_0^\infty a(s-\tilde{s})\,d\tilde{\alpha}(\tilde{s}) - b(s)\right] = 0, \qquad \alpha \in \mathscr{S}; \tag{349}$$

where

$$Ax = \int_0^\infty x(t-s)\,d\alpha(s),$$

$$\tilde{A}x = \int_0^\infty x(t-s)\,d\tilde{\alpha}(s); \qquad \alpha, \tilde{\alpha} \in \mathscr{S}.$$

Now (348) with α replaced by $\tilde{\alpha}$ certainly implies (349). This completes the proof.

It is perfectly possible that the normal equation (348) has a solution $\alpha \notin \mathscr{S}$. Then the solution α would not correspond to an operator $A \in \mathscr{A}$. Thus Theorem 347 tends to be useful when $\mathscr{A}$ is large.

350. REMARK. Under certain hypotheses, a condition like (348) would be necessary as well as sufficient for (349). For example, if $\mathscr{S}$ includes all complex measures α with compact support, then the relation (349) implies (348) with α replaced by $\tilde{\alpha}$. For, if (348) fails for one t, one could construct an α for which (349) would fail. Alternatively, if $\mathscr{S}$ includes all absolutely continuous complex measures with compact support, then (349) implies that

$$b(t) - \int_0^\infty a(t-s)\,d\tilde{\alpha}(s) = 0$$

for almost all t (Lebesgue measure). If the correlations a and b are continuous, the last relation will hold for all t (cf. [Doob 1, pp. 518, 519]).

The amount by which an operator $A \in \mathscr{A}$ fails to satisfy the normal equation (348) may be used to calculate how near stationary efficiency A is, providing that the basis $\mathscr{Z}_t$ for M_t is known, according to the following lemma.

351. LEMMA. *Consider an operator $\tilde{A}$, where*

$$\tilde{A}x = \int_0^\infty x(t-s)\,d\tilde{\alpha}(s), \qquad \tilde{\alpha} \in \mathscr{S}.$$

Suppose that $\tilde{A}$ satisfies the normal equation to within $\zeta(t)$; that is, that

$$\int_0^\infty a(t-s)\,d\tilde{\alpha}(s) = b(t) + \zeta(t), \qquad t \in T. \tag{352}$$

Then A is within $\rho + 0$ of stationary efficiency, where

$$\rho^2 = \sum_{j \in J} |\zeta^j|^2, \tag{353}$$

$$\zeta^j = \int_0^\infty \zeta(s)\,d\bar{\alpha}^j(s), \qquad j \in J. \tag{354}$$

Indeed the distance in Ψ *between* $\tilde{e}_t$ *and* $\tau_t - y_t$, *for each* $t \in T$, *equals* ρ, *where*

$$\tilde{e}_t = (\tilde{A}z)_t - y_t,$$
$$\tau_t = \operatorname{Proj}_{M_t} y_t.$$

Thus $\tilde{A}$ may be efficient even though $\zeta \neq 0$. For the efficiency of $\tilde{A}$, it is necessary that ρ in (353) vanish.

The measures α^j that appear in (354) are those which correspond to the operators A^j in the basis $\mathscr{Z}_t$ for M_t.

PROOF. The relation (352) may be written as

$$\int_0^\infty a(s - \bar{s})\, d\tilde{\alpha}(\bar{s}) = b(s) + \zeta(s), \qquad s \in T;$$

or

$$\int_0^\infty Ez(t - \bar{s})\bar{z}(t - s)\, d\tilde{\alpha}(\bar{s}) = Ey(t)\bar{z}(t - s) + \zeta(s), \qquad s, t \in T;$$

or

$$E[(\tilde{A}z)_t - y_t]\bar{z}(t - s) = \zeta(s),$$

or

$$E\tilde{e}_t\bar{z}(t - s) = \zeta(s).$$

Hence

$$E\tilde{e}_t \int_0^\infty \bar{z}(t - s)\, d\bar{\alpha}(s) = \int_0^\infty \zeta(s)\, d\bar{\alpha}(s), \qquad \alpha \in \mathscr{S};$$

and

$$(\tilde{e}_t, (Az)_t)_\Psi = \int_0^\infty \zeta(s)\, d\bar{\alpha}(s),$$

where

$$Ax = \int_0^\infty x(t - s)\, d\alpha(s), \qquad \alpha \in \mathscr{S}.$$

In particular

$$(\tilde{e}_t, (A^j z)_t)_\Psi = \int_0^\infty \zeta(s)\, d\bar{\alpha}^j(s) = \zeta^j, \qquad j \in J.$$

Thus the coordinates of $\tilde{e}_t$ are $\{\zeta^j\}$.

On the other hand, by the Theorem of Pythagoras,

$$\tilde{e}_t - f_t = \operatorname{Proj}_{M_t} \tilde{e}_t = \sum_{j \in J} (\tilde{e}_t, (A^j z)_t)_\Psi (A^j z)_t,$$

and

$$E|\tilde{e}_t|^2 - E|f_t|^2 = E|\tilde{e}_t - f_t|^2 = \sum_j |(\tilde{e}_t, (A^j z)_t)_\Psi|^2 = \sum_j |\zeta^j|^2 = \rho^2,$$

where

$$f_t = \tau_t - y_t, \qquad t \in T.$$

The diagram of § 33 is pertinent here.

This proves the lemma, since $E|f_t|^2$ is the infimum of $E|e_t|^2$, $A \in \mathscr{A}$.

§ 355. **A calculation.** It is perhaps of interest to cite an example in which the normal equation is readily solved.

For background, we start with the stochastic processes z and y and deduce the correlations a and b. For the solution it would be sufficient to start with a and b.

The nature of the probability space Ω, p is immaterial to our example; Ω, p may be simple or complicated or in between.

A *stochastic variable* is a complex function measurable p on almost all of Ω.

Suppose that

$$\xi_j, \qquad j \in J, \quad J \textit{ finite},$$

are stochastic variables such that

$$E\xi_j\bar{\xi}_k = \delta^{j,k}\sigma_j^2; \qquad \sigma_j^2 > 0, \quad j, k \in J. \tag{356}$$

Suppose that

$$z(s) = \sum_{j \in J} \xi_j e^{2\pi i \lambda_j s}, \qquad s \in T,$$

where $\lambda_j, j \in J$, *are distinct real numbers.* As a matter of fact any weakly stationary stochastic process may be approximated by a process of the above form [Doob 1, p. 524]. *Suppose that*

$$y(t) = \sum_{j \in J} \frac{\xi_j e^{2\pi i \lambda_j t}}{1 + 2\pi i \lambda_j}, \qquad t \in T.$$

Then the autocorrelation of z is

$$\begin{aligned} a(s + h, h) &= Ez(s + h)\bar{z}(h) = E \sum_{j \in J} \xi_j e^{2\pi i \lambda_j (s+h)} \sum_{k \in J} \bar{\xi}_k e^{-2\pi i \lambda_k h} \\ &= \sum_j \sigma_j^2 e^{2\pi i \lambda_j s} = a(s), \qquad s \in T, \end{aligned}$$

by (356). Thus a is indeed a function of s alone. Similarly the cross-correlation of y into z is

$$\begin{aligned} b(t + h, h) &= Ey(t + h)\bar{z}(h) = E \sum_j \frac{\xi_j e^{2\pi i \lambda_j (t+h)}}{1 + 2\pi i \lambda_j} \sum_k \bar{\xi}_k e^{-2\pi i \lambda_k h} \\ &= \sum_j \frac{\sigma_j^2 e^{2\pi i \lambda_j t}}{1 + 2\pi i \lambda_j} = b(t), \qquad t \in T. \end{aligned}$$

Thus b is a function of t alone.

From now on, we deal with a and b. The normal equation (348) is

$$\int_0^\infty \sum_j \sigma_j^2 e^{2\pi i\lambda_j(t-s)}\,d\alpha(s) = \sum_j \frac{\sigma_j{}^2 e^{2\pi i\lambda_j t}}{1 + 2\pi i\lambda_j}.$$

The form of this equation suggests that we try

$$d\alpha(s) = e^{-cs}\,ds, \qquad c \in \mathsf{C}.$$

Now $c = 1$ affords a solution, since

$$\int_0^\infty e^{-2\pi i\lambda_j s}e^{-s}\,ds = \int_0^\infty e^{-(1+2\pi i\lambda_j)s}\,ds = \frac{1}{1 + 2\pi i\lambda_j}.$$

Furthermore

$$\alpha(s) = -e^{-s}$$

is indeed of bounded variation on $\{0 \leqq s \leqq \infty\}$.

Hence a strongly efficient operator in the present example is A, where

$$Ax = \int_0^\infty x(t - s)\,e^{-s}\,ds,$$

providing that the set $\mathscr{A}$ of operators relative to which the problem is posed includes A. It may be however that $\mathscr{A}$ includes neither A nor anything near A.

Chapter 10

Minimal Response to Error

§ 1. **Introduction.** If in the preceding chapter we put $y = Gx$, we there studied the approximation of Gx by $A(x + \delta x)$, where both x and δx are stochastic processes, G is a given operator, and A is the operator which is intended to filter out the effect of the error δx and to approximate G. The rôle of probability is to describe the anticipated importance of individual inputs x and δx.

In the present chapter we again approximate Gx by $A(x + \delta x)$. The error δx is a stochastic process, as before. Our hypothesis about x, however, is different. We suppose that we are given a closed linear subspace $M \subset X$ and that x is an arbitrary element of M. In some fashion out of our control, x is determined in each instance in which we are to approximate Gx. All elements of M are considered to be equally important.

We define and study minimal operators: these are operators which provide the least possible response to error subject to the condition of their being unbiased approximations of G on M (§ 2). Minimal operators were introduced by Gauss in connection with least square approximation [Plackett 1].

In least square approximation a weight W is given and the approximation is such as to minimize a measure of the residuals

$$A(x + \delta x) - G(x + \delta x)$$

based on W. Least square approximation is therefore sensitive to W and the choice of W is important. That choice, according to Gauss, should depend on the variance V of the error δx in $x + \delta x$ (§ 70). The rôle of W in least square approximation is that W is or can be just the suitable counterfoil to the error δx. The suitable W can be characterized in terms of the variance V.

The principal results of this chapter are Theorems 104 and 137 on minimal operators and variance.

§ 2. **Approximations which are unbiased and have the minimal expected response to errors.** Suppose that X and Y are separable Hilbert spaces of more than one point and that G is a given fixed linear continuous operator on X to Y. Suppose that M is a nonempty closed linear subspace of X. In applications M will often be finite dimensional.

Suppose that $\Psi = H(\Omega, p)$ is a separable L^2-space of functions absolute square integrable on a space Ω relative to a probability p. Suppose that an element δx of the direct product $X\Psi$ is given. For each fixed $\omega \in \Omega$ with null exceptions, $\delta x_\omega \in X$ and δx_ω is a possible error in the input of our calculation (cf. § 9 : 175).

We seek a linear continuous operator A on X to Y such that, for each $x \in X$, $A(x + \delta x)$ will approximate Gx. The constituent x of the input is determined in each instance by something or someone other than the mathematician. The mathematician is told that x is an element of M. In the design of the process of approximation, the mathematician treats all elements of M as equally important. The error δx_ω is determined in each instance by a stochastic mechanism, and the probability p that enters in the definition of $\Psi = H(\Omega, p)$ measures the anticipated importance of different errors δx_ω, $\omega \in \Omega$.

In the preceding chapter both y and $x + \delta x$ were stochastic processes. To compare that chapter and the present one, put y in Chapter 9 equal to Gx, where x is a stochastic process (element of $X\Psi$). Then the inputs x in the two chapters are different; the inputs δx are similar.

Assume that

(3) $$E\delta x = 0 \in X;$$

and

(4) $$E\|\delta x\|_X^2 < \infty.$$

Condition (3) is that the error δx is unbiased. We did not assume (3) in the preceding chapter.

We say that a linear continuous operator A on X to Y is *unbiased* if

(5) $$EA(x + \delta x) = Gx \quad \text{whenever } x \in M.$$

Thus, for each $x \in M$, $A(x + \delta x)$ is an unbiased estimate of Gx. Since we will estimate Gx by $A(x + \delta x)$, it will be natural to specify that A be an unbiased operator.

We now define a *minimal operator* A as an operator which for each $x \in M$ minimizes

(6) $$E\|A(x + \delta x) - Gx\|_Y^2$$

among all linear continuous unbiased operators. If $\rho > 0$, we say that A is *within* ρ *of minimality* if A is a linear continuous unbiased operator and if the quantity (6) exceeds its infimum by less than ρ^2. We say that a sequence $\{A^n : n = 1, 2, \cdots\}$ is a *minimizing sequence* if for each n, A^n is a linear continuous unbiased operator and if the sequence

$$\{E\|A_n(x + \delta x) - Gx\|_Y^2\}$$

of numbers converges to the infimum of (6) for each $x \in M$.

If $\delta x = 0 \in X\Psi$, we may take $A = G$. *Assume* henceforth *that*

$$\delta x \neq 0 \in X\Psi.$$

Let

(7) $$\mathscr{T} = \mathscr{T}(X, Y)$$

denote the set of all linear continuous operators on X to Y. Let $\mathscr{U}$ denote the set of unbiased operators:

$$\mathscr{U} = \{A \in \mathscr{T}(X, Y) : EA(x + \delta x) = Gx \quad \text{whenever } x \in M\}.$$

8. Lemma. *An operator* $A \in \mathscr{T}(X, Y)$ *is unbiased iff*

$$Ax = Gx \quad \textit{whenever } x \in M. \tag{9}$$

If $A \in \mathscr{U}$, *then*

$$A(x + \delta x) - Gx = e = A\delta x, \qquad x \in M, \tag{10}$$

and

$$E\|A(x + \delta x) - Gx\|_Y^2 = E\|A\delta x\|_Y^2. \tag{11}$$

Thus, by (9),

$$\mathscr{U} = \{A \in \mathscr{T}(X, Y) : (A - G)M = 0\}. \tag{12}$$

Proof. Suppose that $x \in M \subset X$. Then

$$x = x \times 1 \in X\Psi,$$

since $1 \in \Psi$. In (5), A is considered as an operator on $X\Psi$ to $Y\Psi$ (Theorem 9: 156). Now, by Theorem 9: 156,

$$EA(x + \delta x) = EAx + EA\delta x = Ax + AE\delta x = Ax + A0 = Ax.$$

Thus (5) is equivalent to (9).

Suppose that $A \in \mathscr{T}(X, Y)$ is unbiased. Then

$$A(x + \delta x) - Gx = Ax + A\delta x - Gx = A\delta x \quad \text{whenever } x \in M,$$

by (9). Thus (10) and (11) are established. This completes the proof.

An alternative definition of a minimal operator may now be given. Let $\mathscr{U}$ denote the set of linear continuous operators A on X to Y such that

$$Ax = Gx \quad \text{whenever } x \in M.$$

An operator $A \in \mathscr{U}$ is minimal if it minimizes

$$E\|A(x + \delta x) - Gx\|^2 = E\|A\delta x\|^2 \quad \text{for each } x \in M.$$

In the rest of this chapter we will deal with the above problem and nowhere use the hypothesis (3) that δx is unbiased.

The reader may ask why we did not start with the second form of the problem. The reason is that the second form refers to Ax, an element which is not of itself material to the preproblem. The preproblem deals with $A(x + \delta x)$ and Gx. These elements enter in condition (5). It is because δx is unbiased that Ax becomes pertinent.

One may wish to compare the concepts of minimal and efficient operators. An operator A is minimal relative to G, M, and δx; it minimizes

$$E\|A(x + \delta x) - Gx\|_Y^2 = E\|A\delta x\|_Y^2 \quad \text{for each } x \in M,$$

among unbiased linear continuous operators. On the other hand an operator A is efficient relative to $y = Gx$, $x + \delta x$, and $\mathscr{A}$; it minimizes

$$E\|A(x + \delta x) - Gx\|_Y^2, \qquad A \in \mathscr{A},$$

where x is a stochastic process (element of $X\Psi$) and $\mathscr{A}$ is a given set of operators. In both cases δx is a stochastic process.

§ 13. **Minimal operators and projections.** Minimal operators are related to projections in $Y\Psi$, as we shall see.

We continue to denote by $\mathscr{T}(X, Y)$ the set of linear continuous operators on X to Y. Let $\mathscr{B}$ be the set of operators in $\mathscr{T}(X, Y)$ which vanish on M:

(14) $$\mathscr{B} = \{B \in \mathscr{T}(X, Y) : BM = 0\}.$$

Then, by (9),

(15) $$\mathscr{U} = G + \mathscr{B} = \{G + B : B \in \mathscr{B}\};$$

thus the set $\mathscr{U}$ of unbiased operators is the translation of $\mathscr{B}$ by G.

A minimal operator A is one which minimizes

$$E\|A\delta x\|_Y^2, \qquad A \in \mathscr{U};$$

an operator within ρ of minimality, $\rho > 0$, is an $A \in \mathscr{U}$ for which $E\|A\delta x\|_Y^2$ is within ρ^2 of its infimum, $A \in \mathscr{U}$, by Lemma 8. A minimizing sequence $\{A^n : n = 1, 2, \cdots\}$ is one for which $A^n \in \mathscr{U}$, $n = 1, 2, \cdots$, and $E\|A^n\delta x\|_Y^2$ converges to the infimum just described.

Let τ be the set of images of δx under elements of $\mathscr{T}(X, Y)$:

(16) $$\tau = \mathscr{T}(X, Y)\delta x = \{A\delta x : A \in \mathscr{T}(X, Y)\} \subset Y\Psi.$$

Let $\hat{\tau}$ be the closure of τ in $Y\Psi$. Since $\delta x \neq 0$, τ consists of more than the element 0, and $\hat{\tau}$ is a Hilbert space of positive dimension contained in $Y\Psi$. Since $\mathscr{T}(X, Y)$ is part but not all of $\mathscr{T}(X\Psi, Y\Psi)$, the space $\hat{\tau}$ need not be all of $Y\Psi$. There may be elements in $\hat{\tau} - \tau$ because it is perfectly possible that

$$\{A^n\delta x\}, \qquad A^n \in \mathscr{T}(X, Y),$$

be a Cauchy sequence in $Y\Psi$ even though there is no element $A \in \mathscr{T}(X, Y)$ such that

$$A^n\delta x \to A\delta x$$

(cf. § 150).

Let β be the set of images of δx under elements of $\mathscr{B}$:

(17) $$\beta = \mathscr{B}\delta x = \{B\delta x : B \in \mathscr{B}\} \subset \tau \subset Y\Psi.$$

Then

$$\beta = \{B\delta x : B \in \mathscr{T}(X, Y) \quad \text{and} \quad BM = 0\}.$$

Let α be the set of images of δx under elements of $\mathscr{U}\}$:

$$\alpha = \mathscr{U}\delta x = \{A\delta x : A \in \mathscr{U}\}. \tag{18}$$

Then

$$\alpha = \{A\delta x : A \in \mathscr{T}(X, Y) \quad \text{and} \quad (A - G)M = 0\}.$$

Let γ be the orthogonal complement of β in $\hat{\tau}$ (cf. § 9 : 19). Thus γ is the closure in $Y\Psi^{\cdot}$ of the set

$$\{A\delta x : A \in \mathscr{T}(X, Y), \quad \text{and} \quad E(A\delta x, B\delta x) = 0 \quad \text{whenever } B \in \mathscr{B}\} \tag{19}$$

of elements of the form $A\delta x$, $A \in \mathscr{T}(X, Y)$, each of which is orthogonal to all elements $B\delta x$, $B \in \mathscr{B}$. Let $\beta^{\perp}$ be the orthogonal complement of β in $Y\Psi^{\cdot}$. Then

$$\gamma \subset \beta^{\perp},$$

since each element of γ is surely an element of $\beta^{\perp}$.

Put

$$\theta = \operatorname{Proj}_{\gamma} G\delta x \in \gamma \subset Y\Psi^{\cdot}. \tag{20}$$

Thus θ is the projection of $G\delta x$ onto γ. Note that θ is not the origin.

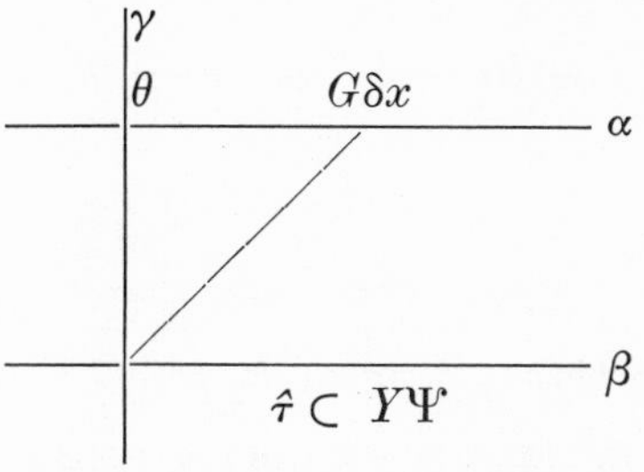

21. Lemma.

$$\theta = \operatorname{Proj}_{\gamma} G\delta x = \operatorname{Proj}_{\beta^{\perp}} G\delta x.$$

Proof. By their definitions, β and γ are orthogonal complements in the Hilbert space $\hat{\tau}$. Furthermore

$$G\delta x \in \tau \subset \hat{\tau}.$$

Hence, by Theorem 9 : 21,

$$G\delta x = \operatorname{Proj}_{\beta} G\delta x + \operatorname{Proj}_{\gamma} G\delta x,$$

and

$$\begin{aligned}\operatorname{Proj}_{\beta^{\perp}} G\delta x &= \operatorname{Proj}_{\beta^{\perp}} \operatorname{Proj}_{\beta} G\delta x + \operatorname{Proj}_{\beta^{\perp}} \operatorname{Proj}_{\gamma} G\delta x \\ &= 0 + \operatorname{Proj}_{\gamma} G\delta x,\end{aligned}$$

by Theorem 9 : 26, since

$$\mathrm{Proj}_\gamma\, G\delta x \in \gamma \subset \beta^\perp.$$

This completes the proof.

We denote the closure of a set by adding a roof $\wedge$ to its symbol. Thus $\hat{\alpha}$ is the closure of α in $Y\Psi$.

22. Lemma. *The set $\hat{\alpha}$ has one and only one element in common with γ or with $\beta^\perp$, and that element is θ:*

$$\hat{\alpha} \cap \gamma = \hat{\alpha} \cap \beta^\perp = \{\theta\}. \tag{23}$$

There exists a sequence $\{A^n : n = 1, 2, \cdots\}$ such that

$$A^n \in \mathscr{U}, \qquad n = 1, 2, \cdots,$$

and

$$A^n \delta x \rightarrow \theta \quad \mathit{in} \quad Y\Psi \quad \mathit{as} \quad n \rightarrow \infty.$$

Proof. By (20),

$$\theta \in \gamma,$$

and γ is the orthogonal complement of β in $\hat{\tau}$. Hence θ is a limit point of τ and there exists a sequence $\{\tilde{A}^n\}$ such that

$$\tilde{A}^n \in \mathscr{T}(X, Y)$$

and

$$\tilde{A}^n \delta x \rightarrow \theta \quad \text{as} \quad n \rightarrow \infty.$$

We may write

$$\{\tilde{A}^n \delta x\} = \theta \in \gamma.$$

Now, by Lemma 21,

$$G\delta x - \theta = G\delta x - \mathrm{Proj}_{\beta^\perp} G\delta x = \{(G - \tilde{A}^n)\delta x\} \in \hat{\beta}.$$

Since $\hat{\beta}$ is the closure of β, there is a sequence $\{B^n\}$ such that

$$\{(G - \tilde{A}^n)\delta x\} = \{B^n \delta x\}, \qquad B^n \in \mathscr{B}. \tag{24}$$

Put

$$A^n = G - B^n.$$

Then

$$A^n \in \mathscr{U},$$

since $(A^n - G)M = 0$. Also

$$\begin{aligned}\{A^n\delta x\} - \theta &= \{A^n\delta x\} - \{\tilde{A}^n\delta x\} = \{(G - B^n)\delta x\} - \{\tilde{A}^n\delta x\} \\ &= \{(G - B^n - \tilde{A}^n)\delta x\} = 0,\end{aligned}$$

by (24). Hence

$$\theta = \{A^n \delta x\} \in \hat{\alpha}.$$

Thus

$$\theta \in \hat{\alpha} \cap \gamma \subset \hat{\alpha} \cap \beta^{\perp}.$$

Furthermore, the sequence of the conclusion of the lemma exists.

It remains to show that θ is the only element of $\hat{\alpha} \cap \beta^{\perp}$. Thus, suppose that

$$\theta' \in \hat{\alpha} \cap \beta^{\perp}.$$

Then

$$\theta' = \{A'^n \delta x\} \in \beta^{\perp}, \tag{25}$$

where $A'^n \in \mathscr{U}$, $n = 1, 2, \cdots$, and $\{A'^n \delta x\}$ is a Cauchy sequence in $Y\Psi$, since $\alpha = \mathscr{U}\delta x$. Then

$$(A'^n - G)M = 0, \qquad n = 1, 2, \cdots.$$

Hence

$$A'^n - G \in \mathscr{B},$$

and

$$\{(G - A'^n)\delta x\} \in \hat{\beta}. \tag{26}$$

Now

$$G\delta x = \{(G - A'^n)\delta x\} + \{A'^n \delta x\}.$$

By (25), (26), and Theorem 9: 21,

$$\{A'^n \delta x\} = \text{Proj}_{\beta^{\perp}} G\delta x = \theta = \theta'.$$

This completes the proof.

In the next theorem, $\mathscr{U}$ continues to be the set (15) of unbiased operators;

$$\theta = \text{Proj}_{\gamma} G\delta x = \text{Proj}_{\beta^{\perp}} G\delta x,$$

where β and γ are defined in (17) and (19); and τ is the set defined in (16).

27. THEOREM. *For each $\rho > 0$, an operator $A \in \mathscr{U}$ is within ρ of minimality iff*

$$E\|A\delta x - \theta\|_Y^2 < \rho^2. \tag{28}$$

An operator $A \in \mathscr{U}$ is minimal iff

$$A\delta x = \theta. \tag{29}$$

A minimal operator exists iff

$$\theta \in \tau. \tag{30}$$

For any $A \in \mathscr{U}$,

$$E\|A\delta x\|_Y^2 = E\|A\delta x - \theta\|_Y^2 + E\|\theta\|_Y^2. \tag{31}$$

Also

$$\inf_{A \in \mathscr{U}} E\|A\delta x\|_Y^2 = E\|\theta\|_Y^2. \tag{32}$$

Thus if an operator A is minimal, the approximation $A(x + \delta x)$ of Gx, $x \in M$, is

$$A(x + \delta x) = Ax + A\delta x = Gx + \theta,$$

where $\theta \in Y\Psi$ is uniquely determined. If A is within ρ of minimality, then $A(x + \delta x)$ is within ρ of $Gx + \theta$ in $Y\Psi$ for each $x \in M$.

PROOF. *Part* 1. Consider $A \in \mathscr{U}$. Then

$$A\delta x - \theta = (A - G)\delta x + G\delta x - \theta.$$

Now

$$(A - G)\delta x \in \beta$$

since

$$A - G \in \mathscr{B};$$

and

$$G\delta x - \theta = G\delta x - \{A^n\delta x\} = \{(G - A^n)\delta x\} \in \hat{\beta},$$

where $\{A^n\}$ is the sequence of Lemma 22. Hence

$$A\delta x - \theta \in \hat{\beta}.$$

This establishes (31), by orthogonality in $Y\Psi$, since $\theta \in \beta^\perp$.

Part 2. By Lemma 22 we may choose $A \in \mathscr{U}$ so as to make

$$E\|A\delta x - \theta\|_Y^2$$

less than any preassigned positive quantity. By (31), then, the infimum of $E\|A\delta x\|_Y^2$, $A \in \mathscr{U}$, is $E\|\theta\|_Y^2$. This establishes (32). It follows that $A \in \mathscr{U}$ is minimal iff (29) holds; and $A \in \mathscr{U}$ is within ρ of minimality, $\rho > 0$, iff

$$E\|A\delta x\|_Y^2 - E\|\theta\|_Y^2 = E\|A\delta x - \theta\|_Y^2 < \rho^2;$$

that is, iff (28) holds.

Part 3. If $\theta \in \tau$, then there is an $A \in \mathscr{U}$ such that (29) holds; that A is minimal. Conversely, if A is a minimal operator, then (29) holds and therefore (30) holds.

This completes the proof of the theorem.

An illustration of the use of Theorem 27 is given in §§ 150, 172 below.

33. REMARK. Suppose that $\{\beta^i : i \in \mathscr{I}\}$ is a basis for $\hat{\beta}$, where

$$\beta^i = B^i\delta x, \qquad B^i \in \mathscr{B},$$

and $\mathscr{I}$ consists of all the positive integers or the first m positive integers for some m. It is easy to calculate a minimizing sequence $\{A^n\}$ in terms of the basis $\{\beta^i\}$. Thus

$$\text{Proj}_\beta\, G\delta x = \sum_i E(G\delta x, \beta^i)_Y B^i\delta x$$

by (9 : 57), and

$$\theta = \text{Proj}_{\beta^\perp}\, G\delta x = G\delta x - \sum_i E(G\delta x, \beta^i)_Y B^i\delta x.$$

Put

$$A^n = G - \sum_{i \leqq n} E(G\delta x, \beta^i)B^i.$$

Then

$$A^n \in \mathscr{U}, \qquad n = 1, 2, \cdots,$$

and $\{A^n\}$ is a minimizing sequence, since

$$\{A^n \delta x\} = \theta.$$

In the calculation of A^n one uses only the first n elements of the basis $\{\beta^i\}$.

Theorem 27 affords a direct and complete technique for the calculation of minimal operators or nearly minimal operators. The element θ can be calculated if the stochastic process δx as an element of $Y\Psi'$ is known.

We next develop a theory involving the variance of δx rather than δx itself.

§ 34. **Linear continuous functionals on a Hilbert space. Adjoint operators.** In the present section, X and Y are arbitrary Hilbert spaces, not necessarily separable.

35. Theorem. *Suppose that F is a linear continuous functional on a Hilbert space X. Then there exists a unique vector $f \in X$ such that*

(36) $$Fx = (x, f)_X, \qquad x \in X.$$

The element f may be obtained as follows. If $F = 0$, then $f = 0$. If $F \neq 0$, put

(37) $$L = \{x \in X : Fx = 0\}.$$

Let g be any nonzero element of $L^\perp$. Then

$$f = \frac{\overline{Fg}}{\|g\|^2} g$$

and

(38) $$Fx = (x, f)_X = \frac{Fg}{\|g\|^2}(x, g)_X, \qquad x \in X.$$

Conversely, for each $f \in X$, the functional F defined by (36) *is linear and continuous and its Banach norm $\|F\|$ equals $\|f\|_X$.*

Proof. For each $f \in X$, (36) clearly defines a linear continuous functional on X, because of the properties of the inner product. Furthermore

$$|Fx| \leqq \|x\| \, \|f\|, \qquad x \in X;$$

so that

$$\|F\| \leqq \|f\|.$$

On the other hand, putting $x = f$, we see that

$$Ff = \|f\|^2 = \|x\| \, \|f\|.$$

Hence

$$\|F\| \geqq \|f\|.$$

Thus the Banach norm $\|F\|$ of F is the norm $\|f\|$ in X of the element f.

That f in (36) is unique is immediate, because

$$(x, f) = (x, f'), \qquad x \in X,$$

implies that $f - f' \in X^\perp = \{0\}$ (Theorem 9 : 21).

If $F = 0$, then $f = 0$ satisfies (36).

Finally suppose that F is a given linear continuous functional on X and that $F \neq 0$. Let L be the set on which F vanishes:

$$L = \{x \in X : Fx = 0\}.$$

Let g be any nonzero element of $L^\perp$. Such elements exist, else $L = X$ and $Fx = 0$, $x \in X$. Then

$$Fg \neq 0,$$

else $g \in L \cap L^\perp$ and $g = 0$. Put

$$f = \frac{\overline{Fg}}{\|g\|^2}\, g.$$

Then, for all $x \in X$,

(39) $$(x, f) = \left(x, \frac{\overline{Fg}}{\|g\|^2}\, g\right) = \frac{Fg}{\|g\|^2}\,(x, g).$$

On the other hand

$$x - \frac{Fx}{Fg}\, g \in L,$$

since

$$F\left(x - \frac{Fx}{Fg}\, g\right) = Fx - \frac{Fx}{Fg}\, Fg = 0.$$

Hence

$$\left(x - \frac{Fx}{Fg}\, g, g\right) = 0. \qquad x \in X;$$

and

$$(x, g) - \frac{Fx}{Fg}\, \|g\|^2 = 0,$$

$$Fx = \frac{Fg}{\|g\|^2}\,(x, g).$$

This establishes (38) and (36).

The proof is complete.

40. Remark. Theorem 35 implies that $L^\perp$ is one-dimensional, except in the case $F = 0$ where $L^\perp$ is zero-dimensional.

The element g in (38) is any nonzero element of X such that

(41) $$(g, x) = 0 \quad \text{whenever} \quad x \in X \quad \text{and} \quad Fx = 0.$$

In Theorem 35, F is an element of the space X^* which is adjoint to X (§ 3 : 13). The adjoint space is sometimes called the conjugate space or dual space.

We now consider the adjoint of an operator, a different concept.

Suppose that A is a linear continuous operator on a Hilbert space X to a Hilbert space Y. The *adjoint* A^* of A is defined as an operator on Y to X such that

(42) $$(Ax, y)_Y = (x, A^*y)_X \quad \text{for all } x \in X,\ y \in Y.$$

An operator B on X to X is *self-adjoint* if $B = B^*$. Projections are self-adjoint, by Theorem 9 : 26.

43. Theorem. *If A is a linear continuous operator on a Hilbert space X to a Hilbert space Y, then the adjoint A^* exists, is unique, and is a linear continuous operator on Y to X. The Banach norms of A and A^* are equal. If*

$$A,\ B \in \mathscr{T}(X, Y), \quad c \in \mathsf{C},$$

then

$$A^{**} = A,$$
$$(cA)^* = \bar{c}A^*,$$
$$(A + B)^* = A^* + B^*,$$
$$(AB^*)^* = BA^*,$$
$$0^* = 0.$$

The matrix of A^* is the conjugate transpose of the matrix of A.

Proof. [Halmos 2, pp. 39, 40.] Note that products of operators are defined if the range of the first to act is in the domain of the second.

44. Lemma. *Suppose that M is a linear subspace of X and that*

$$B \in \mathscr{T}(X, Y).$$

Then

(45) $$BM = 0$$

iff

(46) $$B^*Y \subset M^\perp.$$

PROOF. Let P be the operator of projection onto $\hat{M}$ (P is an operator on X to X). Then $BM = 0$ is equivalent to

$$BP = 0,$$

or

$$(BP)^* = 0^* = 0,$$

or

$$PB^* = 0,$$

or

$$B^*Y \subset M^\perp,$$

since $P = P^*$ and $Px = 0$, $x \in X$ iff $x \in M^\perp$, by Theorem 9:26. This completes the proof. An alternative proof may be based on partitioning the space X (cf. § 123).

§ 47. **Operators of finite Schmidt norm.** Suppose that X and Y are separable Hilbert spaces with bases $\{\xi^j : j \in J\}$ and $\{\eta^k : k \in K\}$, respectively. Consider a linear continuous operator B on X to Y. We define the *Schmidt norm* $\|B\|_{\mathscr{S}}$ of B by the relation

(48) $$\|B\|_{\mathscr{S}}^2 = \sum_{j,k} |(B\xi^j, \eta^k)_Y|^2, \qquad 0 \leqq \|B\|_{\mathscr{S}} \leqq \infty.$$

We continue to denote the Banach norm of B by $\|B\|$.

Thus $\|B\|_{\mathscr{S}}$ appears to depend on the bases $\{\xi^j\}$, $\{\eta^k\}$. The series in (48) is the sum of the absolute squares of the elements of the matrix of B relative to $\{\xi^j\}$, $\{\eta^k\}$ (§ 9 : 132).

49. LEMMA. *Suppose that*

$$B \in \mathscr{T}(X, Y).$$

Then $\|B\|_{\mathscr{S}}$ *is independent of the bases used in its definition. Furthermore*

(50) $$\|B\| \leqq \|B\|_{\mathscr{S}},$$

and

(51) $$\begin{aligned}\|B\|_{\mathscr{S}}^2 &= \sum_{j,k} |(B\xi^j, \eta^k)_Y|^2 = \sum_j \|B\xi^j\|_Y^2 \\ &= \sum_k \|B^*\eta^k\|_X^2 = \sum_{j,k} |(\xi^j, B^*\eta^k)_X|^2 = \|B^*\|_{\mathscr{S}}^2.\end{aligned}$$

PROOF. The series in (48) consists of nonnegative terms and therefore converges absolutely to a nonnegative number or to $+\infty$. In either case its terms may be summed in any order. It follows that

$$\|B\|_{\mathscr{S}}^2 = \sum_j \|B\xi^j\|_Y^2,$$

since $(B\xi^j, \eta^k)_Y$ is the kth coordinate of $B\xi^j$ relative to $\{\eta^k\}$. This establishes part of (51) and also the fact that $\|B\|_{\mathscr{S}}$ is independent of the basis $\{\eta^k\}$.

A similar argument applies to the rest of (51), since

$$(B\xi^j, \eta^k)_Y = (\xi^j, B^*\eta^k)_X.$$

Hence $\|B\|_{\mathscr{S}}$ is independent of $\{\xi^j\}$ and $\{\eta^k\}$.

To establish (50), we use coordinates. Consider $x \in X$. Put

$$x = \{_j\, x^j\} = \sum_j x^j \xi^j, \qquad x^j = (x, \xi^j)_X;$$

$$B = \{_k\, b^{k,j}\, _j\}, \qquad b^{k,j} = (B\xi^j, \eta^k)_Y.$$

As in (9: 142, 143), the index attached to the left brace is the row index; the right, the column index. Then

$$Bx = \{b^{k,j}\}\{x^j\} = \left\{\sum_j b^{k,j} x^j\right\}$$
$$= \sum_k \eta^k \sum_j b^{k,j} x^j.$$

Hence

$$\|Bx\|^2 = \sum_k \left|\sum_j b^{k,j} x^j\right|^2 \leqq \sum_k \left[\sum_j |b^{k,j}|^2\right]\left[\sum_j |x^j|^2\right]$$
$$= \|x\|^2 \sum_{j,k} |b^{k,j}|^2 = \|x\|^2 \|B\|^2_{\mathscr{S}}.$$

Hence

$$\|B\| \leqq \|B\|_{\mathscr{S}};$$

and the proof is complete.

The Schmidt norm $\|B\|_{\mathscr{S}}$ of an operator $B \in \mathscr{T}(X, Y)$ may be infinite. We denote by $\mathscr{S}(X, Y)$ the subset of $\mathscr{T}(X, Y)$ consisting of operators of finite Schmidt norm. Thus

(52) $$\mathscr{S}(X, Y) = \{B \in \mathscr{T}(X, Y) : \|B\|_{\mathscr{S}} < \infty\}.$$

53. Corollary. *The conditions*

$$B \in \mathscr{S}(X, Y)$$

and

$$B^* \in \mathscr{S}(Y, X)$$

are equivalent.

Proof. By (51), $\|B\|_{\mathscr{S}} = \|B^*\|_{\mathscr{S}}$. Hence both are finite together.

54. Lemma. *Suppose that*

$$A, B \in \mathscr{S}(X, Y), \qquad c \in \mathbf{C}.$$

Then

$$cA \in \mathscr{S}(X, Y),$$

and

$$A + B \in \mathscr{S}(X, Y).$$

PROOF. Let $\{\xi^j\}$ be a basis for X and $\{\eta^k\}$ a basis for Y.
The first conclusion follows from (48). Furthermore

$$((A + B)\xi^j, \eta^k)_Y = (A\xi^j, \eta^k)_Y + (B\xi^j, \eta^k)_Y$$

and

$$|((A + B)\xi^j, \eta^k)|^2 \leqq 2|(A\xi^j, \eta^k)|^2 + 2|(B\xi^j, \eta^k)|^2,$$

since

$$2uv \leqq u^2 + v^2$$

for real numbers u, v. Hence, by (51),

$$\|A + B\|_{\mathscr{S}}^2 \leqq 2\|A\|_{\mathscr{S}}^2 + 2\|B\|_{\mathscr{S}}^2 < \infty;$$

and

$$A + B \in \mathscr{S}(X, Y).$$

This completes the proof.

55. LEMMA. *Suppose that X, Y, Z are separable Hilbert spaces and that*

$$A \in \mathscr{S}(X, Y), \qquad B \in \mathscr{T}(Y, Z), \qquad C \in \mathscr{T}(Z, X).$$

Then

$$BA \in \mathscr{S}(X, Z), \qquad AC \in \mathscr{S}(Z, Y)$$

and

$$\|BA\|_{\mathscr{S}} \leqq \|B\|\,\|A\|_{\mathscr{S}}, \qquad \|AC\|_{\mathscr{S}} \leqq \|C\|\,\|A\|_{\mathscr{S}}.$$

This elementary lemma is extremely useful because of the generality of the operators B and C; they must be linear and continuous and operate on the space appropriate to the multiplication, but are otherwise arbitrary.

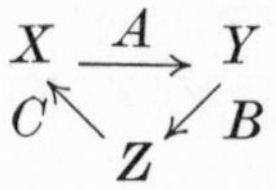

PROOF. Let $\{\xi^j\}$ be a basis for X. By (51) and § 3 : 8,

$$\begin{aligned}\|BA\|_{\mathscr{S}}^2 &= \sum_j \|BA\xi^j\|_Z^2 \leqq \|B\|^2 \sum_j \|A\xi^j\|_Y^2 \\ &= \|B\|^2\|A\|_{\mathscr{S}}^2 < \infty.\end{aligned}$$

Similarly, let $\{\eta^k\}$ be a basis for Y. Then

$$\|AC\|_{\mathscr{S}}^2 = \sum_k \|C^*A^*\eta^k\|_Z^2 \leqq \|C^*\|^2 \sum_k \|A^*\eta^k\|_X^2$$
$$= \|C\|^2 \|A\|_{\mathscr{S}}^2 < \infty,$$

by (51) and Theorem 43. This completes the proof.

56. LEMMA. *Suppose that*

$$A, B \in \mathscr{S}(X, Y)$$

and that $\{\xi^j\}$ *is a basis for* X. *Then the series*

$$(57) \qquad \sum_j (A\xi^j, B\xi^j)_Y \underset{\text{def}}{=} (A, B)_{\mathscr{S}}$$

is absolutely convergent to a finite sum independent of the basis $\{\xi^j\}$.

The function $(A, B)_{\mathscr{S}}$ defined in (57) is in fact an inner product and our notation is consistent, since $\|A\|_{\mathscr{S}}^2$ as previously defined is $(A, A)_{\mathscr{S}}$ as above defined. The space $\mathscr{S}(X, Y)$ with the inner product (57) is a Hilbert space [Schatten 1, pp. 76, 110]. We note these facts but do not use them.

PROOF. The prefixes

Real, Imag

will indicate real and imaginary parts, respectively. Now

$$4 \text{ Real } (A\xi^j, B\xi^j)_Y = \|(A + B)\xi^j\|_Y^2 - \|(A - B)\xi^j\|_Y^2.$$

Hence

$$4 \text{ Real } \sum_j (A\xi^j, B\xi^j)_Y = \|A + B\|_{\mathscr{S}}^2 - \|A - B\|_{\mathscr{S}}^2,$$

a finite quantity independent of the basis $\{\xi^j\}$. If we replace A by $-iA$, where $i^2 = -1$, the expansion on the left becomes

$$4 \text{ Imag } \sum_j (A\xi^j, B\xi^j)_Y,$$

which therefore is finite and independent of the basis. Hence the series (57) is convergent to a sum independent of the basis.

Since any rearrangement of a basis $\{\xi^j\}$ is itself a basis, the terms of the series (57) may be rearranged in any fashion without affecting the sum. Hence the series is absolutely convergent. The absolute convergence may also be seen directly from the fact that

$$2|(A\xi^j, B\xi^j)_Y| \leqq \|A\xi^j\|_Y^2 + \|B\xi^j\|_Y^2.$$

This elementary relation follows immediately from Schwarz's inequality, since

$$2|(y, y')_Y| \leqq 2\|y\|_Y \|y'\|_Y \leqq \|y\|_Y^2 + \|y'\|_Y^2; \qquad y, y' \in Y.$$

The proof is complete.

§ 58. **Trace.** Consider a linear continuous operator A on a separable Hilbert space X of more than one point to X. Let $\{\xi^j\}$ be a basis for X. Form the series

$$\sum_j (A\xi^j, \xi^j)_X. \tag{59}$$

If this series converges to the same value, finite or infinite, for all bases $\{\xi^j\}$, that value is defined as the *trace of* A and is denoted

$$\text{trace } A.$$

Since any rearrangement of a basis is a basis, the existence of trace A implies that the series (59) converges to trace A no matter how its terms may be rearranged and hence that the series (59) is absolutely convergent.

Thus trace A is the sum of the diagonal elements of the matrix of A, when that sum is absolutely convergent and the same for all bases.

Consider separable Hilbert spaces X and Y of more than one point.

60. Theorem. *Suppose that*

$$A, B \in \mathscr{S}(X, Y).$$

Then trace AB^* *exists and is finite. Furthermore*

$$\text{trace } AB^* = (B^*, A^*)_{\mathscr{S}}. \tag{61}$$

Proof. The operator AB^* is on Y to Y. Let $\{\eta_k\}$ be any basis for Y. Then

$$\sum_k (AB^* \eta^k, \eta^k)_Y = \sum_k (B^*\eta^k, A^*\eta^k)_X = (B^*, A^*)_{\mathscr{S}} < \infty,$$

by (57) and Corollary 53. This sum is independent of the basis $\{\eta^k\}$, by Lemma 56. Hence it is trace AB^*, and the proof is complete.

§ 62. **Nonnegative operators. Square roots.** Consider a linear continuous operator B on X to X. We say that B is *nonnegative* if

$$(Bx, x)_X \geqq 0 \quad \text{whenever } x \in X;$$

and that B is *positive* if

$$(Bx, x)_X > 0 \quad \text{whenever } 0 \neq x \in X.$$

63. Lemma. *If* $B \in \mathscr{T}(X, X)$ *is nonnegative, then* B *is self-adjoint.*

Proof [Loève 1, p. 466]. Consider $x, y \in X$. Then

$$\begin{aligned} (B(y + x), y+x) &= (By, y) + (Bx, y) + (By, x) + (Bx, x) \geqq 0, \\ (B(y + ix), y + ix) &= (By, y) + i(Bx, y) - i(By, x) + (Bx, x) \geqq 0, \end{aligned} \tag{64}$$
$$i^2 = -1.$$

Put

$$(Bx, y) + (By, x) = a,$$
$$i[(Bx, y) - (By, x)] = b.$$

Then (64) implies that a and b are real. Now

$$(Bx, y) - (By, x) = -ib,$$
$$(Bx, y) = \frac{a - ib}{2},$$
$$(By, x) = \frac{a + ib}{2}.$$

Hence

$$\overline{(By, x)} = (x, By) = (Bx, y),$$

and

$$B = B^*.$$

This completes the proof.

In the real domain the analogue of the preceding lemma does not hold. There when we consider nonnegative operators, we specify that those operators be self-adjoint.

65. THEOREM. *Suppose that V is a nonnegative self-adjoint linear continuous operator on a Hilbert space X to X. There exists a unique operator $V^{1/2}$ with the following properties:*

(i) *$V^{1/2}$ is nonnegative, self-adjoint, linear, and continuous on X to X.*

(ii) $V = V^{1/2}V^{1/2}$.

The operator $V^{1/2}$ is called the *square root* of V.

PROOF. [Riesz-Nagy 1, p. 262.]

66. THEOREM. *Suppose that V is a nonnegative self-adjoint linear continuous operator on a separable Hilbert space X to X. Then* trace *V exists and is nonnegative. Furthermore*

$$\text{trace } V = \|V^{1/2}\|_{\mathscr{S}}^2; \tag{67}$$

and trace *V is finite iff*

$$V^{1/2} \in \mathscr{S}(X, X).$$

PROOF. Consider $V^{1/2}$. By Lemma 49,

$$\|V^{1/2}\|_{\mathscr{S}}$$

exists and is nonnegative, though perhaps ∞. Let $\{\xi^j\}$ be any basis for X.

Then

$$\begin{aligned}(68)\qquad \sum_j (V\xi^j, \xi^j) &= \sum_j (V^{1/2}V^{1/2}\xi^j, \xi^j) = \sum_j (V^{1/2}\xi^j, V^{1/2}\xi^j) \\ &= \sum_j \| V^{1/2}\xi^j\|^2 = \| V^{1/2}\|^2_{\mathscr{S}},\end{aligned}$$

by (51). Hence the series (68) is independent of the basis $\{\xi^j\}$, trace V exists, and (67) holds. Hence

$$\text{trace } V < \infty$$

iff

$$\| V^{1/2}\|_{\mathscr{S}} < \infty.$$

This completes the proof.

69. THEOREM. *Suppose that X, Y are separable Hilbert spaces, that V is a nonnegative self-adjoint linear continuous operator on X to X of finite trace, and that A, B are linear continuous operators on X to Y. Then*

$$\text{trace } AVB^*$$

exists and is finite.

PROOF. By Theorem 66,

$$\| V^{1/2}\|_{\mathscr{S}} < \infty,$$

since trace $V < \infty$. Hence

$$V^{1/2} \in \mathscr{S}(X, X),$$

and

$$AV^{1/2} \in \mathscr{S}(X, Y), \qquad BV^{1/2} \in \mathscr{S}(X, Y),$$

by Lemma 55. Hence

$$\text{trace } AV^{1/2}(BV^{1/2})^* = \text{trace } AV^{1/2}V^{1/2}B^* = \text{trace } AVB^* < \infty,$$

by Theorem 60. This completes the proof.

§ 70. **The variance of δx.** We have assumed that the error δx is an element of $X\Psi$, where X is a separable Hilbert space and $\Psi = H(\Omega, p)$ is a separable L^2-space of functions on Ω absolute square integrable relative to a probability p. Then

$$E\|\delta x\|^2_X = \|\delta x\|^2_{X\Psi} < \infty.$$

Our assumption that $E\delta x = 0$ is not essential to the present section.

The variance

$$V = \text{Var } \delta x$$

of δx is an operator on X to X; its definition is motivated by the idea that Vx, $x \in X$, should be something like

$$E(x, \delta x)_X\, \delta x$$

(cf. Remark 86 below). Now $\delta x \in X\Psi^{\cdot}$ and, for each fixed ω with null exceptions, $\delta x_\omega \in X$. So

$$(x, \delta x)_X = (x, \delta x_\omega)_X$$

is a numerical function on almost all of Ω. Hence

$$(x, \delta x_\omega)_X \, \delta x_\omega \in X \quad \text{for each fixed } \omega \in \Omega \text{ with null exceptions.}$$

It might therefore be natural to consider the expected value

(71) $$E(x, \delta x)_X \, \delta x.$$

Here E would be a generalized integral to X rather than to the complex numbers. If X is finite dimensional, no difficulties are involved. The expression (71) can be used as the definition of Vx, $x \in X$. If X is infinite dimensional, an appropriate theory can be developed: one which permits the interchange of the operator E with certain other operators in later calculations.

Alternatively, we shall use a different definition of variance: one which avoids having the operator E somewhat out of position for our purposes.

As will be seen, the variance that we define is precisely the ordinary variance in all cases in which the latter is defined (Remarks 86, 96).

For convenience, we *write f for δx*:

(72) $$f = \delta x \in X\Psi^{\cdot}.$$

Let $\{\xi^j : j \in J\}$ be a basis in X and $\{\psi^\nu : \nu \in N\}$ a basis in $\Psi^{\cdot}$. The coordinates of f are

(73) $$f^{j,\nu} = (f, \xi^j \psi^\nu)_{X\Psi^{\cdot}}, \qquad j \in J, \quad \nu \in N.$$

We may write

(74) $$f = \{_j \, f^{j,\nu} \, _\nu\}.$$

Then

(75) $$\|f\|^2_{X\Psi^{\cdot}} = E\|f\|^2_X = \sum_{j,\nu} |f^{j,\nu}|^2.$$

We now define the *operator F associated with f* as the operator on $\Psi^{\cdot}$ to X whose matrix relative to the bases $\{\xi^j\}$, $\{\bar{\psi}^\nu\}$ is

(76) $$F = \{_j \, f^{j,\nu} \, _\nu\}.$$

Note that the conjugate set $\{\bar{\psi}^\nu\}$ is certainly a basis in $\Psi^{\cdot}$, since $\Psi^{\cdot}$ is an L^2-space. The reason for using the basis $\{\bar{\psi}^\nu\}$ instead of $\{\psi^\nu\}$ is that F will now be independent of bases.

77. Lemma. *The operator F associated with f is of finite Schmidt norm*

$$F \in \mathscr{S}(\Upsilon, X),$$

and

$$\|F\|^2 \leqq \|F\|_{\mathscr{S}}^2 = E\|f\|_X^2 = E\|\delta x\|_X^2. \tag{78}$$

Furthermore F is independent of the bases used in its definition.

Proof. The matrix (76) defines F by linearity on span $\{\bar{\psi}^\nu\}$. Now the sum of the absolute squares of the elements of the matrix (76) is

$$\|F\|_{\mathscr{S}}^2 = \sum_{j,\nu} |f^{j,\nu}|^2 = \|f\|_{X\Upsilon}^2 = E\|f\|_X^2 = E\|\delta x\|_X^2 < \infty.$$

If follows, by exactly the argument used to establish (50), that F is bounded on span $\{\bar{\psi}^\nu\}$, with bound $\leqq \|F\|_{\mathscr{S}}$. Therefore F is continuous on span $\{\bar{\psi}^\nu\}$. Therefore F may be defined by continuity on

$$\text{Span}\,\{\bar{\psi}^\nu\} = \Upsilon.$$

Thus

$$F \in \mathscr{S}(X, Y)$$

and

$$\|F\| \leqq \|F\|_{\mathscr{S}}.$$

It remains to show that F is independent of the bases $\{\xi^j\}$, $\{\psi^\nu\}$, $\{\bar{\psi}^\nu\}$.

Suppose that $\{\xi_1^j\}$, $\{\psi_1^\nu\}$ are arbitrary bases in X, Υ, respectively. We shall prove that the operator F_1 defined analogously in terms of the new bases $\{\xi_1^j\}$, $\{\psi_1^\nu\}$, $\{\bar{\psi}_1^\nu\}$ is precisely F. The coordinates of $f = \delta x$ relative to $\{\xi_1^j\}$, $\{\psi_1^\nu\}$ are $\{_j f_1^{j,\nu}{}_\nu\}$, where

$$f_1^{j,\nu} = (f, \xi_1^j \psi_1^\nu)_{X\Upsilon}.$$

Now by (74),

$$f = \sum_{j,\nu} f^{j,\nu} \xi^j \psi^\nu.$$

Hence, by (9 : 129) and (9 : 51),

$$\begin{aligned} f_1^{j_0,\nu_0} &= \left(\sum_{j,\nu} f^{j,\nu} \xi^j \psi^\nu,\ \xi_1^{j_0} \psi_1^{\nu_0}\right)_{X\Upsilon} \\ &= \sum_{j,\nu} f^{j,\nu} (\xi^j \psi^\nu,\ \xi_1^{j_0} \psi_1^{\nu_0})_{X\Upsilon} \\ &= \sum_{j,\nu} f^{j,\nu} (\xi^j, \xi_1^{j_0})_X (\psi^\nu, \psi_1^{\nu_0})_\Upsilon, \qquad j_0 \in J, \quad \nu_0 \in N. \end{aligned} \tag{79}$$

The operator F_1 is the operator whose matrix relative to $\{\xi_1^j\}$, $\{\bar{\psi}_1^\nu\}$ is

$$F_1 = \{_j\, f_1^{j,\nu}\ {}_\nu\}.$$

The matrix of F relative to these bases is

$$\{_j\ (F\bar{\psi}_1^\nu,\ \xi_1^j)_X\ {}_\nu\}.$$

By coordinates relative to $\{\xi^j\}$, $\{\bar{\psi}^\nu\}$,

$$\begin{aligned} F\bar{\psi}_1^{\nu_0} &= \{_j\, f^{j,\nu}\,{}_\nu\}\{_\nu\,(\bar{\psi}_1^{\nu_0},\ \bar{\psi}^\nu)_\Psi\} = \Big\{_j\ \sum_\nu f^{j,\nu}\overline{(\psi_1^{\nu_0},\ \psi^\nu)_\Psi}\Big\} \\ &= \sum_j \xi^j \sum_\nu f^{j,\nu}(\psi^\nu,\ \psi_1^{\nu_0})_\Psi \in X; \\ \xi_1^{j_0} &= \{_j\,(\xi_1^{j_0},\ \xi^j)_X\} = \sum_j \xi^j(\xi_1^{j_0},\ \xi^j)_X \in X; \\ (F\bar{\psi}_1^{\nu_0},\ \xi_1^{j_0})_X &= \sum_j \Big[\sum_\nu f^{j,\nu}(\psi^\nu,\ \psi_1^{\nu_0})_\Psi\Big]\ \overline{(\xi_1^{j_0},\ \xi^j)}_X \\ &= \sum_{j,\nu} f^{j,\nu}(\psi^\nu,\ \psi_1^{\nu_0})_\Psi(\xi^j,\ \xi_1^{j_0})_X = f_1^{j_0,\nu_0}, \qquad j_0 \in J, \quad \nu_0 \in N, \end{aligned}$$

since the series in (79) is absolutely convergent by Schwarz's inequality.
Thus

$$F = F_1,$$

and the proof is complete.

The adjoint F^* of F is the operator on X to Ψ whose matrix is the conjugate transpose of that of F, by Theorem 43. Thus

(80) $$F^* = \{_\nu\ \bar{f}^{j,\nu}\ {}_j\}, \qquad F = \{_j\, f^{j,\nu}\ {}_\nu\}.$$

By Corollary 53,

$$F^* \in \mathscr{S}(X,\ \Psi).$$

We now define the *variance* of δx as the operator

(81) $$V = FF^*$$

on X to X. We sometimes write

$$V = \operatorname{Var} \delta x.$$

82. Theorem. *The variance V of δx is a linear continuous nonnegative self-adjoint operator on X to X of finite trace. Indeed*

(83) $$\|V\| \leqq \operatorname{trace} V = E\|\delta x\|_X^2 < \infty.$$

The operator V depends on δx alone and not on the choice of bases in X and Ψ.

PROOF. The definition (81) implies that

$$V \in \mathscr{S}(X, X) \subset \mathscr{T}(X, X),$$

by Lemma 55, since

$$F \in \mathscr{S}(\Psi, X), \qquad F^* \in \mathscr{S}(X, \Psi).$$

Also, V is nonnegative, since

$$(Vx, x)_X = (FF^*x, x)_X = (F^*x, F^*x)_\Psi = \|F^*x\|_\Psi^2 \geqq 0, \qquad x \in X.$$

Hence V is self-adjoint by Lemma 63. Alternatively,

$$V^* = (FF^*)^* = F^{**}F^* = FF^* = V.$$

Since F and F^* do not depend on the bases used in their definition, V does not depend on the bases.

By Theorem 60, Lemma 77, and (51),

$$\begin{aligned} \text{trace } V &= \text{trace } FF^* = (F^*, F^*)_{\mathscr{S}} = \|F^*\|_{\mathscr{S}}^2 \\ &= \|F\|_{\mathscr{S}}^2 = E\|\delta x\|_X^2. \end{aligned}$$

Finally

$$\|V\| = \|FF^*\| \leqq \|F\|\,\|F^*\|,$$

since the Banach norm of a product is $\leqq$ the product of the Banach norms. Hence, by (50),

$$\|V\| \leqq \|F\|_{\mathscr{S}}\|F^*\|_{\mathscr{S}} = \|F\|_{\mathscr{S}}^2 = E\|\delta x\|_X^2.$$

This completes the proof.

84. LEMMA. *The matrix of the variance V of δx relative to any basis $\{\xi^j\}$ in X is*

$$V = \{_{\bar{j}}\ v^{\bar{j},j}\ _j\},$$

where

$$v^{\bar{j},j} = \sum_\nu f^{\bar{j},\nu}\bar{f}^{j,\nu}, \tag{85}$$

$f^{j,\nu}$ are the coordinates of δx relative to $\{\xi^j\}$, $\{\psi^\nu\}$; and $\{\psi^\nu\}$ is any basis in Ψ.

PROOF. This is immediate, since

$$\begin{aligned} F &= \{_j\ f^{j,\nu}\ _\nu\}, \\ F^* &= \{_\nu\ \bar{f}^{j,\nu}\ _j\}, \\ V &= FF^* = \{_{\bar{j}}\ f^{\bar{j},\nu}\ _\nu\}\{_\nu\ \bar{f}^{j,\nu}\ _j\} = \left\{_{\bar{j}}\ \sum_\nu f^{\bar{j},\nu}\bar{f}^{j,\nu}\ _j\right\}. \end{aligned}$$

86. REMARK. Suppose that X is a separable L^2-space,

$$X = H(S, \mu),$$

where μ is a measure on a space S. Then the variance V is the integral operator whose kernel is the autocorrelation (§ 9 : 311):

$$(87)\qquad Vx = \int_S a(s, s')x(s')\,d\mu(s'), \qquad x \in X,$$

where

$$a(s, s') = E\delta x(s)\overline{\delta x}(s').$$

Also

$$(88)\qquad Vx = E(x, \delta x)_X \delta x, \qquad x \in X.$$

There is no assumption here that δx is stationary.

PROOF. Define the integral operator B as

$$(89)\qquad Bx = \int_S a(s, s')x(s')\,d\mu(s'), \qquad x \in X.$$

We shall show that $B = V$ and that (88) holds.

Part 1. B is linear and continuous on X to X. The function a is defined for almost all s, s'. That B is linear is immediate. Now

$$\begin{aligned} |Bx|^2 &\leqq \int_S |a(s, s')|^2\,d\mu(s') \int_S |x(s')|^2\,d\mu(s') \\ &= \|x\|_X^2 \int_S |a(s, s')|^2\,d\mu(s'), \quad \text{almost all } s. \end{aligned}$$

Hence

$$\begin{aligned} \|B\|_X^2 = \int_S |Bx|^2\,d\mu(s) &\leqq \|x\|_X^2 \int_S \int_S |a(s, s')|^2\,d\mu(s)\,d\mu(s') \\ &\leqq \|x\|_X^2 \int_S \int_S E|f(s)|^2 E|\bar{f}(s')|^2\,d\mu(s)\,d\mu(s') \\ &= \|x\|_X^2 [E\|f\|_X^2]^2, \qquad f = \delta x. \end{aligned}$$

Thus B is bounded, with norm $\leqq E\|f\|_X^2$.

Part 2. We show that

$$(90)\qquad Bx = E(x, \delta x)_X \delta x, \qquad x \in X.$$

Thus

$$(91)\qquad Bx = \int_S Ef(s, \omega)\bar{f}(s', \omega)x(s')\,d\mu(s'),$$

and $f(s, \omega)\bar{f}(s', \omega)x(s')$ is integrable $p(\omega)\mu(s')$ by Schwarz's inequality, since

$$(92)\qquad \int_S E|\bar{f}(s', \omega)|^2\,d\mu(s') = E\|f\|_X^2 < \infty$$

and

$$\int_S E|f(s, \omega)x(s')|^2\,d\mu(s') = \|x\|_X^2 E|f(s, \omega)|^2 < \infty, \quad \text{almost all } s,$$

because (92) implies that

$$E|f(s,\omega)|^2 < \infty, \quad \text{almost all } s.$$

Hence, by (91), Corollary 9: 114, and Lemma 9: 88,

$$\begin{aligned} Bx &= E \int_S f(s,\omega)\bar{f}(s',\omega)x(s')\,d\mu(s') \\ &= Ef(s,\omega)\int_S x(s')\bar{f}(s',\omega)\,d\mu(s') \\ &= Ef(s,\omega)(x,f)_X = E(x,f)_X f, \quad \text{almost all } s. \end{aligned}$$

This establishes (90).

Part 3. We show that

$$Bx = Vx, \qquad x \in X.$$

Let $\{\xi^j : j \in J\}$, $\{\psi^\nu : \nu \in N\}$ be bases in X, Ψ, respectively. Since B and V are linear continuous operators, it will be sufficient to show that

$$B\xi^{j_0} = V\xi^{j_0}, \qquad j_0 \in J.$$

By Lemma 9: 88,

$$\begin{aligned} f &= \sum_{j,\nu} f^{j,\nu}\xi^j\psi^\nu, \\ f^j &= \sum_\nu f^{j,\nu}\psi^\nu \in \Psi, \\ f_\omega &= \sum_j f^j(\omega)\xi^j \in X, \quad \text{almost all } \omega, \end{aligned}$$

and by coordinates,

$$(f,\xi^{j_0})_X = (f_\omega,\xi^{j_0})_X = f^{j_0}(\omega), \quad \text{almost all } \omega.$$

Thus

$$(f,\xi^{j_0})_X = f^{j_0} \in \Psi.$$

Now

$$\begin{aligned} B\xi^{j_0} &= E(\xi^{j_0},f)_X f = (f,(f,\xi^{j_0})_X)_\Psi \\ &= (f,f^{j_0})_\Psi = (f_s,f^{j_0})_\Psi, \quad \text{almost all } s. \end{aligned}$$

Also by Lemma 9: 88 with X and Ψ interchanged,

(93)
$$\begin{aligned} f^\nu &= \sum_j f^{j,\nu}\xi^j \in X, \\ f_s &= \sum_\nu f^\nu(s)\psi^\nu \in \Psi, \quad \text{almost all } s, \end{aligned}$$

and by coordinates,

(94)
$$B\xi^{j_0} = \sum_\nu f^\nu(s)\bar{f}^{j_0,\nu}, \quad \text{almost all } s.$$

On the other hand, by Lemma 84,

$$(95)\qquad \begin{aligned} V\xi^{j_0} &= \Big\{\sum_{\nu} f^{j,\nu}\bar{f}^{j',\nu}\Big\}_{j,j'}\Big\{\delta^{j',j_0}\Big\}_{j'} = \Big\{\sum_{\nu} f^{j,\nu}\bar{f}^{j_0,\nu}\Big\}_j \\ &= \sum_j \xi^j \sum_\nu f^{j,\nu}\bar{f}^{j_0,\nu} = \sum_\nu \sum_j \bar{f}^{j_0,\nu} f^{j,\nu}\xi^j. \end{aligned}$$

By (9 : 51), the last change of order of summation is valid if the last series $\sum_\nu \cdots$ is convergent in X. Now that series is indeed convergent, by Cauchy's criterion and coordinates, since

$$\begin{aligned} \Big\| \sum_{n<\nu\leqq n'} \sum_j \bar{f}^{j_0,\nu} f^{j,\nu}\xi^j \Big\|_X^2 &= \Big\| \sum_j \sum_{n<\nu\leqq n'} \bar{f}^{j_0,\nu} f^{j,\nu}\xi^j \Big\|_X^2 = \sum_j \Big| \sum_{n<\nu\leqq n'} \bar{f}^{j_0,\nu} f^{j,\nu} \Big|^2 \\ &\leqq \sum_j \sum_{n<\nu\leqq n'} |\bar{f}^{j_0,\nu}|^2 \sum_{n<\nu\leqq n'} |f^{j,\nu}|^2 \\ &= \sum_{n<\nu\leqq n'} |\bar{f}^{j_0,\nu}|^2 \sum_{n<\nu\leqq n',\, j} |f^{j,\nu}|^2 \to 0 \quad \text{as } n\to\infty \end{aligned}$$

because

$$\sum_{j,\nu} |f^{j,\nu}|^2 < \infty.$$

By (95) and (93),

$$V\xi^{j_0} = \sum_\nu \bar{f}^{j_0,\nu} f^\nu.$$

It follows by Corollary 9 : 122 that

$$V\xi^{j_0} = \sum_\nu{}' \bar{f}^{j_0,\nu} f^\nu(s), \quad \text{almost all } s,$$

where the $'$ indicates that a suitable sequence of partial sums is used. With (94) this implies that

$$V\xi^{j_0} = B\xi^{j_0}, \quad \text{almost all } s,$$

and

$$V\xi^{j_0} = B\xi^{j_0} \in X.$$

The proof of Remark 86 is complete.

96. Remark. If $X = H(S, \mu)$ and the measure μ is purely atomic, with a finite number of atoms all of measure unity, then the matrix of V is precisely the variance-covariance matrix of δx: The autocorrelation $a(s, s')$ gives the elements of the variance-covariance matrix, if s and s' are taken as row and column indices. This follows from (87).

97. Lemma. *If*

$$B \in \mathscr{T}(X, Y),$$

then

$$(98)\qquad \operatorname{Var}(B\delta x) = B(\operatorname{Var}\delta x)B^* = BVB^*.$$

PROOF. Let $\{\xi^j\}$, $\{\eta^k\}$, $\{\psi^\nu\}$ be bases in X, Y, Ψ, respectively. Put

$$f = \delta x \in X\Psi,$$
$$g = Bf = B\delta x \in Y\Psi.$$

The variance of g is

$$GG^*,$$

where G is the operator on Ψ to Y associated with g. Then

$$G = BF$$

because

$$g = Bf$$

and because the matrix of Bf is precisely the matrix of B times the matrix of f. Hence the variance of $B\delta x$ is

$$GG^* = BF(BF)^* = BFF^*B^* = BVB^*,$$

where

$$V = \text{Var } \delta x = FF^*.$$

This completes the proof. Alternatively one could prove the lemma by calculating the matrix of Var $(B\delta x)$ relative to $\{\eta^k\}$ and observing that the matrix is the matrix of BVB^*.

§ 99. **Variance and inner product.** The variance V of δx is important because it permits us to find minimal operators without using the space Ψ, as we shall see. In Theorem 27 we characterized minimal operators in terms of

$$\theta = \text{Proj}_\gamma\, G\delta x.$$

Using the technique of projection in the space $Y\Psi$ we may find θ or at any rate approximate θ, if we know δx, G, M. In Theorem 104 we will characterize minimal operators in terms of V, G, M.

100. THEOREM. *If A, B are linear continuous operators on X to Y, then*

$$E(A\delta x, B\delta x)_Y = \text{trace } AVB^*. \tag{101}$$

PROOF. By Theorems 69 and 82, trace AVB^* exists and is finite. Take bases $\{\xi^j\}$, $\{\eta^k\}$, $\{\psi^\nu\}$ in X, Y, Ψ, respectively. Then describe A, B by their matrices; and δx by its coordinates:

$$A = \{_k\, a^{k,j}\, _j\}, \qquad a^{k,j} = (A\xi^j, \eta^k)_Y;$$
$$B = \{_k\, b^{k,j}\, _j\}, \qquad b^{k,j} = (B\xi^j, \eta^k)_Y;$$
$$\delta x = f = \{_j\, f^{j,\nu}\, _\nu\}, \qquad f^{j,\nu} = (f, \xi^j\psi^\nu)_{X\Psi}.$$

Also

$$V = \left\{ {}_{\bar{j}} \sum_{\nu} f^{\bar{j},\nu} \bar{f}^{j,\nu} {}_{j} \right\},$$

by (85).

Hence

$$A\delta x = \left\{ {}_{k} \sum_{\bar{j}} a^{k,\bar{j}} f^{\bar{j},\nu} {}_{\nu} \right\},$$

$$B\delta x = \left\{ {}_{k} \sum_{j} b^{k,j} f^{j,\nu} {}_{\nu} \right\}.$$

Since these are the coordinates of $A\delta x$, $B\delta x$ in $Y\Psi$,

$$E(A\delta x, B\delta x)_Y = (A\delta x, B\delta x)_{Y\Psi} = \sum_{k,\nu} \sum_{\bar{j}} a^{k,\bar{j}} f^{\bar{j},\nu} \sum_{j} \bar{b}^{k,j} \bar{f}^{j,\nu}. \tag{102}$$

Now

$$V = FF^*,$$

where

$$F = \{{}_j\, f^{j,\nu}\, {}_\nu\}$$

and the matrix refers to the bases $\{\xi^j\}$, $\{\bar{\psi}^\nu\}$. Hence

$$AVB^* = A(FF^*)B^* = (AF)(F^*B^*),$$

since multiplication of operators is associative. Hence

$$AVB^* = [\{{}_{\bar{k}}\, a^{\bar{k},\bar{j}}\, {}_{\bar{j}}\}\{{}_{\bar{j}}\, f^{\bar{j},\nu}\, {}_{\nu}\}]\, [\{{}_{\nu}\, \bar{f}^{j,\nu}\, {}_{j}\}\{{}_{j}\, \bar{b}^{k,j}\, {}_{k}\}]$$

$$= \left\{ {}_{\bar{k}} \sum_{\nu} \sum_{\bar{j}} \sum_{j} a^{\bar{k},\bar{j}} f^{\bar{j},\nu} \bar{f}^{j,\nu} \bar{b}^{k,j} {}_{k} \right\};$$

and

$$\operatorname{trace} AVB^* = \sum_{k} \sum_{\nu} \sum_{\bar{j}} \sum_{j} a^{k,\bar{j}} f^{\bar{j},\nu} \bar{f}^{j,\nu} \bar{b}^{k,j} = E(A\delta x, B\delta x)$$

by (59) and (102). This completes the proof.

§ 103. **Minimality in terms of variance.** We continue to denote by $\mathscr{U}$ the set (15) of unbiased linear continuous operators on X to Y. An operator $A \in \mathscr{U}$ is minimal if it minimizes

$$E\|A(x + \delta x) - Gx\|^2 = E\|A\delta x\|^2, \qquad x \in M,$$

among all $A \in \mathscr{U}$ (§ 2).

104. Theorem. *A linear continuous operator A on X to Y is minimal iff*

$$VA^*Y \subset M, \qquad (A - G)M = 0 \tag{105}$$

or equivalently iff

$$AVM^\perp = 0, \qquad (A - G)M = 0. \tag{106}$$

This theorem is due to the author [7], as are Theorems 137, 187, and 189.

PROOF. By Lemma 44, conditions (105) and (106) are equivalent. By Lemma 8, the condition (105) implies that A is unbiased.

We first consider the case

$$X \neq M \neq \{0\}.$$

Suppose that A is minimal. By Theorem 27,

$$A\,\delta x = \theta;$$

and therefore

$$E(A\,\delta x,\ B\,\delta x) = 0 \quad \text{whenever } B \in \mathscr{B},$$

by (19) since $\theta \in \gamma$. Hence

$$\text{(107)} \qquad \operatorname{trace} AVB^* = 0 \quad \text{whenever } B \in \mathscr{B},$$

by (101).

Let $\{\xi^j : j \in J' \cup J''\}$ be a basis for X such that $\{\xi^j : j \in J'\}$ is a basis for $M^\perp$ and $\{\xi^j : j \in J''\}$ a basis for M. Let $\{\eta^k : k \in K\}$ be a basis for Y. Suppose that, relative to these bases,

$$A = \{_k\, a^{k,j}\, _j\}, \qquad B = \{_k\, b^{k,j}\, _j\}, \qquad V = \{_{\bar{\jmath}}\, v^{\bar{\jmath},j}\, _j\},$$

where $k \in K$, $j, \bar{\jmath} \in J' \cup J''$. Then (107) may be written

$$\text{(108)} \qquad \sum_k \sum_{\bar{\jmath}} \sum_j a^{k,\bar{\jmath}} v^{\bar{\jmath},j} \bar{b}^{k,j} = 0 \quad \text{whenever } B \in \mathscr{B}.$$

Now

$$B \in \mathscr{B} \quad \text{iff} \quad b^{k,j''} = 0, \qquad j'' \in J'', \quad k \in K.$$

For, $B \in \mathscr{B}$ iff $Bx = 0$, $x \in M$. Now $x = \{x^j\} \in M$ iff $x^{j'} = 0, j' \in J'$, by construction of the basis $\{\xi^j\}$. And

$$Bx = \left\{_k \sum_j b^{k,j} x^j\right\} = \left\{_k \sum_{j''} b^{k,j''} x^{j''}\right\} \quad \text{whenever } x \in M.$$

We may take $x^{j''} = \delta^{j'',\, j''_0}, j''_0 \in J''$. Hence $BM = 0$ iff

$$\text{(109)} \qquad b^{k,j''} = 0, \qquad j'' \in J''.$$

In particular, we may take B as

$$B = \{\delta^{k,k_0}\, \delta^{j,j'_0}\}, \qquad k_0 \in K, \quad j'_0 \in J'.$$

Then (108) becomes

$$\text{(110)} \qquad \sum_k \sum_{\bar{\jmath}} \sum_j a^{k,\bar{\jmath}} v^{\bar{\jmath},j}\, \delta^{k,k_0}\, \delta^{j,j'_0} = 0 = \sum_{\bar{\jmath}} a^{k_0,\bar{\jmath}} v^{\bar{\jmath},j'_0}, \qquad k_0 \in K, \quad j'_0 \in J'.$$

That is, the elements of the matrix of AV in the column j all vanish whenever $j \in J'$. Now $x = \{x^j\} \in M^{\perp}$ iff $x^{j''} = 0, j'' \in J''$. Hence (110) implies that

$$AVx = 0 \quad \text{whenever } x \in M^{\perp}, \tag{111}$$

that is,

$$AVM^{\perp} = 0.$$

Conversely, suppose that (106) and therefore (111) holds. Then, reversing the above argument,

$$\sum_{\bar{\jmath}} a^{k,\bar{\jmath}} v^{\bar{\jmath},j} = 0, \qquad j \in J', \quad k \in K.$$

Hence

$$\sum_{j} \sum_{\bar{\jmath}} a^{k,\bar{\jmath}} v^{\bar{\jmath},j} \bar{b}^{\tilde{k},j} = 0, \qquad k, \tilde{k} \in K, \quad \text{whenever } B \in \mathscr{B},$$

by (109). Hence

$$\begin{aligned} AVB^* &= 0 \quad \text{whenever } B \in \mathscr{B}; \\ \operatorname{trace} AVB^* &= 0 \quad \text{whenever } B \in \mathscr{B}; \\ E(A\delta x, B\delta x)_Y &= 0 \quad \text{whenever } B \in \mathscr{B}; \end{aligned} \tag{112}$$

by (101). This implies that

$$A\delta x \in \beta^{\perp} \cap \alpha \subset \beta^{\perp} \cap \hat{\alpha},$$

by (19) and (18). Hence

$$A\delta x = \theta$$

by Lemma 22, and A is minimal by Theorem 27.

It remains to consider the extreme cases.

If $M = X$, then $A = G$ is the only unbiased operator and is therefore the unique minimal operator. The theorem is true because the condition

$$AVM^{\perp} = AV0 = 0$$

is satisfied by all operators $A \in \mathscr{T}(X, Y)$.

If $M = \{0\}$, then

$$\mathscr{B} = \mathscr{T}(X, Y), \qquad \beta = \tau, \qquad \gamma = \{0\},$$

and

$$\theta = 0,$$

by (14), (16), and (20). Hence $A \in \mathscr{U}$ is minimal iff

$$A\delta x = \theta = 0,$$

by Theorem 27. This equality implies that

$$AF = 0,$$
$$AFF^* = AV = 0,$$
$$AVM^\perp = AVX = 0,$$

by § 70. Conversely, the last relation implies that (112) holds and, by the argument following (112), that

$$A\delta x = \theta.$$

Thus A is minimal, and the proof is complete.

An alternative proof of Theorem 104, independent of Theorem 27, is given in [Sard 7, pp. 432-434], where G is taken as the identity. The modifications for our G are immediate.

113. REMARK. If A is minimal,

$$\text{trace } AVA^* = E\|A\delta x\|_Y^2 = E\|\theta\|_Y^2, \tag{114}$$

by (32). If $\{A^n\}$ is a minimizing sequence,

$$\text{trace } A^n VA^{n*} \to E\|\theta\|_Y^2 \text{ as } n \to \infty, \tag{115}$$

since

$$\text{trace } A^n VA^{n*} = E\|A^n\delta x\|_Y^2.$$

116. THEOREM. *Suppose that A is a minimal operator. Then*

$$AVA^* = GVA^* = AVG^*, \tag{117}$$

$$(G - A)V(G - A)^* = GVG^* - AVA^*, \tag{118}$$

$$\text{Var }(G\delta x) = \text{Var }(A\delta x) + \text{Var }(G - A)\delta x, \tag{119}$$

$$E\|G\delta x\|_Y^2 = E\|A\delta x\|_Y^2 + E\|(G - A)\delta x\|_Y^2, \tag{120}$$

$$\text{trace } GVG^* = \text{trace } AVA^* + \text{trace }(G - A)V(G - A)^*. \tag{121}$$

These conditions are necessary for minimality, but not sufficient. For example, (117)–(121) are satisfied if $A = G$.

The relation (119) is important in the statistical theory of the analysis of variance, where it is often established under more demanding hypotheses than ours.

PROOF. Suppose that A is a minimal operator. If $y \in Y$, then

$$AVA^*y = A(VA^*y) = G(VA^*y),$$

by (105). Hence

$$AVA^* = GVA^*.$$

Also

$$(AVA^*)^* = AVA^* = (GVA^*)^* = AVG^*.$$

This establishes (117).

Hence, by (117),

$$\begin{aligned}(G - A)V(G - A)^* &= GVG^* - AVG^* - GVA^* + AVA^* \\ &= GVG^* - AVG^* = GVG^* - AVA^*.\end{aligned}$$

This establishes (118) and therefore (119), by Lemma 97.

The relation (121) follows directly from (118); and (120) is equivalent to (121), by (101).

This completes the proof.

§ 122. **A digression on statistical estimation.** Relations like (119), (120), (121) are important in statistics. If V, G, and a minimal operator A are known, we may calculate the traces that appear in (121) and check the validity of (121).

Now

$$(G - A)\delta x = (G - A)(x + \delta x) \quad \text{if } x \in M,$$

by Lemma 8 and the fact that A is unbiased. Furthermore

$$(G - A)(x + \delta x)$$

is simply the *residual* in our calculation. In any instance we may calculate the residual and its square norm:

$$\|(G - A)\delta x_\omega\|_Y^2.$$

This may be compared with its expected value

$$E\|(G - A)\delta x\|_Y^2 = \text{trace } (G - A)V(G - A)^*,$$

calculated earlier. If the values of $\|(G - A)\ \delta x_\omega\|_Y^2$ differ repeatedly from their expected value, an anomaly is present which may indicate that one of our fundamental hypotheses is not in force.

In order to use Theorem 104 it is sufficient to know $V = \text{Var } \delta x$ to within a constant factor, for we may replace V by kV, where $k > 0$, without changing (105). *Suppose that*

$$V = k\tilde{V},$$

where $\tilde{V}$ is known and the positive constant k is not known. A minimal operator A can be recognized by (105). Then, by Theorem 116,

$$\begin{aligned}E\|(G - A)\delta x\|_Y^2 &= E\|G\delta x\|_Y^2 - E\|A\delta x\|_Y^2 \\ &= \text{trace } GVG^* - \text{trace } AVA^* \\ &= k\,(\text{trace } G\tilde{V}G^* - \text{trace } A\tilde{V}A^*).\end{aligned}$$

Since $x \in M$, the residual is

$$(G - A)\delta x = (G - A)(x + \delta x),$$

and we may calculate

$$\|(G - A)\delta x_\omega\|_Y^2 = \|(G - A)(x + \delta x_\omega)\|_Y^2.$$

We may choose to take the latter quantity as an estimate of its expected value

$$E\|(G - A)\delta x\|_Y^2,$$

as is often done in statistical work. Then we obtain the following estimate of k:

$$\frac{\|(G - A)\delta x_\omega\|_Y^2}{\text{trace } G\tilde{V}G^* - \text{trace } A\tilde{V}A^*}. \tag{123}$$

The denominator in the estimate (123) sometimes is the number of degrees of freedom in $M^\perp$. For example, suppose that

$$\begin{aligned} X &= Y = N\text{-dimensional space;} \\ G &= \text{identity on } X; \\ M &= \text{an } n\text{-dimensional subspace of } X,\ n < N; \\ \tilde{V} &= \text{the identity on } X. \end{aligned}$$

This means that the different components of δx are uncorrelated and of equal standard deviation. Then

$$\text{trace } \tilde{V} = \text{trace } G\tilde{V}G^* = \underbrace{1 + \cdots + 1}_{\text{N terms}} = N.$$

Furthermore the minimal operator is

$$A = \text{Proj}_M \in \mathscr{T}(X, X),$$

by (105). Hence, by Theorem 9: 26,

$$\text{trace } A\tilde{V}A^* = \text{trace } AA^* = \text{trace } A^2 = \text{trace } A = n.$$

Thus the denominator of the estimate (123) is

$$N - n,$$

the number of degrees of freedom in $M^\perp$.

§ 124. **Partitioned form.** We may express some of our conditions in useful alternative form by partitioning X into M and $M^\perp$. For each $x \in X$, we write

$$x = x_0 + x_1, \qquad x_0 \in M, \quad x_1 \in M^\perp.$$

Let A be a linear operator on X to Y. We write

$$A = (A_0 \quad A_1), \tag{125}$$

where

$$y = Ax = A(x_0 + x_1) = A_0x_0 + A_1x_1, \tag{126}$$

and A_0 is the operator on M to Y such that

$$A_0x_0 = Ax_0 \quad \text{for all } x_0 \in M,$$

and A_1 is the operator on $M^\perp$ to Y such that

$$A_1x_1 = Ax_1 \quad \text{for all } x_1 \in M^\perp.$$

Thus A_0 is the restriction of A to M and A_1 is the restriction of A to $M^\perp$. We think of (125) as a 1×2 matrix and we write

$$x = \begin{pmatrix} x_0 \\ x_1 \end{pmatrix}$$

as a 2×1 matrix. Then matrix algebra is valid:

$$y = Ax = (A_0 \quad A_1)\begin{pmatrix} x_0 \\ x_1 \end{pmatrix} = A_0x_0 + A_1x_1.$$

Similarly we write linear operators on X to X as 2×2 matrices. For example

$$V = \begin{pmatrix} V_{00} & V_{01} \\ V_{10} & V_{11} \end{pmatrix},$$

where

V_{00} is an operator on M to M,
V_{01} is an operator on $M^\perp$ to M,
V_{10} is an operator on M to $M^\perp$,
V_{11} is an operator on $M^\perp$ to $M^\perp$;

and, for all $x \in X$,

$$\tilde{x} = Vx = \begin{pmatrix} \tilde{x}_0 \\ \tilde{x}_1 \end{pmatrix} = V(x_0 + x_1) = \begin{pmatrix} V_{00} & V_{01} \\ V_{10} & V_{11} \end{pmatrix}\begin{pmatrix} x_0 \\ x_1 \end{pmatrix}$$
$$= \begin{pmatrix} V_{00}x_0 + V_{01}x_1 \\ V_{10}x_0 + V_{11}x_1 \end{pmatrix}; \qquad x_0, \tilde{x}_0 \in M; \qquad x_1, \tilde{x}_1 \in M^\perp.$$

Let P be the projection in X onto M and Q the projection in X onto $M^\perp$. Then

V_{00} is the operator such that $V_{00}x_0 = PVx_0, \quad x_0 \in M$;
V_{01} is the operator such that $V_{01}x_1 = PVx_1, \quad x_1 \in M^\perp$;
V_{10} is the operator such that $V_{10}x_0 = QVx_0, \quad x_0 \in M$;
V_{11} is the operator such that $V_{11}x_1 = QVx_1, \quad x_1 \in M^\perp$.

Since the variance V is continuous, so are V_{00}, V_{01}, V_{10}, V_{11}. Since V is self-adjoint and nonnegative, so are V_{00} and V_{11}. Furthermore

$$V_{01}^* = V_{10}, \qquad V_{10}^* = V_{01},$$
$$(Vx, x) = (V_{00}x_0, x_0) + (V_{01}x_1, x_0) + (V_{10}x_0, x_1) + (V_{11}x_1, x_1) \geqq 0,$$
$$x = x_0 + x_1 \in X, x_0 \in M, x_1 \in M^\perp.$$

Note that

$$P = \begin{pmatrix} I_{00} & 0 \\ 0 & 0 \end{pmatrix}, \qquad Q = \begin{pmatrix} 0 & 0 \\ 0 & I_{11} \end{pmatrix},$$

where I_{00} is the identity on M and I_{11} is the identity on $M^{\perp}$. This follows from Theorem 9 : 21, since

$$Px = \begin{pmatrix} I_{00} & 0 \\ 0 & 0 \end{pmatrix} \begin{pmatrix} x_0 \\ x_1 \end{pmatrix} = x_0,$$

$$Qx = x_1,$$

and

$$x = x_0 + x_1, \qquad x_0 \in M, \quad x_1 \in M^{\perp}.$$

We have now expressed elements of X as 2×1 matrices, elements of Y as 1×1 matrices, operators on X to Y as 1×2 matrices, and operators on X to X as 2×2 matrices.

127. LEMMA. *The condition*

$$(A - G)M = 0$$

holds iff

(128) $$A_0 = G_0.$$

PROOF. If $x \in M$, then

$$x = \begin{pmatrix} x_0 \\ 0 \end{pmatrix}, \qquad x_0 \in M,$$

and

$$(A - G)x = (A_0 - G_0 \quad A_1 - G_1)\begin{pmatrix} x_0 \\ 0 \end{pmatrix} = (A_0 - G_0)x_0.$$

Thus

$$(A - G)x = 0 \quad \text{for all } x \in M$$

iff

$$(A_0 - G_0)x_0 = 0 \quad \text{for all } x_0 \in M.$$

This establishes the lemma.

129. LEMMA. *The condition*

(130) $$AVM^{\perp} = 0$$

holds iff

(131) $$A_0V_{01} + A_1V_{11} = 0.$$

As we have seen, (130) is equivalent to

$$VA^*Y \subset M,$$

by Lemma 44.

PROOF. Suppose that $x \in M^1$. Then

$$x = \begin{pmatrix} 0 \\ x_1 \end{pmatrix}, \qquad x_1 \in M^\perp;$$

and

$$AVx = (A_0 \quad A_1)\begin{pmatrix} V_{00} & V_{01} \\ V_{10} & V_{11} \end{pmatrix}\begin{pmatrix} 0 \\ x_1 \end{pmatrix} = (A_0 V_{01} + A_1 V_{11})x_1.$$

Thus (130) holds iff (131) holds. This completes the proof.

132. THEOREM. *The linear continuous operator*

$$A = (A_0 \quad A_1)$$

on X to Y is minimal iff

(133) $$A_0 = G_0,$$

(134) $$A_1 V_{11} = -G_0 V_{01}.$$

If $V_{1,1}$ *is invertible, then*

(135) $$A_1 = -G_0 V_{0,1} V_{1,1}^{-1},$$

and the minimal operator exists and is unique.

PROOF. By (106) and Lemmas 127, 129, the operator A is minimal iff (128) and (131) hold. The latter are equivalent to (133) and (134).

If $V_{1,1}$ is invertible, then (134) implies (135). Then A_0 and A_1 exist and are unique [Halmos 2, p. 37]. This completes the proof.

Thus if $V_{1,1}$ is invertible, there is a unique minimal operator for each $G \in \mathscr{T}(X, Y)$. Since $V_{1,1}$ is self-adjoint, any one-sided inverse is necessarily two-sided and therefore unique [Riesz-Nagy 1, p. 263].

§ 136. **Minimizing sequences.** It may be impossible to find an operator

$$A = (A_0 \quad A_1) \in \mathscr{T}(X, Y)$$

which satisfies (133), (134), since minimal operators need not exist. Even if a minimal operator does exist, it may be impractical to solve (134). It is therefore natural to consider whether an operator A which satisfies (133) exactly and (134) approximately is near minimality. It is not possible to calculate how near minimality A is in terms of only the residue

$$A_1 V_{11} + G_0 V_{01}$$

in (134). This may be seen as follows. An operator $A \in \mathscr{U}$ is within $\rho + 0$ of minimality, where

$$\rho^2 = E\|A\delta x\|^2 - E\|\theta\|^2 = \text{trace } AVA^* - E\|\theta\|^2,$$

since

$$E\|\theta\|^2 = \inf_{A \in \mathscr{U}} E\|A\delta x\|^2;$$

by Theorem 27. Thus in order to calculate ρ we need $E\|\theta\|^2$ or its equivalent.

If a minimizing sequence $\{A^n\}$ is known, we may obtain an operator within ρ of minimality, for any $\rho > 0$, by taking A^n with n sufficiently large. Furthermore minimizing sequences $\{A^n\}$ surely exist, by Lemma 22.

Theorems which permit us to recognize minimizing sequences are useful. Theorem 27 is such a theorem, but requires knowledge of θ. A theorem which involves only the variance V and the spaces X, Y will be given.

Consider a sequence $\{A^n\}$ of elements of $\mathscr{U}$. When A^n is expressed in partitioned form $(A_0^n \quad A_1^n)$, the first component A_0^n is precisely G_0, by Lemma 127.

137. THEOREM. *Suppose that*

$$\{A^n\} = \{(G_0 \quad A_1^n)\}, \qquad n = 1, 2, \cdots,$$

is a sequence of linear continuous operators on X to Y such that $\{A^n\delta x\}$ is a Cauchy sequence in $Y\Psi$. In order that $\{A^n\}$ be a minimizing sequence it is sufficient that

$$\sum_k \|(V_{10}G_0^* + V_{11}A_1^{n*})\eta^k\|_X \to 0 \quad \textit{as } n \to \infty, \tag{138}$$

where $\{\eta^k\}$ is one basis in Y.

Note that $\{A^n\delta x\}$ is a Cauchy sequence iff

$$\begin{aligned}\text{trace}\,(A^{n'} - A^n)V(A^{n'} - A^n)^* \\ = \text{trace}\,(A_1^{n'} - A_1^n)V_{11}(A_1^{n'} - A_1^n)^* \to 0 \quad \text{as } n', n \to \infty,\end{aligned} \tag{139}$$

since

$$\text{trace}\,(A^{n'} - A^n)V(A^{n'} - A^n)^* = E\|(A^{n'} - A^n)\delta x\|_Y^2.$$

One may therefore establish that $\{A^n\delta x\}$ is a Cauchy sequence without using δx, if V and A^n are known.

PROOF. Put

$$\theta^0 = \lim_n A^n\delta x \in Y\Psi,$$

as is permissible since $\{A^n\delta x\}$ is a Cauchy sequence. We shall prove that $\theta^0 = \theta$.

Since

$$A^n\delta x \in \alpha,$$

it follows that

$$\theta^0 \in \hat{\alpha}.$$

We now show that

$$E(A^n\delta x, B\delta x) \to 0 \quad \text{as } n \to \infty, \tag{140}$$

for each $B \in \mathscr{B}$. Thus

$$E(B\delta x, A^n\delta x) = \text{trace}\, BVA^{n*},$$

by (101). Now $B \in \mathscr{B}$ iff

(141) $$B = (B_0 \quad B_1) = (0 \quad B_1),$$

since $B_0 = 0$ iff $BM = 0$. Assume (141). Then

$$V = \begin{pmatrix} V_{00} & V_{01} \\ V_{10} & V_{11} \end{pmatrix}, \qquad A^{n*} = \begin{pmatrix} G_0^* \\ A_1^{n*} \end{pmatrix},$$

$$VA^{n*} = \begin{pmatrix} V_{00}G_0^* + V_{01}A_1^{n*} \\ V_{10}G_0^* + V_{11}A_1^{n*} \end{pmatrix},$$

$$BVA^{n*} = B_1(V_{10}G_0^* + V_{11}A_1^{n*}).$$

Hence

(142) $$\begin{aligned} \text{trace } BVA^{n*} &= \sum_k (B_1(V_{10}G_0^* + V_{11}A_1^{n*})\eta^k, \eta^k)_Y \\ &= \sum_k ((V_{10}G_0^* + V_{11}A_1^{n*})\eta^k, B_1^*\eta^k)_X, \end{aligned}$$

by § 58. Hence

$$\begin{aligned} \text{trace } BVA^{n*} &\leqq \sum_k \|(V_{10}G^* + V_{11}A_1^{n*})\eta^k\|_X \|B_1^*\eta^k\|_X \\ &\leqq \|B_1\| \sum_k \|(V_{10}G^* + V_{11}A_1^{n*})\eta^k\|_X, \end{aligned}$$

since

$$\|B_1^*\| = \|B_1\| \quad \text{and} \quad \|\eta^k\|_Y = 1.$$

By (138),

$$\text{trace } BVA^{n*} \to 0 \quad \text{as } n \to \infty.$$

This establishes (140). Since the inner product in $Y\Psi$ is continuous in its arguments, it follows that

$$E(\theta^0, B\delta x)_Y = 0, \qquad B \in \mathscr{B}.$$

Hence

$$\theta^0 \in \beta^\perp$$

and

$$\theta^0 \in \hat{\alpha} \cap \beta^\perp.$$

Hence

$$\theta^0 = \theta,$$

by Lemma 22. Hence $\{A^n\}$ is a minimizing sequence, and the proof is complete.

The condition (138) of Theorem 137 is sufficient to insure that $\{A^n\}$ be a minimizing sequence. Let us consider conditions that are necessary and sufficient. Suppose that

$$\{A^n\} = \{(G_0 \quad A_1^n)\} \subset \mathscr{T}(X, Y)$$

and that $\{A^n \delta x\}$ is a Cauchy sequence in $Y\Psi$. A necessary and sufficient condition that $\{A^n\}$ be a minimizing sequence is that

$$\text{trace } A^n V A^{n*} \to E\|\theta\|_Y^2 \quad \text{as } n \to \infty,$$

by (32). We can use this condition only if we know $E\|\theta\|_Y^2$. Another necessary and sufficient condition is that

$$\text{(143)} \qquad \text{trace } BVA^{n*} \to 0 \quad \text{as} \quad n \to \infty \quad \text{for each } B \in \mathscr{B},$$

by (140). Now if $B \in \mathscr{B}$,

$$\text{trace } BVA^{n*} = (V_{10}G_0^* + V_{11}A_1^{n*}, B_1^*)_{\mathscr{S}}, \qquad B = (0 \quad B_1),$$

by (142) and Lemma 56. Thus (143) is equivalent to the condition that

$$(V_{10}G_0^* + V_{11}A_1^{n*}, B_1^*)_{\mathscr{S}} \to 0 \quad \text{as } n \to \infty \quad \text{for each } B_1^* \in \mathscr{T}(Y, M^{\perp}).$$

This condition amounts to a kind of weak convergence of $V_{10}G_0^* + V_{11}A_1^{n*}$ to 0 in the space $\mathscr{S}(Y, M^{\perp})$ of operators on Y to $M^{\perp}$ of finite Schmidt norm [Riesz-Nagy 1, p. 60]. It would be precisely that weak convergence if B_1^* were an arbitrary element of $\mathscr{S}(Y, M^{\perp})$ instead of $\mathscr{T}(Y, M^{\perp})$.

The search for a minimal or near minimal operator in terms of V may be carried out as follows. Attempt to solve (134) for A_1. If a continuous solution A_1 is found, then

$$A = (G_0 \quad A_1)$$

is minimal. If the solution A_1 is not continuous, then consider the sequence $\{A^n\}$ of truncations of $(G_0 \quad A_1)$. Each truncation is continuous and the fact that A_1 satisfies (134) makes it natural to expect that $\{A^n\}$ is a minimizing sequence. Test the sequence of truncations to see if it satisfies the hypotheses of Theorem 137. We give an instance of the calculation in §§ 150, 161.

§ 144. **The approximation of x by $A(x + \delta x)$.** A special case of the problem of minimal approximation is that in which $X = Y$ and G is the identity I on X.

A linear continuous operator A on X to itself is now unbiased if

$$EA(x + \delta x) = x, \qquad x \in M.$$

A linear continuous operator A on X to itself is minimal if A minimizes

$$E\|A(x + \delta x) - x\|^2$$

among all unbiased operators, for each $x \in M$.

By Theorem 104, a linear continuous operator A is minimal iff

$$\text{(145)} \qquad (A - I)M = 0 \quad \text{and} \quad VA^*X \subset M;$$

or iff

$$\text{(146)} \qquad (A - I)M = 0 \quad \text{and} \quad AVM^{\perp} = 0.$$

If

$$A \in \mathscr{T}(X, X),$$

we write

$$(147) \qquad A = \begin{pmatrix} A_{00} & A_{01} \\ A_{10} & A_{11} \end{pmatrix}.$$

Thus the operators A_0, A_1 of (125) are

$$A_0 = \begin{pmatrix} A_{00} \\ A_{10} \end{pmatrix}, \qquad A_1 = \begin{pmatrix} A_{01} \\ A_{11} \end{pmatrix}.$$

Also

$$G = I = \begin{pmatrix} I_{00} & 0 \\ 0 & I_{11} \end{pmatrix}, \qquad G_0 = \begin{pmatrix} I_{00} \\ 0 \end{pmatrix}, \qquad G_1 = \begin{pmatrix} 0 \\ I_{11} \end{pmatrix},$$

where I_{00} is the identity on M and I_{11} the identity on $M^{\perp}$.

We may now rephrase Theorem 132 for the present problem as follows.

148. THEOREM. *A linear continuous operator*

$$A = \begin{pmatrix} A_{00} & A_{01} \\ A_{10} & A_{11} \end{pmatrix}$$

on X to X is minimal for the approximation of x by $A(x + \delta x)$ iff

$$(149) \qquad \begin{aligned} A_{00} &= I_{00} = \textit{identity on } M, \\ A_{10} &= 0, \\ A_{01}V_{11} &= -V_{01}, \\ A_{11}V_{11} &= 0. \end{aligned}$$

PROOF. The conditions (133) and (134) are now

$$\begin{pmatrix} A_{00} \\ A_{10} \end{pmatrix} = \begin{pmatrix} I_{00} \\ 0 \end{pmatrix},$$

$$\begin{pmatrix} A_{01} \\ A_{11} \end{pmatrix} V_{11} = -\begin{pmatrix} I_{00} \\ 0 \end{pmatrix} V_{01}.$$

This completes the proof.

§ 150. **Illustration.** We shall illustrate the theory of minimal approximation by an example in which G is the identity and $A(x + \delta x)$ approximates x.

Suppose that $X = Y$ is an infinite dimensional separable Hilbert space and that $\Psi = H(\Omega, p)$ is an infinite dimensional separable L^2-space based on a space Ω and a probability p. Let $\{\psi^{\nu} : \nu = -1, 0, 1, 2, \cdots\}$ be a basis for Ψ in which ψ^{-1} is the function which is identically 1 on Ω:

$$(151) \qquad \psi^{-1}(\omega) = 1, \qquad \omega \in \Omega.$$

Such a basis exists since ψ^{-1} is measurable and

$$\|1\|_{\Psi}^{2} = E|1|^{2} = E1 = 1.$$

Then

$$E\psi^{\nu} = E\psi^{\nu}1 = (\psi^{\nu}, \psi^{-1})_{\Psi} = \delta^{\nu,-1}, \qquad \nu = -1, 0, 1, 2, \cdots.$$

Let $\{\xi^{j} : j = 0, 1, 2, \cdots\}$ be a basis for X.

Suppose that M is the one-dimensional subspace of X spanned by ξ^{0}, and that G is the identity on X to X.

Let $v_r, w_r, r = 1, 2, \cdots$, be numbers such that

$$\text{(152)} \qquad v_r > 0, \quad w_r > 0, \quad \sum_r v_r^2 < \infty, \quad \sum_r w_r < \infty; \qquad \sum_r \frac{v_r^2}{w_r} < 1.$$

Throughout the present and succeeding sections, the ranges of the indices are to be as follows:

$$q, q_0, r, m, n = 1, 2, 3, \cdots,$$

$$j, j_0, k, k_0 = 0, 1, 2, \cdots,$$

and

$$\nu = -1, 0, 1, 2, \cdots.$$

The fact that these three ranges are different will be important for some of our discussion.

Suppose that

$$\text{(153)} \qquad \delta x = \xi^{0}\psi + \sum_r w_r^{1/2}\xi^{r}\psi^{r} \in X\Psi,$$

where

$$\text{(154)} \qquad \psi = c\psi^{0} + \sum_r \frac{v_r}{w_r^{1/2}}\psi^{r} \in \Psi,$$

$$\text{(155)} \qquad c^2 = 1 - \sum_r \frac{v_r^2}{w_r}, \qquad c > 0,$$

and the exponent $1/2$ indicates the positive square root. Note that $c^2 > 0$ by (152); that (154) does indeed define an element of Ψ since

$$\text{(156)} \qquad \|\psi\|_{\Psi}^{2} = |c|^{2} + \sum_r \frac{v_r^2}{w_r} = 1;$$

and that (153) does indeed define an element of $X\Psi$ since $\xi^{0}\psi \in X\Psi$ by Lemma 9: 127 and $\sum_r w_r < \infty$ by (152). Note also that

$$\text{(157)} \qquad (\psi, \psi^{r})_{\Psi} = \frac{v_r}{w_r^{1/2}}.$$

Furthermore

$$E\delta x = 0,$$

since $E\psi^\nu = \delta^{\nu,-1}$ and ψ^{-1} is absent from (153).

Having defined

$$X = Y, \quad \Psi, \qquad M = \operatorname{span}\{\xi^0\}, \quad G = \text{identity}, \quad \text{and} \quad \delta x,$$

we seek to approximate x by $A(x + \delta x)$, $x \in M$, where A is to be a linear continuous unbiased operator:

$$EA(x + \delta x) = x \quad \text{whenever } x \in M.$$

We shall choose as A an operator which is minimal or within ρ of minimality for sufficiently small positive ρ.

The problem is now posed and may be solved on the basis of the above data by the use of projections. Such a solution will be given in § 172.

We next calculate the variance V of δx. By (153),

$$\delta x = f = \xi^0[c\psi^0 + \sum_r \frac{v_r}{w_r^{1/2}} \psi^r] + \sum_q w_q^{1/2} \xi^q \psi^q.$$

In matrix form, by (151),

$$f = \{_j f^{j,\nu}{}_\nu\} = \left\{_j\ \delta^{j,\nu} w_\nu^{1/2} + \delta^{j,0} \frac{v_\nu}{w_\nu^{1/2}}\ _\nu\right\}, \tag{158}$$

where we have put

$$v_{-1} = v_0 = 0, \qquad w_{-1} = w_0 = c^2. \tag{159}$$

Hence, by (81),

$$\begin{aligned} V = FF^* &= \left\{_j\ \delta^{j,\nu} w_\nu^{1/2} + \delta^{j,0} \frac{v_\nu}{w_\nu^{1/2}}\ _\nu\right\} \left\{_\nu\ \delta^{k,\nu} w_\nu^{1/2} + \delta^{k,0} \frac{v_\nu}{w_\nu^{1/2}}\ _k\right\} \\ &= \left\{_j\ \sum_\nu \left(\delta^{j,\nu} w_\nu^{1/2} + \delta^{j,0} \frac{v_\nu}{w_\nu^{1/2}}\right) \left(\delta^{k,\nu} w_\nu^{1/2} + \delta^{k,0} \frac{v_\nu}{w_\nu^{1/2}}\right)\ _k\right\} \\ &= \left\{_j\ \delta^{j,k} w_k + \delta^{k,0} v_j + \delta^{j,0} v_k + \delta^{j,0} \delta^{k,0} \sum_\nu \frac{v_\nu^2}{w_\nu}\ _k\right\}. \end{aligned}$$

Now

$$\sum_\nu \frac{v_\nu^2}{w_\nu} = 1 - c^2 = 1 - w_0,$$

by (155) and (159). Hence

$$V = \begin{pmatrix} V_{00} & V_{01} \\ V_{10} & V_{11} \end{pmatrix} = \begin{pmatrix} \{\ 1\ \} & \{v_r\ _r\} \\ \{_q\ v_q\ \} & \{_q\ \delta^{q,r} w_r\ _r\} \end{pmatrix}. \tag{160}$$

§ 161. **First solution.** We now solve the problem by means of Theorem 148, using the variance (160) but not the explicit formula (153) for δx.

We seek a solution

$$A = \begin{pmatrix} A_{00} & A_{01} \\ A_{10} & A_{11} \end{pmatrix} = \begin{pmatrix} \{a^{0,0}\} & \{a^{0,r}{}_r\} \\ \{_q a^{q,0}\} & \{_q a^{q,r}{}_r\} \end{pmatrix}$$

of (149). Thus

$$\begin{aligned} A_{00} &= I_{00} = \{1\} = \{a^{0,0}\}, \\ A_{10} &= 0 = \{_q a^{q,0}\}, \\ A_{01}V_{11} &= -V_{01} = \{a^{0,r}{}_r\}\{_r \delta^{r,m} w_m{}_m\} = \{-v_m{}_m\} = \{a^{0,m} w_m{}_m\}, \\ A_{11}V_{11} &= 0 = \{_q a^{q,r}{}_r\}\{_r \delta^{r,m} w_m{}_m\} = \{_q 0{}_m\} = \{_q a^{q,m} w_m{}_m\}. \end{aligned}$$

Hence

$$a^{0,m} = -\frac{v_m}{w_m}, \qquad a^{q,m} = 0;$$

(162) $$A_{01} = \left\{-\frac{v_r}{w_r}{}_r\right\}, \qquad A_{11} = 0;$$

(163) $$A = \begin{pmatrix} 1 & \left\{-\frac{v_r}{w_r}{}_r\right\} \\ 0 & 0 \end{pmatrix}.$$

The matrix (163) is the unique solution of (149). Hence the minimal operator, if existent, is unique. If the matrix (163) represents a continuous operator, that operator is the minimal operator.

We now distinguish two cases, depending on whether the series

(164) $$\sum_r \frac{v_r^2}{w_r^2}$$

converges or not. Both cases occur. For example, if

$$v_r = \frac{r}{3^r}, \qquad w_r = \frac{r^2}{3^r},$$

then (152) is satisfied and the series (164) is

$$\sum_r \frac{1}{r^2} < \infty.$$

On the other hand, if

$$v_r = \frac{r^{1/2}}{3^r}, \qquad w_r = \frac{r}{3^r},$$

then (152) is satisfied and the series (164) is

$$\sum_r \frac{1}{r} = \infty.$$

Case i. $\sum_r v_r^2/w_r^2 < \infty$. Here the matrix (163) describes a continuous operator A, as we shall see. We may alternatively describe A as follows. Put

$$a = \xi^0 - \sum_r \frac{v_r}{w_r} \xi^r \in X.$$

Then

$$(165) \qquad Ax = (x, a)\xi^0, \qquad x \in X,$$

since the matrix multiplication

$$A\begin{pmatrix} (x, \xi^0) \\ \{_r\ (x, \xi^r)\ \} \end{pmatrix}$$

gives Ax as defined by (165). It is clear from (165) that A is bounded, with

$$\|A\| = \|a\|_X,$$

and therefore that A is continuous.

Case ii. $\sum_r v_r^2/w_r^2 = \infty$. Here the matrix (163) characterizes an unbounded operator, as can be seen by considering the truncations

$$(166) \qquad a^n \underset{\text{def}}{=} \xi^0 - \sum_{i \leqq n} \frac{v_i}{w_i} \xi^i \in X, \qquad n = 1, 2, \cdots,$$

of a and observing that

$$\frac{\|Aa^n\|}{\|a^n\|} = \frac{\|a^n\|^2}{\|a^n\|} = \left[1 + \sum_{i \leqq n} \frac{v_i^2}{w_i^2}\right]^{1/2} \to \infty \quad \text{as } n \to \infty.$$

Let $\{A^n : n = 1, 2, \cdots\}$ be the sequence of linear continuous operators whose matrices are the matrix (163) truncated after the column of index n. Thus

$$(167) \qquad A^n x \underset{\text{def}}{=} (x, a^n)\xi^0, \qquad x \in X,$$

where a^n is given by (166).

The fact that the formal limit of A^n satisfies the conditions (149) indicates that $\{A^n\}$ may be a minimizing sequence. We shall show that this is indeed so, by using Theorem 137.

Thus, the operators A^n all are unbiased by construction. Also the sequence $\{A^n \delta x\}$ is a Cauchy sequence, by (139). For, $A^{n'} - A^n =$ a matrix of zeros except that $-v_i/w_i$ appears in the first row in columns $i = n+1, \cdots, n'$; $n' > n$. Hence

$$\text{trace } (A^{n'} - A^n)V(A^{n'} - A^n)^* = \sum_{n<i\leqq n'} w_i \frac{v_i^2}{w_i^2}$$
$$= \sum_{n<i\leqq n'} \frac{v_i^2}{w_i} \to 0 \quad \text{as } n' > n \to 0,$$

by (160) and (152). Finally the sequence $\{A^n\}$ satisfies the condition (138), with $\eta^k = \xi^k$. Thus, by (160) and (163), with

$$A^n = (A_0^n \quad A_1^n) = (G_0 \quad A_1^n),$$
$$V_{11} = \{_q\ \delta^{q,r} w_r\ _r\}, \qquad V_{10} = \{_q\ v_q\ \},$$
$$A_0 = G_0 = A_0^n = \{_j\ \delta^{j,0}\ \}, \qquad A_0^* = \{\ \delta^{j,0}\ _j\},$$
$$A_1 = \{_j\ -\delta^{j,0} v_q/w_q\ _q\}, \qquad A_1^* = \{_q\ -\delta^{j,0} v_q/w_q\ _j\},$$

$A_1^n = A_1$ truncated after the nth column, that is, A_1 with elements in which $q > n$ replaced by zeros, $\qquad A_1^{n*} = A_1^*$ truncated after the nth row,

$$V_{10}G_0^* = \{_q\ v_q \delta^{j,0}\ _j\},$$
$$V_{11}A_1^* = \{_q\ -v_q \delta^{j,0}\ _j\}, \qquad V_{11}A_1^{n*} = V_{11}A_1^* \text{ truncated after the } n\text{th row},$$

$$V_{10}G_0^* + V_{11}A_1^* = 0, \tag{168}$$

$$V_{10}G_0^* + V_{11}A_1^{n*} = \{_q\ c^{q,j}\ _j\}, \tag{169}$$

where

$$c^{q,j} = \begin{cases} 0 & \text{if } q \leqq n, \\ \delta^{j,0} v_q & \text{if } q > n. \end{cases} \tag{170}$$

The relation (168) is equivalent to (134); this checks our construction of A.

Now

$$\xi^{j_0} = \{_j\ \delta^{j,j_0}\ \}.$$

Hence

$$(V_{10}G_0^* + V_{11}A_1^{n*})\xi^{j_0} = \{_q\ c^{q,j_0}\ \},$$

and

$$\|(V_{10}G_0^* + V_{11}A_1^{n*})\xi^{j_0}\|_X = \sum_q |c^{q,j_0}|^2 = \delta^{j_0,0} \sum_{q>n} v_q^2,$$
$$\sum_j \|(V_{10}G_0^* + V_{11}A_1^{n*})\xi^j\|_X = \sum_{q>n} v_q^2.$$

By (152), the last quantity approaches 0 as $n \to \infty$. Hence (138) is satisfied and the sequence $\{A^n\}$, defined by (167), is a minimizing sequence.

If we wish we may now calculate

$$E\|\theta\|^2 = \inf_{A \in \mathscr{U}} E\|A\,\delta x\|^2 = \lim_n \operatorname{trace} A^n V A^{n*}.$$

We anticipate that this quantity will equal trace AVA^*, as is indeed the case. Thus

$$\text{(171)}\qquad \begin{aligned} VA^{n*} &= \begin{pmatrix} V_{00} & V_{01} \\ V_{10} & V_{11} \end{pmatrix} \begin{pmatrix} G_0^* \\ A_1^{n*} \end{pmatrix} = \begin{pmatrix} V_{00}G_0^* + V_{01}A_1^{n*} \\ V_{10}G_0^* + V_{11}A_1^{n*} \end{pmatrix} \\ &= \begin{pmatrix} \left\{\left(1 - \sum_{r \leqq n} \dfrac{v_r^2}{w_r}\right) \delta^{j,0} \;{}_j\right\} \\ \left\{{}_q\; c^{q,j} \;{}_j\right\} \end{pmatrix}, \end{aligned}$$

by (160) and (169), since

$$V_{00} = \{1\}, \qquad V_{01} = V_{10}^* = \{\, v_r \;{}_r\},$$

$$V_{00}G_0^* = \{\, \delta^{j,0} \;{}_j\}, \qquad V_{01}A_1^{n*} = \left\{ -\,\delta^{j,0} \sum_{q \leqq n} \frac{v_q^2}{w_q} \;{}_j\right\},$$

$$V_{00}G_0^* + V_{01}A_1^{n*} = \left(1 - \sum_{q \leqq n} \frac{v_q^2}{w_q}\right) \{\, \delta^{j,0} \;{}_j\}.$$

The numerical factor here approaches c^2 as $n \to \infty$, by (155).

Hence

$$A^n V A^{n*} = (G_0 \quad A_1^n) V A^{n*} = \left(\{{}_j\; \delta^{j,0}\} \left\{{}_j\; -\,\delta^{j,0} \frac{v_q}{w_q} \;{}_q\right\}^T \right) V A^{n*},$$

where the T indicates that the matrix is truncated, elements with $q > n$ being replaced by zeros. By (171),

$$A^n V A^{n*} = \left\{{}_j \left(1 - \sum_{r \leqq n} \frac{v_r^2}{w_r}\right) \delta^{j,0}\, \delta^{k,0} \;{}_k\right\} + \{{}_j\; 0 \;{}_k\},$$

since

$$\sum_{q \leqq n} -\,\delta^{j,0} \frac{v_q}{w_q}\, c^{q,j} = 0$$

by (170). Hence

$$\operatorname{trace} A^n V A^{n*} = 1 - \sum_{q \leqq n} \frac{v_q^2}{w_q} \to c^2$$

as $n \to \infty$. Hence

$$E\|\theta\|^2 = c^2.$$

This completes the first solution, one which uses the variance V but not the explicit stochastic process δx.

§ 172. **Second solution.** We now give an independent second solution, one which uses the formula for δx but not V.

The data of the problem are the following:

$X = Y$ is a separable Hilbert space with basis $\{\xi^j : j = 0, 1, 2, \cdots\}$.

$M = \text{span}\,\{\xi^0\}$.

G is the identity on X.

$\Psi = H(\Omega, p)$ is a separable L^2-space, with basis $\{\psi^\nu : \nu = -1, 0, 1, 2, \cdots\}$, where $p(\Omega) = 1$ and $\psi^{-1}(\omega) = 1,\ \omega \in \Omega$.

$\delta x = f$ is the element of $X\Psi$ given by (153) or equivalently (158).

We shall calculate

$$\theta = \text{Proj}_{\beta^\perp} G\delta x = \text{Proj}_{\beta^\perp}\delta x,$$

where the projection is in $X\Psi$ and

$$\beta = \mathscr{B}\delta x,$$
$$\mathscr{B} = \{B \in \mathscr{T}(X, X) : BM = 0\}.$$

Now, if the matrix of an operator $B \in \mathscr{T}(X, X)$ is

$$\{_k\, b^{k,j}\, _j\},$$

relative to the basis $\{\xi^j\}$ in X and in Y, then $B \in \mathscr{B}$ iff

$$b^{k,0} = 0, \qquad k = 0, 1, 2, \cdots. \tag{173}$$

For, $B \in \mathscr{B}$ iff

$$B\xi^0 = 0,$$

since $M = \text{span}\,\{\xi^0\}$; and the coordinates of $B\xi^0$ are

$$\left\{_k \sum_j b^{k,j}\, \delta^{j,0} \right\} = \{_k\, b^{k,0}\}.$$

It follows that β consists of all elements in $X\Psi$ with coordinates

$$\left\{_k \sum_j b^{k,j} f^{j,\nu}\, _\nu\right\}, \tag{174}$$

for all matrices $\{b^{k,j}\}$ of operators in $\mathscr{T}(X, X)$ such that (173) holds, where $\{f^{j,\nu}\}$ is given by (158). In particular, $\{b^{k,j}\}$ may consist entirely of zeros except for a solitary 1 in any position after the zeroth column:

$$\{b^{k,j}\} = \{\delta^{k,k_0}\, \delta^{j,q_0}\}.$$

Hence β contains the elements with coordinates

$$\{_k\, \delta^{k,k_0} f^{q_0,\nu}\, _\nu\} = \{_k\, \delta^{k,k_0}\, \delta^{q_0,\nu} w_{q_0}^{1/2}\, _\nu\},$$

by (174), since

$$f^{q,\nu} = \delta^{q,\nu} w_q^{1/2} \tag{175}$$

by (158). It is essential here that q and q_0 never equal 0 or -1. Thus

$$\beta \supset \text{span}\,\{\xi^{k_0}\psi^{q_0} : k_0 = 0, 1, 2, \cdots \text{ and } q_0 = 1, 2, \cdots\},$$

since $w_{q_0} \neq 0$; and by (174),

$$\beta \subset \text{Span}\,\{\xi^{k_0}\psi^{q_0} : \text{all } k_0 \text{ and } q_0\}.$$

Since $\{\xi^k\psi^\nu\}$ is a basis for $X\Psi$, it follows that $\{\xi^k\psi^{-1}, \xi^k\psi^0 : \text{all } k\}$ is a basis for $\beta^\perp$. Hence

$$\begin{aligned}\theta = \text{Proj}_{\beta^\perp}\,\delta x &= \sum_k (\delta x, \xi^k\psi^{-1})_{X\Psi}\xi^k\psi^{-1} + \sum_k (\delta x, \xi^k\psi^0)_{X\Psi}\xi^k\psi^0 \\ &= \sum_k c\delta^{k,0}\xi^k\psi^0 = c\xi^0\psi^0,\end{aligned}$$

by (153) or (158), since the column of δx of index $\nu = -1$ consists entirely of zeros and that of index $\nu = 0$ has c in its first row and zeros elsewhere. Hence

$$E\|\theta\|^2 = c^2.$$

We seek $A \in \mathscr{U}$ such that

(176) $$A\delta x = \theta = c\xi^0\psi^0 = c\{_j\ \delta^{j,0}\,\delta^{\nu,0}\ _\nu\}.$$

Now

$$\mathscr{U} = G + \mathscr{B} = \text{identity} + \mathscr{B}.$$

Put

$$A = \text{identity} + B, \qquad B \in \mathscr{B}.$$

Then

$$A\delta x = \delta x + B\delta x.$$

The matrix of δx is (158). Let the matrix of B be

$$\{_k\ b^{k,j}\ _j\},$$

where

$$b^{k,0} = 0$$

by (173). Then

$$\begin{aligned}B\delta x &= \{b^{k,j}\}\,\{f^{j,\nu}\} = \left\{\sum_j b^{k,j}\left(\delta^{j,\nu}w_\nu^{1/2} + \delta^{j,0}\frac{v_\nu}{w_\nu^{1/2}}\right)\right\} \\ &= \{_k\ b^{k,\nu}w_\nu^{1/2}\ _\nu\},\end{aligned}$$

by (158) and (173), where we take

$$b^{k,-1} = 0.$$

Hence

$$A\delta x = \delta x + B\delta x = \left\{_j\ \delta^{j,\nu}w_\nu^{1/2} + \delta^{j,0}\frac{v_\nu}{w_\nu^{1/2}} + b^{j,\nu}w_\nu^{1/2}\ _\nu\right\},$$

and $A\delta x = \theta$ iff

$$\delta^{j,\nu}w_\nu^{1/2} + \delta^{j,0}\frac{v_\nu}{w_\nu^{1/2}} + b^{j,\nu}w_\nu^{1/2} = c\delta^{j,0}\delta^{\nu,0},$$

by (176); that is, iff

$$(177)\qquad b^{j,\nu} = \frac{c\delta^{j,0}\delta^{\nu,0}}{w_\nu^{1/2}} - \delta^{j,\nu} - \delta^{j,0}\frac{v_\nu}{w_\nu} = \delta^{j,0}\delta^{\nu,0} - \delta^{j,\nu} - \delta^{j,0}\frac{v_\nu}{w_\nu},$$

since $w_\nu^{1/2} = c$ when $\nu = 0$, by (159), and the leading term vanishes for $\nu \neq 0$. Note that

$$b^{j,0} = \delta^{j,0} - \delta^{j,0} = 0, \qquad b^{j,-1} = 0,$$

since $v_{-1} = v_0 = 0$. Now

$$A = \text{identity} + B = \{_k\ \delta^{k,j}\ _j\} + B = \left\{_k\ \delta^{k,0}\,\delta^{j,0} - \delta^{k,0}\frac{v_j}{w_j}\ _j\right\},$$

or

$$A = \begin{pmatrix} 1 & \left\{-\dfrac{v_r}{w_r}\ _r\right\} \\ 0 & 0 \end{pmatrix}.$$

Thus A is given by the matrix (163), as before.

Case i. $\sum_r v_r^2/w_r^2 < \infty$. Here the minimal operator exists, is unique, and may alternatively be written as

$$Ax = (x, a)\xi^0, \qquad x \in X,$$

where

$$a = \xi^0 - \sum_r \frac{v_r}{w_r}\xi^r,$$

as in (165).

Case ii. $\sum_r v_r^2/w_r^2 = \infty$. Here the operator (163) is not continuous, as before. Consider the sequence $\{A^n\}$ of the truncations of (163). The operators A^n are defined in (167). Then

$$A^n \in \mathscr{U}.$$

To show that $\{A^n\}$ is a minimizing sequence, it is necessary and sufficient to show that

$$E\|A^n\delta x - \theta\|_X^2 = E\|A^n\delta x\|^2 - E\|\theta\|^2 = E\|A^n\delta x\|^2 - c^2 \to 0,$$

by Theorem 27. Now, by (167), (166), (153) and (154),

$$A^n\delta x = (\delta x, a^n)_X\xi^0 = \left[\psi - \sum_{i\leqq n}\frac{v_i}{w_i}w_i^{1/2}\psi^i\right]\xi^0$$

$$= \left[c\psi^0 + \sum_{i>n}\frac{v_i}{w_i^{1/2}}\psi^i\right]\xi^0.$$

Hence, by coordinates in $X\Psi'$ and (152),

$$E\|A^n\delta x\|^2 = c^2 + \sum_{i>n} \frac{v_i^2}{w_i} \to c^2 \quad \text{as } n \to \infty.$$

Thus we have shown that $\{A^n\}$ is a minimizing sequence and also that a minimal operator exists iff

$$\sum_r \frac{v_r^2}{w_r^2} < \infty;$$

in the latter case, the minimal operator is A.

§ 178. **Least square approximation.** We conclude this chapter with a discussion of least square approximation of a function relative to a weight W. Such approximation is sensitive to the weight W, as one would expect. One is led therefore to consider the question of which W to use. For certain weights W, the least square approximation is in fact a minimal approximation. It is reasonable to say that such weights W are the ones to use.

Least square approximation with a suitable weight is equivalent to minimal approximation. Least square approximation of a function is, apart from its historical interest, an indirect way to obtain minimal approximation. Direct methods are those of the preceding sections.

§ 179. **The precise definition.** Suppose for the rest of the chapter that $X = Y$ is a separable Hilbert space, that M is a closed linear subset of X of more than one point, and that we wish to approximate x by

$$A(x + \delta x), \qquad x, \delta x \in X;$$

where A is an operator on X to X. How x and δx are determined is not of primary concern. We imagine that $x + \delta x$ is to be given and that we seek an operator A which will filter out the error δx and leave x intact insofar as possible.

Unless something more is specified, the problem is too vague. We need information about x and δx; and we need a criterion that involves the error

$$A(x + \delta x) - x$$

in the approximation or the apparent error or *residual*

$$A(x + \delta x) - (x + \delta x) = Az - z,$$

where

$$z = x + \delta x.$$

In least square approximation it will be the residual that is considered, perhaps because the residual can be calculated when $x + \delta x$ and A are known, even though x is unknown. Furthermore the condition that $A(x + \delta x)$ be an element of M will be imposed, perhaps because it is known that $x \in M$.

Suppose that W, called the weight, is a given nonnegative self-adjoint linear continuous operator on X to X. An operator A on X to X is said to be a *least square operator*, relative to W and M, if A minimizes the quantity

$$q \underset{\text{def}}{=} (W[Az - z], Az - z)_X \quad \text{for each } z \in X, \tag{180}$$

subject to the condition

$$Az \in M. \tag{181}$$

If W is the identity, then q is the sum of the absolute squares of the components of the residual $Az - z$. This accounts for the name least square. If W is diagonal, then q is a weighted sum of the absolute squares of the components of the residual. The diagonal case is natural, as we shall see, when the errors in the different components of z are uncorrelated. When those errors are correlated, the appropriate weight will not be diagonal. This is why we have admitted general weights, and not merely diagonal weights.

If the space X is finite dimensional, then q is a nonnegative quadratic form in the components of the residual $Az - z$. If X is infinite dimensional, we may still think of q as a nonnegative quadratic form.

In the above definition of a least square operator A we did not specify that A be linear or continuous. We minimized q among all operators, of whatsoever sort, on X to M. We will see, however, that least square operators must be linear and continuous. It is this property of being linear and continuous which has been a strong inducement in the past to mathematicians to use least square operators.

There are situations in which a mathematician wishes to approximate x and knows that $x \in M$. It is then natural to adopt condition (181). It is then perhaps also natural to use q as a measure of the success of the approximation. The generality of W allows flexibility. The approximation will depend on W. If a mathematician is able to carry out the efficient approximation of x in the sense of § 9 : 176 or the minimal approximation (§ 144), he may prefer to do so, since these approximations minimize the error

$$A(x + \delta x) - x$$

rather than the residual

$$A(x + \delta x) - (x + \delta x).$$

Suppose that A is a least square operator; that is, an operator which minimizes q in (180) subject to the condition (181). One might consider that q is a new square norm on X. This could be effected by introducing a new inner product

$$((x, y)) \underset{\text{def}}{=} (Wx, y)_X, \qquad x, y \in X.$$

The space X with the new inner product might itself be a Hilbert space. If so, the projection in the new Hilbert space onto M would be a least square approximation A.

We do not follow this attack, because details of closure and completion and complications relative to the fact that $(Wx, y)_X$ may vanish even though $x \neq 0 \neq y$ must be treated. The proofs which we cite are simple, and perhaps simpler than others.

In any case, the facts about least square approximation, which we will set forth, are perhaps of greater interest than the proofs of the facts. Complete references to one set of adequate proofs will be given. The paper [Sard 7] will be designated simply as [7].

§ 182. **Existence of least square operators.** We say that W is a *proper weight* if W is a nonnegative self-adjoint linear continuous operator on X to itself and if there exists a positive constant b such that

$$\|\text{Proj}_M\, Wx\| \geqq b\|x\| \quad \text{whenever } x \in M. \tag{183}$$

The hypothesis that W be a proper weight will appear in Theorems 185 and 190. This hypothesis is quite mild. Furthermore Theorem 193 insures the existence of proper weights whenever minimal operators exist.

If W is a proper weight, then

$$Wx \notin M^{\perp} \quad \text{whenever } 0 \neq x \in M. \tag{184}$$

For, if $Wx \in M^{\perp}$, then $\text{Proj}_M\, Wx = 0$ and (183) implies that $x = 0$ when $x \in M$.

If M is finite dimensional, the converse holds. That is, (184) implies that a positive b exists for which (183) holds [7, Lemma 17]. If M is finite dimensional, the condition that W be a proper weight is equivalent to the condition that W be positive on M and not merely nonnegative on M [7, Lemmas 10, 17].

185. THEOREM. *If W is a proper weight, then the least square operator exists, is unique, and is linear and continuous. Furthermore a linear continuous operator A is the least square operator iff the following conditions are all satisfied:*

$$(A - I)M = 0,$$
$$AX \subset M,$$
$$WA = A^*W,$$

where I is the identity on X.

PROOF. [7, Theorem 3.]

The least square operator is a projection or something like a projection onto M relative to a new inner product.

§ 186. **The choice of a suitable** W. The theory of the preceding section has the advantage of referring only to X, M, and W. It has two disadvantages: (1) the residual rather than the error is controlled and (2) the result depends on W. Different weights lead to different approximations $A(x + \delta x)$ of x.

Suppose that the hypotheses of § 144 are satisfied; that is, that

$X = Y$ is a separable Hilbert space;

M is a closed linear subspace of X of dimension $\geqq 1$;

$\Psi = H(\Omega, p)$ is a separable L^2-space of functions absolute square integrable on a space Ω relative to a probability p;

δx is an element of the direct product $X\Psi$;

$E\delta x = 0 \in X$;

$0 < E\|\delta x\|_X^2 < \infty$.

Then the concepts of minimal operators and operators near minimality in the approximation of x by $A(x + \delta x)$, $A \in \mathscr{U}$, are defined (§§ 2, 13, 144).

187. THEOREM. *The unique least square operator relative to* W, M *is itself a minimal operator iff*

$$VWM \subset M, \tag{188}$$

where W *is a proper weight and* V *is the variance of* δx.

PROOF. [7, Theorem 4.]

This theorem is a generalization of earlier results of Gauss [1, 2, 3] and Aitken [1, 2], who considered the case in which X is finite dimensional. Gauss supposed in addition that the matrix of V is diagonal (the components of the error δx are uncorrelated). Gauss and Aitken have shown that the unique least square approximation is a minimal approximation if V is invertible and if

$$W = V^{-1}.$$

Now this condition implies (188), but is of restricted scope because V^{-1} need not exist. Indeed, *if* X *is infinite dimensional, then the inverse* V^{-1} *surely does not exist!* This is a consequence of the fact that

$$E\|\delta x\|_X^2 = \text{trace } V < \infty$$

[7, § 11]. Even in Gauss's case in which the matrix of V is a finite diagonal matrix, it is perfectly possible that one of the components of the error have zero variance, that is, that one of the diagonal elements of the matrix of V be zero. Then V^{-1} would not exist.

Thus the invertibility of V is not really pertinent to either least square or minimal approximation.

189. THEOREM. *Proper weights W satisfying condition* (188) *exist iff minimal operators exist. Suppose that A is a minimal operator. Then*

$$W = A^*BA + C$$

is a proper weight and is positive on X, if B and C are any nonnegative self-adjoint linear continuous operators on X such that B is positive on X and proper on M, C is positive on $M^\perp$, and $CM = 0$.

PROOF. [7, Lemma 9.]

Thus whenever a minimal operator exists, it is possible to obtain a minimal operator as a least square operator in the following way: One finds a W which is a proper weight and which satisfies (188). Thereafter one finds the least square operator relative to W, perhaps by using Theorem 185. In this calculation one must know the variance V in order to solve (188) for W. If one knows V, however, one may calculate the minimal operator directly by using Theorem 148. The calculation is shorter than by least squares, because it is not necessary to solve (188).

If a minimal operator does not exist, an operator within ρ of minimality may be sought, for any $\rho > 0$. Our direct methods† apply, whereas proper weights satisfying condition (188) will not exist.

† Remark 33 and Theorems 27, 137.

CHAPTER 11

The Step Functions θ and ψ

§ 1. **Introduction.** Heaviside's [1, 2] function θ and the function ψ have entered in the theory of the spaces B^*, Z^*, and K^*. We now establish a number of elementary formulas involving integrals of θ and ψ. The formulas were needed in Chapters 1–7.

As θ occurs in nature, so do its integrals. One may therefore expect that the results of the present chapter will be of general interest and will have applications elsewhere. Formulas involving θ are of broad scope because any step function constant on intervals and zero outside a compact set is a linear combination of functions θ, except possibly at transition points where its values are often immaterial.

The source of the importance of ψ is equation (14) of Chapter 1. In that equation a directed integral with variable limits is converted into an integral with fixed limits.

§ 2. **The functions θ, ϕ, ψ.** The function θ on $\mathsf{R} \times \mathsf{R}$ and the function ψ on $\mathsf{R} \times \mathsf{R} \times \mathsf{R}$ are defined as follows:

(3)
$$\theta(t, s) = \begin{cases} 0 & \text{if } t < s, \\ 1 & \text{if } t \geqq s; \end{cases}$$

and

(4)
$$\psi(u, t, s) = \theta(t, u) - \theta(t, s).$$

Then

(5)
$$\psi(s, t, u) = -\psi(u, t, s), \qquad \psi(s, t, s) = 0.$$

Also

(6)
$$\psi(u, t, s) = \begin{cases} 1 & \text{if } u \leqq t < s, \\ -1 & \text{if } s \leqq t < u, \\ 0 & \text{otherwise}; \end{cases}$$

as may be verified by considering the cases

$$u < s, \qquad u > s, \qquad u = s.$$

For convenience in earlier chapters, we defined the function ϕ, where

(7)
$$\phi(t, s) = 1 - \theta(t, s).$$

The present chapter does not use ϕ.

§ 8. **Integral formulas.** In the following formulas s, t, u, v, a, b are real variables, m is a positive integer, and

$$(9) \qquad s^{(m)} = \frac{s^m}{m!}; \qquad s^{(0)} = 1.$$

Thus $s^{(m)}$ is a normalized power. Proofs will be given in the next section. Formulas (15) and (19) are [Sard 5, (4: 11); and 13, (17.10)], respectively.

The first formulas involve θ.

$$(10) \qquad \int_a^t (u - s)^{(m-1)}\theta(t, s)\, ds = [(u - a)^{(m)} - (u - t)^{(m)}]\theta(t, a).$$

$$(11) \qquad \int_a^b (u - s)^{(m-1)}\theta(t, s)\, ds = (u - a)^{(m)}\theta(t, a) - (u - b)^{(m)}\theta(t, b) - (u - t)^{(m)}[\theta(t, a) - \theta(t, b)].$$

$$(12) \qquad \int_a^t (t - s)^{(m-1)}\theta(t, s)\, ds = (t - a)^{(m)}\theta(t, a).$$

$$(13) \qquad \int_t^u (u - s)^{(m-1)}\theta(t, s)\, ds = (u - t)^{(m)}\theta(t, u).$$

$$(14) \qquad \int_a^b (t - s)^{(m-1)}\theta(t, s)\, ds = (t - a)^{(m)}\theta(t, a) - (t - b)^{(m)}\theta(t, b).$$

$$(15) \qquad \int_a^u (u - s)^{(m-1)}\theta(t, s)\, ds = (u - a)^{(m)}\theta(t, a) - (u - t)^{(m)}[\theta(t, a) - \theta(t, u)].$$

The above formulas (10)–(15) remain valid if the arguments of θ are interchanged throughout each formula. For example, (10) induces

$$(10') \qquad \int_a^t (u - s)^{(m-1)}\theta(s, t)\, ds = [(u - a)^{(m)} - (u - t)^{(m)}]\theta(a, t).$$

The formula (15) may be written in an alternative form involving the Taylor operator

$$T = T_s$$

of § 3: 69. Indeed the first member of (15) is precisely

$$[T_s^m\theta(t, s)]_{s = u},$$

by (3: 71). Hence (15) is equivalent to

$$(16) \qquad T_s^m\theta(t, s) = (s - a)^{(m)}\theta(t, a) - (s - t)^{(m)}[\theta(t, a) - \theta(t, s)].$$

The following formulas involve ψ.

$$\int_a^b (u - s)^{(m-1)}\psi(v, t, s)\, ds = (u - b)^{(m)}\psi(b, t, v) - (u - a)^{(m)}\psi(a, t, v) + (u - t)^{(m)}\psi(a, t, b). \tag{17}$$

$$\int_a^u (u - s)^{(m-1)}\psi(a, t, s)\, ds = (u - t)^{(m)}\psi(a, t, u). \tag{18}$$

In terms of T_s the last formula may be written

$$T_s^m\psi(a, t, s) = (s - t)^{(m)}\psi(a, t, s). \tag{19}$$

$$\int_t^u (u - s)^{(m-1)}\psi(a, t, s)\, ds = (u - t)^{(m)}\psi(a, t, u). \tag{20}$$

$$\int_a^u (t - s)^{(m-1)}\psi(u, t, s)\, ds = -(t - a)^{(m)}\psi(a, t, u). \tag{21}$$

$$\int_a^t (t - s)^{(m-1)}\psi(u, t, s)\, ds = -(t - a)^{(m)}\psi(a, t, u). \tag{22}$$

§ 23. **Proofs.** Consider (10). If $t = a$, the formula reduces to $0 = 0$. If $t < a$, then except at the limits of integration,

$$t < s < a$$

and

$$\theta(t, s) = \theta(t, a) = 0.$$

Thus the formula reduces to $0 = 0$. If $t > a$, then except at the limits of integration,

$$a < s < t$$

and

$$\theta(t, s) = \theta(t, a) = 1.$$

Thus the formula reduces to the correct relation

$$\int_a^t (u - s)^{(m-1)}\, ds = (u - a)^{(m)} - (u - t)^{(m)}. \tag{24}$$

In similar fashion any of the formulas (10)–(22) may be established directly by considering cases. Alternatively we shall deduce the formulas from (10).

To establish (11), we write

$$\int_a^b = \int_a^t - \int_b^t$$

and use (10) twice. The bracket in (11) may be written $\psi(a, t, b)$.

To establish (12), put $u = t$ in (10).

To establish (13), put $(a, b) = (u, t)$ in (11) and interchange limits.

To establish (14), put $u = t$ in (11).

To establish (15), put $b = u$ in (11). The bracket in (15) may be written $\psi(a, t, u)$.

In order to show that (10)–(15) remain valid if the arguments of θ in each equation are interchanged, it is sufficient to establish (10′), since (11)–(15) were derived from (10). Now (10′) may be established just as (10) was, by considering cases. Alternatively we may deduce (10′) from (10), by using the relations

$$\theta(t, s) = 1 - \theta(s, t), \qquad t \neq s; \tag{25}$$
$$\theta(t, a) = 1 - \theta(a, t), \qquad t \neq a;$$

these relations convert (10) into (10′), by (24).

We have seen that (16) is another form of (15).

Consider (17). By (4), (24) and (11),

$$\begin{aligned}\int_a^b (u - s)^{(m-1)}\psi(v, t, s)\,ds &= \theta(t, v)\int_a^b (u - s)^{(m-1)}\,ds \\ &\quad - \int_a^b (u - s)^{(m-1)}\theta(t, s)\,ds \\ &= \theta(t, v)[(u - a)^{(m)} - (u - b)^{(m)}] \\ &\quad - (u - a)^{(m)}\theta(t, a) + (u - b)^{(m)}\theta(t, b) \\ &\quad + (u - t)^{(m)}[\theta(t, a) - \theta(t, b)] \\ &= (u - b)^{(m)}\psi(b, t, v) - (u - a)^{(m)}\psi(a, t, v) \\ &\quad + (u - t)^{(m)}\psi(a, t, b).\end{aligned}$$

Thus (17) is established.

To establish (18) and (19), put $(b, v) = (u, a)$ in (17) and use (5).

One may now derive subsidiary formulas from (17) by identifying any of the free variables a, b, u, v, t. We have cited (20), (21), (22) because of their simplicity.

To establish (20), put $(b, a, v) = (u, t, a)$ in (17) and use the relation

$$\psi(t, t, u) - \psi(t, t, a) = \psi(a, t, u).$$

Formulas (18) and (20) are consistent, because $\psi(a, t, s)$ vanishes for s between a and t.

To establish (21), put $(b, u, v) = (u, t, u)$ in (17).

To establish (22), put $(b, u, v) = (t, t, u)$ in (17). Formulas (21) and (22) are consistent, because $\psi(u, t, s)$ vanishes for s between u and t.

Formulas involving $\psi(a, s, t)\,ds$ may also be derived from (10)–(15).

Chapter 12

Stieltjes Integrals, Integration by Parts, Functions of Bounded Variation

§ 1. **Introduction.** There are many alternative constructions of the theory of Lebesgue integration, doubtless each with its own interest. The present chapter, which is really an appendix, discusses the method of F. Riesz. As regards single integrals it would be sufficient to refer the reader to [Riesz-Nagy 1]. There are important theorems about multiple integrals, however, which are not readily available. Our treatment of multiple integrals is based on the work of W. H. Young.

Multiple integration by parts is of general interest. So too is the theory of discontinuities of functions of bounded variation in several variables.

We first consider single integrals and then double integrals. The subsequent step to m-fold integrals will be left to the reader. For brevity we speak of Riemann and Lebesgue integrals, dropping the reference to Stieltjes. For simplicity of exposition we consider only compact intervals, the case needed in Chapters 1–7. Infinite intervals may be treated similarly for those theorems which remain true in the infinite case.

§ 2. **The integral $\int_\alpha^{\tilde\alpha} x(s)\, df(s)$.** Let I be the interval

$$[\alpha, \tilde\alpha] = \{\alpha \leqq s \leqq \tilde\alpha\},$$

where

$$-\infty < \alpha < \tilde\alpha < \infty.$$

By a *partition* P of I we mean a finite ordered set

$$\tilde s^0, s^0, \tilde s^1, s^1, \tilde s^2, s^2, \cdots, \tilde s^m, s^m, \tilde s^{m+1}$$

of real numbers such that

$$(3) \qquad \alpha = \tilde s^0 = s^0 \leqq \tilde s^1 \leqq s^1 \leqq \tilde s^2 \leqq \cdots \leqq \tilde s^m \leqq s^m = \tilde s^{m+1} = \tilde\alpha.$$

Thus s^0 and $\tilde s^0$ are merely alternative designations of α; and s^m, $\tilde s^{m+1}$ of $\tilde\alpha$. We define the *norm* of the partition P as

$$(4) \qquad \|P\| = \max_{i=1,\cdots,m} (s^i - s^{i-1}).$$

The norm $\|P\|$ depends on the constituent intervals $[s^{i-1}, s^i]$, $i = 1, \cdots, m$, of P and not on the points $\tilde s^i$. The partition P without the latter points is called a *subdivision* of I.

Suppose that x and f are functions on I to the reals R. For each partition P of I, consider the sum

$$(5)\qquad \sum \underset{\text{def}}{=} \sum_{i=1,\cdots,m} x(\tilde s^i)[f(s^i) - f(s^{i-1})] = \sum_i x(\tilde s^i)\,\Delta f(s^{i-1}).$$

The *Riemann integral*

$$(6)\qquad \int_\alpha^{\tilde\alpha} x(s)\,df(s) = \int_I x(s)\,df(s) = \int_I x\,df$$

is defined as the limit of $\sum$ as the norm of P approaches zero, if the limit exists. Thus the integral (6) is a real number, determined by $x, f, \alpha, \tilde\alpha$, with the following property. For each $\eta > 0$ there exists $\zeta > 0$ such that

$$(7)\qquad \left|\int_\alpha^{\tilde\alpha} x(s)\,df(s) - \sum\right| < \eta$$

whenever

$$\|P\| < \zeta.$$

The integral (6) with $\tilde\alpha = \alpha$ is defined as zero.

8. Theorem (integration by parts). *If*

$$\int_\alpha^{\tilde\alpha} x(s)\,df(s)$$

exists, then so does

$$\int_\alpha^{\tilde\alpha} f(s)\,dx(s)$$

and

$$(9)\qquad \int_\alpha^{\tilde\alpha} x(s)\,df(s) + \int_\alpha^{\tilde\alpha} f(s)\,dx(s) = x(\tilde\alpha)f(\tilde\alpha) - x(\alpha)f(\alpha).$$

Thus integration by parts is valid providing merely that one of the integrals exists.

Proof. The theorem is an immediate consequence of the elementary identity

$$(10)\qquad \begin{aligned}\sum_{i=1,\cdots,m} f^i(x^i - x^{i-1}) + \sum_{i=0,\cdots,m} x^i(f^{i+1} - f^i) &= x^m f^{m+1} - x^0 f^0\\ &= x(\tilde\alpha)f(\tilde\alpha) - x(\alpha)f(\alpha);\end{aligned}$$

where

$$f^j = f(\tilde s^j), \qquad x^i = x(s^i), \qquad i = 0, \cdots, m; \qquad j = 0, \cdots, m+1;$$

and $\tilde s^j$, s^i are the elements of a partition P of I. By hypothesis the second sum in (10) approaches $\int_I x\,df$ as $\|P\| \to 0$. Hence the first sum also approaches a limit and (9) is established. This completes the proof.

The definition of the integral implies that

$$\int_{\alpha}^{\tilde{\alpha}} df(s) = f(\tilde{\alpha}) - f(\alpha).$$

If $f(s)$ is constant, $s \in I$, then

$$\int_{\alpha}^{\tilde{\alpha}} x(s)\, df(s) = 0.$$

The replacement of $f(s)$ by $f(s) - c$, where $c \in \mathsf{R}$, does not change the sum $\sum$ or the integral (6). In particular, we may replace f by g, where

$$g(s) = f(s) - f(\alpha).$$

Note that g vanishes at $s = \alpha$, that is, on the lower boundary of I.

The integral (6) is linear in x and in f. That is, if

$$\int_I x\, df, \qquad \int_I y\, df$$

exist, then

$$\int_I (ax + by)\, df, \qquad a, b \in \mathsf{R},$$

exists and equals

$$a \int_I x\, df + b \int_I y\, df.$$

Also if

$$\int_I x\, df, \qquad \int_I x\, dg$$

exist, then

$$\int_I x\, d(af + bg), \qquad a, b \in \mathsf{R},$$

exists and equals

$$a \int_I x\, df + b \int_I x\, dg.$$

If

$$\int_{\alpha}^{\tilde{\alpha}} x(s)\, df(s)$$

exists, then for all $a \in I$,

$$\int_{\alpha}^{a} x\, df, \qquad \int_{a}^{\tilde{\alpha}} x\, df$$

exist and

$$\int_{\alpha}^{a} x\, df + \int_{a}^{\tilde{\alpha}} x\, df = \int_{\alpha}^{\tilde{\alpha}} x\, df.$$

If however the integrals on the left exist for one a, it does not follow that the integral on the right must exist. This is because the inclusion or omission of $s = a$ as a point of subdivision may affect the sum (5).

§11. **Increasing functions.** In considering a function f on I to R, we shall always extend f to a function on R to R by putting

$$(12) \qquad f(s) = \begin{cases} f(\alpha) & \text{if } s < \alpha, \\ f(s) & \text{if } \alpha \leqq s \leqq \tilde{\alpha}, \\ f(\tilde{\alpha}) & \text{if } \tilde{\alpha} < s. \end{cases}$$

We say that f is an *increasing function* if

$$f(s') \geqq f(s) \quad \text{whenever } s' \geqq s.$$

If f is an increasing function, the limits

$$f(s + 0) \underset{\text{def}}{=} \lim_{\eta \to 0+} f(s + \eta),$$

$$f(s - 0) \underset{\text{def}}{=} \lim_{\eta \to 0+} f(s - \eta),$$

always exist, and

$$(13) \qquad f(s - 0) \leqq f(s) \leqq f(s + 0), \qquad s \in \mathsf{R}.$$

Furthermore these three quantities are equal and f is continuous at s, except for a countable set of points in I. This is because we may count the discontinuities by considering them in order of size of jump. The number of points s at which

$$f(s + 0) - f(s - 0) \geqq \rho > 0$$

is less than or equal to

$$\frac{f(\tilde{\alpha}) - f(\alpha)}{\rho},$$

by (13).

§ 14. **Functions of bounded variation.** Consider a function f on I to R and its extension (12). For any interval $H \subset \mathsf{R}$ we define the *variation of f on H* as

$$(15) \qquad \operatorname{var}(f; H) = \sup \sum |\Delta f|,$$

where the supremum is taken over all subdivisions of H and the summation is taken over the constituent intervals of the subdivision. In particular,

$$\operatorname{var}(f; H) = 0$$

if H does not overlap I or if H is a point or if $f(s)$ is constant, $s \in I$.

Thus

$$0 \leqq \operatorname{var}(f; H) \leqq \infty,$$

$$\operatorname{var}(f \pm g; H) \leqq \operatorname{var}(f; H) + \operatorname{var}(g; H),$$

and

(16) $$\left|\int_H x(s)\, df(s)\right| \leqq \sup_{s \in H} |x(s)| \operatorname{var}(f; H),$$

whenever the integral exists.

Consider a subdivision of an interval H and the corresponding sum

$$\sum |\Delta f|.$$

If we refine the subdivision by dividing some of its constituent intervals, we increase the sum or at any rate leave it unchanged. This is because certain increments Δf are replaced by $\Delta^1 f$, $\Delta^2 f$, where

$$\Delta f = \Delta^1 f + \Delta^2 f$$

and consequently

$$|\Delta f| \leqq |\Delta^1 f| + |\Delta^2 f|.$$

Since $\operatorname{var}(f; H)$ is a supremum, it follows that

(17) $$\operatorname{var}(f; [s, u]) = \operatorname{var}(f; [s, t]) + \operatorname{var}(f; [t, u])$$

whenever

$$s \leqq t \leqq u.$$

Thus $\operatorname{var}(f; H)$ *is an additive function of* H.

For all intervals $H \subset \mathsf{R}$,

(18) $$\operatorname{var}(f; H) \leqq \operatorname{var}(f; I).$$

We say that f is of *bounded variation on* I and we write

$$f \in V,$$

if

$$\operatorname{var}(f; I) < \infty.$$

Consider a function $f \in V$. We define the *total variation* v, the *positive variation* p, and the *negative variation* q of f as follows:

(19) $$v(s) = \begin{cases} \operatorname{var}(f; [\alpha, s]) & \text{if } s \geqq \alpha, \\ 0 & \text{otherwise}; \end{cases}$$

(20) $$p(s) = \frac{v(s) + f(s) - f(\alpha)}{2},$$

(21) $$q(s) = \frac{v(s) - f(s) + f(\alpha)}{2}.$$

22. THEOREM. *Suppose that* $f \in V$. *Then the variations* v, p, q *of* f *are increasing, vanish at* $s = \alpha$, *and are bounded by* var $(f; I)$. *Also*

$$f(s) = p(s) - q(s) + f(\alpha), \tag{23}$$

$$v(s) = p(s) + q(s), \qquad s \in \mathsf{R}. \tag{24}$$

PROOF. The relations (23) and (24) follow from (20) and (21). By (12),

$$f(s) - f(\alpha) = 0, \qquad s \leqq \alpha.$$

Hence $v(s)$, $p(s)$, $q(s)$ all vanish for $s \leqq \alpha$.

Consider s and Δs, where

$$\alpha \leqq s \leqq s + \Delta s.$$

By (19) and (17),

$$\Delta v(s) = v(s + \Delta s) - v(s) = \text{var}\,(f; [s, s + \Delta s]).$$

Now a simple subdivision of $[s, s + \Delta s]$ is the interval itself. Hence, by the definition of the variation as a supremum,

$$\Delta v \geqq |\Delta f| \geqq 0. \tag{25}$$

Now (20) and (21) imply that

$$\Delta p = \frac{\Delta v + \Delta f}{2},$$

$$\Delta q = \frac{\Delta v - \Delta f}{2}.$$

Hence, by (25),

$$\Delta p \geqq 0, \qquad \Delta q \geqq 0.$$

Thus the functions v, p, q are all increasing and therefore nonnegative. By (18), v is bounded by var $(f; I)$; and so are p, q, by (24).

This completes the proof.

Consider a function $f \in V$ and its variations v, p, q. Since v, p, q are increasing functions, they are continuous except at countably many points. Furthermore v is continuous at a point iff both p and q are continuous there, since

$$\Delta v = \Delta p + \Delta q, \qquad \Delta p \geqq 0, \qquad \Delta q \geqq 0 \quad \text{when } \Delta s \geqq 0.$$

Hence each continuity of v is a continuity of f. The limits

$$f(s - 0) \quad \text{and} \quad f(s + 0)$$

exist for all s. Except for countably many points,

$$f(s - 0) = f(s) = f(s + 0).$$

Likewise for v, p, and q.

Consider a function $f \in V$. The relation (23) implies that f is the difference of two increasing functions: p plus the constant $f(\alpha)$, and q. Conversely, if f^1 and f^2 are increasing functions on I, then

$$f^1 - f^2 \in V.$$

This is immediate, because

$$\begin{aligned} \operatorname{var}(f^1 - f^2; I) &\leqq \operatorname{var}(f^1; I) + \operatorname{var}(f^2; I) \\ &= f^1(\tilde{\alpha}) - f^1(\alpha) + f^2(\tilde{\alpha}) - f^2(\alpha) < \infty. \end{aligned}$$

It may be of interest to note the following facts about the variations. As we do not use these facts, we shall not establish them. Suppose that $f \in V$. The decomposition (23) is minimal in the following sense: If

$$f(s) - f(\alpha) = f^1(s) - f^2(s),$$

where f^1 and f^2 are increasing functions, then

$$\begin{aligned} \Delta f^1(s) &\geqq \Delta p(s), \\ \Delta f^2(s) &\geqq \Delta q(s), \end{aligned} \qquad s \in \mathsf{R}, \quad \Delta s \geqq 0.$$

For all $s \in \mathsf{R}$,

$$p(s + 0) = p(s) \quad \text{or} \quad q(s + 0) = q(s).$$

It cannot be that both p and q are discontinuous on the right at s. The dual statements hold for $s - 0$.

§ 26. **Integration relative to a function of bounded variation.**

27. THEOREM. *If x is continuous on I and f is of bounded variation on I, then*

(28)
$$\int_I x(s)\, df(s)$$

exists.

PROOF. The definition of the integral involves Δf rather than f. Now

$$\Delta f = \Delta p - \Delta q,$$

by (23). It is therefore sufficient to show that the integrals

(29)
$$\int_I x(s)\, dp(s), \qquad \int_I x(s)\, dq(s)$$

exist. Since p and q are increasing functions, the classical proof of the existence of the Riemann integral

$$\int_I x(s)\, ds, \qquad x \in C_0(I),$$

carries over to the integrals (29). This completes our discussion of the proof.

30. THEOREM. *Suppose that f is of bounded variation on I. In order that*

$$\int_I x(s)\, df(s) = 0$$

for all continuous functions x on I, it is necessary and sufficient that the function f be constant except on a countable set of points strictly interior to I.

The condition may be stated as follows. There exists a countable set $\mathscr{J}_s$ of points strictly interior to I such that

$$f(s) = f(\alpha) = f(\tilde{\alpha}), \qquad s \notin \mathscr{J}_s.$$

The hypothesis $f \in V$ could be omitted because of the known theorem that the integral

$$\int_I x(s)\, df(s)$$

exists for all $x \in C_0$ only if $f \in V$ [Graves 1, Chapter 12, Theorems 9 and 6].

PROOF [Riesz-Nagy 1, p. 111]. *Sufficiency.* Since $f \in V$ and $x \in C_0$, the integral must exist. It follows that the integral must vanish, because we may construct partitions of I with arbitrarily small norm such that

$$f(s^i) = f(\alpha)$$

for all points s^i in (3). Then, by (5),

$$\sum = 0 = \int_I x\, df.$$

The fact that $\mathscr{J}_s$ excludes α and $\tilde{\alpha}$ is essential.

Necessity. Note first that

$$\int_I 1\, df(s) = f(\tilde{\alpha}) - f(\alpha) = 0,$$

since we may take x as unity.

Let $\mathscr{J}_s$ be the set of those discontinuities of the variation v which are strictly interior to I. Then $\mathscr{J}_s$ is countable, since v is increasing.

Consider any fixed s^0 such that

$$\alpha < s^0 < \tilde{\alpha}, \qquad s^0 \notin \mathscr{J}_s.$$

Define the continuous function x^ν for each positive integer ν as

$$x^\nu(s) = \theta^\nu(s^0, s),$$

where

$$\theta^\nu(s^0, s) = \begin{cases} 1, & \alpha \leqq s \leqq s^0, \\ 0, & s^0 + \dfrac{1}{\nu} \leqq s, \\ 1 + \nu(s^0 - s), & s^0 < s < s^0 + \dfrac{1}{\nu}. \end{cases} \tag{31}$$

Thus θ^ν is the same function as that defined in (3: 29). For sufficiently large ν,

$$0 = \int_\alpha^{\tilde{\alpha}} x^\nu(s)\, df(s) = \int_\alpha^{s^0} x^\nu\, df + \int_{s^0}^{s^0+1/\nu} x^\nu\, df + \int_{s^0+1/\nu}^{\tilde{\alpha}} x^\nu\, df$$
$$= \int_\alpha^{s^0} df + \int_{s^0}^{s^0+1/\nu} x^\nu\, df = f(s^0) - f(\alpha) + \int_{s^0}^{s^0+1/\nu} x^\nu\, df.$$

Now, by (16) and (17),

$$\left| \int_{s^0}^{s^0+1/\nu} x^\nu\, df \right| \leqq 1 \operatorname{var}\left(f; \left[s^0, s^0 + \frac{1}{\nu}\right]\right)$$
$$= v\left(s^0 + \frac{1}{\nu}\right) - v(s^0) \to 0 \quad \text{as } \nu \to \infty,$$

since s^0 is a point of continuity of v. Hence

$$f(s^0) = f(\alpha),$$

and the proof is complete.

Consider a function $f \in V$. By the *normalization* of f we mean the function h, where

$$(32) \qquad h(s) = \begin{cases} f(s+0) - f(\alpha), & s > \alpha, \\ 0, & s \leqq \alpha. \end{cases}$$

Thus

$$h(\alpha) = 0$$

and

$$h(s + 0) = h(s), \qquad s \neq \alpha.$$

Furthermore, h is a function of bounded variation, because

$$\left.\begin{aligned} f(s) - f(\alpha) &= p(s) - q(s), \\ f(s+0) - f(\alpha) &= p(s+0) - q(s+0), \end{aligned}\right\} \qquad s \in \mathsf{R},$$

and, omitting details,

$$\operatorname{var}(h; I) \leqq \operatorname{var}(f; I).$$

Hence

$$h \in V^0,$$

where V^0 is the space, defined in (3: 60), of functions of bounded variation which vanish on the lower boundary and which are continuous from above except possibly on the lower boundary.

Now, by (12),

$$h(s) - f(s) = \begin{cases} f(s+0) - f(s) - f(\alpha), & s > \alpha, \\ 0 - f(\alpha), & s \leqq \alpha; \end{cases}$$

and

$$f(s+0) = f(s), \qquad s \geqq \tilde{\alpha}.$$

Hence

$$h(s) - f(s) = -f(\alpha),$$

except on a countable set $\subset (\alpha, \tilde{\alpha})$. It follows by Theorem 30 that

$$\int_I x \, d(h - f) = 0$$

and

$$\int_I x \, dh = \int_I x \, df,$$

for all functions x continuous on I.

The Lebesgue integral will be defined in the next sections in terms of the Riemann integral of continuous integrands. It will follow that measurability and integrability of a function relative to f imply their counterparts relative to the normalization of f, with equality of the integrals.

§ 33. **$|f|$-null sets.** We now indicate how the theory of Lebesgue integration may be constructed, following F. Riesz. The first step will be to define $|f|$-null sets (sets of $|f|$-measure zero). Then we will define the Lebesgue integral relative to f of a function and the f-measurable functions. Then, at the end, one may define the $|f|$-measure of f-measurable sets. The construction is based on the dominant rôle of sets of measure zero in integration.†

Consider a function f of bounded variation on I. The variation v of f is an increasing function.

A set A of points in R is said to be an $|f|$-*null set* (or a set of f-variation zero or a set of $|f|$-measure zero) if for each $\eta > 0$ there exists a countable set of open intervals whose union contains A and which are such that

$$\sum \Delta v < \eta.$$

It follows that any subset of an $|f|$-null set is $|f|$-null, and that a countable union of $|f|$-null sets is $|f|$-null.

---

† F. Riesz [5] has given an elegant review of the rôle of null sets in analysis. One might add to his list of theorems involving null sets, theorems about Hausdorff dimension [Szpilrajn 1] and theorems on the nullity of the images of critical sets [Sard 11].

§ 34. **The Lebesgue integral.** Consider a function f of bounded variation on I and its variations v, p, q. Since v vanishes on $(-\infty, \alpha]$ and is constant on $[\tilde{\alpha}, \infty)$, it follows that the open intervals

$$(-\infty, \alpha) \quad \text{and} \quad (\tilde{\alpha}, \infty)$$

are $|f|$-null sets. Now the values of an integrand x on an $|f|$-null set do not affect the value of $\int x\, df$, as we shall see. For this reason we define

$$\int_{\mathsf{R}} x(s)\, df(s) = \int x(s)\, df(s) \tag{35}$$

as

$$\int_I x(s)\, df(s).$$

We sometimes write $|f|$ for v; thus

$$\int x(s)\, d|f(s)| = \int x(s)\, dv(s) = \int x(s)\, d[p(s) + q(s)]. \tag{36}$$

The integrals (35) and (36) surely exist if x is continuous on I.

Consider a function x defined on R, except for an $|f|$-null set, to R. We say that x is Lebesgue *integrable* relative to f if

$$x = y - z,$$

where y is the limit, except on an $|f|$-null set, of an increasing sequence $\{y^\nu\}$ of functions continuous on I, if similarly z is the limit, except on an $|f|$-null set, of an increasing sequence $\{z^\nu\}$ of functions continuous on I, and if the sequences

$$\left\{\int y^\nu(s)\, d|f|(s)\right\}, \qquad \left\{\int z^\nu(s)\, d|f|(s)\right\}, \qquad \nu = 1, 2, \cdots,$$

are bounded; and we then define

$$\int x(s)\, df(s) \tag{37}$$

as

$$\lim_{\nu\to\infty} \left[\int y^\nu(s)\, df(s) - \int z^\nu(s)\, df(s)\right].$$

Following [Riesz-Nagy 1, §§ 56, 17, 22], one may now show that the integral (37) is unambiguously defined. In particular, then, if x is continuous, the Lebesgue integral (37) equals the Riemann integral

$$\int_\alpha^{\tilde{\alpha}} x(s)\, df(s).$$

We say that x is *measurable* relative to f if x is the limit, except on an $|f|$-null set, of a sequence (monotone or not) of functions continuous on I.

For any set $A \subset \mathsf{R}$, we put

(38) $$\int_A x(s)\, df(s) = \int x(s) c_A(s)\, df(s),$$

where c_A is the characteristic or *autofunction* of A:

$$c_A(s) = \begin{cases} 1 & \text{if } s \in A, \\ 0 & \text{otherwise.} \end{cases}$$

The integral (38) exists iff the function xc_A is Lebesgue integrable relative to f.

One may now establish the known properties of Lebesgue integration, including the equivalence of the present definition with other definitions that have been used.

It may be of interest for us to discuss the following theorem, which we used in the study of the space Z^* (§ 3 : 58).

39. Theorem. *Suppose that $f \in V$. Then*

$$\int_{[t,u]} df(s) = f(u+0) - f(t-0), \qquad t \leqq u,$$

$$\int_{[t,u)} df(s) = f(u-0) - f(t-0), \qquad t \leqq u,$$

$$\int_{(t,u]} df(s) = f(u+0) - f(t+0), \qquad t \leqq u,$$

$$\int_{(t,u)} df(s) = f(u-0) - f(t+0), \qquad t < u;$$

$$\int_{\{t\}} df(s) = f(t+0) - f(t-0).$$

Proof. The formulas are consequences of the following two:

(40) $$\int_{[\alpha,t]} df(s) = f(t+0) - f(\alpha),$$

$$\alpha < t < \tilde{\alpha},$$

(41) $$\int_{\{t\}} df(s) = f(t+0) - f(t-0),$$

because of the additivity of the integral on measurable sets, because f is constant on $(-\infty, \alpha]$ and on $[\tilde{\alpha}, \infty)$, and because

$$\int_I df(s) = f(\tilde{\alpha}) - f(\alpha).$$

Furthermore (41) is a consequence of (40). Thus

$$\int_{[\alpha,t-\eta]} df + \int_{(t-\eta,t]} df = \int_{[\alpha,t]} df, \qquad \alpha < t - \eta < t.$$

Hence (40) implies that

$$f(t - \eta + 0) - f(\alpha) + \int_{(t-\eta,t]} df = f(t + 0) - f(\alpha),$$

$$\int_{(t-\eta,t]} df = f(t + 0) - f(t - \eta + 0).$$

Let $\eta \to 0$ monotonely. The integral on the left approaches

$$\int_{\{t\}} df,$$

since the autofunction of $(t - \eta, t]$ approaches that of $\{t\}$ monotonely. The expression on the right approaches

$$f(t + 0) - f(t - 0).$$

Thus (41) is established.

It remains to establish (40). Let x^ν, for each positive integer ν, be the continuous function $\theta^\nu(t, s)$ of s, where θ^ν is defined in (31). The bounded decreasing sequence $\{x^\nu\}$, $\nu = 1, 2, \cdots$, converges to the autofunction of $[\alpha, t]$. Hence the limit of

$$\int_\alpha^{\tilde{\alpha}} x^\nu(s)\, df(s) \quad \text{as } \nu \to \infty$$

exists and equals

$$\int_{[\alpha,t]} df(s).$$

Now

$$\int_\alpha^{\tilde{\alpha}} x^\nu(s)\, df(s) = x^\nu(\tilde{\alpha}) f(\tilde{\alpha}) - x^\nu(\alpha) f(\alpha) - \int_\alpha^{\tilde{\alpha}} f(s)\, dx^\nu(s). \tag{42}$$

The last integral exists as a Riemann integral, by Theorem 9. For sufficiently large ν, then,

$$\int_\alpha^{\tilde{\alpha}} x^\nu(s)\, df(s) = 0 - f(\alpha) - \int_t^{t+1/\nu} f(s)\, dx^\nu(s), \tag{43}$$

by (31). We now evaluate the last integral, which we know to exist as a Riemann integral, using a particular sequence of partitions of $[t, t + 1/\nu]$ with

$$\Delta s = \frac{1}{n\nu}, \qquad n = 1, 2, \cdots.$$

Thus

$$-\int_t^{t+1/\nu} f(s)\,dx^\nu(s) = \lim_{n\to\infty}\left[f\left(t+\frac{1}{n\nu}\right)\frac{1}{n}+f\left(t+\frac{2}{n\nu}\right)\frac{1}{n}+\cdots+f\left(t+\frac{n}{n\nu}\right)\frac{1}{n}\right],$$

since

$$\Delta x^\nu(s) = -\nu\frac{1}{n\nu} = -\frac{1}{n}.$$

Hence

$$-\int_t^{t+1/\nu} f\,dx^\nu = \lim_{n\to\infty}\frac{1}{n}\left[f\left(t+\frac{1}{n\nu}\right)+f\left(t+\frac{2}{n\nu}\right)+\cdots+f\left(t+\frac{1}{\nu}\right)\right].$$

This limits exists. It is near $f(t+0)$, as we now show. Thus

$$-\int_t^{t+1/\nu} f\,dx^\nu - f(t+0) = \lim_{n\to\infty}\frac{1}{n}\sum_{i=1,\cdots,n}\left[f\left(t+\frac{i}{n\nu}\right)-f(t+0)\right].$$

Now

$$\left|f\left(t+\frac{i}{n\nu}\right)-f(t+0)\right| \leqq v\left(t+\frac{i}{n\nu}\right)-v(t+0),$$

a consequence of the fact that

$$\left|f\left(t+\frac{i}{n\nu}\right)-f(t+\eta)\right| \leqq \operatorname{var}\left(f;\left[t+\eta, t+\frac{i}{n\nu}\right]\right)$$

$$= v\left(t+\frac{i}{n\nu}\right)-v(t+\eta), \qquad 0<\eta<\frac{i}{n\nu}.$$

Hence

$$\left|f\left(t+\frac{i}{n\nu}\right)-f(t+0)\right| \leqq v\left(t+\frac{1}{\nu}\right)-v(t+0), \qquad i=1,\cdots,n;$$

and

$$\left|-\int_t^{t+1/\nu} f\,dx^\nu - f(t+0)\right| \leqq v\left(t+\frac{1}{\nu}\right)-v(t+0).$$

Now

$$v\left(t+\frac{1}{\nu}\right)-v(t+0)\to 0 \quad \text{as } \nu\to\infty,$$

whether t is a continuity of v or not. Hence

$$\lim_\nu -\int_t^{t+1/\nu} f\,dx^\nu = f(t+0),$$

and, by (43),

$$\int_{[\alpha,t]} df(s) = f(t+0)-f(\alpha).$$

This completes the proof.

§ 44. **Absolutely continuous masses.** A function f on I is *absolutely continuous* if f is differentiable almost everywhere (relative to Lebesgue measure) on I, if the derivative f_1 of f is Lebesgue integrable on I, and if

$$f(s) = \int_{\alpha}^{s} f_1(\tilde{s})\, d\tilde{s} + f(\alpha), \qquad s \in I. \tag{45}$$

In the notation of § 1 : 2,

$$f \in \boldsymbol{C}_1.$$

Then

$$\Delta f(s) = \int_{s}^{s+\Delta s} f_1(\tilde{s})\, d\tilde{s}, \qquad s,\, s + \Delta s \in I;$$

$$f \in V;$$

and it is natural to suppose that one may replace $df(s)$ by $f_1(s)\, ds$ in

$$\int x(s)\, df(s).$$

The strongest theorem to this effect is on page 126 of [Riesz-Nagy 1] and refers to Lebesgue integrals.

The following elementary lemma is adequate for our applications, including the proof of Corollary 3 : 99.

46. Lemma. *Suppose that f is absolutely continuous on I, with derivative f_1 almost everywhere; and that x is either of bounded variation on I or continuous on I or both. Then the Riemann integral*

$$\int_{\alpha}^{\tilde{\alpha}} x(s)\, df(s) \tag{47}$$

and the Lebesgue integral

$$\int_{I} x(s) f_1(s)\, ds \tag{48}$$

exist and are equal.

Proof. Under either hypothesis on x, by Theorems 27 and 8, the Riemann integral (47) exists and equals

$$\lim_{\|P\| \to 0} \sum,$$

where P is a partition (§ 2) of I,

$$\begin{aligned} \sum = \sum_{i=1,\cdots,m} x(\tilde{s}^i)\, \Delta f(s^{i-1}) &= \sum_i x(\tilde{s}^i) \int_{s^{i-1}}^{s^i} f_1(s)\, ds \\ &= \int_I x^P(s) f_1(s)\, ds, \end{aligned} \tag{49}$$

and x^P is the step function such that

$$x^P(s) = x(\bar{s}^i) \quad \text{if} \quad s^{i-1} < s < s^i, \qquad i = 1, 2, \cdots, m;$$
$$x^P(s^i) \text{ is undefined.}$$

The integrals in (49) come from (45) and are Lebesgue integrals.

Consider a countable sequence of partitions P with $\|P\| \to 0$. Let $\mathscr{J}_s$ be the countable set of points of subdivision of all the partitions and also points of discontinuity of x. If $s \notin \mathscr{J}_s$, then

$$x^P(s) \to x(s) \quad \text{as} \quad \|P\| \to 0,$$

since x is continuous at s. Hence

$$x^P(s)f_1(s) \to x(s)f_1(s) \quad \text{almost everywhere,}$$

since $f_1(s)$ exists almost everywhere. Now

$$|x^P(s)f_1(s)| \leqq |f_1(s)|M,$$

for a suitable constant M; and $|f_1(s)|$ is integrable by hypothesis. Furthermore $x^P(s)f_1(s)$ is integrable, since it is a finite sum of integrable pieces. Hence,

$$\int_I x^P(s)f_1(s)\,ds \to \int_I x(s)f_1(s)\,ds \quad \text{as} \quad \|P\| \to 0,$$

by Lebesgue's Theorem [Riesz-Nagy 1, p. 37]. This completes the proof.

§ 50. *m*-**fold integrals.** For clarity and brevity, we will consider double integrals. The generalization to *m*-fold integrals is quite direct.

Let I be the interval

$$I = I_s \times I_t,$$

where

$$I_s = \{\alpha \leqq s \leqq \tilde{\alpha}\}, \qquad I_t = \{\beta \leqq t \leqq \tilde{\beta}\},$$
$$-\infty < \alpha < \tilde{\alpha} < \infty, \qquad -\infty < \beta < \tilde{\beta} < \infty.$$

By a *partition* P of I we mean the direct product of partitions of I_s and I_t; that is, ordered sets

$$\bar{s}^0, s^0, \bar{s}^1, s^1, \bar{s}^2, \cdots, \bar{s}^m, s^m, \bar{s}^{m+1};$$
$$\bar{t}^0, t^0, \bar{t}^1, t^1, \bar{t}^2, \cdots, \bar{t}^n, t^n, \bar{t}^{n+1};$$

of real numbers such that

(51)
$$\alpha = \bar{s}^0 = s^0 \leqq \bar{s}^1 \leqq s^1 \leqq \cdots \leqq \bar{s}^m \leqq s^m = \bar{s}^{m+1} = \tilde{\alpha},$$
$$\beta = \bar{t}^0 = t^0 \leqq \bar{t}^1 \leqq t^1 \leqq \cdots \leqq \bar{t}^n \leqq t^n = \bar{t}^{n+1} = \tilde{\beta}.$$

Thus $\tilde{s}^0$, s^0 are merely alternative descriptions of α; s^m, $\tilde{s}^{m+1}$ of $\tilde{\alpha}$; and similarly for β and $\tilde{\beta}$. The point $(\tilde{s}^i, \tilde{t}^j)$ is an element of the interval

$$(52) \qquad [s^{i-1}, s^i] \times [t^{j-1}, t^j]; \qquad i = 1, \cdots, m; \qquad j = 1, \cdots, n.$$

A more general definition of partition, which we do not need or use, would replace our $(\tilde{s}^i, \tilde{t}^j)$, for each (i, j), by an arbitrary point $(\tilde{s}^{i,j}, \tilde{t}^{i,j})$ of the interval (52). Our definition of partition leads to simpler theorems and at the same time is entirely adequate because it engenders the full class of Lebesgue integrals, as we shall see.

The *norm* of the partition P is defined as

$$\|P\| = \max\,[\max_{i=1,\cdots,m} (s^i - s^{i-1}), \max_{j=1,\cdots,n} (t^j - t^{j-1})].$$

We describe the intervals (52) as the constituent intervals of P. Thus $\|P\|$ depends on the constituent intervals and not on the points $(\tilde{s}^i, \tilde{t}^j)$. The partition P without the latter points is called a *subdivision* of I.

Suppose that x and f are functions on I to R. For each partition P of I consider the sum

$$(53) \quad \sum \underset{\text{def}}{=} \sum_{\substack{i=1,\cdots,m;\\ j=1,\cdots,n}} x(\tilde{s}^i, \tilde{t}^j)[f(s^i, t^j) - f(s^{i-1}, t^j) - f(s^i, t^{j-1}) + f(s^{i-1}, t^{j-1})].$$

The Riemann integral

$$(54) \qquad \int_\alpha^{\tilde{\alpha}} \int_\beta^{\tilde{\beta}} x(s, t)\, df(s, t) = \iint_I x(s, t)\, df(s, t) = \iint_I x\, df$$

is defined as the limit of $\sum$ as the norm of P approaches zero, if the limit exists. Thus the integral (54) is a real number, determined by x, f, and I, with the following property. For each $\eta > 0$ there exists $\zeta > 0$ such that

$$\left| \iint_I x\, df - \sum \right| < \eta$$

whenever

$$\|P\| < \zeta.$$

The integral (54) with $\tilde{\alpha} = \alpha$ or $\tilde{\beta} = \beta$ is defined as zero.

We denote the *boundary* of I by ∂I, and we say that

$$\int_{\partial I} x\, df$$

exists if the four single integrals

$$(55) \qquad \int_\alpha^{\tilde{\alpha}} x(s, \beta)\, df(s, \beta), \qquad \int_\alpha^{\tilde{\alpha}} x(s, \tilde{\beta})\, df(s, \tilde{\beta}), \qquad \int_\beta^{\tilde{\beta}} x(\alpha, t)\, df(\alpha, t), \qquad \int_\beta^{\tilde{\beta}} x(\tilde{\alpha}, t)\, df(\tilde{\alpha}, t),$$

exist.

56. THEOREM (INTEGRATION BY PARTS). *If*

$$\iint_I x\,df \quad \textit{and} \quad \int_{\partial I} x\,df$$

exist, then so do

$$\iint_I f\,dx \quad \textit{and} \quad \int_{\partial I} f\,dx.$$

Furthermore

$$\begin{aligned}(57)\qquad \int_\alpha^{\tilde\alpha}\int_\beta^{\tilde\beta} f(s,t)\,dx(s,t) &= x(\tilde\alpha,\tilde\beta)f(\tilde\alpha,\tilde\beta) - x(\alpha,\tilde\beta)f(\alpha,\tilde\beta) - x(\tilde\alpha,\beta)f(\tilde\alpha,\beta)\\ &\quad + x(\alpha,\beta)f(\alpha,\beta) - \int_\alpha^{\tilde\alpha} x(s,\tilde\beta)\,df(s,\tilde\beta)\\ &\quad + \int_\alpha^{\tilde\alpha} x(s,\beta)\,df(s,\beta) - \int_\beta^{\tilde\beta} x(\tilde\alpha,t)\,df(\tilde\alpha,t)\\ &\quad + \int_\beta^{\tilde\beta} x(\alpha,t)\,df(\alpha,t) + \int_\alpha^{\tilde\alpha}\int_\beta^{\tilde\beta} x(s,t)\,df(s,t).\end{aligned}$$

PROOF [Young 4]. That $\int_{\partial I} f\,dx$ exists follows from the theory for functions of one variable (Theorem 8).

Put

$$f^{i,j} = f(\tilde s^i, \tilde t^j) \quad \text{and} \quad x^{i,j} = x(s^i, t^j).$$

Then, as the reader may verify,

$$\begin{aligned}\sum_{\substack{i=1,\cdots,m;\\ j=1,\cdots,n}} & f^{i,j}(x^{i,j} - x^{i-1,j} - x^{i,j-1} + x^{i-1,j-1})\\ &= x^{m,n}f^{m+1,n+1} - x^{0,n}f^{0,n+1} - x^{m,0}f^{m+1,0} + x^{0,0}f^{0,0}\\ &\quad - \sum_{i=0,\cdots,m} x^{i,n}(f^{i+1,n+1} - f^{i,n+1}) + \sum_{i=0,\cdots,m} x^{i,0}(f^{i+1,0} - f^{i,0})\\ &\quad - \sum_{j=0,\cdots,n} x^{m,j}(f^{m+1,j+1} - f^{m+1,j}) + \sum_{j=0,\cdots,n} x^{0,j}(f^{0,j+1} - f^{0,j})\\ &\quad + \sum_{\substack{i=0,\cdots,m;\\ j=0,\cdots,n}} x^{i,j}(f^{i+1,j+1} - f^{i,j+1} - f^{i+1,j} + f^{i,j}).\end{aligned}$$

Let $\|P\| \to 0$. The several terms on the right approach the corresponding terms in (57). Hence the sum on the left must approach a limit; and (57) is established. This completes the proof.

By the *lower boundary* of I we mean the two closed segments of the boundary abutting at the corner (α, β). Thus f vanishes on the lower boundary iff

$$(58)\qquad f(s,\beta) = 0 \quad \text{for all} \quad s \in I_s; \qquad \text{and} \quad f(\alpha,t) = 0 \quad \text{for all} \quad t \in I_t.$$

The function f vanishes on the entire boundary iff

$$f(s, t) = 0$$

whenever $s = \alpha$ or $s = \tilde{\alpha}$ or $t = \beta$ or $t = \tilde{\beta}$.

59. COROLLARY. *Suppose that*

$$\iint_I x\, df \quad \text{and} \quad \int_{\partial I} x\, df$$

exist. If f vanishes on the lower boundary,

$$\int_\alpha^{\tilde{\alpha}} \int_\beta^{\tilde{\beta}} f(s, t)\, dx(s, t) = x(\tilde{\alpha}, \tilde{\beta}) f(\tilde{\alpha}, \tilde{\beta}) - \int_\alpha^{\tilde{\alpha}} x(s, \tilde{\beta})\, df(s, \tilde{\beta}) - \int_\beta^{\tilde{\beta}} x(\tilde{\alpha}, t)\, df(\tilde{\alpha}, t) + \int_\alpha^{\tilde{\alpha}} \int_\beta^{\tilde{\beta}} x(s, t)\, df(s, t). \tag{60}$$

If f vanishes on the entire boundary,

$$\int_\alpha^{\tilde{\alpha}} \int_\beta^{\tilde{\beta}} f(s, t)\, dx(s, t) = \int_\alpha^{\tilde{\alpha}} \int_\beta^{\tilde{\beta}} x(s, t)\, df(s, t). \tag{61}$$

PROOF. The relation (57) simplifies to (60) and (61). This completes the proof.

The definition of the integral implies that

$$\int_\alpha^{\tilde{\alpha}} \int_\beta^{\tilde{\beta}} df(s, t) = f(\tilde{\alpha}, \tilde{\beta}) - f(\alpha, \tilde{\beta}) - f(\tilde{\alpha}, \beta) + f(\alpha, \beta). \tag{62}$$

The integral (54) is linear in x and in f.

If the integral (54) exists and if I^1, I^2 are nonoverlapping intervals† whose union is I, then the integrals

$$\iint_{I^1} x\, df, \qquad \iint_{I^2} x\, df$$

exist, and

$$\iint_{I^1} x\, df + \iint_{I^2} x\, df = \iint_I x\, df. \tag{63}$$

64. LEMMA. *If the integrand x is independent of s or t, the double integral*

$$\iint_I x\, df$$

reduces to single integrals. Indeed if x is independent of t,

$$\int_\alpha^{\tilde{\alpha}} \int_\beta^{\tilde{\beta}} x(s)\, df(s, t) = \int_\alpha^{\tilde{\alpha}} x(s)\, df(s, \tilde{\beta}) - \int_\alpha^{\tilde{\alpha}} x(s)\, df(s, \beta). \tag{65}$$

† Definitions are in § 66.

The existence of the integrals on the right implies the existence of the integral on the left. If x is independent of s, the dual relation holds.

Thus the integration with respect to the uncoupled variable may be carried out.

PROOF. The sum in (53) now is

$$\begin{aligned}\sum &= \sum_{i=1,\cdots,m} x(\tilde{s}^i) \sum_{j=1,\cdots,n} [f(s^i, t^j) - f(s^{i-1}, t^j) - f(s^i, t^{j-1}) + f(s^{i-1}, t^{j-1})] \\ &= \sum_i x(\tilde{s}^i)[f(s^i, t^n) - f(s^i, t^0) - f(s^{i-1}, t^n) + f(s^{i-1}, t^0)] \\ &= \sum_i x(\tilde{s}^i)[f(s^i, \tilde{\beta}) - f(s^{i-1}, \tilde{\beta})] - \sum_i x(\tilde{s}^i)[f(s^i, \beta) - f(s^{i-1}, \beta)],\end{aligned}$$

by (51). The last two sums approach

$$\int_\alpha^{\tilde{\alpha}} x(s)\, df(s, \tilde{\beta}), \qquad \int_\alpha^{\tilde{\alpha}} x(s)\, df(s, \beta),$$

respectively, as $\|P\| \to 0$, if the integrals exist. This implies (65), and proves the lemma.

§ 66. **Intervals and increments.** By an *interval* we mean a set

$$H = [a, \tilde{a}] \times [b, \tilde{b}] = \{(s, t) : a \leqq s \leqq \tilde{a} \text{ and } b \leqq t \leqq \tilde{b}\},$$

where

$$-\infty < a \leqq \tilde{a} < \infty, \qquad -\infty < b \leqq \tilde{b} < \infty.$$

Thus H may reduce to a line segment or a point. Two intervals are *non-overlapping* if they have no common interior points.

If f is a function on part of $\mathsf{R} \times \mathsf{R}$ to R, we write

$$\begin{aligned}\Delta_s f &= \Delta_s f(s, t) = f(s + \Delta s, t) - f(s, t), \\ \Delta_t f &= \text{dual},\end{aligned}$$

(67) $$\begin{aligned}\Delta_s \Delta_t f &= \Delta_{s,t} f = \Delta_{s,t} f(s, t) \\ &= f(s + \Delta s, t + \Delta t) - f(s, t + \Delta t) - f(s + \Delta s, t) + f(s, t).\end{aligned}$$

These increments are defined iff f is defined at the appropriate points. If $\Delta s \geqq 0$, $\Delta t \geqq 0$, we sometimes write

$$\Delta_{s,t} f = \Delta_H f,$$

where

$$H = [s, s + \Delta s] \times [t, t + \Delta t].$$

If $\Delta s = 0$, then

$$\Delta_s f = 0 \quad \text{and} \quad \Delta_{s,t} f = 0.$$

Likewise if $\Delta t = 0$.

If f is independent of s, then

$$\Delta_s f = 0 \quad \text{and} \quad \Delta_{s,t} f = 0.$$

Likewise if f is independent of t.

The sum (53) which enters in the definition of

$$\iint_I x(s, t)\, df(s, t) \tag{68}$$

may be written

$$\sum = \sum_{\substack{i=1,\cdots,m;\\ j=1,\cdots,n}} x(\tilde{s}^i, \tilde{t}^j)\, \Delta_{H^{i,j}} f, \tag{69}$$

where

$$H^{i,j} = [s^{i-1}, s^i] \times [t^{j-1}, t^j].$$

It follows that *the integral* (68) exists and *vanishes if f is independent of s or if f is independent of t.* Hence we may replace f in the definition of (68) by

$$f - \phi - \psi,$$

where ϕ is a function independent of s and ψ is a function independent of t. In particular, we may replace f by g, where

$$g(s, t) = f(s, t) - f(\alpha, t) - f(s, \beta) + f(\alpha, \beta).$$

Note that g vanishes on the lower boundary of I. We call g the *partial normalization* of f.

70. LEMMA. *If an interval H is the union of intervals $H^1, H^2, \cdots, H^q$, no two of which overlap, and f is a function, then*

$$\Delta_H f = \Delta_{H^1} f + \Delta_{H^2} f + \cdots + \Delta_{H^q} f, \tag{71}$$

providing that the terms on the right are defined.

PROOF. It is sufficient to prove the lemma for the case $q = 2$. Suppose that H is the union of nonoverlapping intervals H^1 and H^2. Then H^1 and H^2 have a common edge, parallel to the s or t-axis. For preciseness assume the first. Then

$$H^1 = [a, a'] \times [b, b'],$$
$$H^2 = [a, a'] \times [b', b''],$$
$$H = [a, a'] \times [b, b''].$$

The relation

$$\Delta_H f = \Delta_{H^1} f + \Delta_{H^2} f$$

follows; and the proof is complete.

§ 72. **The extension of a function.** If f is a function on I to R, we define the *extension* of f as the function e such that

$$e(s, t) = f(s', t'), \qquad s, t \in \mathsf{R},$$

where

$$s' = \begin{cases} \alpha & \text{if } s < \alpha, \\ s & \text{if } \alpha \leqq s \leqq \tilde{\alpha}, \\ \tilde{\alpha} & \text{if } \tilde{\alpha} < s; \end{cases} \qquad t' = \begin{cases} \beta & \text{if } t < \beta, \\ t & \text{if } \beta \leqq t \leqq \tilde{\beta}, \\ \tilde{\beta} & \text{if } \tilde{\beta} < t. \end{cases}$$

Thus e is defined everywhere on $\mathsf{R} \times \mathsf{R}$. If we fix one of the variables s or t, the extension as now defined is consistent with the extension as defined in § 11.

73. Lemma. *If f is a function on I and e is the extension of f, then*

(74) $$\Delta_H\, e = \Delta_{H \cap I} f$$

for all intervals H. In particular

(75) $$\begin{aligned} \Delta_H\, e &= \Delta_H f \quad \text{if } H \subset I, \\ \Delta_H\, e &= 0 \qquad\ \ \text{if } H \text{ and } I \text{ do not overlap.} \end{aligned}$$

Proof. Produce the boundaries of I and thereby divide the plane $\mathsf{R} \times \mathsf{R}$ into nine closed nonoverlapping regions, one of which is I itself. In any one of these closed regions other than I, the extension e is either constant or independent of s or independent of t. Hence

$$\Delta_H\, e = 0$$

whenever $H \subset$ one of the eight closed regions.

If $H \subset I$, then

$$e(s, t) = f(s, t), \qquad (s, t) \in H;$$

and

$$\Delta_H\, e = \Delta_H f.$$

Now any interval H may be written as the union of $H \cap I$ and a finite number of other intervals, each in one of the other eight closed regions. By Lemma 70,

$$\Delta_H\, e = \Delta_{H \cap I} f + 0 = \Delta_{H \cap I} f.$$

This establishes (74), which implies (75). The proof is complete.

In considering functions defined on the basic interval I, we will henceforth replace each function f by its extension and denote the latter by the same letter f.

§ 76. **Entirely increasing functions.** Consider a function f on I and the extension of f. We say that f is *entirely increasing* if

(77) $$\Delta_H f \geqq 0 \quad \text{for all intervals } H,$$

and for every fixed s^0, $f(s^0, t)$ is an increasing function of t, and for every fixed t^0, $f(s, t^0)$ is an increasing function of s.

78. Lemma. *A function f is entirely increasing if*

(79) $$\Delta_H f \geqq 0 \quad \textit{for all intervals } H \subset I$$

and f is an increasing function on each of the two segments of the lower boundary of I.

Proof. The condition (79) implies (77), by Lemma 73.

Consider a fixed s^0. If $s^0 \geqq \alpha$, put

$$H = [\alpha, s^0] \times [t, t'], \qquad t' \geqq t;$$

then (77) implies that

$$f(s^0, t') - f(\alpha, t') - f(s^0, t) + f(\alpha, t) \geqq 0$$

and

$$f(s^0, t') - f(s^0, t) \geqq f(\alpha, t') - f(\alpha, t) \geqq 0,$$

since f is increasing on the lower boundary. If, on the other hand, $s^0 < \alpha$, then

$$f(s^0, t) = f(\alpha, t), \qquad t \in \mathsf{R}.$$

In either case, $f(s^0, t)$ is an increasing function of t.

Since the dual argument applies to $f(s, t^0)$ for each fixed t^0, the proof is complete.

80. Lemma. *If a function f is entirely increasing, then*

(81) $$|f(s', t') - f(s, t)| \leqq |f(s', \tilde{\beta}) - f(s, \tilde{\beta})| + |f(\tilde{\alpha}, t') - f(\tilde{\alpha}, t)|$$

for all $s, t, s', t' \in \mathsf{R}$.

Proof. Consider the difference

$$f(s, t') - f(s, t)$$

first. If $t' \geqq t$ and $s \leqq \tilde{\alpha}$, then by (77),

$$f(\tilde{\alpha}, t') - f(s, t') - f(\tilde{\alpha}, t) + f(s, t) \geqq 0;$$

hence, since f is increasing in each variable separately,

$$f(\tilde{\alpha}, t') - f(\tilde{\alpha}, t) \geqq f(s, t') - f(s, t) \geqq 0$$

and

(82) $$|f(s, t') - f(s, t)| \leqq |f(\tilde{\alpha}, t') - f(\tilde{\alpha}, t)|.$$

It follows by interchange of t and t' that (82) holds if $t' \leqq t$ and $s \leqq \tilde{\alpha}$. Thus (82) holds whenever $s \leqq \tilde{\alpha}$. If $s > \tilde{\alpha}$, then (82) with equality holds, by the definition of the extension of f. Thus (82) holds in all cases.

Likewise

$$|f(s', t') - f(s, t')| \leqq |f(s', \tilde{\beta}) - f(s, \tilde{\beta})|.$$

This relation and (82) imply (81). Thus the proof is complete.

The next theorem involves limits such as $f(s - 0, t + 0)$ or $f(s - 0, t)$. These are defined in the natural way:

$$f(s - 0, t + 0) = \lim_{(\eta,\zeta)\to(0+,0+)} f(s - \eta, t + \zeta),$$

$$f(s - 0, t) = \lim_{\eta\to 0+} f(s - \eta, t).$$

83. THEOREM. *If a function f is entirely increasing, then the limits*

(84) $f(s + 0, t + 0),\quad f(s - 0, t + 0),\quad f(s + 0, t - 0),\quad f(s - 0, t - 0)$

in the four open quadrants exist, and the limits

(85) $f(s + 0, t),\quad f(s - 0, t),\quad f(s, t + 0),\quad f(s, t - 0)$

on the four half axes exist, for all $s, t \in \mathsf{R}$. Also,

$$f(s - 0, t - 0) \leqq \begin{Bmatrix} f(s - 0, t) \\ f(s, t - 0) \end{Bmatrix} \leqq f(s, t) \leqq \begin{Bmatrix} f(s + 0, t) \\ f(s, t + 0) \end{Bmatrix} \leqq f(s + 0, t + 0), \tag{86}$$

$$\begin{aligned} &f(s - 0, t) \leqq f(s - 0, t + 0) \leqq f(s, t + 0), \\ &f(s, t - 0) \leqq f(s + 0, t - 0) \leqq f(s + 0, t). \end{aligned} \tag{87}$$

It follows from the theorem that f is continuous at (s, t) iff

$$f(s - 0, t - 0) = f(s + 0, t + 0).$$

PROOF. We will use Lemma 80 and Cauchy's criterion for the existence of a limit. If (s, t) and (s', t') approach (s^0, t^0) staying in one open quadrant, then s and s' stay on one side of s^0; and t and t' stay on one side of t^0. Since $f(s, \tilde{\beta})$ is an increasing function of s, the limits $f(s^0 + 0, \tilde{\beta})$ and $f(s^0 - 0, \tilde{\beta})$ surely exist. Hence

$$|f(s', \tilde{\beta}) - f(s, \tilde{\beta})| \to 0$$

as s' and $s \to s^0$ on one side. Likewise for $f(\tilde{\alpha}, t)$. It follows that

$$|f(s', t') - f(s, t)| \to 0$$

as (s', t') and $(s, t) \to (s^0, t^0)$ in one open quadrant, by Lemma 80. Hence the limits (84) exist.

The limits (85) exist, since f is an increasing function in each variable separately. For the same reason the inequalities (86) and (87) hold. This completes the proof.

88. THEOREM. *Suppose that a function* f *is entirely increasing. Let* $\mathscr{J}_s \subset I_s$ *be the countable set of discontinuities of* $f(s, \tilde{\beta})$ *and* $\mathscr{J}_t \subset I_t$ *the dual. Then* f *is continuous in* (s, t) *at* (s^0, t^0) *if*

(89) $$s^0 \notin \mathscr{J}_s \quad \text{and} \quad t^0 \notin \mathscr{J}_t.$$

Thus the discontinuities of f lie on countably many lines parallel to one or other axis. The condition (89) is sufficient but not necessary.

PROOF. Since $f(s, \tilde{\beta})$ is an increasing function of s, its discontinuities $\mathscr{J}_s$ are indeed a countable subset of I_s.

The theorem follows immediately from the fact that

$$|f(s, t) - f(s^0, t^0)| \leqq |f(s, \tilde{\beta}) - f(s^0, \tilde{\beta})| + |f(\tilde{\alpha}, t) - f(\tilde{\alpha}, t^0)|,$$

by Lemma 80. Because of (89), the two absolutes on the right $\to 0$ as $s \to s^0$ and $t \to t^0$. The proof is complete.

For further study (which we do not need) of the discontinuities of monotone functions, the reader may consult [Young 5].

§ 90. **Functions of bounded variation.** Consider a function f on I and the extension of f. For any interval H we define the *variation* of f on H as

(91) $$\operatorname{var}(f; H) = \sup \sum |\Delta_{s,t} f|,$$

where the supremum is taken over all subdivisions (§ 50) of H and the summation is taken over the constituent intervals of the subdivision. In particular

$$\operatorname{var}(f; H) = 0$$

if H does not overlap I or if H is a line segment or if H is a point or if f is independent of s or if f is independent of t.

As in the one-dimensional case,

$$\operatorname{var}(f \pm g; H) \leqq \operatorname{var}(f; H) + \operatorname{var}(g; H);$$

and

(92) $$\left| \iint_H x(s, t)\, df(s, t) \right| \leqq \sup_{(s,t) \in H} |x(s, t)| \operatorname{var}(f; H)$$

whenever the integral exists.

Consider a subdivision of an interval H and the corresponding sum

(93) $$\sum |\Delta_{s,t} f|.$$

If we further divide H by adding a segment to the lines of subdivision, we thereby do not decrease the sum (93). This is because certain differences $\Delta_{s,t} f$ are replaced by two others whose algebraic sum equals the original difference (Lemma 70). Since $\operatorname{var}(f; H)$ is a supremum, it follows that

(94) $$\operatorname{var}(f; H) = \operatorname{var}(f; H^1) + \operatorname{var}(f; H^2)$$

whenever H^1, H^2 are nonoverlapping intervals whose union is H. Thus var $(f; H)$ *is an additive function of* H.

For all intervals H in $\mathsf{R} \times \mathsf{R}$,

$$0 \leqq \text{var}\,(f; H) \leqq \text{var}\,(f; I). \tag{95}$$

We say that f is of *bounded variation* on I and we write

$$f \in V,$$

if

$$\text{var}\,(f; I) < \infty$$

and for every fixed s^0, $f(s^0, t)$ is of bounded variation on I_t, and for every fixed t^0, $f(s, t^0)$ is of bounded variation on I_s.

96. LEMMA. *A function f is of bounded variation if*

$$\text{var}\,(f; I) < \infty,$$

and for one s^0, $f(s^0, t)$ is of bounded variation on I_t, and for one t^0, $f(s, t^0)$ is of bounded variation on I_s.

PROOF [Young 3]. It will be sufficient to show that for each fixed s, $f(s, t)$ is of bounded variation on I_t. Now

$$\begin{aligned}\Delta_t f(s, t) &= f(s, t + \Delta t) - f(s, t) \\ &= [f(s, t + \Delta t) - f(s, t) - f(s^0, t + \Delta t) + f(s^0, t)] \\ &\quad + [f(s^0, t + \Delta t) - f(s^0, t)].\end{aligned}$$

Take $\Delta t \geqq 0$. Then

$$|\Delta_t f(s, t)| \leqq |\Delta_{s,t} f| + |\Delta_t f(s^0, t)|$$

whether $s \geqq s^0$ or $s < s^0$. For each s and for any subdivision of I, then,

$$\sum |\Delta_t f(s, t)| \leqq \text{var}\,(f; I) + \text{var}\,(f(s^0, t); I_t) < \infty,$$

where the sum on the left is the sum that corresponds to a subdivision of I_t. Hence for each fixed s, $f(s, t)$ is of bounded variation on I_t. This completes the proof.

Consider a function f such that

$$\text{var}\,(f; I) < \infty. \tag{97}$$

Let g be the partial normalization of f, that is, the function such that

$$g(s, t) = f(s, t) - f(\alpha, t) - f(s, \beta) + f(\alpha, \beta), \quad \text{all } s, t. \tag{98}$$

We have seen in § 66 that

$$\Delta_{s,t}\, g = \Delta_{s,t} f$$

for all intervals. Hence

$$\text{var}\,(g; I) = \text{var}\,(f; I). \tag{99}$$

Now g vanishes on the lower boundary of I and so is of bounded variation on each segment of the lower boundary. It follows by Lemma 96 that g is of bounded variation on I. Thus the condition (97) alone implies that

$$g \in V,$$

where g is the partial normalization of f.

The extension of g, as defined in § 72, is consistent with g itself, as based on the extension of f.

§ 100. **The variations of** f. Consider a function $f \in V$. Let g be the partial normalization (98) of f. Define functions

$$v, \quad p, \quad q, \quad v^1, \quad p^1, \quad q^1, \quad v^2, \quad p^2, \quad q^2$$

as follows:

$$v(s, t) = \begin{cases} \operatorname{var}(f; [\alpha, s] \times [\beta, t]) = \operatorname{var}(g; [\alpha, s] \times [\beta, t]) & \text{if } s \geqq \alpha \text{ and } t \geqq \beta, \\ 0 & \text{otherwise;} \end{cases} \tag{101}$$

$$p(s, t) = \frac{v(s, t) + g(s, t)}{2}; \tag{102}$$

$$q(s, t) = \frac{v(s, t) - g(s, t)}{2}; \tag{103}$$

$$v^1(s) = \begin{cases} \operatorname{var}(f(s, \beta); [\alpha, s]) & \text{if } s \geqq \alpha, \\ 0 & \text{otherwise;} \end{cases} \tag{104}$$

$$p^1(s) = \frac{v^1(s) + f(s, \beta) - f(\alpha, \beta)}{2}; \tag{105}$$

$$q^1(s) = \frac{v^1(s) - f(s, \beta) + f(\alpha, \beta)}{2}; \tag{106}$$

$$v^2(t) = \begin{cases} \operatorname{var}(f(\alpha, t); [\beta, t]) & \text{if } t \geqq \beta, \\ 0 & \text{otherwise;} \end{cases} \tag{107}$$

$$p^2(t) = \frac{v^2(t) + f(\alpha, t) - f(\alpha, \beta)}{2}; \tag{108}$$

$$q^2(t) = \frac{v^2(t) - f(\alpha, t) + f(\alpha, \beta)}{2}. \tag{109}$$

The functions v, v^1, v^2 are called *total variations*, p, p^1, p^2 *positive variations*, and q, q^1, q^2 *negative variations*.

110. THEOREM. *Suppose that $f \in V$. Then the variations v, p, q are entirely increasing, vanish on the lower boundary of I, and are bounded by* var $(f; I)$. *The variations v^1, p^1, q^1 are increasing, vanish on the lower boundary of I_s, and are bounded by* var $(f(s,\beta); I_s)$. *Likewise for v^2, p^2, q^2. Also*

$$(111) \qquad v(s, t) = p(s, t) + q(s, t),$$

$$(112) \qquad g(s, t) = p(s, t) - q(s, t),$$

$$(113) \qquad v^1(s) = p^1(s) + q^1(s),$$

$$(114) \qquad f(s, \beta) - f(\alpha, \beta) = p^1(s) - q^1(s),$$

$$(115) \qquad v^2(t) = p^2(t) + q^2(t),$$

$$(116) \qquad f(\alpha, t) - f(\alpha, \beta) = p^2(t) - q^2(t),$$

$$(117) \qquad f(s, t) = p(s, t) - q(s, t) + p^1(s) - q^1(s) + p^2(t) - q^2(t) + f(\alpha, \beta), \qquad s, t \in \mathsf{R}.$$

PROOF. The relations (111)–(116) are immediate and imply (117), since

$$f(s, t) = g(s, t) + f(\alpha, t) + f(s, \beta) - f(\alpha, \beta)$$

by (98). The stated properties of $v^1, p^1, q^1, v^2, p^2, q^2$ have been established in the theory for functions of one variable (Theorem 22).

It remains to show that v, p, q are entirely increasing, vanish on the lower boundary of I, and are bounded by var $(f; I)$.

Consider

$$\Delta_{s,t}\, v = v(s + \Delta s, t + \Delta t) - v(s, t + \Delta t) - v(s + \Delta s, t) + v(s, t),$$

where

$$\alpha \leqq s \leqq s + \Delta s, \qquad \beta \leqq t \leqq t + \Delta t.$$

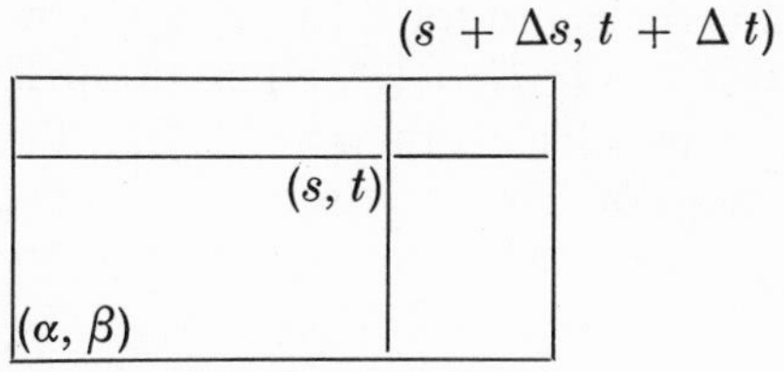

By (94) and the diagram,

$$\Delta_{s,t}\, v = \text{var}\,(f; [s, s + \Delta s] \times [t, t + \Delta t]).$$

Now a simple subdivision of $[s, s + \Delta s] \times [t, t + \Delta t]$ is the interval itself. Hence, by the definition of the variation as a supremum,

$$\Delta_{s,t}\, v \geqq |\Delta_{s,t} f| = |\Delta_{s,t}\, g|.$$

Hence

$$\Delta_{s,t}\, v \geqq 0$$

and, by (102), (103),

$$\Delta_{s,t}\, p \geqq 0, \qquad \Delta_{s,t}\, q \geqq 0.$$

Since v, p, q all vanish whenever $s \leqq \alpha$ and whenever $t \leqq \beta$, the last inequalities hold for all (s, t). Also, v, p, q are increasing functions on each segment of the lower boundary of I, since zero is an increasing function. Hence v, p, q are entirely increasing, by Lemma 78. Hence v, p, q are nonnegative.

Finally

$$v(s, t) \leqq \operatorname{var}(f; I), \qquad s, t \in \mathsf{R},$$

by (95); and

$$p(s, t) \leqq v(s, t), \qquad q(s, t) \leqq v(s, t),$$

by (111). This completes the proof.

Consider a function $f \in V$ and the variations of f. Theorem 110 implies the following. Let $\mathscr{J}_s$ be the set of points at which

$$p(s, \tilde{\beta}) \quad \text{or} \quad q(s, \tilde{\beta}) \quad \text{or} \quad p^1(s) \quad \text{or} \quad q^1(s)$$

is discontinuous. Then $\mathscr{J}_s$ is a countable subset of I_s. Similarly let $\mathscr{J}_t$ be the countable subset of I_t at which

$$p(\tilde{\alpha}, t) \quad \text{or} \quad q(\tilde{\alpha}, t) \quad \text{or} \quad p^2(t) \quad \text{or} \quad q^2(t)$$

is discontinuous. *If*

$$s^0 \notin \mathscr{J}_s \quad \textit{and} \quad t^0 \notin \mathscr{J}_t,$$

then

$$\begin{aligned} &p^1, q^1, v^1 \quad \textit{are continuous at} \quad s^0, \\ &p^2, q^2, v^2 \quad \textit{are continuous at} \quad t^0, \textit{ and} \\ &p, q, v, f \quad \textit{are continuous at} \quad (s^0, t^0). \end{aligned}$$

Furthermore for all s^0, t^0 without exception the limits of f and all its variations as $(s, t) \to (s^0, t^0)$ in an open quadrant or on a half axis all exist.

Consider a function $f \in V$. The relation (117) implies that f is the difference of two entirely increasing functions: $p + p^1 + p^2 + f(\alpha, \beta)$ and $q + q^1 + q^2$. Conversely, if f^1 and f^2 are entirely increasing functions, then

$$f^1 - f^2 \in V.$$

For, $f^1 - f^2$ is of bounded variation on each segment of the lower boundary, since f^1, f^2 are increasing there. Furthermore,

$$\begin{aligned} \operatorname{var}(f^1 - f^2; I) &\leqq \operatorname{var}(f^1; I) + \operatorname{var}(f^2; I) \\ &= \Delta_I f^1 + \Delta_I f^2 < \infty, \end{aligned}$$

since, for any subdivision of I,

$$\sum |\Delta_{s,t} f^k| = \sum \Delta_{s,t} f^k = \Delta_I f^k, \qquad k = 1, 2,$$

because f^k is entirely increasing. Hence $f^1 - f^2 \in V$.

It may be of interest to note the following facts about the variations, which we do not prove or use. Suppose that $f \in V$. Let g be the partial normalization (98) of f. The decomposition (112)

$$g = p - q$$

is minimal in the following sense: If

$$g = f^1 - f^2$$

where f^1, f^2 are entirely increasing functions, then

$$\Delta_{s,t} f^1 \geqq \Delta_{s,t}\, p,$$
$$\Delta_{s,t} f^2 \geqq \Delta_{s,t}\, q,$$

for all $\Delta s, \Delta t \geqq 0$ and all s, t.

For all $s, t \in \mathsf{R}$, either

$$p(s + 0, t + 0) - p(s, t + 0) - p(s + 0, t) + p(s, t) = 0$$

or

$$q(s + 0, t + 0) - q(s, t + 0) - q(s + 0, t) + q(s, t) = 0$$

or both. Similar statements hold for

$$(s - 0, t + 0), \quad (s + 0, t - 0), \quad \text{and} \quad (s - 0, t - 0).$$

§ 118. Integration relative to $f \in V$.

119. THEOREM. *If x is continuous on I and f is of bounded variation on I, then*

$$\iint_I x\, df \quad \textit{and} \quad \int_{\partial I} x\, df$$

exist.

It follows that the integrals with x and f interchanged also exist, by Theorem 56.

PROOF. Since f is of bounded variation on I, f is also of bounded variation on the boundary of I. Hence

$$\int_{\partial I} x\, df$$

exists, by the one-dimensional theory.

Now consider

$$\iint_I x\, df = \iint_I x\, dg = \iint_I x\, (dp - dq),$$

where g is the partial normalization of f and p, q are the positive and negative variations (102), (103) of f. By Theorem 110, p and q are entirely increasing. The classical argument implies that

$$\iint_I x\, dp, \qquad \iint_I x\, dq$$

exist. This completes the proof.

120. THEOREM. *Suppose that f is of bounded variation on I. In order that*

$$\iint_I x(s, t)\, df(s, t) = 0 \tag{121}$$

for all continuous functions x on I, it is necessary and sufficient that the partial normalization g of f vanish except on a countable set of lines different from the sides of I and parallel to a side.

The condition may be stated as follows. There exist countable sets $\mathscr{I}_s$ and $\mathscr{I}_t$ such that

$$\begin{aligned} &g(s, t) = 0 \quad \text{whenever} \quad s \notin \mathscr{I}_s \quad \text{and} \quad t \notin \mathscr{I}_t; \\ &\mathscr{I}_s \subset (\alpha, \tilde{\alpha}) = \text{interior of } I_s, \qquad \mathscr{I}_t \subset (\beta, \tilde{\beta}). \end{aligned} \tag{122}$$

Thus g must vanish at the corners of I.

PROOF. Replace f in the integral by g, as is permissible by § 66.

The condition (122) is sufficient. For, we may evaluate the integral

$$\iint_I x(s, t)\, dg(s, t),$$

known to exist, by a sequence of partitions (§ 50) of I, with arbitrarily small norm, in all of which the points s^i of subdivision are not in $\mathscr{I}_s$ and the points t^j of subdivision are not in $\mathscr{I}_t$. For each of these partitions, $\sum$ vanishes, since

$$\Delta_{s,t}\, g = 0.$$

This implies (121).

We shall now establish the necessity of (122). Note first that

$$g(\alpha, \beta) = g(\tilde{\alpha}, \beta) = g(\alpha, \tilde{\beta}) = 0,$$

since g vanishes on the lower boundary of I. Now we may put x equal to unity in (121). Hence

$$\iint_I df = 0 = \iint_I dg = g(\tilde{\alpha}, \tilde{\beta}) - g(\alpha, \tilde{\beta}) - g(\tilde{\alpha}, \beta) + g(\alpha, \beta) = g(\tilde{\alpha}, \tilde{\beta}),$$

by (62). Thus g vanishes at the corners of I.

Next suppose that x is independent of t; that is, that

$$x \in C_0(I_s).$$

Then, by (65),

$$\iint_I x(s)\, dg(s, t) = 0 = \int_{I_s} x(s)\, dg(s, \tilde{\beta}).$$

It follows by Theorem 30 that

$$g(s, \tilde{\beta}) = 0 \tag{123}$$

with countable exceptions interior to I_s. The dual argument applies to $g(\tilde{\alpha}, t)$.

Let $\mathscr{J}_s$ be the countable set of discontinuities of $v(s, \tilde{\beta})$ other than $s = \alpha$ and $s = \tilde{\alpha}$ together with the points at which (123) fails, where v is the total variation (101). Define $\mathscr{J}_t$ dually.

Since g vanishes on the lower boundary of I, its behaviour on the entire boundary is in accord with condition (122).

Consider any point (s^0, t^0) such that

$$\alpha < s^0 < \tilde{\alpha}, \qquad s^0 \notin \mathscr{J}_s,$$
$$\beta < t^0 < \tilde{\beta}, \qquad t^0 \notin \mathscr{J}_t.$$

We shall show that

$$g(s^0, t^0) = 0.$$

Define the continuous function x^ν for each positive integer ν as follows:

$$x^\nu(s, t) = \theta^\nu(s^0, s)\theta^\nu(t^0, t),$$

where θ^ν is given by (31). Thus $x^\nu(s, t)$ is always between 0 and 1, equals unity when $s \leqq s^0$ and $t \leqq t^0$, and vanishes when either $s \geqq s^0 + 1/\nu$ or $t \geqq t^0 + 1/\nu$.

For sufficiently large ν, by the additivity of the integral,

$$\iint_I x^\nu\, dg = 0 = \int_\alpha^{s^0} \int_\beta^{t^0} dg + \gamma = g(s^0, t^0) + \gamma,$$

where

$$\gamma = \int_{s^0}^{s^0+1/\nu} \int_\beta^{t^0} x^\nu\, dg + \int_\alpha^{s^0} \int_{t^0}^{t^0+1/\nu} x^\nu\, dg + \int_{s^0}^{s^0+1/\nu} \int_{t^0}^{t^0+1/\nu} x^\nu\, dg + 0.$$

Now

$$|\gamma| \leqq \int_{s^0}^{s^0+1/\nu} \int_\beta^{t^0} dv + \int_\alpha^{s^0} \int_{t^0}^{t^0+1/\nu} dv + \int_{s^0}^{s^0+1/\nu} \int_{t^0}^{t^0+1/\nu} dv$$
$$= v\left(s^0 + \frac{1}{\nu}, t^0 + \frac{1}{\nu}\right) - v(s^0, t^0) \to 0 \qquad \text{as } \nu \to \infty,$$

because v is continuous at (s^0, t^0) by Theorem 88. Hence

$$g(s^0, t^0) = 0,$$

and the proof is complete.

Consider a function $f \in V$. We have defined the partial normalization g of f in § 66. We now define the *normalization* of f as the function h, where

$$(124) \qquad h(s, t) = \begin{cases} g(s + 0, t + 0) & \text{if } s > \alpha \text{ and } t > \beta, \\ 0 & \text{otherwise.} \end{cases}$$

Thus h vanishes on the lower boundary of I; and, everywhere except possibly on the lower boundary of I,

$$(125) \qquad h(s + 0, t + 0) = h(s, t).$$

Furthermore, h is a function of bounded variation, because by (112),

$$\left.\begin{aligned} g(s, t) &= p(s, t) - q(s, t), \\ g(s + 0, t + 0) &= p(s + 0, t + 0) - q(s + 0, t + 0), \end{aligned}\right\} \text{all } s, t;$$

p, q are entirely increasing functions; and, omitting details,

$$\text{var}\,(h; I) \leqq \text{var}\,(f; I).$$

Thus

$$h \in V^0,$$

where V^0 is the space of normalized functions of bounded variation defined in § 6 : 3.

Now the difference $h - g$ vanishes except possibly on a countable set of lines different from the sides of I and parallel to a side. For, both $h(s, t)$ and $g(s, t)$ vanish unless $\alpha < s$ and $\beta < t$. Suppose $\alpha < s$ and $\beta < t$. Then the difference $h(s, t) - g(s, t)$ vanishes if

$$(126) \qquad g(s + 0, t + 0) = g(s, t).$$

This equality holds at

$$(s, t) = (\tilde{\alpha}, \tilde{\beta}),$$

by the definition of the extension of a function. The equality (126), with $s = \tilde{\alpha}$, holds except for countably many values of t interior to I_t. Likewise if $t = \tilde{\beta}$. Now consider points (s, t) strictly interior to I. The equality (126) then holds except possibly when s takes on a countable set of values interior to I_s or when t takes on a countable set of values in I_t.

Thus $h - g$ satisfies the hypothesis of Theorem 120, with f replaced by $h - g$. Hence

$$\iint_I x\, d(g - h) = 0,$$

$$\iint_I x\, dh = \iint_I x\, dg = \iint_I x\, df,$$

for all functions x continuous on I. It will follow that measurability and integrability of a function relative to f imply as their counterparts relative to the normalization of f, with equality of the integrals.

§ 127. **The Lebesgue double integral.** Consider a function $f \in V$. The total variation v, defined in (101), is an entirely increasing function. We sometimes write $|f|$ for v.

A set A of points in $\mathsf{R} \times \mathsf{R}$ is said to be an $|f|$-*null set* if for each $\eta > 0$ there exists a countable set of open intervals whose union contains A and which are such that

$$\sum \Delta_{s,t}\, v < \eta.$$

Measurability relative to f, integrability relative to f, and the Lebesgue integral

$$\iint x(s, t)\, df(s, t) = \iint\limits_{\mathsf{R}\times\mathsf{R}} x(s, t)\, df(s, t) = \iint\limits_{I} x(s, t)\, df(s, t)$$

are now defined just as in § 34.

The five formulas of Theorem 39 generalize to twenty-five formulas, all of which can be deduced from the following assertion. Suppose that f vanishes on the lower boundary of I. Then

$$\text{(128)} \qquad \iint\limits_{\substack{\alpha \leqq s \leqq s^0,\\ \beta \leqq t \leqq \tilde{\beta}}} df(s, t) = f(s^0 + 0, \tilde{\beta}), \qquad \alpha < s^0 \leqq \tilde{\alpha}.$$

To prove this assertion, note that the integral on the left is the limit as $\nu \to \infty$ of

$$\int_{\alpha}^{\tilde{\alpha}} \int_{\beta}^{\tilde{\beta}} x^{\nu}(s)\, df(s, t),$$

where

$$x^{\nu}(s) = \theta^{\nu}(s^0, s)$$

and θ^{ν} is given in (31). Now,

$$\int_{\alpha}^{\tilde{\alpha}} \int_{\beta}^{\tilde{\beta}} x^{\nu}(s)\, df(s, t) = \int_{\alpha}^{\tilde{\alpha}} x^{\nu}(s)\, df(s, \tilde{\beta}) \to \int_{\alpha \leqq s \leqq s^0} df(s, \tilde{\beta}) \quad \text{as } \nu \to \infty.$$

The last integral equals $f(s^0 + 0, \tilde{\beta})$, by Theorem 39. Thus (128) is established.

§ 129. **Absolutely continuous f.** A function f on I is *absolutely continuous* if there exist functions $f^{1,1}, f^{1,0}, f^{0,1}$ such that

(i) $$f(s, t) = \int_\alpha^s \int_\beta^t f^{1,1}(s, t)\, ds\, dt + \int_\alpha^s f^{1,0}(s)\, ds + \int_\beta^t f^{0,1}(t)\, dt + f(\alpha, \beta), \quad (s, t) \in I;$$

(ii) $f^{1,1}$ is defined almost everywhere on I and is Lebesgue integrable on I;

(iii) $f^{1,0}$ is defined almost everywhere on I_s and is Lebesgue integrable on I_s;

(iv) $f^{0,1}$ satisfies the dual condition.

[Carathéodory 1, p. 654.] Then $f \in V$; and

$$\Delta_{s,t} f = \int_s^{s+\Delta s} \int_t^{t+\Delta t} f^{1,1}(\tilde{s}, \tilde{t})\, d\tilde{s}\, d\tilde{t}$$

$$= \int_s^{s+\Delta s} \int_t^{t+\Delta t} f_{1,1}(\tilde{s}, \tilde{t})\, d\tilde{s}\, d\tilde{t},$$

where the integrals are Lebesgue integrals and $f_{1,1}$ is the cross-derivative $D_s D_t f$ which exists almost everywhere and equals $f^{1,1}$ almost everywhere.

130. LEMMA. *Suppose that f is absolutely continuous on I with cross-derivative $f_{1,1}$ almost everywhere; and that x is of bounded variation on I or continuous on I or both. Then the Riemann integral*

$$\int_\alpha^{\bar{\alpha}} \int_\beta^{\bar{\beta}} x(s, t)\, df(s, t)$$

and the Lebesgue integral

$$\int_\alpha^{\bar{\alpha}} \int_\beta^{\bar{\beta}} x(s, t) f_{1,1}(s, t)\, ds\, dt$$

exist and are equal.

The proof is precisely like that of Lemma 46.

131. REMARK. There are some theorems on the relation of Riemann and Lebesgue integrals of functions of a single variable whose analogues for functions of two variables do not seem to be in the literature. An instance is the theorem that a bounded function x which is Riemann integrable relative to f is Lebesgue integrable relative to f, where $f \in V$ [Graves 1, p. 279]. For continuous x the theorem is easily proved, as we have seen. If the integrator f is entirely increasing, the theorem is easily proved.

Riesz's principle of transition does not apply to Riemann integrals. It appears that Riemann integration is important insofar as its use simplifies Lebesgue integration. Where the relationship between the integrals is elusive, one tends to deal directly with the Lebesgue integral.

Bibliography

AITKEN, A. C.

1. *Studies in practical mathematics.* IV, *On linear approximation by least squares,* Proc. Roy. Soc. Edinburgh. Sect. A **62** (1945), 138–146.
2. *On least squares and linear combinations of observations,* ibid. **55** (1935), 42–48.

BAIRE, R.

1. *Sur les fonctions de variables réelles,* Ann. Mat. Pura Appl. (3) **3** (1899), 1–123.

BANACH, S.

1. *Théorie des opérations linéaires,* Warsaw, 1932.
2 *Sur la divergence des interpolations,* Studia Math. **9** (1940), 156–163.

BOURBAKI, N.

1. *Intégration,* Éléments de Mathématique, Livre VI, Chapitres I–IV, Paris, 1952.

BUCK, R. C.

1. *Linear spaces and approximation theory,* On numerical approximation, pp. 11–23, R. E. Langer, ed., Madison, Wis., 1959.

CARATHÉODORY, C.

1. *Vorlesungen über reele Funktionen,* 2nd ed., Berlin, 1927.

DAHLQUIST, G.

1. *Convergence and stability in the numerical integration of ordinary differential equations,* Math. Scand. **4** (1956), 33–53.
2. *Stability and error bounds in the numerical integration of ordinary differential equations,* Trans. Roy. Inst. Tech. Stockholm No. 130 (1959), 85 pp.

DIXMIER, J.

1. *Les algèbres d'opérateurs dans l'espace Hilbertien,* Paris, 1957.

DOOB, J. L.

1. *Stochastic processes,* New York, 1953.

DUNFORD, N. and SCHWARTZ, J. T.; with the assistance of Bade, W. G. and Bartle, R. G.

1. *Linear operators.* I, New York, 1958.

ÈZROHI, I. A.

1. *General forms of remainder terms of linear formulas in multidimensional approximate analysis,* Mat. Sb. (N.S.) **38** (**80**) (1956), 389–416; **43** (**85**) (1957), 9–28. (Russian)

GAUSS, C. F.

1. *Theoria combinationis observationium erroribus minimus obnoxiae* 1821, 1823, 1826, Werke IV, Göttingen, 1873, pp. 1–94.
2. *Méthode des moindres carrés,* J. Bertrand, trans., Paris, 1855.
3. *Abhandlungen zur Methode der kleinsten Quadrate,* Berlin, 1887; pp. 1–91.
4. *Methodus nova integralium valores per approximationem inveniendi* 1814 = Werke III, Göttingen, 1866; pp. 163–196.

GÖDEL, K.

1. *The consistency of the axiom of choice and the generalized continuum-hypothesis with the axioms of set theory,* Princeton, N.J., 1940.

GOLOMB, M. and WEINBERGER, H. F.

1. *Optimal approximation and error bounds,* On numerical approximation, pp. 117–190, R. E. Langer, ed., Madison, Wis., 1959.

GOURSAT, E.

1. *Cours d'analyse.* II, Paris, 1905; p. 421 = *Differential equations,* Part 2, Vol. 2, Mathematical Analysis, Translated by E. R. Hedrick and O. Dunkel, New York, 1917; pp. 108–109.

GRAVES, L. M.
1. *The theory of functions of real variables*, 1st ed., New York, 1946.

HALMOS, P.
1. *Measure theory*, New York, 1950.
2. *Introduction to Hilbert space and the theory of spectral multiplicity*, New York, 1951.

HAMEL, G.
1. *Eine Basis aller Zahlen und die unstetigen Lösungen der Funktionengleichung* $f(x + y) = f(x) + f(y)$, Math. Ann. **60** (1905), 459–462.

HARDY, G. H., PÓLYA, G., and LITTLEWOOD, J. E.
1. *Inequalities*, Cambridge, 1934.

HAUSDORFF, F.
1. *Mengenlehre*, 2nd ed., Berlin, 1927.

HEAVISIDE, O.
1. *On operators in mathematical physics*, Proc. Roy. Soc. London **52** (1893), 504–529; particularly p. 513.
2. *Electromagnetic theory*, London, 1893, 1899, 1912. Reprint New York, 1950; particularly Vol. 2, p. 36.

HENRICI, P.
1. *Discrete variable methods in ordinary differential equations*, New York, 1962.

KOLMOGOROV, A. N.
1. *Interpolation und extrapolation von stationären zufälligen Folgen*, Izv. Akad. Nauk SSSR Ser. Mat. **5** (1941), 3–14. (Russian with German summary)
2. *Stationary sequences in Hilbert space*, Bull. Math. Univ. Moscou **2**, No. 6 (1941), 40 pp. (Russian)
3. *On the proof of the method of least squares*, Uspehi Mat. Nauk **1** (**11**) (1946), 57–70. (Russian)

LANING, J. H., Jr. and BATTIN, R. H.
1. *Random processes in automatic control*, New York, 1956.

LEBESGUE, H.
1. *Leçons sür l'intégration et la recherche des fonctions primitives*, 2nd ed., Paris, 1928.

LOÈVE, M.
1. *Probability theory*, New York, 1955.

MEYERS, L. F. and SARD, A.
1. *Best approximate integration formulas*, J. Math. Phys. **29** (1950), 118–123.
2. *Best interpolation formulas*, ibid., 198–206.

MUNROE, M. E.
1. *Introduction to measure and integration*, Cambridge, Mass., 1953.

MURRAY, F. J. and VON NEUMANN, J.
1. *On rings of operators*, Ann. of Math. **37** (1936), 116–229 = Collected works of J. von Neumann, III, New York, 1961, pp. 6–119.

NAIMARK, M. A.
1. *Normed rings*, translated by L. F. Boron, Groningen, 1959.

VON NEUMANN, J.
1. *Mathematical foundations of quantum mechanics*, translated by R. T. Beyer, Princeton, N.J., 1955 = *Mathematische Grundlagen der Quantenmechanik*, Berlin, 1932.
2. *Functional operators*. I, II, Princeton, N.J., 1950.
3. *On infinite direct products*, Compositio Math. **6** (1938), 1–77 = Collected works III, New York, 1961; pp. 322–399.

NIKODYM, O.
1. *Sur un theorème de M. S. Zaremba concernant les fonctions harmoniques*, J. Math. Pures Appl. (**9**) **12** (1933), 94–108.

NIKOLSKII, S. M.
1. *Concerning estimation for approximate quadrature formulas*, Uspehi Mat. Nauk **5** (1950), no. 2 (36), 165–177. (Russian)
2. *Quadrature formulas*, Izv. Akad. Nauk SSSR Ser. Mat. **16** (1952), 181–196. (Russian)
3. *Quadrature formulas*, Moscow, 1958; 124 pp. (Russian)

PEANO, G.
1. *Resto nelle formule di quadratura espresso con un integrale definito*, Rend. Accad. Lincei (5^a) $\mathbf{22}_1$ (1913), 562–569 = Opere Scelte I, Roma, 1957, pp. 410–418.
2. *Residuo in formulas de quadratura*, Mathesis (4) **4** (1914), 5–10 = Opere Scelte I, pp. 419–425.

PLACKETT, R. L.
1. *A historical note on the method of least squares*, Biometrika **36** (1949), 458–460.

RADON, J.
1. *Theorie und Anwendungen der absolut additiven Mengenfunktionen*, Sitzungsber. der Math.-Naturwiss. Klasse der K. Akademie der Wiss., Wien, 122, IIa (1913), 1295–1438.
2. *Restausdrücke bei Interpolations- und Quadraturformeln durch bestimmte Integrale*, Monatsh. Math. Phys. **42** (1935), 389–396.

RÉMÈS, E. J.
1. *Sur les termes complémentaires de certaines formules d'analyse approximative*, Dokl. Akad. Nauk SSSR **26** (1940), 129–133.
2. *Sur certaines classes de fonctionelles linéaires dans les espaces C_p et sur les termes complémentaires des formules d'analyse approximative*, Acad. Sci. RSS Ukraine Rec. Trav. **3** (1939), 21–62; **4** (1940), 47–82. (Ukrainian)

RIESZ, F.
1. *Sur les opérations fonctionelles linéaires*, C. R. Acad. Sci. Paris **149** (1909), 974–977 = Oeuvres complètes, Budapest, 1960; pp. 400–402.
2. *Sur certains systèmes singuliers d'équations intégrales*, Ann. École Norm. Sup. (3) **28** (1911), 33–62 = Oeuvres complètes, pp. 798–827.
3. *Démonstration nouvelle d'un théorème concernant les opérations fonctionnelles linéaires*, Ann. École Norm. Sup. (3) **31** (1914), 9–14 = Oeuvres complètes, pp. 490–495.
4. *L'évolution de la notion d'intégrale depuis Lebesgue*, Ann. Inst. Fourier Grenoble **1** (1949), 29–42 = Oeuvres complètes, pp. 327–340.
5. *Les ensembles de mesure nulle et leur rôle dans l'analyse*, Comptes rendus du premier congrès des mathématiciens Hongrois 1950, Akadémiai Kiadó, Budapest, 1952 = Oeuvres complètes, pp. 363–372.

RIESZ, F. and SZ-NAGY, B.
1. *Leçons d'analyse fonctionnelle*, 2nd ed., Budapest, 1952 = *Functional analysis*, translated by L. F. Boron, New York, 1955.

SARD, A.
1. *Integral representations of remainders*, Duke Math. J. **15** (1948), 333–345.
2. *The remainder in approximations by moving averages*, Bull. Amer. Math. Soc. **54** (1948), 788–792.
3. *Best approximate integration formulas; best approximation formulas*, Amer. J. Math. **71** (1949), 80–91.
4. *Smoothest approximation formulas*, Ann. Math. Statist. **20** (1949), 612–615.
5. *Remainders: functions of several variables*, Acta Math. **84** (1951), 319–346.

6. *Remainders as integrals of partial derivatives*, Proc. Amer. Math. Soc. **3** (1952), 732–741.
7. *Approximation and variance*, Trans. Amer. Math. Soc. **73** (1952), 428–446.
8. *Linear functionals on $K_{p,q}$, $B_{p,q}$*, Proceedings of the International Congress of Mathematicians II, 1954, Amsterdam, pp. 167–168.
9. *Function spaces and approximation*, Numerical Analysis, Proc. Sympos. Appl. Math. Vol. 6, pp. 177–185, Amer. Math. Soc., J. H. Curtiss, ed., Providence, R.I., 1956.
10. *Approximation and projection*, J. Math. Phys. **35** (1956), 127–144.
11. *Images of critical sets*, Ann. of Math. **68** (1958), 247–259.
12. *The rationale of approximation*, On numerical approximation, pp. 191–207, R. E. Langer, ed., Madison, Wis., 1959.
13. *New function spaces and their adjoints*, Ann. New York Acad. Sci. **86** (1960), 700–757.

SCHATTEN, R.

1. *A theory of cross-spaces*, Princeton, N.J., 1950.

SCHAUDER, J.

1. *Über die Umkehrung linearer stetige Funktionaloperationen*, Studia Math. **2** (1930), 1–6.

SCHMIDT, E.

1. *Auflösung der allgemeinen linearen Integralgleichung*, Math. Ann. **64** (1907), 161–174.
2. *Über die auflösung linearer Gleichungen mit unendlich vielen Umbekannten*, Rend. Circ. Mat. Palermo **25** (1908), 53–77.

SCHWARTZ, L.

1. *Théorie des distributions*. I, Paris, 1950.

STEFFENSEN, J. F.

1. *Interpolation*, Baltimore, 1927. Reprint, New York, 1950.

SZPILRAJN, E.

1. *La dimension et la mesure*, Fund. Math. **28** (1937), 81–89.

TIETZE, H.

1. *Eine Bemerkung zur interpolation*, Z. Math. Phys. **64** (1914), 74–90.

TYCHONOFF, A.

1. *Eine Fixpunktsatz*, Math. Ann. **111** (1935), 767–776.

WEYL, H.

1. *The method of orthogonal projection in potential theory*, Duke Math. J. **7** (1940), 411–444.

WIENER, N.

1. *Extrapolation, interpolation, and smoothing of stationary time series* (with two appendices by N. Levinson), Cambridge, Mass., 1949.

YOUNG, W. H.

1. *On the new theory of integration*, Proc. Roy. Soc. A **88** (1913), 170–178.
2. *On multiple integrals*, ibid. **93** (1916), 28–41.
3. *On multiple Fourier series*, Proc. London Math. Soc. (2) **11** (1912), 133–184.
4. *On multiple integration by parts and the second theorem of the mean*, ibid. (2) **16** (1917), 273–293.
5. (with G. C. Young) *On the discontinuities of monotone functions of several variables*, ibid (2) **22** (1924), 124–142.

ZAANEN, A. C.

1. *Linear analysis*, Groningen, 1956.

Index

Signs are listed first; then Greek letters; then Latin letters. Numbers refer to pages. The system of references in the book is described in the footnote, page 2.

$\in$, element of 1
$\{a \in A : \mathscr{P}\}$, $\{a : \mathscr{P}\}$, $\{\mathscr{P}\}$, class 146
$\{_k f^{k,j}{}_j\}$, $\{_j x^j\}$, matrices 370
$\supset$, contains 12
$\subset$, is contained in 8
$\cap$, intersection 195
$\cup$, union 182
$(s - a)^{(i)}$, normalized power of $s - a$ 12
$(a, b]$, $[a, b]$, etc., linear intervals from a to b 19
$\| \;\|$, $||| \; |||$, norms 120, 121, 124, 500, 516. If a suffix is attached, see thereunder.
$\hat{X}$, completion of X 302, closure of X 448
(x, y), inner product of x into y 329. If a suffix is attached, see thereunder.
X^*, adjoint of the space X 126, adjoint of the operator X 453
$X/X_0 = X \pmod{X_0}$ 308
A', complement of A 304
$\bar{z}$, complex conjugate of z 317
$\bar{\omega}$, set of pairs of indices in the derivatives which are elements of ω, etc. 183
$|f|$, total variation of f 510, 533
$\ulcorner p, q \urcorner$, set of pairs of integers 191, $\ulcorner p, q, r \urcorner$, set of triples 279
$\perp$, perpendicular 331
$\times$, times 519
α, mass 431
$\alpha = \mathscr{U}\delta x$ 447
σ, boundary of 516
$\beta = \mathscr{B}\delta x$ 446
$\gamma_{j,k}$, coefficient 65
$\gamma = \hat{\tau} - \beta$ 447
∂, boundary of 516
$\delta^{j,i}$, Kronecker delta 153
δ, δ_s, operator 154, δ_t 256
δx, input error 7, 378, 380
θ, origin 118, 120
θ, Heaviside's function 496
θ^ν, continuous function 133
$\theta = \mathrm{Proj}_Y\, G\delta x$ 447
$\{\lambda^g\}$, basis for L 392
ξ, covered core, 170, 195, 282. Likewise for ξ with suffixes.
$\bar{\xi}$ or $\bar{\xi}$ with suffixes 195, 283
Π° 354, Π 355
ρ, retracted core, and $\bar{\rho}$ 262, 284. Likewise for ρ and $\bar{\rho}$ with suffixes.
$\sigma = \mathrm{Proj}_L\, y$ 386
$\tau_t = \mathrm{Proj}_{Mt}\, y$ 393
$\tau = \mathscr{T}(X, Y)\delta x$ 446
ϕ, step function 25
ϕ, full core, and $\bar{\phi}$ 167, 189, 275. Likewise for ϕ and $\bar{\phi}$ with suffixes.
Ψ, space 358, 370, $\tilde{\Psi}$ 381
ψ, step function 496
ψ^ν, continuous function 146
Ω 379, $\tilde{\Omega}$ 381
ω, complete core, and $\bar{\omega}$ 161, 182, 272. Likewise for ω and $\bar{\omega}$ with suffixes.

$\mathscr{A}$, family of operators 379, 380, 431
A, approximating operator, element of $\mathscr{A}$ 380
$\mathscr{A}^*$, family of functionals 105, $\mathscr{A}^*_{m,n}$ 51, 92
A^m_n, best narrow interpolation formula 93
a, autocorrelation 431, 432
Abelian group 119
absolutely continuous functions, masses 514, 534
Adams method 84
addition 118
additive operators 122
adjoint operator 453
adjoint space 126, 453
Aitken, A. C. 494
almost all, almost everywhere 334
analysis of variance 472
appraisals 19, 22, 203, 218
approximate differentiation 111, 123
approximate integration 36, 51, 74, 214, 235
approximate summation 116
approximation 7, 377
approximation based on a table of contaminated values 415
approximation of a projection 339
approximation of Gx by $A(x + \delta x)$ 378, 444
approximation of x by $A(x + \delta x)$ 480
atomic measure 415
autocorrelation 431